ALGEBRA

an introduction to finite mathematics

BOOKS BY ISRAEL H. ROSE

A Modern Introduction to College Mathematics
Algebra: An Introduction to Finite Mathematics

ALGEBRA
an introduction to finite mathematics

ISRAEL H. ROSE

Associate Professor, Department of Mathematics

Hunter College of The City University of New York

John Wiley & Sons, Inc., New York • London

to my father
and the memory of my mother

PREFACE

Mathematicians today pretty generally agree that what distinguishes the algebraically minded mathematician from other mathematicians is a special taste for processes that are finite and discrete rather than infinite and continuous. From this point of view, not only do polynomials, vectors, matrices, groups, fields, and the like fall within the purview of algebra but also such areas of study as logic, boolean algebra, linear programming, and significant parts of set and probability theory.

My goal in writing this textbook has been threefold: First of all, to construct a course that would be suitable for early college or late high school use; secondly, to present what I consider to be valuable mathematics traditionally taught in colleges ("college algebra") and high schools ("advanced algebra"), developed with the help of modern clarifying and unifying concepts (modern, it should be noted, only in the sense that they are just coming into use in the schools—most, if not all, are over half a century old); and finally, to arrive at a course that would reflect, in content and spirit, the "finite mathematics" point of view described above.

We are now encountering college freshmen in greater and greater number whose high school study has included training in the "new mathematics," in programs like that of the School Mathematics Study Group. It is my hope that this textbook will, on the one hand, serve to better the articulation between the freshman college course and the new high school programs in mathematics and, on the other, introduce this mathematics to those who have not yet encountered it. I think that students preparing to teach mathematics in the schools and students going on to full-scale courses in modern algebra will find the "new mathematics" content of this course especially useful.

Parts of this book have been borrowed from my earlier book (*A Modern Introduction to College Mathematics*), either verbatim or in many cases revised in the light of comments of users and appropriateness to the central algebraic theme.   I have also included review material in high school algebra, but I have tried to present this review as far as possible in new contexts to avoid tedious and sterile retreading of old ground.

The book may be used for various one- or two-semester courses, meeting three times a week.   A one-semester course, for example (given from a preliminary version of the book) covered (with some omissions) Chapters 1–8 and Chapter 10; another course substituted Chapter 12 for Chapter 10. For students requiring extensive review, it might be advisable in a one-semester course to concentrate on the review aspects of Chapter 4, touching only lightly on its deductive and field-theoretic content, and to omit some or all of the last two chapters mentioned.

It is a pleasure to acknowledge here the helpful suggestions of students and teachers at Hunter College who used preliminary versions of the material of the book, and to thank Lenore L. Feigelson, Doris Grossman, Nancy L. Knaff and Diane J. Polley for assistance in working out answers to problems.   I also wish to thank Mrs. Bernice Martin for her excellent typing of the manuscript, and the following publishers for permission to reproduce excerpts from their books or tables: Simon and Schuster, J. B. Lippincott Company, and the Society of Actuaries.

ISRAEL H. ROSE

New York City
November, 1962

CONTENTS

LIST OF SYMBOLS AND ABBREVIATIONS

(Some, whose inclusion in this list would not be particularly helpful, have been omitted).

Symbol or Abbreviation		See Page or Pages
$\geqslant$	"is greater than or equal to"	60, 113
$\leqslant$	"is less than or equal to"	60, 113
$\mid$	"is a factor of"	60
Q.E.D.	"which was to be proved"	69
$\Rightarrow$, $\Leftarrow$	"implies" (read from left to right and right to left, respectively)	96
$\Leftrightarrow$	"is equivalent to"	97
$\doteq$	"is approximately equal to"	144
$\{x\mid\ \}$	"the set of all x such that"	205
$[a, b], (a, b)$ $[a, b), (a, b]$ $[a, \infty), (a, \infty)$ $(-\infty, a], (-\infty, a)$	intervals	223, 224
$\sum$	"summation"	296, 302
$n!$	"n factorial"	316
nPr	"the number of permutations of a set of n elements taken r at a time"	317
$\binom{n}{r}$	"the number of combinations of a set of n elements taken r at a time"	327

1 SETS AND THEIR NUMBERS

1.1 INTRODUCTION

For 5000 years, the science we now call "algebra" has concerned itself with the study of processes that derive a single number from a pair of given numbers. Such processes are called *operations*. For example, the operation of *addition* derives from the pair of numbers 7, 11 the single number 18; the operation of *multiplication* derives from the same pair the single number 77.

We recognize the resulting numbers, 18 and 77, as being "unequal." Indeed, from earliest times, algebra has found itself dealing not only with *operations* on numbers but also with such concepts as "equality," "inequality," "less than," and "greater than," that is to say, with *relations* between numbers.

However, like all of mathematics, algebra has not confined itself to its original boundaries, but has continually expanded them as practical considerations and the imagination of mathematicians have dictated. *Number*, for example, originally meant one of the numbers we ordinarily use in counting: 1, 2, 3, $\cdots$ (the three dots are read "and so on"). But today we have at our disposal many other types of numbers; in fact, a good part of this book will be devoted to a study of various sorts of numbers, why they were invented, and their important properties and uses.

Progress has occurred in other directions also. Rather than deriving a single number from a pair of numbers, one may derive a single collection of things from a pair of collections of things ("set theory"), a single statement from a pair of statements ("logic"), and so on and on.

We shall see that there are remarkable resemblances between these newer operations and those with which we are more familiar; resemblances that have a great deal to do with the many important applications of these new operations, both to the development of other theories and to the direct solution of practical problems.

In our study of algebra, however, we shall go backward before we go forward. It is perhaps 25,000 years since modern man (" *homo sapiens* ") first appeared upon the scene; it is likely that the foundational ideas we shall discuss in this chapter had their origins even as long ago as that. These foundational ideas pertain not only to algebra; their importance is compounded by the fact that they lie at the roots of and permeate and unify *all* of mathematics. We begin our consideration of these basic concepts in the next section.

1.2 SETS AND ONE-TO-ONE CORRESPONDENCES

There is a method more elementary than counting for determining whether or not two collections of objects are equally numerous. Before defining the method exactly, we shall give several instances of its use. Suppose, for example, that upon entering a classroom we find each student seated in a properly restrained fashion upon only one chair which he shares with no one else. Then if all the chairs are occupied, *without counting either students or chairs*, we can conclude that there are exactly as many of one as there are of the other; or, when we read in the Bible that "There went in two and two unto Noah into the ark, the male and the female · · · ," we know that the males and the females entering into the ark were equally numerous, even though we do not know how many of each there were; and man, placing the tips of his fingers together in the well-known judicious gesture, must have recognized a certain something which the fingers of one hand had in common with the fingers of the other, long before he gave that common property the name "five."

In other words, we recognize that two collections of objects are equally numerous if it is possible to "match," or "pair off," or "associate in pairs" all the members of one collection with all the members of the other.

We pause at this point to remark that even this very early excursion into mathematics is immediately concerned with *collections of objects*. A preoccupation with collections of objects is profoundly characteristic of mathematics. Indeed, because they must refer to it so often in their work, mathematicians usually use the shorter term "set" in place of "collections of objects," and from now on we shall generally do the same; and we shall call the objects which constitute a set the *members* or the *elements* of the set.

Further Terminology. We shall say that an element of a set *belongs to*, or *is contained in*, or simply, *is in* the set; and that a set *contains* its elements. For example, George Washington belongs to the set of all presidents of the United States; the set of all odd whole numbers contains the number 7.

Notation. If x is an element of a set S, we write: $x \in S$ (read: x belongs to S).

Even before he could count 1, 2, 3, and so on, would it have been possible for primitive man to know whether he had as many wives as his neighbor and to record their number? The process we have been discussing would certainly have enabled him to do the first but, as a matter of fact, it would have sufficed for the second also. The oldest mathematical records which exist, some dating back more than 10,000 years, are animal bones on which marks, arranged regularly in equal groups, have been scratched. Each scratch, of course, was associated with some object. Again we have an illustration of the "matching" process, this time used actually to construct a set whose members are to be as numerous as those of a given set.

We see, then, that from earliest times the idea of a perfect matching of the members of two sets occupied an important position in the thought of man. Here we have one of the great foundational concepts of mathematics, to which mathematicians have given the name "one-to-one correspondence:"

> A one-to-one correspondence between two sets is an association of the members of one set with the members of the other in such a way that each member of each set is associated with just one member of the other.

For example, it is possible for a normal person to associate the fingers of his left hand with the fingers of his right in such a way that each finger of each hand is associated with just one finger of the other. Hence we may say that these two sets of fingers may be put into one-to-one correspondence.

Another Example. It is possible to establish a one-to-one correspondence between the set of letters $\{a, b, c\}$ and the set of names $\{$Tom, Dick, Harry$\}$. Here, for example, is a diagram of one such association:

$$a \longleftrightarrow \text{Dick}$$
$$b \longleftrightarrow \text{Tom}$$
$$c \longleftrightarrow \text{Harry}$$

Notation. As in the preceding example, we shall generally use braces, { }, to enclose the elements of a set; "↔" is read "corresponds to," and may be read either from left to right or from right to left.

1.3 THE NUMBER OF A SET

Now, to return to our primitive man and his wives, it is clear that, by scratching a mark for each of his wives, he could establish a one-to-one correspondence between scratches and wives and thus *record* what we now call their number without actually *naming* or *counting* their number. The marks, however, might at the same time have been in one-to-one correspondence with some other set, say, a collection of war-clubs. War-clubs, marks, wives, and, indeed, all other sets which may be put into one-to-one correspondence with each of these sets—what have they in common? It is an abstract property which we call the *number* of each collection. ("Abstract" is used here in its literal sense, "drawn from." An abstract property is one drawn from a number of instances or phenomena, and represents, roughly speaking, something common to all of them, something that they share.)

For example, in Fig. 1.1, the abstract property which each set exhibits by virtue of the fact that one-to-one correspondences exist between any two of the sets is a number which has the name "three."

Somewhere, at some moment in the dim past, there must have existed a prehistoric genius who recognized the abstract property shared by:

the set of his hands
the set of his feet
the set of his eyes
the set of his ears

and, in fact, by all collections of objects that could be put into one-to-one correspondence with each of these sets, and who signalized his recognition by giving this quality which they shared a name corresponding to our word "two."

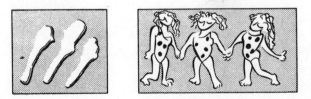

Fig. 1.1 Several concrete examples of the abstract idea "three."

We are led to a second great mathematical idea, one which is related to the first. It is the idea of "the number of a set," or "the number of elements in a set," or "cardinal number." It is the type of number we use to answer the question "How many?"

A *cardinal number* describes an abstract property shared by all sets which can be put into one-to-one correspondence with a given set.

(*Note:* The preceding boxed statement tells something about the concept of a cardinal number, but it is not a precise definition of that concept. A more precise definition will be given in Section 1.8.)

For example, the cardinal number 2 describes an abstract property shared by all sets which can be put into one-to-one correspondence with the set of names: Romeo and Juliet. The cardinal number 5 describes an abstract property exhibited by all sets which can be put into one-to-one correspondence with the set of toes of the author's right foot.

▶ EXERCISE 1

1. List, explain the meaning of, and give original examples to illustrate the most important concepts encountered in Sections 1.1–1.3.

2. Is it possible to set up a one-to-one correspondence different from that of Section 1.2 between the sets {a, b, c} and {Tom, Dick, Harry}? If so, how many are possible in all?

3. Show that a one-to-one correspondence exists between the set of numbers {1, 2} and the set of letters {a, b}. Write down all possible one-to-one correspondences between these sets and tell how many of these correspondences there are.

4. Name a pair of sets, each of which contains only a single element. Write down all possible one-to-one correspondences between these sets. How many of these correspondences are there?

5. Name a pair of sets which can be put into one-to-one correspondence with each other, but not with any of the sets mentioned in Problems 2, 3, and 4. Write down all possible one-to-one correspondences between the pair of sets you have chosen, and tell how many of these correspondences there are.

6. Name, in each of the following cases, an abstract idea drawn from the items included in that case:

(*a*) Sugar and saccharine.

(*b*) A baseball team and the Supreme Court.

(*c*) The sun, a full moon, and a penny.

(*d*) A ray of light and a taut string.

(*e*) "One," "two," "three," "four," "five."

(*f*) "Two and two make four" and "night follows day."

7. Make up a question of your own, similar to Problem 6 and answer it.

8. Sets *A* and *B* are said to be *equivalent* if they can be put into one-to-one correspondence with each other. Give several examples of equivalent sets. Is every set equivalent to itself? Justify your answer.

9. Suppose *A* = {*a*, *b*, *c*}, *B* = {1, 2}. Then we may write $a \in A$, and what other statements involving elements belonging to sets?

*10. What is the total number of one-to-one correspondences which may be established between a pair of sets, each of which contains five elements?

*11. Write down a formula, or state a rule, for computing the total number of one-to-one correspondences possible between a pair of sets if each set of the pair contains *n* elements.

1.4 THE NATURAL NUMBERS

Having mastered the concept of a one-to-one correspondence, prehistoric man found himself ready to count. To the set consisting of all the index fingers on his right hand—and to each set which could be put into one-to-one correspondence with that set—he assigned the cardinal number "1" (or something equivalent to it in his language).

We have already indicated how "2," "3," and "5" may be similarly defined. At this point we shall assume that the student is familiar with the set of all numbers like these, that is to say, with the set of numbers used in ordinary counting: 1, 2, 3, $\cdots$. Following traditional mathematical terminology, we shall call this set of numbers the set of *natural numbers*; later they will appear again, under the name *positive integers*; other names by which they have been known are *whole numbers* and *counting numbers*.

Natural number and cardinal number are not synonymous: although every natural number is a cardinal number, it is *not* true that every cardinal number is a natural number. In fact, zero and the natural numbers are called the *finite* cardinal numbers; there are other cardinal numbers: A cardinal number which is neither zero nor a natural number is called an *infinite* cardinal number. For example, the number of points on a line is certainly not zero, nor is it a natural number; it is an *infinite* cardinal number. Furthermore, a *set* is called finite or infinite, depending upon whether its cardinal number is finite or infinite. (We shall pursue this subject further in Section 1.8.)

Although the natural numbers are the most primitive of all numbers, they play an exceptionally important role in mathematics. The branch of mathematics called the "theory of numbers" is devoted entirely to a study of their properties; many other fields of mathematics build upon the natural numbers as a foundation. A measure of the respect with which mathematicians regard the natural numbers may be gleaned from the following statements, made by two great nineteenth-century mathematicians. (Their terminology is different from ours, but essentially they are talking about the natural numbers):

God made integers, all else is the work of man.

(KRONECKER)

Integral numbers are the fountainhead of all mathematics.

(MINKOWSKI)

1.5 SUBSETS AND THE NULLSET

Suppose we were offered the opportunity to choose, from among the set of people Tom, Dick, and Harry, some to go along on a picnic.

Then here are some choices of picnic companions which we could make:

1. Tom
2. Dick
3. Harry
4. Tom and Dick
5. Tom and Harry
6. Dick and Harry
7. Tom, Dick, and Harry

Each of these seven sets is called a *subset* of the original set of people.

However, we have overlooked one possibility. Just as we might, feeling very friendly toward everyone, have chosen all of the people of the given set to go along with us (choice 7 above), so, in a more disagreeable mood, we might have decided to allow *none* of them to come. To take care of cases like this, mathematicians make use of the concept of a *nullset*, or *empty set*, that is, a set which contains no elements at all. We shall use a pair of braces, { }, containing nothing whatever to denote this set, and occasionally also the symbol $\varnothing$, popular in many texts.

It is plausible to stipulate (and, in fact, with sharper mathematical tools than we have available here at the moment, it may be proved) that the nullset is a subset of any set whatever; for given *any* set, one may choose from it exactly no elements.

We see, then, that it is reasonable to add one more subset, { }, to the seven subsets above, making eight subsets in all derivable from a set of three objects.

We now state the following definitions formally:

> **Definitions:** A set A is said to be a *subset* of a set B if each element of A is also an element of B.
>
> The *nullset* (denoted { } or ∅) is the set which contains no elements.

Further Terminology. If set *A* is a subset of set *B*, we also say that *A is contained in B*, or that *B contains A*; for example the set of all English verbs is contained in the set of all English words.

Notation. If set *A* is contained in set *B*, we write: $A \subset B$ (read: "*A* is contained in *B*"), or $B \supset A$ (read: *B* contains *A*).

Relations among subsets of a set may often be clearly exhibited (see Fig. 1.2) by means of an "inclusion" or "Euler diagram" (the latter is named after the great eighteenth-century Swiss mathematician, who is said to have devised the method).

The first diagram of Fig. 1.2 indicates, for example, that the set of all odd whole numbers is a subset of the set of all whole numbers; the lower indicates that the set of all two-letter English words and the set of all

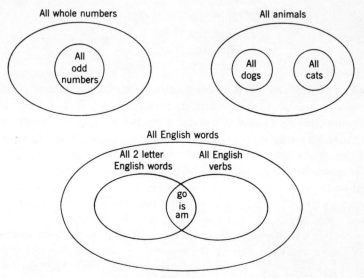

Fig. 1.2

English verbs are subsets of the set of all English words, and that these subsets have certain elements in common, among which are the words *go, is, am*.

1.6 UNION AND INTERSECTION OF SETS

Given a pair of sets A, B, we consider two very natural ways of forming a new set from them.

The first is simply to "combine" the given sets; the result is called the union of the given sets, and denoted $A \cup B$ (read: "A union B or the union of A and B").

Suppose, for example, that at a certain school (in which different students never have the same first name) there is a chess team (which we shall call set A) and a checker team (which we shall call set B), and that the members of the chess team are Tom, Dick, and Harry, and of the checker team, Dick, Harry, and James; that is:

$$A = \{\text{Tom, Dick, Harry}\}$$
$$B = \{\text{Harry, Dick, James}\}$$

Then if we were to combine the two teams into one, the members of the new team would be Tom, Dick, Harry, and James. That is:

$$A \cup B = \{\text{Tom, Dick, Harry, James}\}$$

A second method of forming a new set from a given pair A, B is to choose as elements of the new set only those elements "common" to the given pair. The result is called the "intersection" of the given sets and denoted $A \cap B$ (read: "A intersection B" or "the intersection of A and B").

Thus, if A and B are as in the preceding example,

$$A \cap B = \{\text{Dick, Harry}\}$$

Now we make the formal definitions:

Definitions: Let A and B be sets; then:

$A \cup B$ (read: "A union B") is the set consisting of all elements which belong either to A or to B, or to both.

$A \cap B$ (read: "A intersection B") is the set consisting of all elements which belong both to A and to B.

NOTE 1. The symbols for union and intersection are sometimes, and for obvious reasons, read "cup" and "cap," respectively.

NOTE 2. "either $\cdots$ or $\cdots$," as used in mathematics, does not exclude the possibility "both." That is to say, if an element is both in set A and in set B it is considered to satisfy the condition that it be either in A or in B. As a consequence of this understanding, the definition above is redundant: the words "or to both" may be deleted.

1.7 EQUALITY OF SETS

It may seem superfluous to state the following, but it turns out to be useful to do so:

Two sets are equal (or "the same") if and only if each element of each set is also an element of the other.

This principle not only supplies a handy tool for proving sets equal but also settles certain questions which at first glance are puzzling.

To illustrate the first point, suppose A is the set of all human beings and B is the set of all featherless, furless bipeds. Then we know that $A = B$ as soon as we know that every human being is a featherless, furless biped, and every featherless, furless biped is a human being.

(Symbolically: We may prove that set A = set B by showing that $A \subset B$ and $B \subset A$.)

To illustrate the second point, as an example of a question settled by the principle above, consider the following:

"Is the set of letters in the name $ANNA$, $\{A, N, N, A\}$ or $\{A, N\}$?"

The answer is, it does not matter. Since each letter belonging to one set can be found in the other, the two sets are the same. One might as well, therefore, use the shorter designation $\{A, N\}$ to represent the set of letters in the name $ANNA$.

In fact, it will help to avoid confusion if we agree to avoid writing down more than one symbol for a given element, or a symbol for an element more than once, in listing the elements of a set.

Note also that our principle implies that $\{A, N\} = \{N, A\}$, so that the order in which elements of a set are written is immaterial.

▶ EXERCISE 2

1. List, explain the meaning of, and give original examples to illustrate the most important concepts encountered in Sections 1.4–1.7.

2. In each of the following cases, list all subsets of the given set of letters, and tell how many subsets there are in all.

(a) $\{x\}$.

(b) $\{x, y\}$.

(c) $\{x, y, z\}$.

(d) $\{w, x, y, z\}$.

(e) $\{ \ \}$.

WILAMSD   IAL

3. (a) Suppose A is the set of letters in your first name, B the set of letters in your last name. Find $A \cup B$ and $A \cap B$.

(b) Suppose A and B are sets which have no elements in common. Then $A \cap B = ?$

(c) Draw a pair of intersecting circles on your paper. Let A be the set of points interior to one circle, B the set of points interior to the other. Indicate, by shading, the set of points $A \cap B$.

(d) The same as (c), but shade in $A \cup B$.

(e) Suppose the circles of (c) do *not* intersect. What then can you say about $A \cap B$?

4. (From now on we shall use nn as an abbreviation for "natural number" or "natural numbers.")

(a) What is meant by an *even* nn?

(b) What is meant by an *odd* nn?

(c) Suppose A is the set of all even nn, B the set of all odd nn, C the set of all nn. Then

$$A \cap B = ? \qquad A \cup B = ?$$

*(d) Suppose A is the set of all nn which are integer multiples of 4, B the set of all nn which are integer multiples of 6. What can you say about $A \cap B$? Can you generalize this result?

5. Restricting ourselves to the nn, i.e., considering only those divisions in which the result of dividing one nn by another nn is again a nn, every nn has either exactly one divisor, or exactly two divisors (i.e., 1 and itself), or more than two divisors. The only nn falling into the first class is 1; all those falling into the second class are called "prime nn," or, for short, "primes"; all those falling into the third class are said to be "composite."

An important property of primes is the following ("The Fundamental Theorem of Arithmetic"): Every composite nn may be expressed as the product of primes; furthermore, the set of primes which occur in that product, and the multiplicity with which each prime occurs in that product, are unique.

(a) Define: "prime."

(b) Write down the set of all primes less than 50.

(c) Express each of the composite numbers between 2 and 25 as a product of primes.

(*d*) Suppose that P represents the set of all primes, A the set of all even nn. Then $P \cap A = ?$

*(*e*) Explain the reason for the restriction at the beginning of this problem.

6. Name several important subsets of the nn.

7. Is there a largest nn? Justify your answer.

8. In the following statements, A and B represent sets. Characterize each statement as true or false, and illustrate by means of an inclusion diagram.

(*a*) A is always contained in $A \cup B$.

(*b*) B is always contained in $A \cup B$.

(*c*) A always contains $A \cup B$.

(*d*) B always contains $A \cup B$.

(*e*) A is always contained in $A \cap B$.

(*f*) B is always contained in $A \cap B$.

(*g*) A always contains $A \cap B$.

(*h*) B always contains $A \cap B$.

(*i*) If $A \supset B$, then it always follows that $A \cap B = A$.

(*j*) If $A \supset B$, then it always follows that $A \cap B = B$.

(*k*) If $A \supset B$, then it always follows that $A \cup B = A$.

(*l*) If $A \supset B$, then it always follows that $A \cup B = B$.

9. Consider the sets of letters:

$$R = \{a, b\}, \qquad S = \{a, b, c\}, \qquad T = \{p, q\}$$

(*a*) Which of these sets may be put into one-to-one correspondence? Diagram a one-to-one correspondence between these sets.

(*b*) Which of these sets have the same cardinal number? Why? What is the symbol for this cardinal number?

(*c*) Which of these sets is a subset of which?

(*d*) $R \cap S = ?$

(*e*) $R \cup S = ?$

*10. Find a formula for the total number of subsets which a set with n elements has. How does the concept of the nullset prove itself to be useful in this problem?

*11. What is the cardinal number of the set $\varnothing$? Is it a nn?

*12. Suppose a and b are the cardinal numbers of sets A and B respectively. Then with a certain condition placed on the set $A \cap B$, $a + b$ may be defined to be the cardinal number of a certain set. What is the "certain condition" and what is the "certain set?"

*13. In many situations the order in which elements of sets are written is immaterial; a committee made up of Tom and Dick, for example, is the same as a committee made up of Dick and Tom. There are other situations, however, in which order must be taken into account; for example, the name James Walter is not the same as the name Walter James.

We shall use the symbol (a, b) to represent something which we shall call "an *ordered pair* of elements a, b." In writing an ordered pair, it is, of course, our intention that an order be associated with the given elements; toward that end we define $(a, b) = (a', b')$ *if and only if* $a = a'$ and $b = b'$. With that understanding, there is no ambiguity in our calling a the *first element*, b the *second element* of the ordered pair (a, b) (Section 1.7).

Note, then, that although $\{7, 11\} = \{11, 7\}$, $(7, 11)$ is *not* equal to $(11, 7)$. An example of an equality between ordered pairs which may be justified by the criterion above is: $(7, 11) = (\frac{14}{2}, 10 + 1)$.

Note further that although $\{a, a\} = \{a\}$ (cf. see Section 1.7), the ordered pair (a, a) admits of no such contraction.

For those who would like to see an actual definition of an ordered pair—which we have, as a matter of fact, not yet given—a neat, if not immediately transparent, method of *defining* the ordered pair (a, b) is as the set $\{\{a\}, \{a, b\}\}$.

[The idea of an *ordered pair* leads quite naturally to the idea of an *ordered triple* (a, b, c), and more generally to that of an *ordered n-tuple* $(x_1, \cdots, x_n)$, where n is any nn. Ordered pairs, triples, etc., are examples of *ordered sets*.]

If S and T are sets, the *product set of S and T*, denoted $S \times T$, is defined to be the set whose members are all ordered pairs (s, t), where s is an element of S and t is an element of T.

For example, if S is the set of letters $\{a, b\}$ and T is the set of letters $\{x, y\}$, then $S \times T$ is the set of ordered pairs: $\{(a, x), (a, y), (b, x), (b, y)\}$. On the other hand, $T \times S$ is the set of ordered pairs: $\{(x, a), (y, a), (x, b), (y, b)\}$.

Now, in each of the following cases, write down the members of each of the following product sets: $A \times A$, $A \times B$, $B \times A$, $B \times B$:

(a) $A = \{a, b, c\}$, $B = \{1, 2\}$.

(b) $A = \{x\}$, $B = \{y\}$.

(c) $A = \{1, 2\}$, $B = \{x\}$.

(d) $A = \{a, b, c\}$, $B = \{1, 2, 3\}$.

(e) $A = \{x, y\}$, $B = \{ \ \}$. (What will always be true about the set $A \times B$ if A or $B = \{ \ \}$?)

*14. If S, T, and W are sets, how would you define the product set $S \times T \times W$? Make up an example to illustrate your definition.

*15. Suppose that a and b are the cardinal numbers of sets A and B respectively. Then ab may be defined to be the cardinal number of a certain set. What is that "certain set?"

Verify that your statement is correct in a case where $a = 4$, $b = 3$.

Explain now why the "product set" $A \times B$ is so named.

*16. A jukebox has two rows of buttons, one containing the letters from A to J, the other the numbers from 1 to 10. To play a selection, one button in each row must be pressed. How many selections does the jukebox offer?

Phrase your answer in the language of product sets and in the light of Problem 15.

*17. Suppose A is a set. Then a set of subsets of A is said to be:

Disjoint (or *mutually exclusive*), if no two of the subsets have an element in common.

Exhaustive, if the union of the given subsets is A.

For example, if $A = \{1, 2, 3\}$, then:

(1) The set of subsets $\{1\}$, $\{2\}$ is disjoint but not exhaustive.

(2) The set of subsets $\{1, 2\}$, $\{2, 3\}$ is exhaustive but not disjoint.

(3) The set of subsets $\{1\}$, $\{1, 2\}$ is neither disjoint nor exhaustive.

(4) The set of subsets $\{1\}$, $\{2, 3\}$ is disjoint and exhaustive; so is the set of subsets $\{1\}$, $\{2\}$, $\{3\}$.

Construct examples like (1)–(4) with a set of your own choosing.

*18. Let $\#A$ represent the number of elements in a set A. For example, with A as in the preceding problem $\#A = 3$.

Give an example of a case in which $\#(A \cup B) \neq (\#A) + (\#B)$, ($\neq$ is read "is unequal to"), and another in which $\#(A \cup B) = (\#A) + (\#B)$.

Under what circumstance will the last equation always hold true?

*19. Suppose A and B are finite sets. What equation, involving the quantities $\#A$, $\#B$, $\#(A \cup B)$, $\#(A \cap B)$ will always hold true?

Illustrate, by means of an example and by means of an Euler diagram.

*20. If A and B are sets, $A - B$ (read: A minus B) is defined to be the set of all elements of A which are not in B.

For example, if $A = \{1, 2, 3\}$, $B = \{1, 2, 4\}$, then $A - B = \{3\}$.

If B is a subset of A, then $A - B$ is called the *complement* of B in A.

If $A = B$, what is $A - B$? What if $B \supset A$?

Suppose A and B are unequal intersecting areas in a plane, neither contained in the other. Draw a diagram identifying and shading in $A - B$ and $B - A$.

Suppose A and B are unequal areas in a plane, and $A \subset B$. Draw a diagram identifying and shading in the complement of A in B.

*21. Tell whether each of the following statements is true or false, and justify your answer:

(a) $1 \in \{1, 2\}$ (b) $1 \subset \{1, 2\}$ (c) $\{1\} \in \{1, 2\}$

(d) $\{1\} \subset \{1, 2\}$ (e) $2 \in \{1, 2\}$ (f) $2 \subset \{1, 2\}$

(g) $\{2\} \in \{1, 2\}$ (h) $\{2\} \subset \{1, 2\}$ (i) $1 = \{1\}$

(j) $0 = \{\ \}$ (k) $0 \in \{\ \}$ (l) $0 \subset \{\ \}$

(m) $0 \in \{0\}$ (n) $0 \subset \{0\}$ (o) $\{1, 2\} = \{1, 2\}$

(p) $\{1\} = \{1, 1\}$ (q) $\{\ \} \in \{1\}$ (r) $\{\ \} \subset \{1\}$

(s) $\varnothing \in \varnothing$ (t) $\varnothing \subset \varnothing$

*1.8 INFINITE SETS AND NUMBERS

Now we shall examine some of the surprising consequences of our agreement that two sets will be considered to be equally numerous or, in other words, to have the same cardinal number if there exists a one-to-one correspondence between the two sets.

It seems preposterous, for example, to imagine that a short line segment contains just as many points as a longer line segment. Supposing, however, that it were possible to establish a one-to-one correspondence between two such sets of points, what then? Why then the agreements we have entered into would force us to admit that the points in a short line segment are equal in number to the points on a longer line segment. Since we feel so strongly that this is not true, such a correspondence had better not exist!

But now see Fig. 1.3, in which a is a line segment and b is a line segment longer than a.

A one-to-one correspondence may be set up between the points of line segment a and the points of line segment b in the following way:

Let c be any line through point P which intersects line segments a and b in points Q and R respectively. Then we make the following association:

$$Q \leftrightarrow R$$

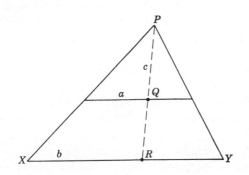

Fig. 1.3

Now is it not true that, if we let the line c assume all possible positions between the lines PX and PY in Fig. 1.3, the points of a and b will be associated in a way which satisfies our definition of a one-to-one correspondence? In other words, can we not match the points of line segment a with the points of line segment b exactly as we match the fingers of one hand with the fingers of the other, and must we not, therefore, conclude that there are as many points on any line segment as there are on any longer line segment?

The answer is that we must. Despite the fact that our intuition is outraged, if we accept our basic assumptions, then we must also accept this conclusion; and since our assumptions are too plausible and too valuable to be discarded, it is our intuition which must, in this case, be rebuffed.

It is not the least of the virtues of mathematics that it so often pricks the bubble of our preconceived notions. There is a lesson of tolerance and respect for new ideas to be learned here. Let us proceed, therefore, to do further violence to our intuition!

How do you imagine the set of all the natural numbers 1, 2, 3, $\cdots$ compares in numerosity with the set of all even numbers 2, 4, 6, $\cdots$? Well now, obviously the second set is only a *proper* subset of the first (a *proper* subset is one that does not contain *all* the elements of the original set) and leaves a good deal out—namely, all of the *odd* natural numbers. It seems certain, then, that the second set could not be as numerous as the first. But consider the following correspondence:

All natural numbers: 1, 2, 3, 4, $\cdots$

$\updownarrow \updownarrow \updownarrow \updownarrow$

Even natural numbers: 2, 4, 6, 8, $\cdots$

In other words, consider the correspondence that associates its double with every number in the first set, and its half with every number in the second. Again, referring to our definition of a one-to-one correspondence, we find that we have established just such a correspondence between these two sets. Like unto the animals entering Noah's ark, two by two the numbers in each set march by, and every number in each set is accounted for. Our definition inexorably wrings from us the admission that there are as many even numbers as even and odd together—intuition, convictions, and prejudices to the contrary notwithstanding.

These startling consequences of what seem to be the most innocent of assumptions disagree even with a hallowed axiom of geometry: that which states that the whole contains more than any of its parts. It appears now that this too must be discarded. But the reader will be happy to learn that there is a way out.

It is a typical device of mathematics to shake new concepts out of a puzzling situation, *enlarging the scope of the matter under discussion*, so that what is contradictory or impossible in a narrow sphere becomes consistent or feasible in a larger one. So it is here (and so we shall discover it to be again and again as we continue our study of mathematics).

In what way, we ask ourselves, do the set of points on a line and the set of whole numbers (i.e., the sets which led us into trouble), in what way do they differ essentially from well-behaved sets like the set of fingers on a hand? The troublesome sets, you will observe, cannot be exhausted by counting 1, 2, 3, $\cdots$, while the set of fingers on a hand can be so exhausted. There is in some sense a *huge* number of objects in the first-named sets—an "infinite" (literally: "endless") number, we are inclined to say. But exactly what do we mean by "infinite"?

It is actually the contradiction that we have been discussing which offers the answer:

A set is said to be *infinite* (and so is its cardinal number) if it can be put into one-to-one correspondence with one of its proper subsets.

A set is said to be *finite* (and so is its cardinal number) if it cannot be put into one-to-one correspondence with any proper subset of itself.

What we have actually demonstrated, then, is that the set of all counting numbers and the set of all points on a line segment are each, according to our definition, infinite sets. As for our axiom of geometry, we need not altogether abandon it. It is still acceptable for finite sets and, with some clarification of terms, in other cases also. For example, a useful form of the axiom might be stated: A whole line segment is greater in *length* than any line segment that is part of it. (The reader will observe, then, that there is a great difference between the length of a line segment and the number of points which it contains.)

We have, of course, far outrun the mathematics of primitive man. The paradox of the whole numbers (although we have altered it slightly) is due to Galileo, who lived in the early seventeenth century. The concept of infinity which we have presented stems from the work of the mathematicians Bolzano, Cantor, and Dedekind, and dates from the middle and late nineteenth century.

We are now able to define "natural number" more precisely than previously. The following definition may be made the basis for a

development of the theory of natural numbers (an approach, however, that we shall not adopt in this course):

> A natural number is a finite nonzero cardinal number.

Before we put away the Pandora's box that the idea of a one-to-one correspondence has opened for us, let us look inside again for just a moment.   The set of all natural numbers, as we have shown, is not finite, and therefore the cardinal number which describes *it* could not be one of the numbers 1, 2, 3, $\cdots$.   (Indeed, no infinite set could be described by a natural number since, by definition, natural numbers describe only *finite* sets.)   In advancing the theory of cardinal numbers, the mathematician Georg Cantor, therefore, had to invent a new symbol to describe the number of natural numbers that exist, and the symbol he chose was the first letter of the Hebrew alphabet, "aleph," followed by the subscript zero: $\aleph_0$.   The symbol as a whole is read: "aleph-null."

The subscript zero was used because it turns out that, in a sense, $\aleph_0$ is the smallest of the "transfinite" numbers, that is, of the cardinal numbers that are not finite.   What is the next larger cardinal number?   We do not know.   Even at this early stage, you see, we have encountered an unsolved problem of mathematics.   We know that there *is* a larger one, for it has been proved that "c", the number that describes the set of all points on a line segment, is larger than $\aleph_0$.   But a great mystery of modern mathematics is the question of whether or not there is a cardinal number between $\aleph_0$ and c.   If the answer were to turn out to be "no," we would finally replace the symbol c by $\aleph_1$.

Other surprising consequences (which again we are constrained to state without proof, since to do so would lead us much too far afield) are the following:

It turns out not only that the number of points on any line segment, however short, is equal to the number of points on any other line segment, however long, but that the cardinal number c which describes either of these sets describes also the set of points on an endless line.   Furthermore, an entire plane has exactly this same number c, of points!   As a matter of fact, all of three-dimensional space is not a bit richer in points than any one of the sets just mentioned.   Any one of these sets can be proved to be in one-to-one correspondence with any other one, so that one symbol, c, may be used to represent the number of points in any of them.

The amazing fact, then, is that the number of points in a space large enough to encompass all of the universe—earth, sun, all the stars, the planets, the comets, the Milky Way and everything else—is not a bit

greater than (in fact is exactly equal to) the number of points in a square just large enough to cover the tiniest flyspeck.

Instead of saying that a set is *described* by a cardinal number, one might say that the set *belongs* to the cardinal number. For example, one might say that the set of letters {a, b, c} belongs to the cardinal number 3. The

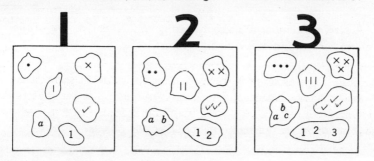

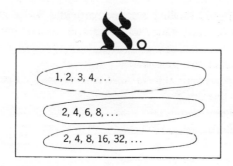

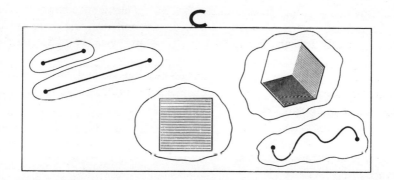

Fig. 1.4

use of the word "belongs" suggests that one may think of a cardinal number as a set. The cardinal number 3, for example, may be thought of as a set to which $\{a, b, c\}$, and $\{2, 4, 6\}$ and $\{+, !, :\}$, and all other sets in one-to-one correspondence with $\{a, b, c\}$ belong. This leads to the following definition of a cardinal number:

A cardinal number is a set consisting of all sets that are in one-to-one correspondence with a given set.

The preceding definition is somewhat sophisticated (it seems a bit odd to say that a *number* is a *set*) but, in terms of ultimate clarity and usefulness, it has turned out to be a very good definition indeed. In Fig. 1.4 several cardinal numbers are (partially) pictured as sets of sets.

▶ ***EXERCISE 3**

1. Tell which of the following sets are finite and which are infinite and, where possible, how many elements there are in each set. Justify your answers.
   (a) The grains of sand on earth.
   (b) The drops of water in all the seas and oceans on earth.
   (c) The stars in the sky.
   (d) The odd natural numbers.
   (e) The natural numbers that are "perfect squares," i.e., 1, 4, 9, 16, $\cdots$.
   (f) All points of a given line segment.
   (g) All points on the circumference of any circle.
   (h) All points on the perimeter of any square.
   (i) All points within a given square.

2. How many proper subsets does a set with n elements contain?

3. Prove, by means of a one-to-one correspondence, that any circle contains exactly as many points as a circle having twice the radius of the given circle.

4. Since a line segment is composed of two halves, and we have seen that the line segment and its halves each contain c points, we are (somewhat roughly and intuitively) led to this odd statement:

$$c + c = c$$

Using similar reasoning, can you complete the following equations of "transfinite arithmetic"?

$$\aleph_0 + \aleph_0 = ? \qquad c \cdot c = ?$$

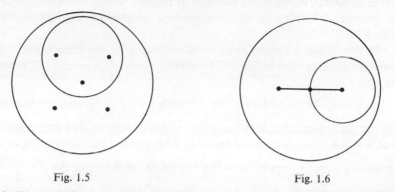

Fig. 1.5   Fig. 1.6

5. The relation "greater than" may be defined for *finite* cardinal numbers as follows: A finite cardinal number p is said to be greater than a finite cardinal number q (written: $p > q$) if there exists a set of p elements which contains a proper subset of q elements.

For example, $5 > 3$ follows from the situation pictured in Fig. 1.5.

This definition fails to work, however, in the case of infinite cardinals. For example, the set of points in any line segment contains as a proper subset the set of points in a shorter line segment (see Fig. 1.6), yet the number of elements in the first set is *not* greater than, but actually equal to, the number of points in the second. (There are, as a matter of fact, c points in each.)

What must be added to the definition to make it work for all cardinal numbers?

What, then, is actually meant by the statement: $c > \aleph_0$?

6. Criticize the following statement:

"By a space of two dimensions is meant any set of objects which may be put into one-to-one correspondence with the totality of $\cdots$."

(The student may assume, in answering this question, that a plane is a space of two dimensions and a line is not.)

7. (*a*) Show that, if J represents the set of all nn, then the set $\{a\} \cup J$ may be put into one-to-one correspondence with the set J. To what equation of transfinite arithmetic does this result lead? Similarly, for the set $\{a, b\}$ rather than for the set $\{a\}$. Generalize as far as you can.

(*b*) The mathematician Hilbert has pointed out that in a hotel with $\aleph_0$ rooms, the arrival of a new guest (or two or three or $\aleph_0$ new guests), even when every room is occupied, need never embarrass the management. How so?

8. (*a*) Prove that a line segment (with end points deleted) and a line have the same cardinal number of points by establishing a one-to-one

correspondence between the two sets of points. (*Hint:* This may be done in geometric fashion, utilizing a method similar to that displayed in Fig. 1.3.)

(*b*) Prove that a line segment (even including its end points) and a line have the same cardinal number of points. (*Hint:* Use results of Problems 8a and 7.)

(*c*) It may be proved that the formula $x \leftrightarrow \dfrac{x}{1 - x^2}$ establishes a one-to-one correspondence between a line segment with its end points deleted and a whole line. For those familiar with graphs, the plausibility of this statement may be seen by drawing the graph of the equation $y = \dfrac{x}{1 - x^2}$ over that part of the X-axis that lies between, but not including, -1 and 1. Draw this graph, and note that it establishes a one-to-one correspondence between a line segment without its end points (that part of the X-axis between, but not including -1 and 1) and a line (the whole Y-axis).

(*d*) For those who have studied trigonometry, it may be pointed out that the formula $x \leftrightarrow \tan x$ (draw the graph of the equation $y = \tan x$) also establishes a one-to-one correspondence between a line segment with end points deleted (which?) and a whole line (which?).

2 FUNCTIONS, OPERATIONS, AND RELATIONS

2.1 FUNCTIONS

The fact that we have up until now spoken always of *one-to-one* correspondences has probably led the reader to suspect that other types of correspondences exist, as indeed they do.

In early times, for example, primitive man must have known very well which of the women in his community were the wives of which men. In other words, there must have existed in his mind a "correspondence" between the set of married men and the set of married women in his community. That correspondence associated with each married man his wives and (or) with each married woman her husbands.

In a monogamous society we are led to our old friend the one-to-one correspondence. But in a polygamous society, we encounter something new. Using an arrow to point from a person to his (or her) spouse, we diagram two such cases in Fig. 2.1.

From these situations (and with many more like them in mind), one may *abstract* the concept of a *function*:

A *function* is said to be defined when:
  (i) A set D is given.
  (ii) To each element of D, one and only one object is assigned.
The set D is called the *domain* of the function.

With regard to functions, most of us are in a position very much like that of Molière's *Bourgeois Gentilhomme*, who learns one day, to his astonishment and delight, that he has been speaking "prose" all his life. Just so with functions; whether we are aware of their existence or not, we

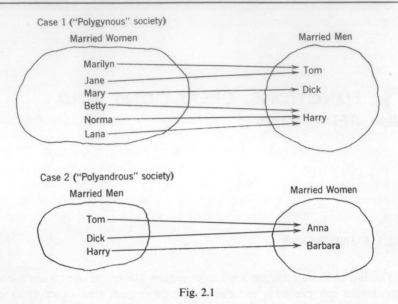

Fig. 2.1

nevertheless deal with them all the time. They are all about us, in situations both mathematical and unmathematical. Simply the frequency with which they occur in mathematical expositions justifies the stress which we shall place upon them.

Now, as an example of a function, consider case 2 in Fig. 2.1. Here we have defined a function whose domain consists of the set {Tom, Dick, Harry}. To Tom this function assigns Anna, etc.

At this point we introduce notation and further special vocabulary useful in discussing functions.

First of all, we often denote a function by a single letter. We shall, for example, use the letter m throughout the remainder of this section to represent the function defined in case 2 above.

When a function f assigns an element b to an element a, we diagram this fact as follows:

(1) $$a \overset{f}{\to} b$$

and we say: "The function f *maps* (or *sends*) a to b."

For example, we write: Tom $\overset{m}{\to}$ Anna, etc.

Another notation which is used to express exactly the same fact as (1) is:

(2) $$f(a) = b$$

which is read: "f of a equals (or is) b."

For example: m(Harry) = Barbara, etc.

If either (1) or (2) is true, we say: "Under the function f, b is the *image* of a, and a is a *pre-image* of b."

For example, we may say: "Under the function m, Anna is the image of Dick; Dick is a pre-image of Anna; etc."

All the pre-images of a given function constitute, of course, the domain of that function. All the images of a given function constitute a set called the *range* of that function.

For example, the range of the function m is the set {Anna, Barbara}.

A function is called *one-one* if each element of its range has exactly one pre-image; otherwise it is called *many-one*.

For example, m is a many-one function, since there is an element in its range (namely, Anna) which has more than one pre-image; or, reading from the diagram, the fact that two arrows point to a single element indicates that m is many-one.

To prove that a function f is one-one, it is sufficient to show:

(3) $$\text{If } f(a) = f(b), \text{ then } a = b$$

For suppose that we can show (3) to be true for a certain function f, and suppose an element c in the range of f has the pre-images a, b in the domain of f. Then $f(a) = c$ and $f(b) = c$; hence $f(a) = f(b)$, hence by (3): $a = b$. Therefore no element in the range of f can have two different pre-images; that is to say, f is one-one.

For example, consider the function f with domain all nn and mapping $f(x) = 3x + 2$. Then if $f(a) = f(b)$, there follows $3a + 2 = 3b + 2$, hence $3a = 3b$, hence $a = b$. Therefore this function f is one-one.

Conversely, if f is a one-one function, (3) must be true. For if (3) were false, then for some a, b in the domain of f we would have $f(a) = f(b)$ without having $a = b$; that is to say, there would exist two different elements a, b in the domain of f with the same image, so that f would *not* be one-one. Thus, finally: *f is a one-one function if and only if (3) is true.*

2.2 HOW A FUNCTION MAY BE SPECIFIED

A particular function may be specified by:

 (i) Telling what its domain is;
 (ii) assigning, to each element of that domain, an object.

When we have given the information (ii) above, we say that we have described the *mapping* of the function. We may, therefore, restate the opening paragraph of this section: A particular function may be specified by giving two pieces of information—its domain and its mapping.

We shall now consider two practical methods for giving the informations (i) and (ii) above. One is to list all the elements of both domain and range, and then state which element of the range is assigned to each element of the domain. This is what we have done in cases 1 and 2 above. Frequently, in using this method, the elements of the domain are written in one column (or row), and the elements of the range in a parallel column (or row), with elements of the domain and their respective images placed next to each other.

This arrangement is already familiar to the student under the name of a "table of values." Here is an example:

LOCAL PARCEL POST RATES

Weight (lbs)	1	2	3	4	5	10
Cost (cents)	18	20	21	23	24	32

We shall call this method of describing a function the "tabular" method.

The tabular method has both advantages and disadvantages; the most serious of its disadvantages is that, when the domain of the function contains a great many elements, tabulation becomes highly inconvenient or even impossible. Consider, for example, the function which assigns to each person on earth his age. To list all the inhabitants of the earth would be a staggering project! Or consider the function which assigns to each n its square. A list of all n is obviously impossible.

But these examples immediately suggest another method of specifying functions: One may *describe* the domain without actually listing all its members (as, for example, when we speak of a function whose domain is "all the inhabitants of the earth"), and one may *describe* a mapping by means of a verbal or symbolic rule (as, for example, when we assign to each person on earth his age, or to each number x of a given domain the number x^2). We speak, in this case, of a *descriptive* definition of domain or mapping.

(The student is reminded that, if x is a number, x^2 is read "x squared" and means the product $x \cdot x$; x^3 is read "x cubed" and means the product $x \cdot x \cdot x$, etc.)

Let us examine a little more closely the symbolic rule just mentioned. Phrases like "x^2 is a function of x" occur often in elementary mathematics. Examining the phrase critically, however, we see that something is lacking. There is no mention of a domain. Therefore, a function cannot have been properly defined. Actually, what the phrase does define for us symbolically is only the *mapping* of a function. We are told by the phrase to assign to each element of a yet nonexistent domain, its square.

In the study of mathematics, a good deal of confusion results from carelessness in the specification of domains of functions. We shall therefore, in the sequel, attach a great deal of importance to the proper specification of functions.

In our notation, the mapping which is implied when we say "x^2 is a function of x," may be expressed by the notation $x \leftrightarrow x^2$; or, if we assign the name g to a function with this mapping, we may express the mapping by means of the equation: $g(x) = x^2$.

It helps, in understanding functions, to form pictures (even if only mental) something like the following: (In Fig. 2.2, we diagram the function g whose domain consists of all nn and whose mapping is given in the preceding paragraph.)

The information imparted by the arrows in Fig. 2.2 may, of course, also be written: $g(1) = 1$, $g(2) = 4$, $g(3) = 9$, etc.

We see, then, that when the mapping of a function g is given by an equation like $g(x) = x^2$ this may be understood to mean that the image of any element of the domain of g may be found by mechanically substituting that element for x in the given equation. Thus.

Since $$g(x) = x^2,$$
it follows that $$g(7) = 7^2 = 49.$$

The letter of the alphabet used in defining the mapping of a function is entirely irrelevant; $y \to y^2$, $a \to a^2$, $x \to x^2$ all say the same thing, namely: "To each element of the domain, assign its square." The same, of course, is true of the alternative notation $g(x) = x^2$. The equations $g(y) = y^2$ or $g(u) = u^2$ define exactly the same mapping. Perhaps best of all (but almost never used) would be the following equation to define this mapping: $g(\ ) = (\ )^2$.

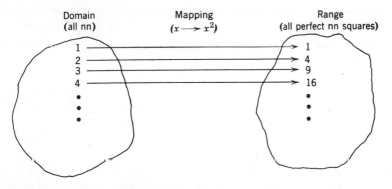

Fig. 2.2

A special type of function is given by the following example: Suppose we define h as a function whose domain is the set of all natural numbers, and whose mapping is given by $h(u) = 7$.   Then,

$$h(1) = 7$$
$$h(2) = 7$$
$$h(3) = 7, \text{ etc.}$$

Figure 2.3 gives a (partial) picture of the function h.

Here the range consists of just a single element.   A function in which the range consists of exactly one element is called a *constant* function.

NOTE 1.   Still another way of saying that $f(a) = b$ is to say: "the value of the function f at a is b;" and when function f has domain D, we say also that f is "defined on" D, or on any subset of D.   Thus a function is always *defined on* elements of its domain, and the *values* of a function are always elements of its range.

NOTE 2.   The following letters are commonly used to identify functions as they arise in a single discussion: f, g, h, F, G, H, ϕ; after that, the student's imagination may take over.

*NOTE 3.   If A is a subset of the domain D of a function f, we define $f(A)$ to be the set of all images of elements of A under the function f.

For example, suppose g is defined as in Fig. 2.2, and $S = \{1, 2, 3\}$. Then $g(S) = \{1, 4, 9\}$; or if S is the set of all even nn, then $g(S)$ is the set of all perfect nn squares that are nn multiples of 4.

Furthermore, if B is a set such that $f(A) \subset B$, we say that f maps A into B; and if actually $f(A) = B$, we say f maps A onto B.

Thus, the function g of Fig. 2.2 maps the nn into (but not onto) the nn; the same function maps the set $\{1, 2, 3\}$ onto (and into) the set $\{1, 4, 9\}$.

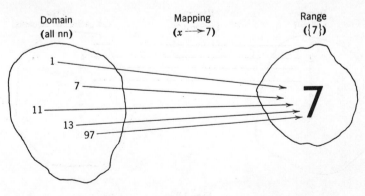

Fig. 2.3

We shall terminate this discussion by pointing out an important application of the concept of function. In the man-to-man defense in basketball, each man on the defending team chooses a man on the opposing team to guard. In this situation, an inability to distinguish between a one-one and a many-one function may spell disaster for the defenders.

2.3 EQUALITY OF FUNCTIONS

We have considered several methods of assigning objects to the elements of a set in order to establish a function. Of primary importance, however, is not *how* the objects are assigned but what the final assignment is.

We shall, therefore, consider two functions to be the same if they have the same domain and if, given any element of that domain, each function assigns the same image to that element.

For example, suppose f and g are functions, and that the domain of each is the set of nn $\{1, 2\}$. Suppose further that the mappings of f and g are given by $f(x) = x^2$, $g(x) = 3x - 2$.
Then

$$f(1) = 1 \qquad f(2) = 4$$
$$g(1) = 1 \qquad g(2) = 4$$

$f(x) = g(x)$ in domain of 1, 2 only

Therefore the functions f and g are the same, and we write: $f = g$.

▶ EXERCISE 4

1. What two pieces of information serve to define (i.e., to specify) a particular *function*? Make up an original example of a function.

2. What is meant by the *domain* of a function? Illustrate by means of an original example.

3. What is meant, in speaking of functions, by an "image?" by a "pre-image?" Illustrate with an original example.

4. What is meant by the *range* of a function? Illustrate by means of an original example.

5. What is meant by a *one-one* function? Illustrate by means of an original example.

6. What is meant by a *many-one* function? Illustrate by means of an original example.

7. Name two ways in which the mapping of a function may be specified, and make up an illustrative example of each.

8. If "f" is the name of a function, what is $f(x)$?

9. What is a *constant* function? Illustrate by means of an original example.

10. (*a*) In each of the following cases, a function is defined. In each case illustrate by means of a diagram, tell what the range of the function is, what the image of the number 3 is, what the pre-images of the given numbers are, whether the function is one-one or many-one, and if the latter, why?

	FUNCTION	DOMAIN	MAPPING	FIND PRE-IMAGES OF
(i)	f	all nn	$f(x) = 2x - 1$	11
(ii)	g	all nn	$g(y) = 2y$	20
(iii)	h	all nn	$h(u) = u^2 - 4u + 5$	2
(iv)	F	all nn	$F(p) = p^2 - 2p + 2$	5
(v)	G	$\{1, 2, 3, 4, 5\}$	$G(a) = a$	4
(vi)	H	$\{1, 2, 3\}$	$H(b) = 11$	11
(vii)	ϕ	$\{3\}$	$\phi(x) = x^2 + 2x + 1$	16
(viii)	q	$\{1, 2, 3\}$	$x \to x^3 - 6x^2 + 11x + 1$	7
(ix)	m	$\{1, 2\}$	$m(x) = x + 1$	2
(x)	r	$\{3\}$	$r(x) = 5x + 1$	16

(*b*) Which of the functions in part *a* are equal? Why?

11. In each of the following tabular functions, express the mapping by means of a formula for $f(x)$:

(*a*)		(*b*)		(*c*)		(*d*)		(*e*)		(*f*)		(*g*)		(*h*)		(*i*)	
x	$f(x)$	x	$f(x)$	x	$f(x)$	x	$f(x)$	x	$f(x)$	x	$f(x)$	x	$f(x)$	x	$f(x)$	x	$f(x)$
1	5	1	1	1	0	1	11	1	12	1	2	1	2	1	2	10	50
2	10	2	4	2	0	2	10	2	6	2	4	2	5	2	6	20	68
3	15	3	9	3	0	3	9	3	4	3	8	3	8	3	12	30	86
4	20	4	16	4	0	4	8	4	3	4	16	4	11	4	20	40	104
5	25	5	25	5	0	5	7			5	32	5	14	5	30	50	122

★(*j*) Let f represent the tabular function "Local Parcel Post Rates" of Section 2.2. *Hint:* Use the symbol ⊗ to mean $\frac{x}{2}$ if x is even, and $\frac{x-1}{2}$ if x is odd; or use.the better-known symbol $[n]$ to mean the largest integer (see Section 2.6) which does not exceed n. In the problem utilize $\left[\frac{3x}{2}\right]$.

★12. Give an example of a correspondence between two sets which might be called "many-many."

★13. As commonly used, "one" and "exactly one" are not always synonymous. Explain and illustrate by means of examples.

*14. Discuss relative advantages and disadvantages of the descriptive and tabular methods in the definition of particular functions.

*15. Suppose $A = \{0\}$, $B = \{1\}$, $C = \{0, 1\}$, $D = \{-1, 0, 1\}$, and f is a function with domain D and mapping $f(x) = x^2$. Which of the sets A, B, C, D does f map into which, and which does f map onto which?

2.4 OPERATIONS

Recorded history dates from the invention of writing, at about 3000 B.C. Before that was the era known as "prehistory." Man's acquaintance with natural numbers undoubtedly antedates recorded history; and probably still well within prehistoric times, man learned to put two and two, and other pairs of numbers, together.

In other words, having secured a firm grip on the natural numbers, man proceeded to do things like addition and multiplication with them.

But what exactly do we mean by "things like addition and multiplication?" We examine the processes of addition and multiplication to see whether we can *abstract* from them a significant general concept.

Addition and multiplication have this in common: Each, given a pair of numbers, returns to us a single number. For example, given the pair of numbers $\{7, 11\}$, addition produces the single number 18, multiplication the single number 77.

We may think in more general terms; combination is not a process which is restricted to numbers. All sorts of things may be combined: colors, for example, or chemicals, or even routes between cities. (A route joining New York and Chicago, for example, may be combined with a route between Chicago and San Francisco to give us a route joining New York and San Francisco.)

The abstraction we are getting at, then, may as well be one which assigns any sort of *object* to a given pair of *objects*, rather than one which necessarily assigns a *number* to a pair of *numbers*.

In the cases of addition and multiplication, and even in the combination of routes, the order in which the elements to be combined are written is immaterial. We should like also to include division, however, in the category of "things like addition and multiplication," and, in the case of division, order *does* make a difference; $8 \div 2$, for example, is not the same as $2 \div 8$.

The abstraction we are getting at, therefore, will be more general if it deals with *ordered* pairs (see Problem 13, Exercise 2) rather than just with pairs of objects.

But now our talking about the "assignment" of objects puts us in mind of functions; we shall call the abstraction of which addition, multiplication, and division are concrete examples an *operation*; and we shall define an operation as follows:

An *operation* in a given set is a function whose domain consists of ordered pairs of elements of the given set.

Alternative definition: An *operation* in a set S is a function whose domain is a subset of $S \times S$.

2.5 ABSTRACT PROPERTIES OF OPERATIONS

In this section we shall abstract, from operations with which we are already familiar, a number of general properties that some operations exhibit and that others do not.

Closure. Consider the well-known operation of addition in the set of nn: We observe that given any pair of nn, it is always possible to add them, and the result of the addition is always again a nn. Similarly for the operation of multiplication in the set of nn: Given any pair of nn, it is always possible to multiply them, and the result of the multiplication is always again a nn. (Note, however, that the situation is different in the case of the operation of division in the set of nn. Example?)

We are led to define an abstract property of operations called *closure*. Roughly speaking, an operation in a set S is said to be *closed* if the "results" of the operation exist for all pairs of elements of S, and are themselves always elements of S; in order to define closure more precisely, we shall introduce a special mathematical symbol.

The student is already familiar with the very useful device of using letters of the alphabet to represent numbers in making general statements about numbers, as for example in the well-known statement: "If a and b are natural numbers, then $a(b + c) = ab + ac$."

In making general statements about operations, we find it similarly useful to have special symbols to represent operations. We shall find just one such symbol, ∘, sufficient for our purposes here. For example, here is how we shall use this symbol to define closure precisely:

An operation ∘ in a set S is said to be *closed* (we also say that S is closed under ∘) if, for all elements a, b belonging to S, $a \circ b$ is defined and belongs to S also.

Commutativity. This property of operations stems from observations such as the following:

$$2 + 3 = 3 + 2 \quad 4 + 7 = 7 + 4 \quad 2 \cdot 3 = 3 \cdot 2 \quad 4 \cdot 7 = 7 \cdot 4$$

However, these statements are not true, and, in fact in some situations (e.g., restricting ourselves to the nn), not even always meaningful when $+$ and $\cdot$ are replaced by $-$ and $\div$.

We are led to the following definition:

> An operation $\circ$ defined in a set S is said to be *commutative* if, for all elements a, b in S, $a \circ b = b \circ a$.

For example, addition in the set of nn is a commutative operation, since, for any pair of nn a, b, $a + b = b + a$.

Associativity. In applying the operation of addition to the numbers 1, 2, 3 in that order, one may add the first to the second, and then that sum to the third:

$$(1 + 2) + 3 = 3 + 3 = 6$$

or one may add the first to the sum of the second two:

$$1 + (2 + 3) = 1 + 5 = 6$$

Parentheses, brackets, and other "grouping symbols" are often used, as above, to enclose symbols for elements of sets (most often sets of numbers). The preceding equation may be read, for example: "The number $1 + 2$ plus the number 3 is equal to $\cdots$," or "The element $1 + 2$ plus the element 3 is equal to $\cdots$." Here the parentheses help us to see that although "$1 + 2$" consists of several marks on the paper, this conglomeration of marks constitutes merely a symbol for a single number; a simpler symbol for the same number is, of course, "3."

Either of the above methods of summing the numbers 1, 2, 3 leads, to no one's surprise, to the same result. In general, if a, b, c are any triple of nn, we all know that both of the following are true:

$$a + (b + c) = (a + b) + c \quad a \cdot (b \cdot c) = (a \cdot b) \cdot c$$

But similar statements are *not* true for all operations. For example, consider the operation of division in the set of all nn. It is easy to verify that $8 \div (4 \div 2)$ and $(8 \div 4) \div 2$ are *not* equal.

We are led to the following definition:

> An operation $\circ$ defined in a set S is said to be *associative* if, for all elements a, b, c in S, $(a \circ b) \circ c = a \circ (b \circ c)$.

We note now that it is only because $+$ is associative that we may write the expression $1 + 2 + 3$ without parentheses; for the associativity of $+$ means that either of the two reasonable interpretations, $1 + (2 + 3)$ and $(1 + 2) + 3$, of the expression $1 + 2 + 3$ leads to the same result.

In general, if $\circ$ is an associative operation, we *define* $a \circ b \circ c$ to mean either of the equal-valued possibilities $a \circ (b \circ c)$ or $(a \circ b) \circ c$.

In the case $1 + 2 + 3 + 4$, parentheses and brackets may be inserted in many more than two ways. However, as a consequence of the associativity of $+$, it turns out that all lead to the same result. In general, when we write an expression like $a \circ b \circ c \circ d$, where $\circ$ is an associative operation (or a similar expression with even more than four elements), we shall mean any one of the different associations of these elements, all of which lead to the same result. (We shall later refer to the definitions in this paragraph and the preceding as the *grouping definitions*.)

Distributivity.   Distributivity properties involve *two* operations rather than one. We shall leave a general statement of these properties to an exercise; here, however, we shall give two very important instances, involving the operations $+$ and $\cdot$, defined on the nn.

We all know that 5 dozen is the sum of 3 dozen and 2 dozen, and that 11 dimes is the sum of 7 dimes and 4 dimes. That is to say:

$$5\cdot12 = 3\cdot12 + 2\cdot12 \quad \text{and} \quad 11\cdot10 = 7\cdot10 + 4\cdot10$$

In other words:

$$(3 + 2)\cdot12 = 3\cdot12 + 2\cdot12 \quad \text{and} \quad (7 + 4)\cdot10 = 7\cdot10 + 4\cdot10$$

In fact, if a, b, c are any triple of nn, then,

$$(a + b)c = ac + bc$$

It follows, since multiplication is commutative among the nn, that if a, b, c are any triple of nn, then also,

$$c(a + b) = ca + cb$$

The last two equations are referred to as the *right* and *left distributive laws*, respectively.

We terminate this section with several notes on its contents.

NOTE 1.   Another use for the symbol $\circ$ is in *defining* particular operations. For example, we may define an operation $\circ$ in the set of nn in the following way: the domain of $\circ$ is defined to be the set of *all* ordered pairs of nn, and if x, y are nn, the mapping of $\circ$ is given by

$$x \circ y = x + 2y$$

Thus
$$1 \circ 1 = 1 + 2\cdot1 = 3$$
$$1 \circ 3 = 1 + 2\cdot3 = 7$$
$$3 \circ 1 = 3 + 2\cdot1 = 5, \text{ etc.}$$

Since for every pair of nn, x, y, it is true that $x + 2y$ is again a nn, the operation is closed.   The fact that $1 \circ 3$ and $3 \circ 1$ have turned out to be unequal justifies our saying that this operation is not commutative.   As for associativity, note that

$$(1 \circ 1) \circ 1 = 3 \circ 1 = 5$$
$$1 \circ (1 \circ 1) = 1 \circ 3 = 7$$

This single "counterexample" proves that our operation is not associative.

As in the case of functions, the "dummy" letters used to define an operation are immaterial. $x \circ y = x + 2y$ might just as well be expressed as $u \circ v = u + 2v$, etc.

NOTE 2.   What we have defined as an *operation* is sometimes called a *binary* operation to emphasize that it works on *pairs* of objects.   Sometimes, however, the word "operation" is used to apply to something like a square root, which works only on one object.   In that case we shall call the operation a "unary".operation.

With regard to the general properties of operations discussed above, only the term "closed" applies to unary operations.   In fact, there is no difference between a unary operation defined on all elements of a set S and a function defined on S.

NOTE 3.   There is ambiguity in writing an expression like $7 \cdot 10 + 4 \cdot 10$, as we have above.   What we intend it to mean is $70 + 40$, or 110.   It might, however, be taken to mean $7 \cdot (10 + 4) \cdot 10$, or 980.   To avoid this possible misinterpretation, we agree that, in ambiguous situations, multiplication and division shall precede addition or subtraction.

▶ **EXERCISE 5**

1. What is an operation?   Make up an original example of an operation.

2. With respect to operations, what is meant by closure? commutativity? associativity?

3. Suppose S is the set of primary colors red, yellow, blue, and the operation $\circ$ in S is that of mixing colors.   Is this operation closed? commutative? associative?   (Justify your answers.)

4. Two nn are said to have the same *parity* if both are even or if both are odd.   We define an operation $\circ$ in the set of nn as follows: The domain of $\circ$ consists of all ordered pairs of nn; $x \circ y = 1$ if x and y are nn of the same parity, and $x \circ y = 0$ if x and y are not of the same parity (referred to sometimes as being of "opposite" parity).   Discuss this operation as in Problem 3.

5. Make up a chart, showing for each of the operations $+$, $\cdot$, $-$, $\div$, defined in the set of nn, whether or not it is closed, associative, or commutative.

6. In each of the following cases, an operation $\circ$ is defined in the set of all nn. In each case, find $8 \circ 2$. Also, in each case discuss the given operation with respect to general properties of operations which it does or does not exhibit, as in Note 1 of this section.

(a) $x \circ y = x + 3y$ (b) $x \circ y = 2x - y$

(c) $x \circ y = 1 + xy$ (d) $x \circ y = x + y + 1$

(e) $x \circ y = x^2 + y$ (f) $x \circ y = \sqrt{xy}$

(g) $x \circ y = x$

7. The numbers of the sum $1 + 2 + 3 + 4$ may be "associated" by finding $1 + 2$ first, then adding the result to 3, and then adding *that* result to 4; i.e.,

$$[(1 + 2) + 3] + 4 = [3 + 3] + 4 = 6 + 4 = 10$$

Indicate, by means of parentheses and brackets, four other associations of the numbers of the given sum, and show that each of them adds up to 10.

*8. Suppose that a, b, c, d are members of a set on which an associative operation $\circ$ is defined. Find all possible associations of the expression $a \circ b \circ c \circ d$ and prove that they are all equal to each other.

*9. Suppose that in the preceding problem, five rather than four elements were given. How many associations would exist in that case?

*10. Devise a method for computing the number of ways in which n elements may be associated, given a particular operation. Use your method to find the number of ways in which 10 elements may be associated.

*11. The first distributive law stated above is more precisely called "the left distributive law of multiplication over addition."

Suppose "$\circ$" and "$*$" represent two operations in a set S. Write and name several distributive laws involving $\circ$ and $*$.

*12. Which of the following subsets of the nn are closed under $+$? under $\cdot$? under $-$? under $\div$?

(a) The set of all even nn.

(b) The set of all odd nn.

(c) The set of all nn.

(d) $\{0\}$.

(e) $\{1\}$.

(f) $\{0, 1\}$.

*13. The same as Problem 4, except that $x \circ y = 3$ if x and y are of opposite parity.

*14. Suppose S is the set of all subsets of a given set T. Then $\cap$ and $\cup$, as defined in Section 1.6, are actually operations in S.

Discuss the operations $\cap$ and $\cup$ in S with respect to closure, etc. (include the question of distributivity).

2.6 RATIONAL NUMBERS AND INTEGERS

A long time ago, when man knew of no numbers but the nn, the operations of subtraction and division in the set of nn were not "complete" (i.e. not defined on *all* pairs of nn).

But probably some time before 3000 B.C., the ancient Egyptians and Babylonians invented *common fractions* (or, as they are usually called by mathematicians, *positive rational numbers*) precisely in order to make the operation of division in the set of nn complete; i.e., to make it possible, given any two nn, to divide either by the other.

This remedied one deficiency in the number system of ancient times. It is a curious fact, however, that *negative numbers* and the number 0, which make it possible to subtract any nn from any other (i.e., which make the operation of subtraction in the set of nn complete), did not come into general use until about 1637 A.D., when Descartes used them in constructing coordinate systems (see Section 2.11).

The following formally defined sets of numbers are essentially enlargements of the set of nn which arose historically in an attempt to make complete, operations which were not complete.

The *positive rational numbers* consist of all those numbers which may be written in the form $\frac{a}{b}$, where a and b are nn.

The *integers* consist of the nn, their negatives, and 0.

The *rational numbers* consist of the positive rational numbers, their negatives, and 0.

Special notice should be taken of the phrase "may be written" in the above definition of a positive rational number. Observe that, because of this phrasing, *all positive (terminating) decimals are positive rational numbers*. For example, 0.23 is a positive rational number, since 0.23 may be written as the following fraction whose numerator and denominator are nn: $\frac{23}{100}$. We say that 0.23 is a positive rational number written in "decimal form."

Since the nn are precisely those integers that are neither negative nor zero, it is not hard to see why the nn are sometimes called the "positive integers."

We shall soon show that every rational number may be written as a "ratio" of (i.e., as a fraction composed of) two integers. For example, the rational number $-\frac{2}{3}$ may be written $\frac{-2}{3}$. It is this expressibility of a rational number as the *ratio* of integers that accounts for the name *ratio*nal number. The student should remember this fact to avoid popular misunderstandings as to the nature of rational and "irrational" (i.e., not-rational) numbers. Thus, to say that a number is irrational means simply that it cannot be represented as the ratio of two integers; it does *not* necessarily mean, for example, that "the number is equal to a square root that does not come out 'exactly.'" A classical example of a number that is irrational, but that has nothing to do with the extraction of roots, is the number that is equal to the circumference of a circle of diameter 1, the number π. (The rational numbers 22/7 and 314/100 and even 314,159/100,000 are all *approximations* to π; none of them is actually equal to π.)

Just as in the cases we have discussed, every enlargement which our number system has undergone may be explained as the consequence of a need or desire to make some particular incomplete operation complete.

In fact, we have introduced "completeness" into our discussion of properties of operations primarily because of the unusually important role that this concept plays in helping us to understand why and how new mathematics has developed out of old.

2.7 THE QUESTION OF DIVISION BY ZERO

What is $6 \div 3$? The answer, of course, is: 2. But why? The reason is: $3 \cdot 2 = 6$.

In fact, the justification for the answer to any problem of division is always a statement involving multiplication. This is because division is *defined* in terms of multiplication; we say $a \div b = c$ only if: $a = bc$.

Now we consider the question: $1 \div 0 = ?$

Here the problem is to find a number such that 0 times that number equals 1.

But it is a fundamental property of our number system that 0 times *any* number is 0, and *not* 1. Therefore $1 \div 0$ can never be defined as a number—unless we are willing to give up the rule that 0 times any number is 0.

To give up that rule, however, would mean a serious loss in the applicability of mathematics to practical problems. For example, the area of a rectangle is the product of its length and its width. Suppose a rectangle has zero width; then no matter what its length, we should not like to assign to it an area of anything but zero.

Furthermore, this property of zero is the consequence of even more fundamental properties of numbers (as we shall demonstrate in Chapter 4), so that defining $1 \div 0$, as indeed defining $N \div 0$ for any real number N different from 0, would necessitate discarding more than one basic and useful property of numbers.

The price is too high. We therefore abandon the project of making the operation of division complete by enlarging the set upon which the operation is defined.

In dividing by zero, a case we have not yet considered is: $0 \div 0 = ?$

In dividing a nonzero number by zero, the difficulty we encountered was that of finding any answer at all; in dividing zero by zero, we find ourselves at an opposite extreme: too many answers are possible. For the problem, in the latter case, is to find a number which, when multiplied by 0, will equal 0. But *any* number times 0 equals 0; *any* number, therefore, might serve as an answer to the problem: $0 \div 0 = ?$

Actually, none of the possibilities would serve any useful purpose. We therefore always refrain from defining $N \div 0$, whether N is zero or not. Thus the expression $a \div b$ will always be meaningless when $b = 0$, as will also be the fraction $\frac{a}{b}$, since $\frac{a}{b} = a \div b$.

The operation of division, then, will always fail to be complete on any set of numbers which contains zero. *Division by zero is never to be allowed.*

▶ **EXERCISE 6**

1. Define and give several examples of each of the following: (*a*) integer; (*b*) positive rational number; (*c*) rational number.

2. The integers serve to make what operation in the set of nn complete?

3. The positive rational numbers serve to make what operation in what set complete?

4. The rational numbers serve to make what operation in what set complete?

5. (*a*) Is 7 a rational number? Justify your answer.

(*b*) Is every integer a rational number? Justify your answer.

6. (*a*) Is 0.13 a rational number? Is 1.13 a rational number? Justify your answers.

(*b*) Define "decimal" or "decimal fraction."

(*c*) Is every decimal a rational number? Justify your answer.

7. Draw an Euler diagram (see Section 1.5) to illustrate the inclusion relationships among the sets in each of the following cases:

(*a*) Integers; nn; rational numbers.

(*b*) Rational numbers; positive rational numbers; positive integers.

8. The same as Problem 5, Exercise 5, except that nn wherever it appears in that problem is to be replaced by: (*a*) integers; (*b*) positive rational numbers; (*c*) rational numbers.

9. An operation ∘ (called "averaging") is defined in the set of positive rational numbers as follows: $x \circ y = (x + y)/2$. Discuss this operation ∘ with respect to general properties of operations which it does or does not exhibit.

10. What number is $6 - 2$ equal to? Why? In terms of what operation may every subtraction be justified? In general, under what circumstance shall we allow ourselves to say that $a - b = c$?

2.8 SYSTEMS OF NOTATION FOR POSITIVE INTEGERS

The system for writing positive integers that is most familiar to us is the "decimal place-value" system, and we shall therefore consider this system first.

From the name "decimal" it would seem that the number ten plays a special role in this system, as indeed it does. We shall therefore find it convenient in this section to use the letter t as an abbreviation for the number ten.

Now observe that, when we write, for example, the number 429, we actually mean 4 hundreds + 2 tens + 9, i.e., $4t^2 + 2t + 9$. (When a positive integer is large, it is easier to carry out its evaluation by reading from right to left. For example, $12{,}345{,}678 = 8 + 7t + 6t^2 + 5t^3 + 4t^4 + 3t^5 + 2t^6 + t^7$.)

Note that only the digits 0, 1, ⋯, 9 are used in writing a positive integer in this system, and that the digit 0 is used only to indicate the omission of a power of t, reading from right to left. Thus 10 (read "one oh") means a number in whose evaluation the "units" place is omitted and $1t$, i.e., t is included; hence $10 = t =$ ten.

The use of the "base" ten in identifying positive integers is the consequence of a physiological accident: ten, of course, is the number of fingers on most pairs of hands. But at various times and places other bases have been used; recently, for example, the base two has found important application in the fast-growing field of electronic computer mathematics.

Because knowledge of nondecimal bases of numerations now has utilitarian value, and because this knowledge helps in gaining insight into more commonly used mathematics, we shall consider nondecimal systems in this section also.

By way of example, we shall begin with an examination of the base five. Just as the decimal system uses the ten digits $0, \cdots, 9$ to write all positive integers, so the base-five system uses only the five digits $0, \cdots, 4$. Writing in the base five, the number 123, for example, means $3 + 2 \cdot 5 + 1 \cdot 5^2$, i.e., the number that in the base ten is written 38. In the sequel, we shall specify the base in which a positive integer is written by the use of a subscript, except that the omission of a subscript will indicate that the base ten is to be understood unless otherwise noted. Thus,

$$(123)_5 = (38)_{10} = 38$$

Similarly, numbers written in other bases may easily be converted to our ordinary decimal notation for numbers. But what about the converse problem? Suppose, for example, that we were asked to express the number 601 in the base-five system. Then we might proceed as follows: First find the highest power of 5 that does not exceed 601, namely, $5^3 = 125$. Then find the largest integer multiple of that power that does not exceed 601, namely, $4 \cdot 125 = 500$. Subtracting this result from 601, we now know that

$$601 = 4 \cdot 5^3 + 101$$

Now repeat the process with 101:

$$101 = 4 \cdot 5^2 + 1$$

Thus,

$$601 = 4 \cdot 5^3 + 4 \cdot 5^2 + 1 = (4401)_5$$

Just as in the decimal system, addition and multiplication tables are useful aids in computation. We work out these tables below:

BASE-FIVE TABLES

+	1	2	3	4
1	2	3	4	10
2	3	4	10	11
3	4	10	11	12
4	10	11	12	13

×	2	3	4
2	4	11	13
3	11	14	22
4	13	22	31

The entry $(4)_5 \cdot (4)_5 = (31)_5$, for example, may be arrived at as follows:

$$(4)_5 \cdot (4)_5 = 4 \cdot 4 = 16 = 3 \cdot 5 + 1 = (31)_5$$

One of the beauties of the results we shall attain in Chapter 4 as consequences of our fundamental assumptions is that among these results will be familiar processes of decimal arithmetic, and we will know that they apply equally well to the base-five system; for it is a single system of numbers with which we deal. Only the way we denote numbers changes. "Carrying" processes in adding and multiplying, for example, remain unchanged, but bear in mind that addition and multiplication *tables* differ in different systems.

Illustrative Example 1. Add and multiply $(13)_5$ and $(44)_5$, and check the results by working out these problems in the decimal system.

SOLUTION. Writing in the base five:

$$
\begin{array}{cc}
13 & 13 \\
+44 & \times 44 \\
\hline
112 & 112 \\
 & 112 \\
\hline
 & 1232
\end{array}
$$

Checking, we first convert to base ten:

$$(13)_5 = 1 \cdot 5 + 3 = 8; \quad (44)_5 = 4 \cdot 5 + 4 = 24.$$
$$8 + 24 = 32; \quad (112)_5 = 1 \cdot 25 + 1 \cdot 5 + 2 = 32 \surd.$$
$$8 \cdot 24 = 192; \quad (1232)_5 = 2 + 3 \cdot 5 + 2 \cdot 25 + 1 \cdot 125 = 192 \surd.$$

The base two demands least in the way of addition and multiplication tables. Indeed, it is only necessary to compute:

$$(1)_2 + (1)_2 = 1 + 1 = 2 = 1 \cdot 2 = (10)_2$$

(Here again 10 is best read "one-oh.")

Illustrative Example 2. Write 23 and 12 in the base-two notation. Add and multiply these numbers in the base-two system and check as above.

SOLUTION,

$$23 = 1 \cdot 2^4 + 1 \cdot 2^2 + 1 \cdot 2 + 1 = (10111)_2$$
$$12 = 1 \cdot 2^3 + 1 \cdot 2^2 = (1100)_2$$

Writing in the base two:

$$
\begin{array}{r}
10111 \\
+ \quad 1100 \\
\hline
100011
\end{array}
\qquad
\begin{array}{r}
10111 \\
\times \quad 1100 \\
\hline
1011100 \\
10111 \quad\ \\
\hline
100010100
\end{array}
$$

Checking:

$23 + 12 = 35; \quad 100,011 = 1 + 1 \cdot 2 + 1 \cdot 2^5 = 35 \checkmark.$
$23 \cdot 12 = 276; \quad 100,010,100 = 1 \cdot 2^2 + 1 \cdot 2^4 + 1 \cdot 2^8 = 276 \checkmark.$

The base twelve has long been advocated (there even exists a "Duodecimal Society") as a replacement for our present decimal system—the main point in its favor being the fact that 12 has more divisors than 10.

We note that in the base twelve two new digits are necessary; we shall use t for ten and e for eleven.

Illustrative Example 3. Find $(t)_{12} + (t)_{12}$ and $(2)_{12} \times (e)_{12}$.

SOLUTION

$$(t)_{12} + (t)_{12} = 10 + 10 = 20 = 1 \cdot 12 + 8 = (18)_{12}$$
$$(2)_{12} \cdot (e)_{12} = 2 \cdot 11 = 22 = 1 \cdot 12 + t = (1t)_{12}$$

▶ **EXERCISE 7**

1. Express the following positive integers in the base ten notation.

(a) $(12)_3$ (b) $(123)_4$ (c) $(13)_2$ (d) $(2345)_6$
(e) $(101,010)_2$ (f) $(200)_{12}$ (g) $(t0e)_{12}$ (h) $(1et)_{12}$

2. Express (a) 1492 and (b) 1776 in each of the following bases:

(i) 2   (ii) 3   (iii) 5   (iv) 10   (v) 12

3. Assuming that the following pairs of numbers are written in the base five, find the sum and product of each pair in the base five, and check by working out these problems in the decimal system.

(a) 10, 4   (b) 3, 11   (c) 13, 11   (d) 12, 21
(e) 22, 33   (f) 123, 4   (g) 123, 41   (h) 123, 42

4. (a) Construct addition and multiplication tables for the base four.

(*b*) Assuming that the following pairs of numbers are written in the base four, find the sum and product of each pair in the base four, and check by working out these problems in the decimal system.

(i) 10, 3   (ii) 3, 11   (iii) 13, 11   (iv) 12, 21
(v) 22, 33   (vi) 123, 3   (vii) 123, 31   (viii) 123, 32

5. (*a*) Construct addition and multiplication tables for the base twelve.

(*b*) Assuming that the following pairs of numbers are written in the base twelve, find the sum and product of each pair in the base twelve, and check by working out these problems in the decimal system.

(i) 10, 4   (ii) 3, 11   (iii) 13, 11   (iv) 12, 21
(v) *e*, *tee*   (vi) *et*, *te*   (vii) 10, 10   (viii) 123, 32

6. A short-cut method of expressing a positive integer n in the base b is the following: Divide n by b, arriving at a quotient and a remainder; divide that quotient by b, arriving at a second quotient and a second remainder; continue until a quotient less than b is obtained. Writing the last quotient and then the successive remainders in an order opposite to that in which they were obtained gives the desired representation of n in the base b.

For example, suppose we wish to write 601 in the base 5. The work may be arranged as follows:

5	601	
	120	1
	24	0
	4	4

Therefore, $601 = (4401)_5$.

Explain why this method works, first in the above example, then in general. (*Hint:* Express 601 in terms of powers of five, n in terms of powers of b, and carry out the above process of division.)

7. Discuss the advantages and disadvantages of the bases two and twelve over the base ten.

2.9 THE REAL NUMBERS

The set of rational numbers contains all the other kinds of numbers we have discussed (which?), but the rational numbers are themselves only a part of a larger collection of numbers, called *the real numbers*.

The real numbers are of overwhelming importance in mathematics: Most of the functions we shall study will be defined on sets of real numbers; very nearly all the mathematics leading into and including calculus may be thought of as a study of the properties of real numbers.

We shall therefore, in due time, study these numbers carefully and in detail. Just now it will be our purpose simply to attain an intuitive grasp of what is meant by a real number.

Suppose that, on a given straight line, we choose two different points, labeling one 0 and the other 1:

(*Note:* From now on, "line" will mean "straight line," unless otherwise noted.)

Then in a "natural" sort of way, every other point on the line may be assigned a label also:

That is to say, we may think of the line segment with end points 0 and 1, as a unit of measure. In the diagram above, the point on our line a distance of one unit to the right of 1 is labeled 2; the point mid-way in distance between 0 and 1 is labeled $\frac{1}{2}$; to the left of 0 we proceed similarly, except that a negative sign is affixed to each label; and so on. If negative signs are disregarded, the label of a point represents its distance from the point 0.

The line so labeled is called a *scaled line*.

The real numbers may be thought of as the numbers that are used to label all the points of a scaled line. The *positive* real numbers are those that are not 0, and that label points on the same side of 0 as the point labeled 1 (on the usual scaled line, the points to the *right* of 0). The *negative* real numbers are those that are not 0, and that label points on the same side of 0 as the point labeled -1 (on the usual scaled line the points to the *left* of 0). (*Note that the real number* 0 *is neither a positive real number nor a negative real number.*) Finally, if a, b are real numbers, we say a is *greater than b* (written $a > b$), and b is *less than a* (written $b < a$) if, on the usual scaled line, the point labeled a lies to the right of the point labeled b.

It is the representation of real numbers by means of points on a line that is responsible for the name "real." They were so named in contrast with "imaginary" numbers, which for a long time had no such pictorial representation. (We shall consider imaginary numbers later on.)

The edge of a ruler and a thermometer scale are examples of scaled line segments. The numbers we see printed on rulers and on thermometer scales are, therefore, examples of real numbers. Hence real numbers include natural numbers and their negatives; zero; positive and negative rational numbers; and, as we shall see, *many other numbers besides.*

2.10 ELEMENTARY OPERATIONS ON REAL NUMBERS

In this section we shall (largely intuitively) review some important properties of the operations addition, subtraction, multiplication, and division as they apply to real numbers.

If we think of a positive real number as representing a gain, a negative real number a loss, and "$+$" as meaning "followed by," the usual rules for addition of signed numbers are easily arrived at. For example, $(-2) + (4) = 2$, since a loss of 2 followed by a gain of 4 amounts to a gain of 2. Similarly, we see that $(-6) + (4) = -2$, and $(-3) + (-4) = -7$.

In phrasing general rules for the addition of real numbers, it is convenient to use the concept of *absolute value.* Every real number a is assigned a value called its absolute (or "numerical") value, and denoted $|a|$ (read "the absolute value of a"). If a is a positive real number, we define both $|a|$ and $|-a|$ to equal a. Thus, $|7| = 7$; $|-7| = 7$. Finally, we define $|0| = 0$. (Later on we shall present an alternative definition of absolute value, more useful in other situations.)

Now we state laws for the addition of real numbers, suggested by examples similar to those above:

(i) *Addition of real numbers is commutative.*

(ii) *If a is any real number, $a + 0 = a$.*

(iii) *The sum of a positive number and a negative number is: the positive difference of their absolute values if the positive number has the greater absolute value; the negative difference of their absolute values if the negative number has the greater absolute value; and zero if the positive number and the negative number are equal in absolute value.*

Or equivalently: If a, b are positive real numbers, we define $a + (-b)$ as follows: $a + (-b) = a - b$ if $a > b$; $a + (-b) = -(b - a)$ if $b > a$; $a + (-b) = 0$ if $a = b$.

[From the last equation, it follows that, if a is any positive real number, $a + (-a) = 0$.]

(iv) *If a and b are positive real numbers, $(-a) + (-b) = -(a + b)$.*

Up to this point, when we have spoken of the real number $-a$, a has always been a positive real number. But now we shall find it convenient to define $-a$ even when a is a negative real number or zero. We are guided by the above remark in brackets to define $-a$, for *any* real number a, as the real number that, when added to a, will yield 0. Thus, $-(-6) = 6$, since 6 is the real number that when added to -6 yields 0. Similarly we see that $-0 = 0$. In fact we may now state:

(v) *If a is any real number, $a + (-a) = 0$, and $-(-a) = a$.*

NOTE: If a is any real number, it is well to read $-a$ as "the opposite of a," reserving the word "minus" to indicate *subtraction of a pair* of numbers and "negative" for numbers known to be less than 0. Thus, reading $7 - (-2)$ as "seven minus the opposite of 2" will help to avoid confusion that may result because of the several senses in which the symbol "$-$" is used.

To work out a rule for the subtraction of real numbers, it is necessary to understand (see Exercise 6, Problem 10) that, if F is a first real number and S is a second real number, then $F - S$ means a third real number T that, when added to the second, S, will yield the first, F. That is to say, when we write $F - S = T$, we mean $F = T + S$. Thus, $6 - 2 = 4$ is true just because $6 = 4 + 2$.

With this understanding, it is not hard to see that, if F, S are any real numbers, then it will always be true that $F - S = F + (-S)$. For if we think of F, S, as before, as being a first real number and a second real number respectively, and $F + (-S)$ as being a third real number, then to demonstrate that the first minus the second is equal to the third it is sufficient to show that the third plus the second is equal to the first. But $[F + (-S)] + S = F + [(-S) + S] = F + 0 = F$, so that the statement $F - S = F + (-S)$ is justified.

We highlight two special cases of the preceding result to serve us in carrying out the subtraction of real numbers:

Suppose $F = a$ and $S = b$, where b is positive. Then the statement that $F - S = F + (-S)$ may be written:

(vi) *If a, b are real numbers and b is positive, then $a - b = a + (-b)$.*
[For example: $7 - 11 = 7 + (-11) = -4$; $-7 - 11 = -7 + (-11) = -18$.]

On the other hand, suppose $F = a$ and $S = -b$, where b is positive. Then the statement $F - S = F + (-S)$ leads to $a - (-b) = a + [-(-b)] = a + b$. Therefore, we may say:

(vii) *If a, b are real numbers and b is positive, then $a - (-b) = a + b$.*
[For example: $7 - (-11) = 7 + 11 = 18$; $-7 - (-11) = -7 + 11 = 4$.]

Finally, directly from statement (ii) there follows (see Exercise 6, Problem 10):

(viii) *If a is any real number, $a - a = 0$.*

It is very much worth noting that our argument, in deriving the equation $F - S = F + (-S)$, has leaned heavily upon certain prior facts—one of which we have not yet demonstrated nor even stated.   When we say above that $[F + (-S)] + S = F + [(-S) + S]$, that statement can be justified only if we know that the operation of addition in the set of all real numbers has the property of *associativity*.   That it does in fact have this property can be shown, but we shall not do so just now, since our goal in this section is not to achieve a watertight logical system but only to arrive at certain useful statements that seem at least not implausible.   In Chapter 4 we shall take a much more careful and extensive look at the real number system.

We come now to the question of *multiplication* of real numbers.   The statements we shall frame will be based upon certain properties that we wish to hold true for real numbers, principally the left and right distributive properties (see Section 2.5).   For example, if the left distributive law is to hold true for real numbers, then $2(2 + 0) = 2 \cdot 2 + 2 \cdot 0 = 4 + 2 \cdot 0$; but on the other hand, $2(2 + 0) = 2(2) = 4$.   Therefore, $4 + 2 \cdot 0 = 4$.   (Why?)   Now the only number that yields 4 when added to 4 is 0.   Therefore $2 \cdot 0$ must be 0, if the left distributive law is to hold true.   Similarly, for $0 \cdot 2$, and indeed for the product of *any* real number and 0.   Since we do wish the very useful distributive laws to hold true for real numbers, we have no choice but to make the following definitions, for any real number a:

(ix) $a \cdot 0 = 0$; $0 \cdot a = 0$.

Consider now the product $2[3 + (-3)]$.   On the one hand, we want to be able to say: $2[3 + (-3)] = 2 \cdot 3 + 2(-3) = 6 + 2(-3)$.   On the other hand, $2[3 + (-3)] = 2(0) = 0$.   Thus, we are led to: $6 + 2(-3) = 0$.   But the only number that yields 0 when added to 6 is -6.   We therefore define $2(-3)$ to be -6.   Similarly, for any positive real numbers a and b, we are forced into defining:

(x) $a(-b) = -(ab)$; $(-a)b = -(ab)$.

(Justification of the second half of the above statement will be left as an exercise for the student.)

Finally, consider the product $-2[(3) + (-3)]$.   On the one hand, still on the assumption that the left distributive law holds true, $-2[(3) + (-3)] = (-2)(3) + (-2)(-3) = -6 + (-2)(-3)$.   On the other hand, $-2[3 + (-3)] = -2(0) = 0$.   Therefore, $-6 + (-2)(-3) = 0$. Since the only number that yields 0 when added to -6 is 6, we define $(-2)(-3)$ to be 6.   Similarly, for any pair of positive real numbers a and b, we are led to define:

(xi) $(-a)(-b) = ab$.

Thus, in defining products of real numbers, we have been guided by the desire that certain useful properties, familiar to us in our work with some of the real numbers, shall be exhibited by all real numbers. It is now something of a problem to show conversely that, having made the only definitions possible under the given desired conditions, the desired laws really do follow from the definitions we have made. Although this can be done, we shall not do so, since our more careful treatment in Chapter 4 will take care of the matter by means of a somewhat different approach.

Finally, we consider *division* of real numbers. As in the past, we make our conclusions concerning division depend upon the relationship between the operations of division and multiplication. (See especially Section 2.7.) For example, we know immediately that $6 \div (-2) = -3$, since (-2) $(-3) = 6$. Similarly, and more generally, we conclude that if a, b are positive real numbers:

(xii) $a \div (-b) = -(a \div b)$; $(-a) \div (b) = -(a \div b)$; $(-a) \div (-b)$ $= a \div b$.

Note that rule statement (xii) may also be written:

$$\frac{a}{-b} = -\frac{a}{b} \qquad \frac{-a}{b} = -\frac{a}{b} \qquad \frac{-a}{-b} = \frac{a}{b}$$

Statements (x) through (xii) may be summarized: *Products and quotients of real numbers maintain absolute values; the product and quotient of two numbers with like sign are positive, of two numbers with unlike sign negative.* (Two real numbers are said to be of *like sign* if they are both positive or both negative; of *unlike sign* if one is positive and the other is negative.)

▶ **EXERCISE 8**

1. In each of the following cases, find the absolute value of each number; the sum of each ordered pair of numbers; the absolute value of the sum; the sum of the absolute values of the numbers.

(a) (2, 1)   (b) (−2, 1)   (c) (2, −1)   (d) (−2, −1)
(e) (2, −2)   (f) (10, 5)   (g) (−10, 5)   (h) (10, −5)
(i) (−10, −5)   (j) (1, −1)   (k) (0, 1)   (l) (0, −1)

2. From the results of Problem 1, induce a conclusion about the relative magnitude of $|a + b|$ and $|a| + |b|$ for any real numbers a, b that are not of like sign. What if a and b are of like sign, or such that at least one of them is zero?

3. (a)–(l) Find the difference, product and quotient of each ordered pair of numbers in Problem 1.

4. Find all real numbers with absolute value:

(*a*) 1   (*b*) 2   (*c*) 0   (*d*) -1 (*e*) -2

5. (*a*)–(*l*) For each ordered pair in Problem 1, write a correct "order" (i.e., magnitude) relationship. [For example in (*a*) we may write $2 > 1$.]

6. Compute each of the following:

(*a*) $8 + (-2) - (-3) + (-11) - (-17) - 5$. {*Hint:* The given expression $= 8 + (-2) + 3 + (-11) + 17 + (-5) = (8 + 3 + 17) + [(-2) + (-11) + (-5)]$.}

(*b*) $-2 + 3 - 7 + 11 - (-4)$ (*c*) $11 + (-7) - 7 - (-3)$

(*d*) $18 - (-19) - 21 + 20$ (*e*) $5 - 17 - (-5) + (-3)$

7. (*a*)–(*l*) For each ordered pair in Problem 1, find the absolute value of the product as well as the product of the absolute values of the given numbers. Induce a general result about the relationship between $|a| \cdot |b|$ and $|ab|$ for any pair of real numbers, a, b.

8. Find what $|a - b|$ is equal to, if a, b are real numbers such that:

(*a*) $a > b$ (*b*) $a = b$ (*c*) $b > a$

9. Label "always true," "sometimes true," "never true," each of the statements $|a| = a$, $|a| > a$, $|a| < a$, $|a| = -a$, in case a is a real number such that:

(*a*) a is positive (i.e., $a > 0$).

(*b*) $a = 0$.

(*c*) a is negative (i.e., $a < 0$).

10. Problem 9 suggests the following definition of the absolute value of a real number a: If a is positive or zero, $|a| = ?$; if a is negative, $|a| = ?$

11. (*a*) What statement justifies our saying that $-0 = ?$

(*b*) What statement justifies our saying that $8 - 3 = 5$?

(*c*) Assuming that the right distributive law holds true, show that $0 \cdot 2$ must equal 0.

(*d*) Assuming that the right distributive law holds true, show that $(-2)(3) = -6$.

12. The same as Problem 5, Exercise 5, except that nn wherever it appears in that problem is to be replaced by "real numbers."

13. The same as Problem 7, Exercise 6, except that "real numbers" is to be appended to parts (*a*) and (*b*).

14. Suppose P is the point on a scaled line labeled 0, and that A and B are points on that line labeled by the real numbers a and b respectively. Then $|a|$ may be thought of as the distance from A to P, and $|b|$ may be thought of as the distance from B to P. What expression will always represent the distance from A to B, no matter where A and B are on the scaled line?

2.11 CARTESIAN COORDINATE PLANES

In his high school study of "graphs," the student has already encountered a method for representing certain functions pictorially. The
functional ideas which we have been discussing throw a great deal of light
on the subject of graphs and, conversely, graphs help us to understand
functions better.

In this section we shall therefore review, in a rough and intuitive way,
the background material upon which the subject of graphs depends; in
the next section, graphs themselves will be considered.

We shall assume that the student already knows that we may think of a
plane as a perfectly flat surface (like a table top) which extends without
limit in all directions.

Suppose then that we are given a plane. On that plane we draw any
pair of perpendicular straight lines, intersecting at a point which we call
the "origin." Then we denote one of the lines the "X-axis," the other
the "Y-axis." (See Fig. 2.4.)

Next let the X- and Y-axes be scaled in the usual way, labeling the
origin with the real number 0 on each axis, and using the same unit of
measure on both axes.

(Most often we draw the X-axis in a horizontal and the Y-axis in a
vertical direction, with the positive real numbers labeling the right-hand
part of the X-axis and the upper part of the Y-axis.)

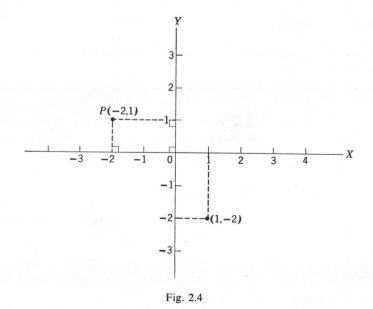

Fig. 2.4

At this point we say that we have established a *Cartesian coordinate system* on our given plane, or that the plane has been made into a *Cartesian coordinate plane*. (The word "Cartesian" is derived from the name of the philosopher and mathematician René Descartes, who in 1637 published the first detailed study of geometry by means of a coordinate system of this sort.) From now on, we shall use the letters "cc" as an abbreviation for Cartesian coordinate.

Now we put our cc system to work: Suppose P is a point of a cc plane. Draw a line through P, perpendicular to the X-axis and intersecting the X-axis in a point whose real-number label will be called the "x-value," or "abscissa," or "first name" of the point P. Similarly, draw a line through P, perpendicular to the Y-axis and intersecting the Y-axis in a point whose real-number label will be called the "y-value," or "ordinate," or "last name," of the point P. For example, the point P of Fig. 2.4 has an x-value of -2 and a y-value of 1.

The first and last names of a point are called its "coordinates," and are used to label, or identify, the point. In identifying a point by means of its coordinates, we write a pair of parentheses, within which we write the first and last names of the point, in that order, separated by a comma.

For example, the label which we assign to the point P of Fig. 2.4 is $(-2, 1)$. Note that the point $(-2, 1)$ is different from the point $(1, -2)$. Pairs of real numbers that identify points of a cc plane are, therefore, considered to be the same only if they consist of the same real numbers *written in the same order*. Such pairs are called *ordered* pairs. (See Problem 13, Exercise 2.)

The fundamental purpose of any coordinate system on a plane is to identify points of that plane by means of ordered pairs of real numbers.

2.12 GRAPHS OF REAL-REAL FUNCTIONS

On a cc plane, every ordered pair of real numbers identifies a unique point. But we have encountered ordered pairs of real numbers before; look again, for example, at the function defined in Problem 11a of Exercise 4.

Here we have *five* ordered pairs of real numbers: (1, 5), (2, 10), etc. Each identifies a point on a coordinate plane. What is more natural, then, than to picture this function by means of the five points on a cc plane identified by these five ordered pairs? (See Fig. 2.5.)

If we do, we may always reconstruct the function from the points on the picture. The existence of the point (1, 5) in the picture would tell us, for example, that 1 is in the domain of the function being described and that, under that function, 5 is the image of 1.

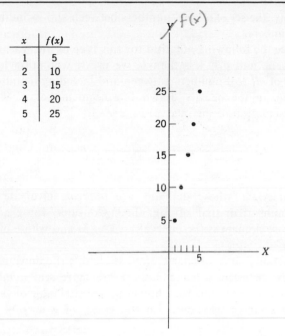

x	f(x)
1	5
2	10
3	15
4	20
5	25

Fig. 2.5

A collection of points, picturing a function in this way, is what we mean by the *graph* of a function. Clearly, the procedure we have illustrated above is possible only if both the domain and the range of the function being pictured contain only real numbers. We make the following definitions:

A *real-real* function is a function whose domain and range both contain only real numbers.

On a cc plane, the *graph* of a real-real function f is the set of all points (a, b), where a is in the domain of f and b is the image of a [i.e., $b = f(a)$].

For example, Fig. 2.5 shows the graph of the real-real function of Problem 11*a*, Exercise 4.

Note especially that the graph consists only of the five points indicated and not of a line passing through these points.

Functions defined on sets of real numbers are most often defined on a special type of set called an *interval*. Intervals themselves are of various sorts; we shall for the moment concern ourselves with just one kind of interval, namely, the set of all real numbers between and including a given pair of real numbers.

We introduce the following notation for this type of interval: If a and b are real numbers, and a is less than b, we use the notation $\{a \longmapsto b\}$ to denote the set of *all* real numbers between and including a and b.

For example, in the heavily drawn line segment below, we have a pictorial representation of the interval $\{-2 \longmapsto 3\}$:

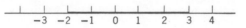

Real-real functions whose domains are *intervals* give rise to more substantial graphs than that of Fig. 2.5. Consider, for example, the function g whose domain is the interval $\{-3 \longmapsto 3\}$ and whose mapping is given by: $g(x) = x^2$.

For this function g, it is, of course, impossible to write down a complete table of values; between -3 and 3 there are more real numbers than could ever be listed.   We construct, however, a partial table of values from which at least *some* of the points on the graph of g may be obtained (Fig. 2.6).

Neither zero nor any natural number could represent the number of points on the graph of this function g.   (In other words, the number of points on the graph of g is *infinite*; see Section 1.4.)   Besides the seven points which we have " plotted " in Fig. 2.6, there are, for example, the points (0.1, 0.01), (0.2, 0.04), (1.1, 1.21), and an infinite number of other points on the graph of g.

The student has probably been in the habit of making what is actually much more than a trivial assumption at this point, namely, that all of the points on the graph of a function like g " stick together " and form a smooth curve as drawn in Fig. 2.7.

x	$g(x)$
-3	9
-2	4
-1	1
0	0
1	1
2	4
3	9

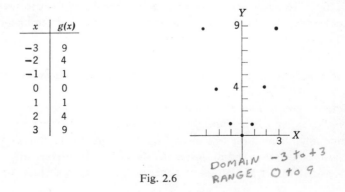

Fig. 2.6

For elementary functions *whose domains are intervals*, this assumption is usually justified. We shall, therefore, often follow the process familiar to the student in drawing graphs. But it should always be kept in mind that the curve which we draw in "plotting" a graph of a function is fundamentally *a set of points*. If the domain of the function contains only a natural number of elements, i.e., a *finite* number of elements, then the graph will consist of only a finite number of separated points; if the domain of the function consists of a whole interval of real numbers, then the graph will consist of an infinite number of points, which, as we have already pointed out, will, in the case of most elementary functions, form a smooth curve.

The graph of a function often brings out significant aspects of the function in a very clear and vivid way. We illustrate this remark in the case of the function g:

The real numbers which appear as x-values of points on the graph of function g constitute the domain of g, which is, of course, the interval $\{-3 \leftrightarrow 3\}$. The domain may therefore be pictured as the shadow of the graph upon the X-axis (cast by light rays parallel to the Y-axis, as shown in Fig. 2.8).

The real numbers which appear as y-values of points on the graph form the range of the function g. This is the interval $\{0 \leftrightarrow 9\}$. Pictorially, it is represented by the shadow of the graph upon the Y-axis (cast by light rays parallel to the X-axis, as shown in Fig. 2.8).

These "shadows" are known in mathematics as "projections." A precise definition of "projection," as it is used in plane geometry, follows:

Let l be a line, S a set of points, all in the same plane. Then the

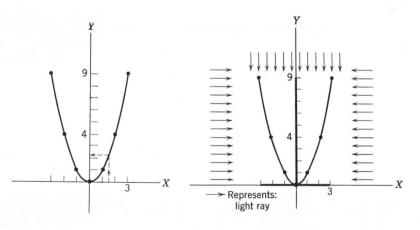

Fig. 2.7   Fig. 2.8

projection of S on l is the set of all points which are the feet of perpendiculars drawn from points of S to l.

The element 1 of the range of g is the image of both 1 and -1 in the domain of g. Hence g is a many-one function. On the graph, this appears as a situation in which we have two different points at the same height above the X-axis—$(-1, 1)$ and $(1, 1)$—so that it is possible for a horizontal line to cut this graph in two different points.

It is clear, in fact, that whenever it is possible for a horizontal line (i.e., a line parallel to the X-axis) to cut the graph of a function in more than one point, then the function is many-one; and when no horizontal line cuts the graph in more than one point, the function is one-one.

A graph may be thought of as simply a link between the domain and the range of a function; the link we call the *mapping*. Consider, for example, the graph of the function g. To find the image of the domain element 1.5 under this function, we may begin at the point 1.5 on the X-axis, move vertically until we encounter the graph, and then horizontally until we meet the Y-axis (Fig. 2.7). We should meet the Y-axis at the point 2.25, which is the image, under the function g, of 1.5. The immediate purpose served by the graph has been to link 1.5 with 2.25.

To serve as another illustrative example, we plot the graph of the function h whose domain is the interval $\{-1 \leftrightarrow 3\}$ and whose mapping is given by: $h(x) = 1 + 4x - x^2$, and we determine the range of h and whether it is one-one or many-one (Fig. 2.9).

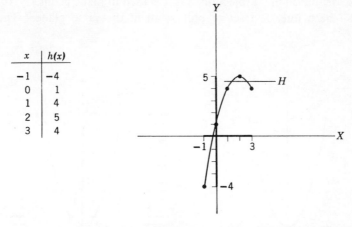

x	$h(x)$
-1	-4
0	1
1	4
2	5
3	4

Fig. 2.9

The range of h is the interval of real numbers $\{-4 \leftrightarrow 5\}$. The function h is many-one, since there is a horizontal line (H in Fig. 2.9) which crosses the graph more than once.

▶ **EXERCISE 9**

1. If a and b are real numbers, and a is less than b, what is meant by the interval $\{a \longrightarrow b\}$? Draw a picture to illustrate each of the following intervals: $\{0 \longrightarrow 1\}$, $\{-1 \longrightarrow 1\}$, $\{2 \longrightarrow 5\}$.

2. Given sets defined as follows: $A = \{2 \longrightarrow 5\}$, $B = \{3 \longrightarrow 7\}$, $C =$ the set of all negative real numbers, $D =$ the set of all natural numbers, $N =$ the null set. Find

(a) $A \cup B$ (b) $A \cap B$ (c) $A \cap C$

(d) $A \cap D$ (e) $A \cup N$ (f) $A \cap N$

(g) $B \cap C$ (h) $B \cap D$ (i) $B \cup N$

(j) $B \cap N$ (k) $C \cap D$ (l) $C \cup N$

(m) $C \cap N$ (n) $D \cup D$ (o) $D \cap D$

(p) $N \cup N$ (q) $N \cap N$

3. What is meant by a cc plane? What is the purpose of establishing a cc system on a plane?

4. On a cc plane, locate the following points: $(1, 1)$, $(7, 0)$, $(0, 7)$, $(-7, 0)$, $(0, -7)$, $(3, 5)$, $(-3, 5)$, $(3, -5)$, $(-3, -5)$.

5. Find the coordinates of (i.e., identify by means of an ordered pair of real numbers) each of the points $A, B, C, \cdots, H, O$ in Fig. 2.10.

6. What sort of correspondence exists between all the points of a cc plane and all ordered pairs of real numbers? Justify your answer.

7. Define and make up an example of a real-real function.

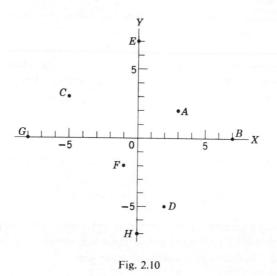

Fig. 2.10

8. What is meant by the graph of a real-real function? What is its purpose?

9. How may one determine, from the graph of a function, whether the function is one-one or many-one?

10. In Fig. 2.9, describe light rays which would cast shadows indicating the domain and the range of the function h.

11. Draw the graph of each of the functions of Problem 10, Exercise 4. (In the first four cases a complete graph is, of course, impossible. Why? In these cases, therefore, draw a partial graph.)

12. Plot the graph of the function f in each of the following cases, and determine the range of f and whether f is one-one or many-one. Also show on the graph how we may find the image of 2.5 in each case and, from the graph, estimate what that image is.

	DOMAIN	MPG. $f(x) =$		DOMAIN	MPG. $f(x) =$
(a)	$\{-1 \cdots 3\}$	x^2	(b)	$\{0 \cdots 3\}$	x^2
(c)	$\{-4 \cdots 3\}$	x	(d)	$\{-4 \cdots 3\}$	$2x$
(e)	$\{-4 \cdots 3\}$	$3x$	(f)	$\{-3 \cdots 3\}$	$2x + 1$
(g)	$\{-3 \cdots 3\}$	$3x - 2$	(h)	$\{-3 \cdots 3\}$	7
(i)	$\{-3 \cdots 3\}$	0	(j)	$\{-3 \cdots 3\}$	-7
(k)	$\{-3 \cdots 3\}$	$x/2$	(l)	$\{-1 \cdots 3\}$	$x^2 - 3x + 2$
(m)	$\{-3 \cdots 3\}$	x^3	(n)	$\{-3 \cdots 3\}$	x^4
(o)	$\{-3 \cdots 3\}$	$x^2 - 2$	(p)	$\{-3 \cdots 3\}$	$2 - x^2$
(q)	$\{-3 \cdots 3\}$	$x^2 + 2$	(r)	$\{2 \cdots 12\}$	$12/x$

13. *The absolute value function.* An especially useful function is the function f which is defined as follows: The domain of f is the set of all real numbers. The mapping of f is given by the rules: If x is positive or zero, $f(x) = x$; if x is negative, $f(x) = -x$.

Thus: $f(7) = 7$; $f(0) = 0$; $f(-7) = -(-7) = 7$.

But: $|7| = 7$; $|0| = 0$; $|-7| = 7$.   (See Section 2.10.)

In fact it is easy to see that, if x is any real number, then $f(x) = |x|$; for if x is positive, we have $f(x) = x$ and $|x| = x$, so that $f(x) = |x|$; if $x = 0$, we have $f(x) = x = 0$ and $|x| = |0| = 0$, so that again $f(x) = |x|$; if x is negative, then $x = -a$, where a is positive, so that $|x| = |-a| = a = -x = f(x)$. Thus, in all cases $f(x) = |x|$. We are led to an alternate definition of absolute value: If a real number x is positive or zero, $|x| = x$; if x is negative, $|x| = -x$.

Now suppose the function g has as domain the interval $\{-5 \cdots 5\}$, and that the mapping of g is given by: $g(x) = |x|$. Draw the graph of g, determine its range, and tell whether it is one-one or many-one, and why.

14. In each of the following cases, draw the graph of f and determine its range and whether it is one-one or many-one.

(a) The domain of f consists of all natural numbers between -1.5 and 10.5. The mapping of f is given by: $f(x) = 7$ if x is even, $f(x) = 11$ if x is odd.

(b) The domain of f is the interval $\{-5 \multimap 5\}$. $f(x) = 1$ if x is positive, $f(x) = -1$ if x is negative, $f(x) = 0$ if x is zero.

(c) The domain of f is the interval $\{-5 \multimap 5\}$. $f(x) = 5 + x$ if x is negative, $f(0) = 10$, $f(x) = 5 - x$ if x is positive.

(d) The domain of f is the interval $\{-5 \multimap 5\}$; $f(x) = x^2 + 10x + 25$ if $x \in \{-5 \multimap -2\}$; $f(x) = (3x/2) + 12$ if $x \in \{-2 \multimap 0\}$; $f(x) = 12 - (3x/2)$ if $x \in \{0 \multimap 2\}$; $f(x) = x^2 - 10x + 25$ if $x \in \{2 \multimap 5\}$.

*15. If R represents the set of all real numbers, use the notation of product sets (see Problem 13, Exercise 2) to name a set which is in one-to-one correspondence with all the points of a cc plane.

*16. Explain why lines are said to be *one*-dimensional and planes *two*-dimensional.

*17. Suppose m is a real number. If $f(x) = mx$ and the domain of f is an interval of real numbers, what do you think may be said about the graph of f? How does the choice of m affect the graph?

*18. Can a vertical line cross the graph of a function more than once? Justify your answer.

2.13 RELATIONS

We return once more to primitive man and his mathematics in order to discover the last of our great basic concepts of mathematics.

As in the case of the others, it is in very simple activities that examples of the concept may be found. Early man not only combined numbers but he compared them with each other as well; and it is likely that the first comparison was with respect to size.

We note this fact about the process of comparing two nn as to size:

Given an ordered pair of nn, the first is either greater than the second or it is not—exactly one of the two possibilities must be true.

Now consider for a moment the concept of "being the father of," as it applies to a set of people. At first glance the concept of "being the father of" seems to have little to do with the concept of "being greater than." But observe the following fact:

Given an ordered pair of people from the given set of people, either the first is the father of the second or he is not—exactly one of the two possibilities must be true.

Other concepts which exhibit the same sort of selectivity with respect to ordered pairs are "being equal to," "dividing," and "being double" (among the nn); "being the brother of" and "loving" (among sets of people).

For example, given the ordered pair of nn (7, 7), one says the first is *equal* to the second; given the ordered pair of nn (7, 6), one says the first is *not equal* to the second. Given the ordered pair of nn (2, 6), one says the first *divides* the second; given the ordered pair of nn (2, 7), one says the first does *not divide* the second. Given the ordered pair of nn (4, 2), one says the first is *double* the second; given the ordered pair of nn (2, 4), one says the first is *not double* the second. Given the ordered pair (Cain, Abel), one says the first is the *brother* of the second; given the ordered pair (Cain, Adam), one says the first is *not the brother* of the second. (It is left to the student similarly to illustrate the remaining concept mentioned in the preceding paragraph.)

Each of these concepts is an example of the abstraction called a *relation*. Our preceding discussion leads to the following definition:

A *relation* R on a set S is a function which associates with each ordered pair of elements of S either the word "yes" or the word "no."

If a relation R associates the word "yes" with the ordered pair (a, b), we say $a \, R \, b$. If a relation R associates the word "no" with the ordered pair (a, b), we say: $a \, \not{R} \, b$ (read "a not R b").

For example, the relation = on the set of nn maps the ordered pair (7, 7) into the word "yes." We therefore say: $7 = 7$; the same relation associates the word "no" with the ordered pair (7, 6). We therefore say: $7 \neq 6$ (read "7 is unequal to 6").

We append a list of names and symbols for certain important relations. The first four are defined on sets of *real numbers*. The last is defined on the set of *all nn*, as follows:

If a and b are nn and we write "$a \mid b$," or we say "a divides b," or "a is a factor of b," or "b is divisible by a," or "b is a multiple of a," we shall in all these cases mean, unless otherwise noted, that there is a *natural number* m such that $b = ma$.

>	Greater than	<	Less than
⩾	Greater than or equal to	⩽	Less than or equal to
|	Divides		

2.14 ABSTRACT PROPERTIES OF RELATIONS

I. **Reflexivity.** It is not overly difficult to find sets of people in which everyone is in love with himself, but to find even one person who is his own father presents a real problem. Or, consider the relation $=$: Any number whatever is equal to itself; that is to say, if a is a number, then $a = a$. The analogous fact is not true, however, of the relation $<$. In fact, for no number a is it true that $a < a$.

We are led to the definition:

A relation R on a set A is said to be *reflexive* if for each a in A:
$$a \ R \ a.$$

II. Symmetry. Some relations are "reversible" and others are not. For example, if Tom is the cousin of Jerry, then it follows that Jerry is the cousin of Tom; but if Tom admires Jerry, it does not *necessarily* follow that Jerry admires Tom.

We make this definition:

A relation R on a set A is said to be *symmetric* if $b \ R \ a$ *always* follows from $a \ R \ b$.

III. Transitivity. Knowing that a first number is equal to a second, and the second number to a third, it is a familiar conclusion that the first number is equal to the third number; i.e., there follows from the information $a = b$ and $b = c$ the conclusion: $a = c$. Not all relations, however, behave in this way. For example, if John loves Mary and Mary loves James, it may be doubted that John loves James.

We make the following definition:

A relation R on a set A is said to be *transitive* if from $a \ R \ b$ and $b \ R \ c$ there *always* follows: $a \ R \ c$.

A relation which is reflexive *and* symmetric *and* transitive is called an *equivalence* or a *congruence* relation.

*2.15 UNIFIED DEFINITION OF FUNCTION, OPERATION, RELATION

There is a neat way of *defining* "function," "operation," and "relation," all in terms of the concept of *ordered pair* (which itself, in Exercise 2, Problem 13, was defined in terms of the concept *set*). We shall find it convenient to begin with the concept "relation."

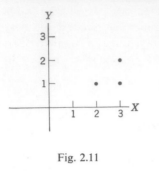

Fig. 2.11

First of all, we note that a relation R defined on a set S may always be associated with a "favored" subset of ordered pairs in $S \times S$ (the ones to which it applies the word "yes"). For example, the relation $>$ defined on the set $\{1, 2, 3\}$ may be associated with the set of ordered pairs $\{(3, 2), (3, 1), (2, 1)\}$. It is only a step, in mathematics, from "associated with" to "defined by"; and from there, only another step to "is."

We find it perfectly adequate to what we wish to do with relations to make the following definition.

Definition. A *relation* R on a set S is a subset of $S \times S$. [If (a, b) belongs to the aforementioned subset of $S \times S$, we write $a\,R\,b$; otherwise we write $a\,\mathcal{R}\,b$.]

The point of view embodied in this definition makes it feasible to draw graphs of certain relations (which?) as well as of real-real functions. When each ordered pair in a given relation represents a point of a cc plane (when does this happen?), the graph of the given relation is defined to be the set of all points in a cc plane so represented.

For example, the graph of the relation $>$, defined on the set $\{1, 2, 3\}$, is given in Fig. 2.11.

Now we recall that in a natural way one may also associate with a *function* a set of ordered pairs—namely, those ordered pairs which may be found in the table of values of the function. The function f whose domain consists of the numbers $\{1, 2, 3\}$, and whose mapping is given by $x \to x^2$, for example, may be associated with the set of ordered pairs $\{(1, 1), (2, 4), (3, 9)\}$.

So far, relations and functions seem to have a great deal in common, as indeed they do. There is a crucial distinction, however: We recall that a function may not assign two different objects to the same element. The ordered pairs, $(3, 2)$, $(3, 1)$ which occur in our relation above, for example, could not occur in the case of a function (as we have defined "function"). We therefore make the following definition:

Definition. A function f is a relation with the following property: If (a, b) and (a, c) are both in the given relation, then $b = c$.

[The set of first elements occurring in the given relation is called the *domain* of f, the set of second elements the *range* of f, and, if (a, b) is in the given relation, then we write: $b = f(a)$.]

Finally, the definition of "operation" which we have given above falls into place in this development without any alteration.

▶ **EXERCISE 10**

1. Make up an original example of a relation, and tell whether it is reflexive, symmetric, or transitive; justify your statements.

2. Discuss, with respect to I, II, and III of Section 2.14, the relations $>$, $<$, $\geqslant$, $\leqslant$, $|$, as defined above; also the relation $=$ on all real numbers. Which are equivalence relations?

3. The relation "$|$" defined above may be generalized as follows: If a, b are elements of a set S in which multiplication is defined, and we say or write that in S "$a|b$," or "a is a factor of b," or "b is a multiple of a," we shall in all these cases mean that there is an element m in S such that $b = ma$; a *divisor* will then be defined to be a nonzero factor.

  (*a*) If a and b are integers, what does it mean to say that a divides b in the set of integers?

  (*b*) Discuss with respect to I, II, III the relation "$|$" in the following sets:

   (i) All integers.
   (ii) All rational numbers.
   (iii) All positive rational numbers.
   (iv) All real numbers.
   (v) $\{1, 2, 4, 8\}$.
   (vi) $\{2, 4, 8\}$.

4. Discuss the following relations with respect to I, II, and III and identify those which are equivalence relations:

RELATION	DEFINED ON
(*a*) "Father"	All Americans
(*b*) "Brother"	All Americans
(*c*) "Cousin"	All Americans
(*d*) "10 miles from"	All U. S. Cities
(*e*) "Parallel"	All lines of a plane
(*f*) "Intersects"	All lines of a plane
(*g*) "Perpendicular"	All lines of a plane
(*h*) "Similar"	All triangles of a plane
(*i*) "Congruent"	All triangles of a plane
(*j*) "Contains"	All subsets of a set
(*k*) "Differs from by an integer multiple of 5"	All integers

5. Why are "equivalence" or "congruence" relations so named?

*6. With respect to the properties I, II, III, every relation must fall into one of eight categories; one of these categories, for example, is: reflexive, symmetric, not transitive. What are the other seven?

For each of these eight categories (or for as many of them as you can), give an example of a relation belonging to that category.

*7. Draw the graphs of the following relations, all defined on the set {1, 2, 3, 4}:

(a) >   (b) ⩾   (c) =   (d) <   (e) ⩽   (f) |

*8. Draw the graphs of the following relations, all defined on the interval {0 ⤙ 1}:

(a) >   (b) ⩾   (c) =   (d) <   (e) ⩽

3 REASON AND IRRATIONALITY

3.1 INTRODUCTION

Up to this point, we have been occupied with the development of ideas and vocabulary necessary to a clear and simple expression of mathematical statements. There is a question which must be settled, however, before we proceed to build mathematics upon the foundation we have laid:

What will the authority for our mathematical statements be? How shall we persuade ourselves and others of their truth? How, in other words, are they to be justified?

Consider, for example, the famous assertion of mathematics known as the Pythagorean theorem, which states that, if c is the length of the hypotenuse of a right triangle whose other sides are of lengths a and b, then $a^2 + b^2 = c^2$.

Pythagoras was a Greek who lived at about 550 B.C. The theorem which bears his name actually was known to the ancient Babylonians, probably before 2000 B.C.; but the Babylonians and the Greeks differed markedly in their attitudes toward that theorem.

Let us first consider the Babylonians. The Babylonian nations of Biblical times together with their contemporary, ancient Egypt, share the distinction of being the earliest of civilizations contributing to our present Western culture. The ancient Babylonians and Egyptians were busy people, with a great many practical problems to solve and a great deal of hard work to do. Their primary interest was in getting the immediate problem solved and the work at hand done.

The governments of Babylonia and Egypt were autocratic, and so indeed was their mathematics (which, incidentally, comprised a good deal of our present high-school algebra and geometry). For example, having somehow stumbled upon the Pythagorean theorem, and having observed that it seemed always to hold true when applied to specific right triangles, the Babylonians were not disposed to pursue any further the matter of its truth. Babylonians accepted the theorem on the authority of their elders and because it was "so written," persuasions which unfortunately even today carry more weight than they properly should.

But the Greek civilization which followed (dating from about 600 B.C.) fostered a leisure class of philosophers (i.e., "lovers of knowledge"), men who lived under a less repressive political structure than did their oriental predecessors, and who pursued their studies in an atmosphere of brave new freedom. These men asked not only "how" but also "why?" Their deeply probing minds raised, and even *answered*, questions which occurred not at all to the Babylonians or to the Egyptians. First among these questions was:

How shall we know that a statement is true?

It is interesting to note that the mathematics which followed from the meditations of the Greeks turned out to be incalculably more useful in science and industry than that which we owe to the very practical-minded Egyptians and Babylonians; and that the down-to-earth Romans, expert in commerce and engineering, were able to contribute absolutely nothing to further the development of the mathematics they used.

We begin our study of the Greek contribution to the problem of how statements may be justified or "proved" by examining several "proofs" occurring early in the development of Greek mathematics, and attributed to Pythagoras or members of his school.

3.2 PYTHAGOREAN PROOFS: SEVERAL EXAMPLES

Many of the statements which we make about real numbers were justified by the Pythagoreans by means of line and area representations. For example, to find a general formula for $(a + b)^2$, where a and b are positive real numbers, a square whose side is of length $a + b$ units may be constructed and subdividing lines may be drawn, as shown in Fig. 3.1.

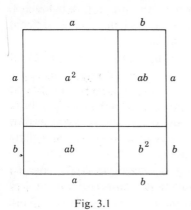

Fig. 3.1

Now the area of the square of side $a + b$ is numerically equal to $(a + b)^2$.

The areas of the four component rectangles are numerically equal to a^2, ab, ab, b^2.

The area of the large square is equal to the sum of the areas of its four component rectangles.   Therefore,

$$(a + b)^2 = a^2 + ab + ab + b^2$$
$$= a^2 + 2ab + b^2$$

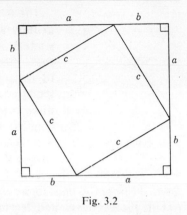

What has been demonstrated, then, is that, if a and b are any positive real numbers, then $(a + b)^2 = a^2 + 2ab + b^2$. (Actually the equation holds true if a and b are any real numbers at all, but we have not shown that.)

Many other rules which we have learned in elementary mathematics may

Fig. 3.2

be justified in similar fashion.   In fact, a very simple and beautiful derivation of Pythagoras' famous theorem results from a slight variation of the preceding diagram:

Starting with four right triangles, each with hypotenuse of length c and arms of lengths a, b, we fit them together as in Fig. 3.2.

It is not hard to see that this time we have a large square of area $(a + b)^2$ composed of a smaller square of area c^2 and four right triangles each of area $\frac{1}{2}ab$.   Therefore:

$$(a + b)^2 = c^2 + 4 \cdot \tfrac{1}{2}ab$$

or

$$a^2 + 2ab + b^2 = c^2 + 2ab$$

Now subtracting $2ab$ from both sides of the preceding equation we have

$$a^2 + b^2 = c^2$$

which is the result we wished to arrive at.

3.3 THE IRRATIONALITY OF $\sqrt{2}$

From their predecessors, the Greeks inherited a system of numbers (the positive rational numbers), which sufficed for most practical needs, and a question of which the ancients were not even aware.   The question is as follows:

Given a unit line segment, can the length of every line segment be expressed, in terms of that unit, as a positive rational number?   In other words, do the positive rational numbers suffice for the measurement of all line segments?

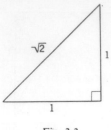

Fig. 3.3

The school which Pythagoras founded at Crotona in Italy was a mystic order, and the scholars who studied there observed many peculiar rules. One of them was anonymity: all discoveries were credited to their leader, Pythagoras. We do not know, therefore, who actually made the remarkable discovery that not all line segments have rational lengths; we know only that he was a Pythagorean. The fact itself was considered a scandal. To the mystic Pythagoreans, everything was based on the whole numbers and the rational numbers which could be constructed from them. Their entire philosophy seemed now to be crumbling. They tried to hide the discovery, and legend even relates that one Pythagorean was drowned because he disclosed the secret to outsiders.

The proof of the Pythagoreans that not all line segments are of rational length is one of the most beautiful in all of mathematics. It goes as follows:

Consider a right triangle whose two arms are of unit length (Fig. 3.3).

If we denote the length of the hypotenuse of this triangle by x, then by the Pythagorean theorem we have:

$$x^2 = 1^2 + 1^2 = 1 + 1 = 2$$

so that

$$x = \sqrt{2}$$

(The student is reminded that the expression $\sqrt{a}$, where a is a non-negative real number, means *the non-negative square root of a*, i.e., *the non-negative number whose square is a*; the symbol $\sqrt{}$ should, in this case, be read: "the non-negative square root of".)

Now we wish to show that $\sqrt{2}$ is *irrational*, i.e., it is *not* rational or, in other words, there is no non-negative rational number whose square equals 2. Obviously, $\sqrt{2}$ cannot be 0, since $0^2 \neq 2$. There is left to consider, then, only the possibility that $\sqrt{2}$ may be a *positive* rational number. The rest of the proof shows that actually no such possibility exists: there is no positive rational number whose square is 2.

Pythagorean Proof of the Irrationality of $\sqrt{2}$. The proof rests principally upon these definitions and assumptions:

1. An *even* nn is one which may be expressed in the form $2k$, where k is a nn.

2. Only *even* nn have squares which are even nn.

3. Every positive rational number p/q, where p and q are nn, may be expressed "in lowest terms," i.e., in such a way that p and q have no common divisor but 1.

(These assumptions may be proved consequences of even more basic assumptions, but they are quite plausible themselves and, therefore, a reasonable basis upon which to build our argument.)

The method of proof is the famous *reductio ad absurdum*. That is, we show that the denial of what we wish to prove leads to an absurdity, so that what we wish to prove cannot be false and must, therefore, be true.

Here we wish to prove that there is *not* a positive rational number whose square is 2. We therefore assume that there *is* a positive rational number whose square is 2, and show that this assumption leads to a contradiction.

By statement 3 if there is a positive rational number whose square is 2, then it may be expressed in the form p/q, where p and q are nn with no common divisor but 1. We have then:

$$\left(\frac{p}{q}\right)^2 = 2 \quad \text{or} \quad \frac{p^2}{q^2} = 2 \quad \text{or} \quad p^2 = 2q^2$$

By statement 1, p^2 is an even nn. Therefore, by statement 2, p is an even nn, i.e., $p = 2k$, where k is a nn.

Substituting this value of p in the equation $p^2 = 2q^2$, we have:

$$(2k)^2 = 2q^2 \quad \text{or} \quad 4k^2 - 2q^2 \quad \text{or} \quad 2k^2 - q^2 \quad \text{or} \quad q^2 = 2k^2$$

But just as we proved p to be even before, so we may prove q to be even now.

However, this is a contradiction, for p and q have no common divisor but 1, and so cannot both be even.

The assumption that $\sqrt{2}$ is a rational number has led to an absurd result. Therefore, $\sqrt{2}$ is irrational, Q.E.D. (*quod erat demonstrandum*, meaning "which was to be proved").

The student has possibly been in the habit of replacing $\sqrt{2}$ by 1.4 or by 1.41 in certain problems. Having proved $\sqrt{2}$ to be irrational, however, we know now that neither 1.4 nor 1.41 could be equal to $\sqrt{2}$; for both 1.4 and 1.41 are *rational* numbers $\left(1.4 = \frac{14}{10}; 1.41 = \frac{141}{100}\right)$. In fact, it is easy to verify that $(1.4)^2 = 1.96$, and not 2, and similarly for 1.41.

Thus 1.4 and 1.41 are approximations to $\sqrt{2}$, in the sense that on a scaled line they label points close to the point labeled $\sqrt{2}$; the first comes as close as any one decimal place approximation could come, the second similarly for two decimal places.

The method which the student may recall for working out successive places of a decimal representation for $\sqrt{2}$ can never terminate, then, for if it did, we would have $\sqrt{2}$ equal to a rational number, which we have proved to be impossible. It is therefore only an *endless* decimal which could possibly represent $\sqrt{2}$.

▶ **EXERCISE 11**

1. Define and give an example of "empirical" knowledge.

2. Prove by means of line and area representations that, if a, b, c, d are real numbers (with certain restrictions), then:

(a) $a(b + c) = ab + ac$ (b) $a(b + c + d) = ab + ac + ad$

(c) $(a + b)(c + d) = ac + bc + ad + bd$

(d) $(a - b)c = ac - bc$ (e) $(a + b + c)^2 = ?$

(f) $(a + b)(a + 2b) = ?$ (g) $(a + b)(a - b) = ?$

3. Show that there exist line segments of the following number of inches in length (*Hint*: See Fig. 3.3).

(a) $\sqrt{3}$ (b) $\sqrt{5}$ (c) $\sqrt{6}$ (d) $\sqrt{7}$ (e) $\sqrt{8}$ (f) $\sqrt{10}$

*4. Prove that $\sqrt{3}$ is irrational.

3.4 REPRESENTATIONS OF REAL NUMBERS

The Greeks (as we have seen in Section 3.2) pictured numbers by means of line segments. We noted, however (in the preceding section), that not all line segments have rational lengths. The Greeks, therefore, were dealing with a more extensive set of numbers than the *positive rational numbers* familiar to the Babylonians and Egyptians. In effect, they extended the number system known to man to include all *positive real numbers*, for the positive real numbers are those which represent the lengths of all possible line segments.

Since they pictured numbers by means of line segments, it follows that the Greeks must have performed operations on numbers by means of geometric operations on line segments. For example, they thought of the operation of adding 2 and 3 as that of adjoining line segments of lengths 2 and 3 units to form a single line segment, 5 units in length:

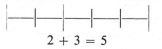

$$2 + 3 = 5$$

A second way of representing not only positive real numbers but in fact *all* real numbers is by means of the points of a scaled line (see Section 2.9).

Now we consider a third way of representing real numbers, quite different from the first two. We have noted, at the end of the last section, that the well-known process for computing $\sqrt{2}$ leads to an endless decimal. This is the clue to our third method for representing real numbers: *The real numbers may be thought of as the set of all endless decimals.*

The real number $\frac{1}{4}$, for example, may be written as the endless decimal $0.25000 \cdots$; the real number $-\frac{1}{3}$ as $-0.33333 \cdots$; (Both of these endless decimals are easily described, although neither, of course, can be written out completely; the first, of course, may also be written as the *terminating* decimal 0.25).

Note that the two preceding cases both had to do with *rational* real numbers, and that in each case the endless decimal expansion involved *repetition*. We note further that sometimes (as in the case $\frac{7}{11} =$ $0.636363 \cdots$) blocks of digits, rather than single digits, occur repeatedly in the endless decimal expansion of a rational number.

The question arises: Does every endless decimal expansion of a rational real number repeat a pattern of one or more digits after some point?

The answer is "yes." We indicate the reason for this by considering the particular rational number $\frac{8}{7}$. In dividing any nn by 7, only seven remainders are possible. Therefore, after seven or fewer steps of the division process, a remainder must be repeated, and a cycle of repetition must begin. In the case of $\frac{8}{7}$,

$$
\begin{array}{r}
1.\,1\,4\,2\,8\,5\,7 \\
\underline{1\ \ 3\ \ 2\ \ 6\ \ 4\ \ 5\ \ 1} \\
7\overline{)8.\,0\,0\,0\,0\,0\,0}
\end{array}
$$

The sequence of digits which occurs between the two remainders "1" will be repeated endlessly.

In the same way, every rational number may be expressed as an endless *repeating* decimal. But what then of those endless decimals which do not display a pattern of repeating blocks of digits? *Nonrepeating endless decimals represent all irrational real numbers.*

As a matter of fact, any repeating decimal must represent a rational number, and we may easily discover which. For example, consider the endless repeating decimal $d = 7.121212 \cdots$. We make the reasonable assumption that, even among endless decimals, ordinary rules for multiplication by powers of 10 and for subtraction hold. Then,

$$
100d = 712.121212 \cdots
$$
$$
d = 7.121212 \cdots
$$

Subtracting,

$$
99d = 705 \qquad d = \tfrac{705}{99} = \tfrac{235}{33}
$$

The student may verify that this result is correct by dividing 33 into 235.

Most of the irrational real numbers (we shall call these simply the *irrational* numbers from now on) which we shall encounter are those arising from the extraction of square roots and cube roots, and so on; but there are many more irrational numbers which do not arise in this way. The most famous of these is π, which the student will recall as the number representing the circumference of a circle whose diameter has a length of 1 unit.

That π is irrational was not known until 1767, A.D. however, when that fact was proved by the German mathematician, J. H. Lambert. His discovery terminated a futile search of thousands of years duration for a rational expression, like 3.14 or $\frac{22}{7}$, which would be equal to π.

In summary: Every real number may be represented as a decimal. If the real number is rational, the decimal is terminating or repeating. If the real number is irrational, the decimal is endless and nonrepeating.

[We now have further light on why Minkowski and Kronecker (see Section 1.4) thought so highly of the natural numbers: For by using *pairs* of natural numbers, one may express all positive rational numbers; by using sequences of natural numbers (together with zero and a decimal point), one may express all positive real numbers. Supplement these with a minus sign, and we may express *all* real numbers. Passing into the field of geometry, whose fundamental building block is the point, we recall that by means of a Cartesian coordinate system every point on a plane may be identified by a pair of real numbers.]

One last word on the representation of real numbers. Actually, all methods of representation of irrational real numbers are awkward. The Greeks worked with physical lines, which is inconvenient. To add lines or endless decimals is a nuisance, and other operations are even more awkward to carry through. We therefore often leave operation symbols in our representations of real numbers, as for example, when we express the sum of 2 and $\sqrt{2}$ as $2 + \sqrt{2}$.

3.5 EUCLID AND THE DEDUCTIVE METHOD

In the year 332 B.C., Alexander the Great founded the city of Alexandria in Egypt. Alexandria very soon became, and for a thousand years remained, one of the great cities of the ancient world and the center of Greek cultural life. There, in about 300 B.C., the world's first university was founded; and it is believed that the first man to serve as head of its department of mathematics was the immortal Euclid.

Euclid's fame rests upon his *Elements*, a book which except for the Bible has been reproduced in more copies than any other ever written. In fact, very nearly all of the high-school texts in geometry in use today are actually only revised editions of a part of Euclid's *Elements*.

It should be underlined that the mathematics in the *Elements* was, for the most part, not the original creation of Euclid but rather an organization and summary of a great deal of the mathematics which was developed by the Greeks in the three centuries preceding the time of Euclid. His genius lay in his selection, organization, and method of presentation of the material at hand.

The method of presentation was that of "deductive logic," a form of reasoning used so skillfully and beautifully by Euclid that his treatment has become a pattern for mathematicians to follow even up to this very day.

What is deductive logic? We have already described it as a method of reasoning or, in other words, as a method of arriving at conclusions. It is, in fact, the method to which the Greeks were driven by the question "why?" which they asked so persistently. They soon realized, as must anyone who has ever tried to answer the questions of a curious child, that there is no end to the "whys" which may be asked. Every explanation involves statements which themselves must be explained. If we are to convince someone of the truth of a particular statement, we must begin with *some* statement or statements with which he agrees, and then from that point proceed to demonstrate that the desired conclusion follows.

The same sort of thing is true of definitions. Words, for example, are defined in terms of other words. But then what do the "other words" mean? If they are to be defined, still *other* words must be utilized. For example, the word "demented" might be defined as "insane;" "insane" as "deranged;" "deranged" as "crazy;" but the process cannot go on forever without repetition, for the number of words in the English language is limited. Eventually one comes to a word which is not defined; in practical terms, a word so simple that everyone agrees he knows what it means without definition.

The beginning of a deductive argument, then, must always consist of a number of words which are never defined and a number of statements which are never proved. In mathematics, these unproved statements are usually called axioms.

In the process of proceeding from statement to statement, precise rules are used—the rules of deductive logic. These very basic precepts of reasoning are used intuitively by everyone, even though they are rarely consciously expressed. One of these rules, for example, affirms that a statement cannot be both true and false; another that if a second statement follows from a first, and a third from the second, then the third statement follows from the first.

Deductive reasoning, then, is a method of arriving at conclusions which begins by making certain statements called "assumptions," or "hypotheses," or "premises," or "postulates," or "axioms," and which proceeds by applying to these statements the rules of deductive logic.

The methods of deductive logic were first systematized and expounded by Aristotle, at about 350 B.C. A classic example of this type of reasoning is his famous "syllogism":

> All men are mortal.
> Socrates is a man.
> Therefore Socrates is mortal.

Here, in the last line, is a conclusion which we feel cannot be escaped, once the two premises which precede it have been granted. It was Aristotle who gave logic the characteristic of a game governed by rules. Every statement after the assumed statements follows from preceding statements by the rules of the game.

It is a surprising fact that the axioms of mathematics need not be "true." To the mathematician, the "truth" of the axioms is irrelevant. Beginning with axioms, he arrives at the consequences of these axioms. *If* you agree to the truth of the axioms, then deductive logic demands that you accept *also* the conclusions deduced from the axioms. But in the process of deduction, we are not in the least concerned with whether the axioms are "true" or "false."

Today, the only conclusions which mathematics stamps with its final seal of approval are those which may be arrived at deductively from sets of axioms. In that sense, high-school geometry, when taught as an exercise in deductive logic, is the most mathematical of high-school courses. Algebra too, however, may be presented in the same deductive fashion, and that is what we shall soon do.

The method of deduction is not by any means the exclusive property of mathematics or even of the sciences. On July 4, 1776, a group of American patriots ratified a document which stated:

> "We hold these truths to be self-evident · · ·,"

and which then proceeded to deduce in masterly style the consequences of its assumptions; and on October 3, 1954, on page 1 of the *New York Times Review of the Week*, there were quoted these lines from a report of a Select Committee of the United States Senate:

We begin with the premise that the Senate of the United States is a responsible political body. · · · From this premise, the committee advanced to its conclusion. · · ·

On the other hand, although the deductive method permeates all fields of human knowledge, it is nowhere to be found in as pure a form, nor may it anywhere be seen as sharply and as clearly as in mathematics. This is one of the most powerful of all arguments in favor of the inclusion of mathematics in all college curricula. The argument fails, however, unless the course in mathematics contains clear examples of careful deductive reasoning. *The following chapter on real numbers is especially intended to serve as an example of careful deductive reasoning.*

3.6 INDUCTION

Another type of reasoning, and one which also plays an important role in mathematics, is *inductive* reasoning. We say that we reason inductively when we come to a general conclusion after observing a number of special instances. Let us consider some examples of this type of reasoning:

Every morning, for as long as I can remember, day has followed night; I am fairly certain, therefore, that tomorrow the sun will rise, just as it has risen always in the past. My reasoning in this case is inductive. That is to say, I have come to a conclusion after observing a number of occurrences of a phenomenon.

Science, with its experiments and observations, is particularly strong in the use of inductive reasoning. In genetics, for example, the conclusion that blondeness is a recessive trait is based upon nothing but the very large number of cases in which blondeness has turned out to be recessive, and the fact that in no case has blondeness turned out to be dominant. Most of our knowledge of the world around us is inductive. The "facts" that fire burns, and sugar is sweet, and even that $2 + 2 = 4$ are conclusions we have all reached inductively.

But our present interest is in mathematics. We therefore now turn our attention to the role of induction in mathematics, beginning with an example of its use:

We observe that the sum of the first two odd numbers, 1 and 3, is 4; the sum of the first three odd numbers, 1, 3, and 5, is 9; and the sum of the first four odd numbers is 16. An alert student will note something special about these sums, namely, that they are all perfect squares (i.e., squares of nn), and from this observation, and perhaps after verifying in a few more cases that his suspicion holds true, he might very well *induce* the general result: The sum of all the odd numbers up to any given odd number is always a perfect square.

Here is an indication of the reason for the importance of inductive reasoning in mathematics: It is a method for *discovering* results. But how certain are we of the truth of the statement induced?

In the example we are considering, our statement says something about *any* odd number, of which there are, of course, an infinite number. Does the fact that the statement holds true for three or four or even a hundred particular odd numbers prove that it holds true for *all* odd numbers?

The answer is *no*. A general statement may hold true in many specific cases and still not be true in all cases. We offer two examples in which this occurs. First, consider the statement:

" All numbers are less than 1,000,000."

Many special cases of this statement happen to be true. If we check in the case of the number 1, it is true, as it is, of course, for the number 2, the number 3, and the number 1.7, and, in fact, for infinitely many numbers. But all the weight of evidence in favor of the theorem does not alter the very obvious fact that it is false, for we know very well that there *are* numbers which are *not* less than 1,000,000. Indeed, although we can never prove the truth of a statement exclusively by verifying that it is true in any subset, however numerous, of the set of all possible cases to which it applies, we can prove that a statement is false by exhibiting only *one* case in which it fails to be true.

For example, when we note that there is a number 1,000,001 which is *not* less than 1,000,000, this "counter-example" suffices to prove that the theorem in question is false. In mathematics, it is very definitely the exception which *dis*proves the rule.

The reader may perhaps consider this example to be somewhat artificial, as indeed it is. We therefore offer another example of a statement to which we might be led inductively, but which turns out to be false.

(The statement has to do with primes, and the student is therefore advised to review the definition of a prime, which will be found in Problem 5 of Exercise 2.)

Consider the result of substituting natural numbers for n in the expression: $n^2 - n + 41$. We construct a table of values:

n	1	2	3	4	5	6	7	8	9	10
$n^2 - n + 41$	41	43	47	53	61	71	83	97	113	131

There is something which may be remarked about the numbers in the second row: They are all primes. Indeed, the table may be continued for quite a way past $n = 10$, and still $n^2 - n + 41$ will be a prime. There is a tendency on the basis of this evidence to jump to the conclusion (i.e., to "induce") that $n^2 - n + 41$ is a formula which will yield a prime no matter *what* natural number is substituted for n.

Successive trials show, indeed, that this conclusion is true for all values of n from 1 up to 40. But alas! For $n = 41$:

$$n^2 - n + 41 = 41^2 - 41 + 41 = 41^2$$

Clearly 41^2 (i.e., 1681) is not a prime, for besides 1 and itself, 1681 has the divisor 41. The statement we have induced is false, even though it works in the first 40 of the cases to which it applies.

(Incidentally, the problem of finding a practicable formula which *will* always yield primes upon substitution of natural numbers for *n* remains one of the unsolved problems of mathematics.)

We see then that a more trustworthy method of arriving at conclusions than that of induction is necessary, and that method, of course, is the method of deduction. We emphasize once more that in mathematics the two methods go hand in hand; we often discover results by induction, but these results do not become part of the accepted body of mathematical science until they have been proved deductively.

In the sciences the inductive method is perhaps even more important than it is in mathematics; for experiments, as well as observations of phenomena which occur repeatedly under certain conditions, are methods which are basic to science in its search for general conclusions—and these, of course, are inductive methods.

Indeed, the famous " scientific method " has been defined as consisting of the following steps:

1. Experiments or observation of phenomena.
2. General conclusions *induced* from step 1.
3. Specific conclusions *deduced* from the general conclusions of step 2.
4. Verification of the conclusions of step 3.

Although these four steps represent an oversimplification of the very complex and varied approach known as the " scientific method," they do constitute a cycle typical in scientific work. One may cite, for example, the work of Newton. On the basis of many experiments and observations (perhaps even helped by the apple falling on his head, as the old, improbable story goes), he induced the very simple " law of universal gravitation," which describes how the force with which any two bodies in the universe attract each other may be computed. Together with several other laws arrived at inductively, this then enabled Newton to *deduce* many specific facts concerning the exact path of the sun and the moon and the planets in the heavens. Finally, the deduced conclusions were verified by actual astronomical observation.

The fact that induced conclusions must always be weighted with some element of uncertainty has by no means led to the abandonment of inductive reasoning in either science or mathematics. In scientific work, there is no alternative. The growth of science, in fact, is a progression from one inductive result to another, in which old theories are discarded when new facts appear which are inconsistent with them, and new theories are framed to jibe with new facts.

In our day the most dramatic evidence of this is in the fall of Newtonian physics. Accepted by science because they worked in all observed cases,

Newton's laws had to be rejected when it was discovered, at the beginning of this century, that there were two places in which their conclusions did not fit all the observed facts: in the very small world of the atom and in the very large world of astronomy.

Einstein's physical theories have therefore superseded Newton's and will stand until new phenomena are discovered which contradict *their* deduced conclusions.

3.7 MATHEMATICS AND ALGEBRA

It is very difficult to define "mathematics" precisely. There have been many attempts to do so, but up until now no one has succeeded in framing a definition upon which all mathematicians can agree. Rather than attempt a definition, therefore, we shall content ourselves with pointing out a number of attributes especially characteristic of mathematics. The student will see in a moment why we have chosen to do so at just this point in the text.

The concepts of set, function, operation, and relation have been selected for discussion in the first two chapters not only because they are logically and historically primitive in the development of mathematics but also because they are pervasive. They occur not only early but often; it is extremely difficult to find a portion of mathematics in which these concepts do not play a role.

In this chapter we spoke briefly of the principal tool used by the mathematician in working with the aforementioned concepts: the method of deductive reasoning.

We are therefore now in a position to say this about mathematics: *It is a distinctive feature of mathematics in general that it deals with functions, operations, and relations defined on sets, and that it reasons about these concepts deductively.*

But where does the raw material, that is, where do the sets, functions, operations, and relations of mathematics come from? The answer is that originally they were *abstracted* from physical situations.

The student will recall, for example, that the concept of a natural number was abstracted from concrete physical situations involving sets (see Section 1.4). The natural numbers themselves form a set, and mathematics goes on to study functions, operations, and relations defined in this set. Both the world of experience and the developing mathematics continually suggest new sets, functions, operations, and relations to study.

This should enable the student to understand that the widespread idea that mathematics is a completed body of knowledge in which nothing very much now remains to be done is grossly inaccurate. Today, for example, although more mathematics journals exist than ever before, it is still a matter of great difficulty to find space to print all the new mathematics being created.

Another misconception we should like to correct is that *all* of the ideas of mathematics are suggested by physical experience. Often it is only the creative imagination of the mathematician which leads him into new paths, and it is only later, if ever, that the practical world finds a use for mathematics of this sort. A case in point would be the invention of negative numbers. Between the time of the Egyptians of 3000 B.C. and the 17th century, many isolated mathematicians conceived of the idea of negative numbers, and some even worked out the rules for their addition and multiplication with which we are now all familiar. But it was not until Descartes showed that negative numbers had a simple, reasonable, and *useful* interpretation on a scaled line, that their use became general.

Concerning mathematics up to and including calculus, we may say a bit more: This mathematics concerns itself especially with two sets abstracted from physical experience, the set of all real numbers, and the set of all points in space. Early school algebra, for the most part, studies the real number system; geometry, sets of points; and trigonometry, functions suggested by the geometric concept of similar triangles.

We have already (in Section 1.1) said something about the nature of algebra, and the fact that algebra, as mathematicians understand it today, goes further than to study only certain classical operations and relations defined in the set of real numbers. Algebra now deals with sets more extensive, more general, and even different from the set of real numbers or any of its well-known subsets; a similar statement may be made about the operations and relations that are the concern of modern algebraists.

Without exception, however, the new trails that algebra has blazed have extended and followed very naturally from the well-worn older paths. In particular, the germ of most, if not all, the mathematics we now call algebra may be found in the familiar operations and relations defined in the set of real numbers and its well-known subsets.

For a number of reasons, then, a careful study of the real numbers is in order, and will be our next concern.

▶ **EXERCISE 12**

1. Name two ways in which all real numbers may be represented, and one more in which all positive real numbers may be represented.

2. Express the following rational numbers as repeating endless decimals:

(a) $\frac{1}{6}$ (b) $\frac{9}{11}$ (c) $\frac{1}{25}$ (d) $\frac{1}{13}$ (e) $\frac{1}{8}$

3. Express the following repeating decimals as rational numbers in lowest terms:

(a) $0.2222\cdots$ (b) $0.450000\cdots$ (c) $1.242424\cdots$
(d) $0.123123123\cdots$ (e) $0.037037\cdots$ (f) $0.123454545\cdots$

4. Having answered Problem 3 of Exercise 11, what do we know about the numbers $\sqrt{3}$, $\sqrt{5}$, $\sqrt{6}$, $\sqrt{7}$, $\sqrt{8}$, and $\sqrt{10}$?

5. Devise a physical experiment to produce a straight line segment of length π inches.   What does the existence of this line segment tell us about the number π?

6. It may be proved that if n is any natural number which is not a perfect square, then $\sqrt{n}$ is irrational.   Therefore we know that $\sqrt{2}$, $\sqrt{3}$, $\sqrt{5}$ are each irrational.

Justify each of the following statements in *two* ways.

(a) $\sqrt{2} \neq 1.41$ (b) $\sqrt{3} \neq 1.73$ (c) $\sqrt{5} \neq 2.24$

7. What is *deductive* logic?   Illustrate by means of an original example.

8. What is *inductive* reasoning?   Illustrate by means of an original example.

9. Describe two outstanding Greek contributions to mathematics, giving associated names and approximate dates.

10. If a number belongs to a class, indicate by a check mark:

	0.77	$\sqrt{3}$	2	$-\frac{3}{4}$	-1.7	4π	0	$\sqrt{4}$	-7	$\frac{7}{11}$	$-\frac{7}{11}$
Natural number			✓								
Integer			✓								
Positive integer			✓								
Negative integer											
Rational number			✓								
Positive rational number			✓								
Negative rational number											
Irrational number											
Real number			✓								

11. (*a*) Prove that the square of an even nn must be an even nn.

(*b*) A nn is *odd* if and only if it can be expressed in what form?

(*c*) Prove that the square of an odd nn must be an odd nn.

12. It follows from the Fundamental Theorem of Arithmetic (see Exercise 2, Problem 5) that, if a nn is not divisible by a particular prime, then neither is its square; that is to say, if the square of a nn is divisible by a particular prime, then so is the nn. Use this to prove $\sqrt{3}$ and $\sqrt{5}$ irrational.

4 THE REAL NUMBER SYSTEM

4.1 INTRODUCTION

We are committed in this course to the thesis that mathematics may best be described and understood in terms of the concepts of sets, functions, operations, and relations, and that the final justification for any mathematical statement must be deductive in nature. That is to say, if a question is asked as to *why* some mathematical statement holds (if one were to ask, for example: "Why does $2 + 2 = 4$?"), the answer must always be either that the statement is an assumption or that it follows from certain assumptions by the methods of deductive logic.

For obvious reasons, the plan of presenting mathematics deductively is called the "Euclidean program." To some degree, the student has seen this program at work in his study of high-school geometry. In this chapter we shall apply the Euclidean program to the development of the real number system. The study of the properties of the real number system includes all of the subject matter of elementary school arithmetic and most of the content of high-school algebra; and based directly upon the real number system are, among other branches of mathematics, analytic geometry and calculus.

We now present a set of axioms which characterize the real numbers. The student will recognize all but the last as statements which we have already remarked to be reasonable and plausible, and in fact, as statements which we would like to hold true for real numbers. From these few assumptions, *all* the properties of real numbers follow.

As a matter of convenience, we shall separate the axioms into three sets, which we shall deal with in separate sections. The first six will be called the "field" axioms (since mathematicians call any set of objects satisfying these axioms a *field*); the next three, because they deal with the concept of order, are called "order" axioms; the last we have called the "Axiom of Dedekind" (since it derives from the work of the great German mathematician, Richard Dedekind, 1831–1916).

4.2 REAL NUMBERS CHARACTERIZED

(In that which follows, the symbols =, <, + and · are read "equals," "less than," "plus," and "times" respectively.)

We shall assume that *the real number system* is a set (the members of which are called *real* numbers) in which there exist two relations, = and <, and two operations, + and ·, satisfying ten axioms.

The ten axioms will be given as six "field" axioms (Section 4.3), three "order" axioms (Section 4.14), and the "Axiom of Dedekind" (Section 4.15).

[*Note:* We shall often write ab or $a(b)$ or $(a)b$ or $(a)(b)$ for $a \cdot b$.]

4.3 THE SIX FIELD AXIOMS

Axiom F1.   = is an equivalence relation (see Section 2.14).

Axiom F2.   + and · are each closed, commutative, and associative operations (see Section 2.5).

Axiom F3.   (*a*) "Sum substitution". In any sum of real numbers, equals may be substituted for equals without altering the value of the sum.

(*b*) "Product substitution". In any product of real numbers, equals may be substituted for equals without altering the value of the product.

More precisely: If a, b, x, y are real numbers such that $a = x$ and $b = y$, then,

$$a + b = a + y \qquad ab = ay$$
$$a + b = x + b \qquad ab = xb$$
$$a + b = x + y \qquad ab = xy$$

Axiom F4.   "Left distributive law". If F, S, T are real numbers, then,

$$F(S + T) = FS + FT$$

Axiom F5.   There are unequal real numbers, 0 and 1 (read "zero" and "one" respectively), which have the property that, if a is any real number, then,

$$(\text{"Zero-axiom"}): a + 0 = a$$
$$(\text{"One-axiom"}): \quad a \cdot 1 = a$$

Axiom F6.   If a is any real number, then there is a real number $\bar{a}$ (read: "a bar") such that:

$$(\text{"Opposite axiom"}): a + \bar{a} = 0$$

and if a is any *nonzero* real number, then there is a real number a' (read: "a prime") such that:

$$(\text{" Reciprocal axiom "}): aa' = 1$$

NOTES ON THE FIELD AXIOMS.   Axiom F3 is sometimes referred to as the "well-definedness" axiom for addition and multiplication, since the axiom guarantees, essentially, that the sum or product of two real numbers is not altered when different names are used for the same number.   Addition, for example, would certainly deserve to be considered badly defined if $\frac{2}{3} + 1$ turned out to be unequal to $\frac{4}{6} + 1$.

The student will recognize axiom F3 as a more precisely stated form of the "equals plus equals" and "equals times equals" axioms of high-school mathematics.

The word "law" in axiom F4 has no special significance; its use is only a matter of custom.

In axiom F6, the number we have denoted $\bar{a}$ is that which the student already knows as $-a$, or "minus a," or "the negative of a." [We shall prefer "the opposite of a" to these terms; see *Note* following Section 2.10, (v).]   Furthermore, a' denotes the number already familiar to the student as $\frac{1}{a}$, or $1/a$, or "the reciprocal of a."   To emphasize that a is in a sense (what sense?) "opposite" to $-a$, we follow tradition in defining the symbols "$+a$" and "a" to represent the same real number.

In the future, we shall use various symbols for the same number interchangeably, most often without formal justification.   If pressed, however, we might say, for example, that $\bar{1} = -1$, and $1' = \frac{1}{1} = 1/1$, and $+1 = 1$, and $+\bar{1} = \bar{1}$, all *by definition*.

The reason for the stipulation $a \neq 0$ in the second part of axiom F6 is, of course, that we have seen that it is unreasonable to ask for an answer to the problem: $1/0 = ?$.   The reason for the change from the usual notation for opposites and reciprocals is to emphasize the similarities between them, and to avoid the confusion which results from the use of the symbol "$-$" to indicate both the *opposite* of a number and the *operation* of subtraction.

4.4 SEVERAL THEOREMS AND THEIR PROOFS

In our deductive processes we shall borrow from the vocabulary and usage of high-school geometry.   For example, relatively important statements following from our axioms will be called "theorems."   In "proving" theorems, that is, in demonstrating that a theorem actually *is* the consequence of our axioms, we shall for some time follow a familiar pattern: Statements will appear in one column, and the reason which justifies each statement will be placed to its right in a parallel column.

It is important to note that only the following are acceptable as entries in the "reason" column:

1. The hypothesis of the theorem to be proved.
2. An axiom.
3. A definition.
4. A previously proved result.

The following are explanations or comments on 1 through 4 above:

1. The Hypothesis of the Theorem to be Proved. Every theorem is made up of statements which may be written in the form: "If $\cdots$, then $\cdots$". For example, the theorem:
"The base angles of an isosceles triangle are equal" may be written:

"If a triangle is isosceles, then its base angles are equal."

When an assertion is written in the "If $\cdots$, then $\cdots$" form, the statement following "if" (and preceding "then") is called the *hypothesis*, and the statement following "then" is called the *conclusion* of the assertion.

2. An axiom. To the Greeks an axiom was a "self-evident truth"; but with the passage of time, mathematicians have become more modest in their claims. Experience (especially the discovery of "non-Euclidean geometry" in the early nineteenth century) has taught that that which seems self-evident is not always even true; in fact, it is very difficult, if not impossible, to be sure about the absolute truth of *any* statement.

Mathematicians today, therefore, do *not* claim that the axioms of mathematics are truths, whether self-evident or otherwise. The axioms are simply statements, mathematicians now say, from which other statements will be made to follow by the rules of deductive logic. *If* one accepts the axioms as "true," and *if* one accepts the rules of deductive logic, then one is constrained to accept the logical consequences of the axioms as "true."

3. A definition. A deductive treatment of a branch of mathematics begins, as we have already pointed out, with a number of unproved statements (called "axioms") and a number of undefined terms. After that, all new terms which are introduced must be defined in terms of the undefined terms and/or in terms of previously defined terms.

For example, in our axiomatic development of real numbers, $=$, $<$, $+$, and $\cdot$ are undefined or, as they are sometimes called, "primitive" terms.

Although the axioms say things *about* these terms, we actually never tell what the terms themselves mean.

However > ("greater than") will be a *defined* term and, in fact, will be defined in terms of the undefined term < ; and "positive" will be a defined term, defined in terms of the previously defined term > ; etc. (See Section 4.14.)

Definitions in mathematics are framed with two things in mind: First of all, we attempt to make a definition agree with intuitive feelings about the things being defined.   Euclid, for example, followed this requirement when he defined a point as "that which has no parts."   But secondly, we attempt to make the definition fruitful, in the sense that the definition lends itself to proving statements about the thing defined.   Euclid's definition of a point fails utterly in this second respect, for not even once do we find Euclid making use of the definition in proving the theorems which follow it.

Since, in fact, only definitions, axioms, and previously proved statements about a mathematical term may be used in proving assertions about that term, these are the resources the student should look to in trying to prove such assertions.   Physical intuition or the imagination may help greatly in indicating the right path to follow, but, in the final write-up of a proof, the raw material must come from one of the four sources listed above.

A word concerning the arbitrariness of mathematical definitions is appropriate here.   It is typical of the English language that many of its words have a multiplicity of meanings.   In mathematics, where we seek for precision of thought and statement, we prefer that one defined term, insofar as is practicable, has only one clearly defined meaning.   Different authors make different choices among a number of meanings, and, as a consequence, the student will find that many texts apparently disagree with each other and with dictionaries as to the meaning of certain terms.

This, however, should not disturb the student.   For him, it is simply a matter of understanding what the author is saying in the light of the *author's* definitions.   In this text, for example, we have arbitrarily chosen a definition of > (see Section 4.14) that coincides with the definition of some texts, differs from others, and that agrees with very few dictionaries. After that definition has been given, > throughout the rest of *this* text will mean nothing more nor less than what that definition states.

Furthermore, the definition agreed upon is what the mathematician seeks when he asks: "What is $\cdots$?" or "What is meant by $\cdots$?"   In ordinary usage, for example, when one is asked: "What is a camel?", there is an inclination to tell as much as possible about that animal, in an attempt to conjure up in the questioner's mind an image resembling as nearly as possible that in the mind of the person answering the question.

But when a mathematician asks: "What is meant by $>$?", he does not want in response a mass of descriptive detail or an enumeration of properties or attributes or characteristics; he wants only to know the *definition* you have agreed upon for $>$, only that and nothing more.

4. A previously proved result. The student may assume that any statement which occurs as a problem to be proved in the exercises which follow, may actually be proved, and may therefore be used in the proof of any statement in the text which follows that problem.

The construction of proofs is one of the more difficult of mathematical activities; in fact, the ability to construct proofs, together with a knack for discovering mathematical statements worth attempting to prove, may generally be considered to be two distinguishing characteristics of the "mathematical mind."

Not everyone, therefore, should be expected to be able to construct any but fairly simple proofs. The reader of this text, however, should in any case be able to follow (i.e. to understand) proofs once they are constructed, since following a proof is in the main only a question of seeing that each step is properly justified.

We now proceed to state and prove our first theorem on real numbers.

Theorem R1. (Right distributive law.) If F, S, T are real numbers, then:

$$(F + S)T = FT + ST$$

PROOF

STATEMENTS	REASONS
1. F and S are real numbers	1. Hypothesis
2. $F + S$ is a real number	2. Closure of $+$
3. T is a real number	3. Hypothesis
4. $(F + S)T = T(F + S)$	4. Commutativity of $\cdot$
5. $T(F + S) = TF + TS$	5. Left distributive law
6. $\therefore (F + S)T = TF + TS$	6. Transitivity of $=$ (steps 4, 5)
7. $TF = FT$, $TS = ST$	7. Commutativity of
8. $\therefore TF + TS = FT + ST$	8. Sum substitution
9. $\therefore (F + S)T = FT + ST$	9. Transitivity of $=$ (steps 6, 8)

A mathematical proof is said to be more or less "rigorous," depending upon the extent to which necessary steps are included and justified. The preceding proof, for example, would be considered to be fairly rigorous.

But exceedingly rigorous proofs often have the disadvantage of being long and tedious; even worse, major ideas tend to be lost in a maze of minor steps. It is customary, therefore, to omit "obvious" statements in proofs. As an example of a proof which is acceptable, although less rigorous than our first, we offer another proof of Theorem R1:

NOTE 1. From now on the headings *Statements* and *Reasons* will be understood, but not written in our proofs.

NOTE 2. "$= TF + TS$" in step 2 below is to be understood as following the expression directly above it; i.e., step 2, as it stands, is an abbreviation for: $T(F + S) = TF + TS$.

ALTERNATE PROOF OF THEOREM R1

1. $(F + S)T = T(F + S)$	1. Commutativity of $\cdot$
2. $\qquad\quad = TF + TS$	2. Left distributive law (LDL)
3. $\qquad\quad = FT + ST$	3. Commutativity of $\cdot$
4. $\therefore (F + S)T = FT + ST$	4. Transitivity of $=$ (more than once)

In further illustration of the process of deductive proof, here is another theorem and its proof:

Theorem R2. If a is any real number, $0 + a = a$.

PROOF

1. $\quad 0 + a = a + 0$	1. Commutativity of $+$
2. $\quad a + 0 = a$	2. Zero axiom
3. $\therefore 0 + a = a$	3. Transitivity of $=$

4.5 PROPERTIES OF EQUALITY

The usefulness of our results on equality is augmented when we note that, because of the symmetric property of equality, any equation may be read either from left to right or from right to left. Therefore, in the following, we shall, for example, read "$a = b$" as either "a equals b" or "b equals a," whichever suits our convenience.

As a consequence of this agreement, two of the familiar axioms of equality encountered in high-school mathematics may now be discarded, for our transitivity of equality axiom can replace both of them. For example, suppose it is given that $a = c$ and $b = c$; then we have been in the habit of using the axiom "Things equal to the same thing are equal to each other," to justify the conclusion: $a = b$. However, if we read the given information: "a equals c and c equals b" (reading the second given equation from right to left, we see that we may give *transitivity of equality* as a reason for the conclusion $a = b$.

As another example, suppose it is given that $a = x$, $b = y$, and $x = y$; here we have used the axiom "Things equal to equal things are equal to each other" to justify the conclusion $a = b$. But using the transitivity of equality, we may conclude from the first and last equations that $a = y$; then using the conclusion $a = y$ together with the given information $b = y$, a second use of transitivity of equality (this time as in the preceding paragraph) justifies the desired conclusion: $a = b$.

In summary, in situations where the student has used "Things equal to the same (or equal) things are equal to each other" as a justification for statements, he may now use "transitivity of equality" instead.

To facilitate writing proofs, we shall in the sequel abbreviate reflexivity, symmetry, and transitivity of equality: $R =$, $S =$, and $T =$, respectively. We shall from now on not bother to say "transitivity of equality more than once" when the axiom has been used more than once, but simply "$T =$," regardless of how many times the axiom has been used.

▶ **EXERCISE 13**

1. Prove: If a is any real number, than $1 \cdot a = a$.
2. Prove: If a is any real number, than $\bar{a} + a = 0$.
3. Prove: If a is any nonzero real number, then $a'a = 1$.
4. Note that in Problem 1, we did not ask for a proof of the statement: $1 \cdot a = a$, but for a proof of the statement: *If a is any real number, then* $1 \cdot a = a$. The italicised prefatory phrase is, in fact, necessary to make sense out of the statement. Beginning algebra is not a subject different from arithmetic, but is a continuation and extension of arithmetic. The child in elementary school who notices that "$3 + 4 = 4 + 3$, and $7 + 11 = 11 + 7$, and it always works like that," may later in his career phrase exactly the same thought: "If F and S are real numbers, then $F + S = S + F$." He has added nothing new in the way of ideas; he has gained only in conciseness and precision of expression. But again note that the expression of the thought in the second form absolutely requires the prefatory phrase: *If F and S are real numbers, then*. Such prefatory phrases, whether expressed or merely understood, are essential parts of many mathematical statements. (More than one prefatory phrase may, of course, be applicable; one may, for example, have numbers other than the real numbers in mind. In this chapter, however, unless otherwise mentioned, we shall have real numbers in mind.)

In the following cases, supply prefatory phrases where necessary, and justify by means of axioms or previously proved statements.

(a) $x + y = y + x$ (b) $(ab)c = a(bc)$
(c) $1 = 1$ (d) $ax + bx = (a + b)x$
(e) $ab = ba$ (f) $1 + (x + y) = (x + y) + 1$
(g) $(1 + a) + b = 1 + (a + b)$ (h) $1 \cdot (x + y) = 1 \cdot x + 1 \cdot y$

(i) $1 \cdot (1 \cdot 1) = (1 \cdot 1) \cdot 1$ (j) $0 + 1 = 1 + 0$

(k) $1 \cdot r = r$ (l) $1 \cdot (x + y) = (x + y) \cdot 1$

(m) $1 \cdot (0 + 0) = 1 \cdot 0 + 1 \cdot 0$ (n) $1 \cdot (0 + 0) = 1 \cdot 0$

(o) $1 \cdot (x + y) = x + y$ (p) $(x + y) \cdot 1 = x + y$

(q) $u + (v + w) = (u + v) + w$ (r) $1 \cdot m = m \cdot 1$

(s) $1 + x = 1 + x$ (t) $1 + x = x + 1$

(u) $1 + (1 + 1) = (1 + 1) + 1$ (v) $1 + (1 \cdot 1) = (1 \cdot 1) + 1$

(w) $1 + (0 + 1) = (0 + 1) + 1$ (x) $0 \neq 1$

(y) $x + \bar{x} = 0$ (z) $xx' = 1$

5 (a). Can a theorem be proved without making use of the hypothesis of the theorem?

(b) How do you explain the fact that the hypothesis of Theorem R2 has not been used in the proof of Theorem R2 above?

NOTE: To facilitate writing out the proofs which follow, we shall combine several statements of this section as follows:

Zero law: The zero axiom and Theorem R2.

One law: The one axiom and Problem 1.

Opposite law: The opposite axiom and Problem 2.

Reciprocal law: The reciprocal axiom and Problem 3.

4.6 ELEMENTARY ARITHMETIC

What is more certain than "two and two make four?" As far as we as mathematicians are concerned, however, no matter how obvious the statement about real numbers, its acceptability must rest finally on whether it can be made to follow from our real number axioms by the methods of deductive logic.

In this section we shall prove that $2 + 2 = 4$, and show how other results of elementary arithmetic are consequences of the real number axioms we have stated so far, that is to say, of the "field" axioms.

Definition R1. $2 = 1 + 1; 3 = 2 + 1; 4 = 3 + 1$; etc.

NOTE: From now on, spaces to be filled in by the student will appear in proofs; also, to prevent proofs from getting too long, we shall sometimes, as in steps 1 and 3 below, combine two or more steps into one.

Theorem R3. $2 + 2 = 4$.

PROOF

1. $\quad 2 + 2 = 2 + (1 + 1)$	1. Def. of 2 and sum sub.
2. $\quad\quad\quad = (2 + 1) + 1$	2.
3. $\quad\quad\quad = 3 + 1$	3. Def. of 3 and sum sub.
4. $\quad\quad\quad = 4$	4.
5. $\therefore 2 + 2 = 4$	5.

Theorem R4. $2 \cdot 2 = 4$.

PROOF

1.	$2 \cdot 2 = 2 \cdot (1 + 1)$	1.
2.	$= 2 \cdot 1 + 2 \cdot 1$	2.
3.	$= 2 + 2$	3.
4.	$= 4$	4.
5. $\therefore$		5.

▶ **EXERCISE 14**

1. Prove each of the following statements:

(a) $2 + 3 = 5$ (b) $3 + 2 = 5$ (c) $2 + 4 = 6$
(d) $4 + 2 = 6$ (e) $3 + 3 = 6$ (f) $3 + 4 = 7$
(g) $4 + 3 = 7$ (h) $2 + 6 = 8$ (i) $6 + 2 = 8$
(j) $2 \cdot 3 = 6$ (k) $3 \cdot 2 = 6$ (l) $2 \cdot 4 = 8$
(m) $4 \cdot 2 = 8$ (n) $3 \cdot 3 = 9$ (o) $2 \cdot 5 = 10$

2. Supply a prefatory statement and prove:

(a) $2x + 3x = 5x$ (b) $x + x = 2x$
(c) $2(2y) = 4y$ (d) $(3y)2 = 6y$
(e) $7a + 7b = 7(a + b)$ (f) $9(x + y) = 9x + 9y$
(g) $(2x)(3x) = 6x^2$ (h) $(2y)(3x) = 6xy$

3. Definition: $a^2 = a \cdot a$; $a^3 = a^2 \cdot a$; $a^4 = a^3 \cdot a$; etc.

(a) Prove: If $a = b$, then $a^2 = b^2$.

(b) Prove: $a \cdot a^2 = a^3$.

(c) Prove: $a^2 \cdot a^2 = a^4$.

(d) Prove: $a \cdot a^3 = a^4$.

(e) Supply necessary prefatory phrases for the definition and (a) through (d) above.

(f) Define a^5, and prove: $a^2 \cdot a^3 = a^5$.

4. Prove: If a and b are real numbers, then $(ab)^2 = a^2 b^2$. (*Hint:* Associative and commutative laws must both be used in the proof.)

4.7 CANCELLATION LAWS

In this section we justify a number of statements concerning cancellations which may be effected on both sides of certain equations, and we use these statements to derive further important results about opposites, reciprocals, one, and zero.

We begin with a "lemma," that is to say, with a statement of relatively minor importance whose chief purpose is to aid in the proof of the theorem which follows it.

Lemma.   If k and x are real numbers, then $(k + x) + \bar{x} = k$.

PROOF

1. $(k + x) + \bar{x} = k + (x + \bar{x})$ 1.
2. $\quad\quad\quad\quad\; = k + 0$ 2.
3. $\quad\quad\quad\quad\; = k$ 3.
4. $\therefore (k + x) + \bar{x} = k$ 4.

Theorem R5.   If a, b, x are real numbers and $a + x = b + x$, then $a = b$.

PROOF

1. $\quad\quad\quad a + x = b + x$ 1.
2. $\therefore (a + x) + \bar{x} = (b + x) + \bar{x}$ 2. Sum sub.
3. $(a + x) + \bar{x} = a$ 3.
     $(b + x) + \bar{x} = b$
4. $\therefore \quad\quad\quad a = b$ 4.

Corollary.   If a, b, x are real numbers and $x + a = x + b$, then $a = b$.

PROOF

1. $x + a = x + b$ 1.
2. $x + a = a + x$ and $x + b = b + x$ 2.
3. $\therefore a + x = b + x$ 3.
4. $\therefore \quad a = b$ 4.

Theorem R6.   If a, b, x, y are real numbers such that $a + x = b + y$ and $x = y$, then $a = b$.

PROOF

1. $\quad\quad x = y$ 1.
2. $\therefore a + x = a + y$ 2.
3. $\quad a + x = b + y$ 3.
4. $\therefore a + y = b + y$ 4.
5. $\therefore \quad a = b$ 5.

Further cancellation theorems having to do with both addition and multiplication will be included in the following exercise.

Using the cancellation theorems above, we are able to arrive at a method *par excellence* for proving that one real number is the opposite of another: Simply show that the sum of the numbers is zero.   This statement is given precisely in Problem 7, Exercise 15.   We sketch a partial proof, leaving a complete proof and formal write-up to the student: Since we are given that $a + b = 0$, and we know that $a + \bar{a} = 0$, we have: $a + b = a + \bar{a}$.   Hence, by one of the cancellation laws (Theorem R5, Corollary), $b = \bar{a}$.   That is to say, if $a + b = 0$, then b is the opposite of a.

Thus, using Problem 7 to prove that the opposite of -8 is 8, i.e., $-(-8) = 8$, it is only necessary to point out that $8 + (-8) = 0$. Indeed, for any real number a, the opposite of $-a$ is a, i.e., $-(-a) = a$, for exactly the same reason: by Problem 7 in Exercise 15, since $a + (-a) = 0$, it follows that $-(-a) = a$. (See Problem 17; again we leave a formal proof to the student.)

Finally, we point out that by Problem 7 we may also prove that the opposite of $a + b$ is $(-a) + (-b)$; i.e., $-(a + b) = (-a) + (-b)$. (We shall find it convenient to make use of the "bar" notation for opposites in several places.)

Theorem R7.   If a, b are real numbers, then $-(a + b) = (-a) + (-b)$ (that is, $\overline{a + b} = \bar{a} + \bar{b}$; verbally, the opposite of $a + b$ is the opposite of a plus the opposite of b).

PROOF

1. $(a + b) + (a + b) = a + b + a + b$ 1. Grouping def. (see page 94)
2. $= a + \bar{a} + b + \bar{b}$ 2. Gr. def., comm. of $+$, sum sub.
3. $= 0 + 0$ 3. Gr. def., opp. law, sum sub.
4. $= 0$ 4.
5. $\therefore (a + b) + (\bar{a} + \bar{b}) = 0$ 5.
6. $\therefore$ $\overline{a + b} = \bar{a} + \bar{b}$ 6. Exercise 15, Problem 7

▶ **EXERCISE 15**

1. Prove: If a, b, x, y are real numbers such that $a + x = b + y$ and $a = b$, then $x = y$.

2. Prove: If k and x are real numbers and $x \neq 0$, then $(kx)x' = k$.

3. Prove: If a, b, x are real numbers such that $ax = bx$ and $x \neq 0$, then $a = b$.

4. Prove: If a, b, x are real numbers such that $xa = xb$ and $x \neq 0$, then $a = b$.

5. Prove: If a, b, x, y are real numbers such that $ax = by$ and $x = y \neq 0$, then $a = b$.

6. Prove: If a, b, x, y are real numbers such that $ax = by$ and $a = b \neq 0$, then $x = y$.

7. Prove: If a and b are real numbers and $a + b = 0$, then $a = \bar{b}$ and $b = \bar{a}$. (*Also:* State this result in more familiar notation.)

8. Prove: $\bar{0} = 0$. (*Also:* State this result in more familiar notation.)

9. Prove: If a and b are real numbers and $ab = 1$, then $a = b'$ and $b = a'$. (*Also:* State this result in more familiar notation.)

10. Prove: $1' = 1$.

11. Prove: (Well-definedness of opposite.) If a and b are real numbers and $a = b$, then $\bar{a} = \bar{b}$.

12. Prove: (Well-definedness of reciprocal.) If a and b are nonzero real numbers and $a = b$, then $a' = b'$.

*13. When $\bar{a}$ is called "*the* opposite of a," there is an implication that only one opposite of a could possibly exist. (In fact, although this is not *always* true, in mathematics we generally understand that an object to which we apply the word "the" is unique; otherwise we tend to use "a" rather than "the").

The defining property of $\bar{a}$ is that, when it is added to a, the result is 0. To prove that $\bar{a}$ *is* unique, and therefore that we are justified in calling $\bar{a}$ *the* opposite of a, show that, if real numbers r and s both have the defining property of $\bar{a}$, then necessarily: $r = s$.

*14. (Uniqueness of 0.) Prove that only the real number 0 has its defining property.

*15. (Uniqueness of 1.) Prove that only the real number 1 has its defining property.

*16. Show that we are justified in referring to a' as *the* reciprocal of a, where a is any nonzero real number.

*17. Prove: If a is a real number, then $\bar{\bar{a}} = a$ (i.e., $-(-a) = a$).

*18. Prove: If a is a real number and $a \neq 0$, then $a'' = a$ (i.e., $1/\frac{1}{a} = a$).

*19. Prove: If a and b are nonzero real numbers, then $(ab)' = a'b'$. (*Also:* State this result in another way.)

*20. Prove: $\bar{1} \neq 0$.

NOTE: We shall refer to Theorem R5 and its corollary, to Theorem R6, and to Problem 1 as "the cancellation laws for addition."

We shall refer to Problems 3, 4, 5, and 6 as "the cancellation laws for multiplication."

4.8 MULTIPLICATION BY ZERO

We all "know" that the result of multiplying any real number by 0 is 0, and that the product of two real numbers cannot be 0 unless at least one of them is 0.

In this section we shall demonstrate that these important properties are consequences of the assumptions that we have made about real numbers.

Theorem R8. If a is any real number, $a \cdot 0 = 0$.

(The idea in this proof is to arrive at the statement: $a \cdot 0 + a \cdot 0 = 0 + a \cdot 0$, from which, by the cancellation Theorem R5, the desired result follows.)

1. $a \cdot 0 + a \cdot 0 = a \cdot (0 + 0)$	1.
2. $ = a \cdot 0$	2.
3. $ = 0 + a \cdot 0$	3.
4. $\therefore a \cdot 0 + a \cdot 0 = 0 + a \cdot 0$	4.
5. $\therefore a \cdot 0 = 0$	5.

Corollary. If a is any real number, then $0 \cdot a = 0$.

(The proof of this corollary is left as an exercise for the student.)

Theorem R8 and its corollary may be combined into a statement that we shall refer to as the "multiplicative property of zero" (MPZ).

MPZ Theorem. If a and b are real numbers, and if either $a = 0$ or $b = 0$, then $ab = 0$.

NOTE. The words "either $\cdots$ or $\cdots$" as used in mathematics connote "at least one and possibly both." Thus "either $a = 0$ or $b = 0$" does not exclude the possibility that *both* a and b are 0 (see Note 2, Section 1.6).

We digress for a moment, to consider a relevant question of logic: A "converse" of a given statement (as we shall understand it in this text) may be arrived at by interchanging all or part of the hypothesis and the conclusion of the given statement. For example, the statement: "If x is *normal*, and x is a man, then x has two eyes" has the converses:

1. If x is normal, and x has two eyes, then x is a man (interchanging second part of hypothesis and conclusion).

2. If x has two eyes and x is a man, then x is normal (interchanging first part of hypothesis and conclusion).

3. If x has two eyes, then x is normal and x is a man (interchanging all of hypothesis and conclusion).

These illustrations show (how?) that a converse of a true statement need not necessarily be true.

A very important converse of the MPZ theorem *is* true, however:

Theorem R9. If a and b are real numbers, and if $ab = 0$, then either $a = 0$ or $b = 0$.

PROOF. We shall prove this theorem by means of the "indirect method," that is, we shall show that the assumption that the theorem is false leads to a contradiction.

If the theorem is false, then there must exist real numbers a and b such that $ab = 0$, but neither a nor b is equal to zero.   We shall assume that such numbers exist, and show that this leads to the situation: $b \neq 0$, $b = 0$.   Since a statement cannot be both true and not true, this result is a contradiction.   The statement $b \neq 0$ is part of our assumption. Therefore, as soon as we have arrived at the statement $b = 0$, we shall know that our theorem cannot be false, and must therefore be true.

1.	$a \neq 0$, $b \neq 0$, $ab = 0$	1. Hyp.
2.	$\therefore a'$ and b' exist	2. Rec. axiom
3.	$a'(ab) = a' \cdot 0$	3.
4.	$= 0$	4.
5.	$\therefore a'(ab) = 0$	5.
6.	$a'(ab) = (a'a)b$	6.
7.	$= 1 \cdot b$	7.
8.	$= b$	8.
9.	$\therefore a'(ab) = b$	9.
10.	$\therefore \qquad b = 0$	10.

4.9 LOGICAL INTERLUDE

In this section we shall further consider certain notation and vocabulary common in logic and useful in mathematics.

If P and Q are statements, the statement "If P, then Q" is often expressed in other ways.   For example, the following are synonymous statements:

1. If P, then Q.
2. P implies Q.
3. From P, there follows Q.
4. P is a *sufficient* condition for Q.
5. Q is a *necessary* condition for P.

The symbol $\Rightarrow$ (read "from left to right') or $\Leftarrow$ (read "from right to left") is used to mean "implies."   For example, the MPZ theorem may be written:

If a and b are real numbers, then:

$$a = 0 \quad \text{or} \quad b = 0 \Rightarrow ab = 0$$

The preceding line is read: "$a = 0$ or $b = 0$ implies $ab = 0$."   This statement may also be expressed in the following ways:

If $a = 0$ or $b = 0$, then $ab = 0$.

From $a = 0$ or $b = 0$, there follows $ab = 0$.

$a = 0$ or $b = 0$ is a *sufficient* condition for $ab = 0$ (i.e., in order for ab to equal 0, it is *sufficient* that $a = 0$ or $b = 0$).

$ab = 0$ is a *necessary* condition for $a = 0$ or $b = 0$ (i.e., if $a = 0$ or $b = 0$ is true, then *necessarily* $ab = 0$ is true also).

When we have statements P and Q such that each implies the other (i.e., such that if either is true, then the other is true), we say and write:

1. P if and only if Q.
2. $P \Leftrightarrow Q$ (read "P is equivalent to Q"; means: $P \Rightarrow Q$ and $Q \Rightarrow P$).
3. P is a necessary and sufficient condition for Q.

Thus the MPZ theorem and Theorem R9 may be combined into the statement:

If a and b are real numbers, then

$$a = 0 \quad \text{or} \quad b = 0 \Leftrightarrow ab = 0$$

4.10 OPPOSITES IN PRODUCTS

In Section 2.10 we derived, somewhat intuitively, statements that are useful in carrying out the elementary operations of addition, subtraction, multiplication, and division in the set of real numbers. The point of this chapter, however, is that as mathematicians we no longer look to intuitive arguments for the final justification of mathematical statements. At this stage only a completely deductive proof based upon our assumptions will convince us. Furthermore, when we have shown that the "laws" stated in Section 2.10 follow logically from our assumptions about real numbers, then we shall be able to say to anyone who accepts our axioms about the real numbers that he must accept these laws also.

Some of the statements, (i) through (xii), of Section 2.10 have already been taken care of in this chapter. We proceed now to deduce others, in particular the laws for multiplication involving opposites of real numbers.

*Lemma. If a and b are real numbers, then:

$$\text{(i) } ab + a\bar{b} = 0.$$
$$\text{(ii) } \bar{a}b + ab = 0.$$
$$\text{(iii) } \bar{a}b + \bar{a}\bar{b} = 0.$$

PROOF OF (i)

1. $ab + a\bar{b} = a(b+\bar{b})$ 1.
2. $\phantom{ab + a\bar{b}} = a \cdot 0$ 2.
3. $\phantom{ab + a\bar{b}} = 0$ 3.
4. $\therefore ab + a\bar{b} = 0$ 4.

[The proofs of (ii) and (iii) are left as exercises for the student.]

*Theorem R10.   If a and b are real numbers, then:

$$\text{(i)} \ \ a\bar{b} = \overline{ab}.$$
$$\text{(ii)} \ \ \bar{a}b = \overline{ab}.$$
$$\text{(iii)} \ \ \bar{a}\bar{b} = ab.$$

PROOF OF (i)

1. $ab + a\bar{b} = 0$ 1. Lemma; (i)
2. $ab + \overline{ab} = 0$ 2. Opp. law
3. $\therefore ab + a\bar{b} = ab + \overline{ab}$ 3.
4. $\therefore$ $a\bar{b} = \overline{ab}$ 4.

PROOF OF (ii)

1. $\bar{a}b + ab = 0$ 1.
2. $\overline{ab} + ab = 0$ 2.
3.   3.
4.   4.

PROOF OF (iii)

1.   1.
2. $\bar{a}b + ab = 0$ 2.
3.   3.
4.   4.

In more familiar notation, the conclusion of Theorem R10 is:

$$\text{(i)} \ \ \ \ a \cdot (-b) = -(ab).$$
$$\text{(ii)} \ \ \ \ (-a) \cdot b = -(ab).$$
$$\text{(iii)} \ (-a) \cdot (-b) = ab.$$

▶ **EXERCISE 16**

1. Prove the corollary to Theorem R8.

2. Suppose x and y are real numbers such that $xy = 0$.   What can you conclude about these numbers?   Why?

3. Suppose x is a real number such that $(x + 1)(x + 2) = 0$.   What can you say about x?   Why?

4. Suppose x is a real number such that $x^2 = 0$ (i.e., $x \cdot x = 0$).   What can you say about x?   Why?

5. Write converses for each of the following statements, and state whether each converse is true or false:

(a) The Pythagorean theorem.

(b) If $x = 5$ and $y = 12$, then $xy = 60$.

(c) If $x = 7$ and $y = 11$, then $xy = 77$.

(d) If $x = 0$, then $x^3 = 0$.

6. Write each of the following statements in other ways:

(a) A necessary condition for good teaching is knowledge of subject matter.

(b) If two angles of a triangle are equal, the triangle is isosceles.

(c) If a triangle is isosceles, two of its angles are equal.

(d) $\triangle ABC$ is isosceles $\Leftrightarrow$ Two angles of $\triangle ABC$ are equal.

7. Prove parts (ii) and (iii) of the lemma preceding Theorem R10.

8. Prove: If k is any real number, then: $\bar{1} \cdot k = \bar{k}$; $k \cdot \bar{1} = \bar{k}$; $\bar{1} \cdot \bar{k} = k$; $\bar{k} \cdot \bar{1} = k$. (*Also:* State these results in more familiar notation, and derive the corollaries: $(1)(-1) = -1$; $(-1)(1) = -1$; $(-1)(-1) = 1$.)

9. "Simplify" each of the following expressions (i.e., find a simpler expression equal to the given one). Do not write out a formal proof but, in each case, state the laws that are involved in the simplifying process.

(a) $0 \cdot \sqrt{2}$	(b) $(-1) \cdot 0$	(c) $7 \cdot (-11)$
(d) $(-11) \cdot 7$	(e) $(-7)(-11)$	(f) $(-1)(-2)(-3)$
(g) $(-2)^3$	(h) $(-2)(-a)(-3)$	(i) $(-2)^2$
(j) -2^2	(k) $(ac)(-b)$	(l) $(-x)^2$
(m) $(-x)^3$	(n) $(-x)^{100}$	(o) $(-x)^{101}$
(p) $-(-2x)$	(q) $(-a)(-b)(-c)$	(r) $-[(-ab)(c)]$
(s) $(-2)(-x)(-3)(-y)$	(t) $(-2x)^4$	(u) $(2x)^3 + (-2x)^3$
(v) $(-2x)^2 + (-3x)^2$	(w) $(-xy)^2$	(x) $x(-xy)^2$

4.11 THE OPERATION OF SUBTRACTION IN THE SET OF REAL NUMBERS

In subtracting 2 from 5, we seek a number which, when added to 2, will yield 5. We already "know" that there is such a number, namely 3, and that there is no other real number which will do the trick.

In general, when we subtract a real number b from a real number a, we seek a real number which, when added to b, will yield a. It is easy to see that $a + \bar{b}$ [i.e., $a + (-b)$], will do the trick, for adding $a + \bar{b}$ to b results in: $(a + \bar{b}) + b = a + (\bar{b} + b) = a + 0 = a$. We call the result of subtracting b from a: $a - b$ (read "a minus b"); in fact, we are led to make the following definition:

Definition R2. The operation of *subtraction* (whose symbol is "$-$") is defined in the set of real numbers as follows: If a, b are real numbers, $a - b = a + \bar{b}$. More generally, any finite sequence of real numbers, some of which are to be added and some subtracted, is defined to be equal to a *sum* in which the numbers originally to be added are unaltered, and those originally to be subtracted are replaced by their opposites.

Examples of the use of Definition R2:

   (i) $4 - 2 = 4 + (-2)$.

   (ii) $2 - 4 = 2 + (-4)$.

   (iii) $2 - 4 - 3 = 2 + (-4) + (-3)$.

   (iv) $a - b - c + d = a + (-b) + (-c) + d$.

   (v) $- a - b = -a + (-b)$.

Note that $- a + (-b)$ and $(-a) + (-b)$ are two different ways of writing the same number. Thus, since we have already seen (Theorem R7) that $- (a + b) = (-a) + (-b)$, it follows, by the transitivity of equality, that $- (a + b) = -a - b$. (It is worth stating this result completely and verbally: If a and b are real numbers, then the opposite of $a + b$ is the opposite of a, *minus b*.)

As a consequence, we are enabled to conclude, for example, that $-2 - 3 = -5$. For, by the preceding rule (read from right to left): $-2 - 3 = -(2 + 3)$.

   (vi) $b - a = b + \bar{a} = \bar{a} + b = -a + b$; hence: $b - a = -a + b$.

The next theorem presents us with an excellent method to use when we wish to prove that the difference of two numbers is equal to a certain third number:

Theorem R11. If F, S, T are real numbers such that $F = S + T$, then $F - S = T$.

PROOF

1. $\quad F = S + T$	1.
2. $\quad F - S = F + \bar{S}$	2.
3. $\quad\quad\quad = (S + T) + \bar{S}$	3.
4. $\quad\quad\quad = (T + S) + \bar{S}$	4.
5. $\quad\quad\quad = T$	5. Lemma, Theorem R5
6. $\therefore F - S = T$	6.

Thus, to prove that $5 - 3 = 2$, Theorem R11 tells us that it is sufficient simply to show that $5 = 3 + 2$. Theorem R11, in other words, enables us to convert a question concerning subtraction into a question in terms of the earlier concept of addition. A formal proof that $5 - 3 = 2$ follows:

1. $\quad 5 = 3 + 2$	1. Exercise 14, Problem 1b
2. $\therefore 5 - 3 = 2$	2. Theorem R11

Now we return to the question of opposites. We have seen above that the opposite of $a + b$ is $-a - b$. But what about the opposite of $a - b$?

Theorem R12. If a, b are real numbers, $-(a - b) = b - a$. (In words: the opposite of a *minus* b is b *minus* a.)

PROOF

1.	$(a - b) + (b - a) = a + \bar{b} + b + \bar{a}$	1. Grouping Def. and ?
2.	$= a + 0 + \bar{a}$	2. Grouping Def. and ?
3.	$= a + \bar{a}$	3. Grouping Def. and ?
4.	$= 0$	4.
5.	$\therefore (a - b) + (b - a) = 0$	5.
6.	$\therefore -(a - b) = b - a$	6. Exercise 15, Problem 7

Corollary. $-(a - b) = -a + b$ [see (vi) above].

[Theorem R12, read from right to left, is often used in the computation of differences; e.g.: $3 - 5 = -(5 - 3) = -2$.]

We shall call a symbol like "$a + b - c - d + e \cdots$" an *algebraic sum*; each of the elements separated by the "$+$" and "$-$" signs, together with the sign, if any, that directly precedes it, is called a *term* of the sum. Thus, the terms of $a + b - c - d + e \cdots$ are a, $+b$, $-c$, $-d$, $+e$, $\cdots$. (Following a convention previously noted, we shall write a term a as $+a$, or $+a$ as a, whenever we find it convenient to do so.)

We shall call a one-term algebraic sum a *monomial*; two-term—*binomial*; three-term—*trinomial*; and an algebraic sum of more than three terms—*multinomial*.

Since the opposite of a number is that which when added to the number yields a result of zero, it is easy to see that the opposite of a number represented by an algebraic sum is a number represented by an algebraic sum which differs from the original only in that the sign of each term has been changed. For example:

$$- (a + b - c - d + \cdots) = -a - b + c + d - \cdots$$

We are now able to frame a useful manipulative rule with respect to parentheses (or other grouping symbols), after noting the following results:

1. $n + (a + b) = n + a + b$.
2. $n + (a - b) = n + (a + \bar{b}) = n + a + \bar{b} = n + a - b$.
3. $n + (-a + b) = n + (\bar{a} + b) = n + \bar{a} + b = n - a + b$.
4. $n - (a + b) = n + \overline{a + b} = n + (\bar{a} + \bar{b}) = n + \bar{a} + \bar{b}$
$$= n - a - b.$$
5. $n - (a - b) = n + \overline{a - b} = n + (\bar{a} + b)$
$$= n + \bar{a} + b = n - a + b.$$
6. $n - (-a + b) = n + \overline{-a + b} = n + (a - b) = n + a - b$.

Thus, in all cases, when the symbol "$+$" precedes a grouping symbol both "+" and grouping symbol may be deleted, provided the sign of each term originally within the grouping symbol is retained and written; when the symbol "−" precedes a grouping symbol, both "−" and grouping symbol may be deleted, provided the sign of each term originally within the grouping symbol is changed and written. [But note that a "+" symbol at the very beginning of an algebraic sum may be, and usually is, omitted. Thus, rather than $-(-a) = +a$, which is the statement we arrive at by using the above rule for parentheses, we most often write: $-(-a) = a$; this agrees, of course, with our previous results, and with our earlier statement concerning the use of the "+" sign.]

▶ **EXERCISE 17**

1. Prove: $b - a = -a + b$.

2. Prove the corollary to Theorem R12.

3. Subtraction and addition are called "inverse" operations because each undoes the work of the other, in the sense that adding and then subtracting (or subtracting and then adding) a number b to a number a leaves a unchanged; i.e.,

   (i) $(a + b) - b = a$ (ii) $(a - b) + b = a$

Prove (i) and (ii). [*Hint:* By Definition R2 and the grouping definition, $(a + b) - b = a + b + \bar{b}$.]

4. Prove:

   (a) $a - 0 = a$ (b) $0 - a = -a$

   (c) $a + b - c = a - c + b$ (d) $a - a = 0$

5. Prove:

   (a) $5 - 2 = 3$ (b) $6 - 2 = 4$

   (c) $6 - 4 = 2$ (d) $6 - 3 = 3$

   (e) $7 - 3 = 4$ (f) $1 - 1 = 0$

6. What statements framed in terms of subtraction follow from Exercise 14, Problems 1g, 1h, 1i and 2a, 2b, 2e, 2f?

7. Prove that multiplication is distributive over subtraction; i.e., prove:

   (i) $a(b - c) = ab - ac$ (ii) $(a - b)c = ac - bc$

8. Using Problem 7, complete each of the following equations:

   (a) $7(x - y) =$ (b) $11x - 11y =$

   (c) $(x - y)z =$ (d) $am - pm =$

   (e) $3a - 2a =$ (f) $2a - 3a =$

9. Simplify each of the following expressions:

   (a) $a(b - c) + ac$ (b) $a(b - c) + (c - b)a$

   (c) $a(b - c) - (b - c)a$ (d) $2(a - b) - (a - b)$

   (e) $-2a - 3a$ (f) $-2a + 7a$

   (g) $(a - 3b + 7c) + (2a - b - 4c) + (a + b + c)$

   (h) $x^2 - 2x + x(1 - x) - 2(3 - x)$

(*i*) $x[2(x - 1) - x(2 - x)] - 2[x(x - 3)]$

(*j*) $x[2(x - 1) - x(2 - x)] + x[x(2 - x) - 2(x - 1)]$

(*k*) $a(1 + \frac{1}{a}) - \frac{1}{a}(a - 1)$

10. (*b*)–(*k*). Each of the expressions in Problem 9 may be regarded as a monomial, binomial, trinomial, or multinomial. In each case, tell which, and identify the terms of the expression; e.g., in part (*a*) we have a binomial whose terms are $a(b - c)$ and ac. (We often omit the quotation marks that distinguish symbols for objects from objects where this leads to no ambiguity.)

11. (*a*)–(*k*). Evaluate each of the expressions in Problem 9, assuming that $a = 1$, $b = -2$, $c = 0$, $x = -3$.

12. Prove:

(*a*) $5 + (-3) = 2$ (*b*) $3 + (-5) = -2$

13 (*a*). State Theorem R11 in several alternative ways.

(*b*) State in several ways, and prove, a converse of Theorem R11.

(*c*) State in two ways a theorem that combines both Theorem R11 and a converse to Theorem R11.

14. (Well-definedness of subtraction.) Prove: $a = x$, $b = y \Rightarrow a - b = x - y$. (What well-known high-school axiom corresponds to this result?)

4.12 THE OPERATION OF DIVISION IN THE SET OF REAL NUMBERS

We have seen (Exercise 17, Problem 3) that subtraction is an operation inverse to addition; the operation of division with which we are familiar turns out to be inverse to multiplication. This similarity suggests a development parallel to a certain extent to that of the preceding section. That, indeed, is the course we shall pursue in our consideration of the operation of division. (The student should compare the following with the development of Section 4.11.)

In dividing 6 by 2, we seek a number which when multiplied by 2 will yield 6. We already "know" that there is such a number, namely 3, and that there is no other real number which will do the trick.

In general, when we divide a real number a by a real number $b \neq 0$, we seek a real number which, when multiplied by b, will yield a. It is easy to see that ab' will do the trick, for in multiplying ab' by b we have: $(ab')b = a(b'b) = a \cdot 1 = a$. We call the result of dividing a by b: $a \div b$ or a/b or $\frac{a}{b}$ (read, respectively: "a divided by b," "a slant b," "a over b"), and we are led to make the following definition:

Definition R3. The operation of *division* (symbols for which are: $\div$, /, $-$) is defined in the set of real numbers as follows: If a, $b \neq 0$ are real numbers, $a \div b = a/b = \dfrac{a}{b} = ab'$.

NOTE: According to Section 4.3, "Notes on the Field Axioms," $1/a = \dfrac{1}{a} = a'$; according to Definition R3, $1/a = \dfrac{1}{a} = 1 \cdot a'$. But, of course, $1 \cdot a' = a'$, so that the two definitions, where they overlap, are in agreement, and no harm has been done by the fact that we have given two definitions for the same symbol.

Indeed, mathematicians often wish to extend the meaning of a word or symbol, so that "overlapping" definitions are a common phenomenon in mathematics. In every such case, however, it is necessary to determine, as we have above, that, where the definitions overlap, they agree.

A remark on notation is also apropos here: Each of the symbols $"\dfrac{a}{b}"$, "a/b" is called a *fraction*, with *numerator* "a" and *denominator* "b".

The next theorem presents us with an excellent method to use when we wish to prove that the quotient of two particular numbers is equal to a certain third number:

Theorem R13. If F, $S \neq 0$, T are real numbers such that $F = ST$, then $F \div S = T$.

(The proof runs parallel to that of Theorem R11, and is left as an exercise for the student.)

Thus, to prove that $6 \div 3 = 2$, Theorem R13 tells us that it is sufficient simply to show that $3 \neq 0$ and that $6 = 3 \cdot 2$. Theorem R13, in other words, enables us to convert a question concerning division into a question in terms of the earlier concept of multiplication. A formal proof that $6 \div 3 = 2$ follows (we do not prove until Section 4.14 that $3 \neq 0$, so that we shall have to utilize a later, although fortunately logically independent, result in the proof):

1. $\quad 3 \neq 0$	1. Exercise 20, Problem ?
2. $\quad 6 = 3 \cdot 2$	2. Exercise 14, Problem 1k
3. $\quad \therefore 6 \div 3 = 2$	3. Theorem R13

If we restrict ourselves to the integers, there is a familiar "algorithm" (i.e., a special computing process), called the *division* algorithm, which enables us, given a "dividend" and a "divisor," to find a "quotient" and a "remainder" such that

$$\text{dividend} = (\text{divisor}) \cdot (\text{quotient}) + (\text{remainder})$$

More precisely:

Division Algorithm Theorem for Integers.   Suppose that D, d are integers, and that $d \neq 0$.   Then there exist unique integers q, r such that

$$D = dq + r \quad \text{and} \quad 0 \leqslant r < |d|$$

(*Note:* Read "$0 \leqslant r < |d|$" as: "r is greater than or equal to zero and less than the absolute value of d.")

We shall not prove this division algorithm theorem, nor shall we justify the division algorithm for integers, since to do either would lead us too far afield.   We assume, however, that the student knows the algorithm in the case of the positive integers.   For example, we assume that the student is able to divide 1234 by 56, and arrive at the quotient 22 and the remainder 2, satisfying the conditions

$$1234 = 56 \cdot 22 + 2, \quad 0 \leqslant 2 < |56|$$

▶ **EXERCISE 18**

1. Prove Theorem R13.
2. Prove that multiplication and division are inverse operations; i.e., prove that, if $b \neq 0$, then:

(i) $\dfrac{ab}{b} = a$ (ii) $\left(\dfrac{a}{b}\right) b = a$

3. (Well-definedness of division.)   Prove that, if $a = x$ and $b = y \neq 0$, then $a \div b = x \div y$.   What well-known high-school axiom corresponds to this result?

4. Prove that, if a, $b \neq 0$ are real numbers, then:

(a) $\dfrac{ba}{b} = a$; $\dfrac{ab}{b} = a$ (b) $b\left(\dfrac{a}{b}\right) = a$; $\left(\dfrac{a}{b}\right) b = a$

(c) $\dfrac{b}{b} = 1$ (d) $\dfrac{0}{b} = 0$

(e) $\dfrac{a}{1} = a$ (f) $b\left(\dfrac{1}{b}\right) = \dfrac{b}{b}$

5. Prove that, if a, $b \neq 0$, c, $d \neq 0$ are real numbers, then:

$$\frac{a}{b} \cdot \frac{c}{d} = \frac{ac}{bd}$$

(*Hint:* Make use of the grouping definition and Exercise 15, Problem 19.)

6 (a). Prove: If a, $b \neq 0$, $k \neq 0$ are real numbers, then:

$$\frac{ak}{bk} = \frac{a}{b} \quad \text{and} \quad \frac{ka}{kb} = \frac{a}{b}$$

(b) As a corollary of (a), prove that, if $a \neq 0$ and $b \neq 0$, then:

(i) $\dfrac{a}{ab} = \dfrac{1}{b}$ $\qquad\qquad\qquad$ (ii) $\dfrac{a}{ba} = \dfrac{1}{b}$

7. Prove: If $a, b, c \neq 0$ are real numbers, then:

$$\frac{a + b}{c} = \frac{a}{c} + \frac{b}{c} \quad \text{and} \quad \frac{a - b}{c} = \frac{a}{c} - \frac{b}{c}$$

8. Prove: If $a, b \neq 0$, $c, d \neq 0$ are real numbers, then

$$\frac{a}{b} + \frac{c}{d} = \frac{ad + bc}{bd}$$

(*Hint:* Use Problems 6, 7 above.)

9. Prove: If $a \neq 0$, $b \neq 0$ are real numbers, then:

$$\frac{a}{b} \cdot \frac{b}{a} = 1$$

[As a corollary, in the light of Exercise 15, Problem 9, it follows that $\left(\dfrac{a}{b}\right)' = \dfrac{1}{\dfrac{a}{b}} = \dfrac{b}{a}$; i.e., the reciprocal of $\dfrac{a}{b}$ is $\dfrac{b}{a}$.]

10. Prove: If $n, a \neq 0$, $b \neq 0$ are real numbers, then:

$$n \div \frac{a}{b} = n \cdot \frac{b}{a}$$

11. Prove:

$$\frac{-1}{-1} = 1 \qquad \frac{-1}{1} = -1 \qquad \frac{1}{-1} = -1$$

(*Hint:* Use Exercise 16, Problem 8, Exercise 15, Problem 20, and Theorem R13.)

12. Prove:

$$r \neq 0 \Rightarrow -r \neq 0$$

(*Hint:* Use the indirect method.)

13. Prove: If $a, b \neq 0$ are real numbers, then:

$$\frac{-a}{-b} = \frac{a}{b}; \quad \frac{-a}{b} = -\frac{a}{b}; \quad \frac{a}{-b} = -\frac{a}{b}$$

14. Prove that if $a, b, \dfrac{a}{b}$ are real numbers such that $\dfrac{a}{b} = 0$, then $b \neq 0$ and $a = 0$.

15. For what real numbers x is it true that $\dfrac{x-7}{x-7} = 1$? Why?

16. For what real numbers x is it true that

$$\frac{(x-7)(x-11)}{(x-7)(x-13)} = \frac{x-11}{x-13}? \quad \text{Why?}$$

17. If $a, b, x \neq 0, y \neq 0$ are real numbers, prove that $a/x = b/y$ if and only if $ay = bx$.

18. Prove:

(a) $6 \div 2 = 3$ (b) $8 \div 2 = 4$

19. What statements, framed in terms of division, follow from Exercise 14, Problems 1*l*, 1*o*, and 2*c* through 2*f*?

20. In each of the following cases, if D represents the dividend and d the divisor, find the quotient q and the remainder r satisfying the division algorithm theorem, and actually show that the theorem is satisfied.

(a) $D = 11, d = 7$ (b) $D = 123, d = 17$

(c) $D = 1024, d = 32$ (d) $D = 0, d = 100$

(e) $D = 17, d = 5$ (f) $D = -17, d - 5$

(g) $D - -17, d = -5$ (h) $D = -5, d = -17$

(i) $D = -5, d = 17$ (j) $D = 5, d = -17$

21 (a). Prove: If D, d, q and r are real numbers such that $D = dq + r$, and if $d \neq 0$, then: $\dfrac{D}{d} = q + \dfrac{r}{d}$.

(b) Use (a) and the results of Problem 20 to express each of the following "improper" fractions as the sum of an integer and a "proper" fraction, or, if possible, as an integer alone.

(i) $\dfrac{11}{7}$ (ii) $\dfrac{123}{17}$ (iii) $\dfrac{1024}{32}$

(c) Assuming we are dealing with rational numbers, what is a *proper* fraction? An *improper fraction*?

4.13 FACTORS AND PRODUCTS

Precisely what do we mean when we say that "$x^2 - 4$ factors into $(x - 2)(x + 2)$?"

What we mean is this: *If x is any real number, then $x^2 - 4 = (x - 2)$* $(x + 2)$. It is very important to note once more that the italicized phrase, whether expressed or simply understood, is an essential part of the statement.

For example, suppose x is the real number 30. Then our statement says: $30^2 - 2^2 = (30 - 2)(30 + 2)$, or (reading from right to left):

$28 \cdot 32 = 900 - 4 = 896$. The student may verify by ordinary multiplication that this result is correct. (As a matter of fact, this and similar "factorizations" may be used to reduce the difficulty of working out certain arithmetic problems mentally.)

In Section 3.2, we saw how Pythagoras justified certain simple factorizations. In this section we shall prove similar formulas, but this time precisely, for now we have the clearly stated field axioms upon which to base our proofs.

The simplest of these formulas is already known to the student as the "common factor" type of factorization. This is only a simple generalization of the distributive laws.

Theorem R14. If a, b, c, k are real numbers, then:

(i) $ka + kb = k(a + b)$ (i') $ak + bk = (a + b)k$

(ii) $ka + kb + kc = k(a + b + c)$ (ii') $ak + bk + ck = (a + b + c)k$

(and so on)

PROOF

(i): 1. $ka + kb = k(a + b)$ 1. LDL

(i'): (Proof left as exercise for student.)

(ii): 1. $ka + kb + kc = ka + (kb + kc)$ 1. Grouping def.

     2. $= ka + k(b + c)$ 2. LDL and sum sub.

     3. $= k[a + (b + c)]$ 3. LDL

     4. $= k(a + b + c)$ 4. Grouping def. and prod. sub.

     5.   5.

(and so on)

Theorem R15. $(a + b)(c + d) = ac + bc + ad + bd$.

NOTE. It is important in the following proof (as in the preceding) to realize that "$a + b$" is a symbol for a single real number—just as "$2 + 3$" is a symbol for a single real number, the single real number more compactly denoted by the symbol "5."

We may therefore treat $a + b$ as a single real number, and this has been done in the following proof, in an application of the left distributive law. That law states that if F, S, T are real numbers (we have used these letters to suggest "first," "second" and "third" respectively), then $F(S + T) = FS + FT$. In the proof which follows, the first real number is $a + b$, the second is c, and the third is d. Hence:

$$(a + b)(c + d) = (a + b)c + (a + b)d$$

PROOF

1. $(a + b)(c + d) = (a + b)c + (a + b)d$ 1. LDL

2. $= ac + bc + ad + bd$ 2. RDL and grouping def.

It is useful to observe that the product of two binomials is thus an algebraic sum (as it happens, of four terms) whose terms are all possible products that may be formed by multiplying a term of one binomial by a term of the other binomial.

For example: $(x + 2)(x + 3) = x^2 + 2x + 3x + 6 = x^2 + 5x + 6$. (Note that we have used the commutativity of multiplication to write $3x$ rather than the $x \cdot 3$ called for by Theorem R15.)

As an important consequence of the above observation we see that:

(1) $$(a + b)(a - b) = a^2 - b^2,$$
for

$$\begin{aligned}(a + b)(a - b) &= (a + b)[a + (-b)] \\ &= a^2 + ab + a(-b) + b(-b) \\ &= a^2 + ab + (-ab) + (-b^2) \\ &= a^2 + (-b^2) = a^2 - b^2.\end{aligned}$$

[Statement (1), when it is used in factoring, is often called the "difference of squares" formula.]

In many situations, especially in the solution of equations and in working with fractions, we find it useful to reverse the process of multiplication in the sense that we seek to discover numbers whose product is equal to a given number; we refer to the sought-for numbers as *factors* of the given number, and to the process of finding such numbers as *factoring*.

The preceding results of this section are very helpful in problems of factoring, as we shall demonstrate by means of illustrative examples.

Illustrative Example 1. Factor $x^2 - 3x + 2$.

SOLUTION. We have seen that the product of binomials may turn out to be a trinomial. We attempt, therefore, to find a pair of binomials whose product is $x^2 - 3x + 2$. Theorem R15 suggests that the first terms in the binomials have the product x^2, the last the product 2. We therefore first write the pattern: ( )( ), which we then fill in: $(x \quad 1)(x \quad 2)$. Now, in order for the product of the last terms to be 2, they must be of like sign. If both are positive, the product of the binomials would not have the required middle term $-3x$. We therefore make the last terms both negative: $(x - 1)(x - 2)$, and verify that this product is indeed equal to $x^2 - 3x + 2$. (Note that the middle term $-3x$ may be thought of as the sum of the product of the *inner* terms, $-x$, and the product of the *outer* terms, $-2x$, of the given product of binomials.)

Illustrative Example 2. Factor $6x^2 - 13x - 8$.

SOLUTION. The above method applies, but considerably more trial and error will probably be necessary. Likely candidates for a pair of first terms are $2x$, $3x$ and x, $6x$; last terms: 1, 8 and 2, 4 (considering only absolute value; eventually the last terms must, of course, be opposite in sign). It turns out that $(2x + 1)(3x - 8) = 6x^2 - 13x - 8$.

Illustrative Example 3. Factor $x^2 - ax - 2x + 2a$.

SOLUTION. The above method may be used, or one may make use of distributive laws directly:

$$x^2 - ax - 2x + 2a = x(x - a) - 2(x - a) = (x - 2)(x - a)$$

Illustrative Example 4. Factor $3x^2 - 27$.

SOLUTION. In all factorization, it is well to keep a weather eye open first for an application of distributivity, i.e., for the so-called "common factor." Using distributivity first, and then Statement (1) above, we have: $3x^2 - 27 = 3(x^2 - 9) = 3(x + 3)(x - 3)$.

Illustrative Example 5. Factor $x^2 - 2$.

SOLUTION. Here, for the first time in our sequence of examples there arises the very important question: What set of numbers are we dealing with? If we restrict ourselves to the integers, $x^2 - 2$ cannot be factored (except trivially, that is, using ± 1 as a factor). However, if we are dealing with the larger set of all real numbers, we may carry out the factorization as follows: $x^2 - 2 = (x + \sqrt{2})(x - \sqrt{2})$ [using Statement (1) above]. We say "over the real numbers," $x^2 - 2$ factors into $(x + \sqrt{2})(x - \sqrt{2})$.

We shall follow the practice common to most texts, of meaning, in most cases, "factor over the integers," when we say "factor." When we wish to utilize a larger set of numbers in our factorization, we shall either say so or it will be obvious from the context.

Illustrative Example 6. Factor $27x^3 - 8a^3$.

SOLUTION. Using the fact [see Exercise 19, Problem 3d] that $(F - S)(F^2 + FS + S^2) = F^3 - S^3$, and letting $F = 3x$, $S = 2a$, we have: $27x^3 - 8a^3 = (3x - 2a)(9x^2 + 6ax + 4a^2)$.

▶ **EXERCISE 19**

1. Prove Theorem R14, (i′) and (ii′).

2. Show how the following products may easily be worked out mentally:

(a) $19 \cdot 21$ (b) $17 \cdot 23$ (c) $29 \cdot 31$

3. Prove, and illustrate each by means of an example in which F and S are particular real numbers:

(a) $(F + S)^2 = F^2 + 2FS + S^2$ (These trinomials are called
(b) $(F - S)^2 = F^2 - 2FS + S^2$ "perfect binomial squares.")
(c) $(F + S)(F^2 - FS + S^2) = F^3 + S^3$

(d) $(F - S)(F^2 + FS + S^2) = F^3 - S^3$

(e) $(F + S)^3 = F^3 + 3F^2S + 3FS^2 + S^3$

(f) $(F - S)^3 = ?$

4. Express each of the following as a different algebraic sum in as simple a form as you can:

✓ (a) $(x + 3)^2$ (b) $(x - 3)^2$

✓ (c) $(x + 3)(x + 2)$ (d) $(x + 3)(x - 2)$

✓ (e) $(x - 3)(x + 2)$ (f) $(x - 3)(x - 2)$

✓ (g) $(2x + 3y)^2$ (h) $(2x - 3y)^2$

✓ (i) $(2x + 3y)(2x - 3y)$ (j) $(2x + 3y)(3x + 2y)$

   (k) $(2x + 3y)(3x - 2y)$ (l) $(2x - 3y)(3x + 2y)$

   (m) $(2x - 3y)(3x - 2y)$ (n) $(a + b)^2 - (a - b)^2$

✓ (o) $(x + 1)(x - 1)(x^2 + 1)$ (p) $[(1 + x)(1 - x)]^2$

(q) $(x + \dfrac{1}{x})^2$ (r) $(x + \dfrac{1}{x})(x - \dfrac{1}{x})$

(s) $(ax + b)(cx + d)$ (t) $(ax - b)(cx - d)$

(u) $(a + b + c)(a + b - c)$ (v) $(a + b + c)(a - b + c)$

(w) $2(2x - y)^2 - 8(x - y)(x + y)$

(x) $(x - y)(x + y) - (x - y)^2 - (x + y)^2$

(y) $2(2x - 1)(3x + 2) - 3(2x + 1)(2x - 3)$

·✓ (z) $(x + 1)[2(x - 2) - (x - 3)] - x[1 - 3(1 - x)]$

5. The product $(x + 1)(2x^2 + x + 2)$ may be expressed as follows: $(x + 1)(2x^2 + x + 2) = x(2x^2 + x + 2) + 1(2x^2 + x + 2) = 2x^3 + x^2 + 2x + 2x^2 + x + 2 = 2x^3 + x^2 + 2x^2 + 2x + x + 2 = 2x^3 + (1 + 2)x^2 + (2 + 1)x + 2 = 2x^3 + 3x^2 + 3x + 2$. What laws of numbers have been used here to show that $(x + 1)(2x^2 + x + 2) = 2x^3 + 3x^2 + 3x + 2$?

6. The observation of page 109 concerning the product of two binomials may be generalized to apply to the product of any number of algebraic sums of any number of terms each.

How many terms are there in the product of two algebraic expressions if one contains two terms, the other three terms? How may each term of the product be described? Generalize to two algebraic sums, supposing one contains m terms, the other n terms. Generalize further, to the product of algebraic sums containing m, n, p, $\cdots$ terms.

Use your general statement to tell first how many terms there are in the algebraic sum equal to each of the following products, and then to write out that algebraic sum.

(a) $(a + b)(c + d + e)$ (b) $(x + 1)(x^2 - x + 2)$

(c) $(2x - 1)(x^2 + 3x - 2)$ (d) $(a + b)(c + d)(e + f)$

(e) $(x + 1)(x + 2)(x + 3)$ (f) $(x - 1)(x + 1)^2$

(g) $(a + b + c)^2$

(Can you make a complete general statement about the square of an algebraic sum of n terms?) To what does your general statement reduce when $n = 2$?

(h) $(x + y + 1)^2$

(i) $(x - y - 1)^2$

(j) $(ax^2 + bx + c)^2$

(k) $(xy + yz + xz)^2$

7. Factor:

(a) $2x + 2y$ $2(x+y)$

(b) $ax + ay + 2x + 2y$

(c) $3x^2 - 3y^2$ $3(x+y)(x-y)$

(d) $16x^4 - 81y^4$

(e) $x^2 + 4x + 4$ $(x+2)(x+2)$

(f) $x^2 + 3x + 2$

(g) $x^2 - 3x + 2$ $(x-2)(x-1)$

(h) $x^2 + x - 2$

(i) $2x^2 - 3x - 2$ $(2x+1)(x-2)$

(j) $4ax^2 + 6ax - 4a$

(k) $x^2 - (a + b)x + ab$

(l) $x^2 - \dfrac{1}{x^2}$

(m) $(a + b)^2 - c^2$

(n) $x^2 - y^2 + (x + y)^2$

(o) $6x^2 - 35x - 6$

(p) $6x^2 + 9x - 6$

(q) $6x^2 + 13x - 8$

(r) $12x^2 - 7x - 12$

(s) $4 + x^2 + \dfrac{4}{x^2}$

(t) $2 - x^2 - \dfrac{1}{x^2}$

(u) $x^3 - x^2 + x - 1$

(v) $x^3 + 1$

(w) $x^3 - 1$

(x) $8x^3 - 27y^3$

(y) $8x^3 + 27y^3$

(z) $x^4 + 8x^2 + 16$

(z') $x^4 + 16$

8. Factor $x^4 - 9$:

(a) Over the integers

(b) Over the rational numbers

(c) Over the real numbers

4.14 THE AXIOMS OF INEQUALITY

We now present three axioms which characterize the relation $<$ on the set of all real numbers. They are known as the "axioms of inequality" or the "order axioms."

Axiom O1. $<$ is a transitive relation.

Axiom O2.   ("Trichotomy" axiom.) If a and b are real numbers, then one and only one of the following three statements is true:

(i) $a < b$ (ii) $a = b$ (iii) $b < a$

Axiom O3.   If a, b, k are real numbers and:

$$a < b$$

then:

$$a + k < b + k$$

and if, furthermore, $0 < k$, then:

$$ak < bk$$

Definition R4. The relation $>$ (greater than) is defined on the set of real numbers in terms of the relation $<$ as follows:

If a and b are real numbers, then we say:

$$a > b$$

if and only if:

$$b < a$$

As a consequence of Definition R4, the statement "$a < b$" may be read either forward ("a is less than b") or backward ("b is greater than a"). Furthermore, it is easily proved that the relation $>$ is transitive also, and we may now restate Axiom O2 in the more symmetric form:

Axiom O2. If a and b are real numbers, then one and only one of the following three statements is true:

(i) $a < b$ (ii) $a = b$ (iii) $a > b$

Definition R5. A real number k is said to be *positive* if $k > 0$, and *negative* if $k < 0$.

Note that the condition "$0 < k$" in Axiom O3 may therefore be read "k is positive."

Now we are ready to prove a theorem involving the substitution of equals for equals in an inequality:

Theorem R16. If a, b, x are real numbers such that $a < b$ and $x = a$, then: $x < b$.

*PROOF. By the trichotomy axiom, $x < b$ must follow if $x = b$ and $x > b$ can both be proved impossible.

We therefore consider two cases.

In the first case we assume $x = b$ and show that this leads to the result $a = b$, which is impossible, since by the trichotomy axiom $a = b$ and $a < b$ cannot both be true.

In the second case we assume $x > b$ and arrive at the result $x > a$, which again is impossible. (Why?)

(The rest of the proof of Theorem R16 is left as an exercise for the student.)

There are two relations which are closely related to those we have been discussing:

Definition R6. The relations $\leqslant$ ("less than or equal to") and $\geqslant$ ("greater than or equal to") are defined on the real numbers as follows:

If a and b are real numbers, we say

$$a \leqslant b \quad \text{if} \quad a < b \quad \text{or} \quad a = b$$

and we say

$$a \geqslant b \quad \text{if} \quad a > b \quad \text{or} \quad a = b$$

We shall call the four relations, $<$, $>$, $\leqslant$, $\geqslant$, the *inequality relations*. It is now possible to prove:

Theorem R17. (i) All the inequality relations are transitive.

(ii) Any real number may be added to (or subtracted from) both sides of an inequality without altering the inequality relation.

(iii) Both sides of an inequality may be multiplied (or divided) by the same *positive* real number without altering the inequality relation.

(iv) Equals may be substituted for equals in any inequality.

[Although (i) through (iv) of Theorem R17 are a little loosely stated, it is assumed that the student will be able to translate them into more precise statements. The proof of Theorem R17 is not difficult, but, since it involves so many separate statements, it is tedious and will, therefore, be omitted here.]

Our next theorem has to do with the effect of "changing the sign" of both sides of an inequality:

Theorem R18. If a and b are real numbers, then:

(i) $a > b \Rightarrow \bar{a} < \bar{b}$.

(ii) $a < b \Rightarrow \bar{a} > \bar{b}$.

PROOF

(i): 1. $a > b$ 1.

    2. $\bar{b} + \bar{a} + a > b + \bar{b} + \bar{a}$ 2.

    3. $\bar{b} + 0 > 0 + \bar{a}$ 3.

    4. $\bar{b} > \bar{a}$ 4.

(ii): (Proof left as exercise for student.)

Corollary. If a is a real number, then:

(i) a is positive $\Rightarrow \bar{a}$ is negative;

(ii) a is negative $\Rightarrow \bar{a}$ is positive.

(Proof of corollary left as exercise for student.)

The comment which follows Theorem R17 applies to the following theorem also:

Theorem R19. Changing the sign of both sides of any inequality relation reverses the symbol of inequality.

With the help of Theorem R18, we can now establish the order relation between 1 and 0, and then we go on to establish a few other order relations:

Theorem R20. $1 > 0$.

*PROOF. By the trichotomy axiom, $1 > 0$ will follow if we can show

$1 = 0$ and $1 < 0$ to be impossible. The first, $1 = 0$, is immediately impossible, however, since Axiom F5 specifically states that 1 and 0 are unequal.

We therefore assume $1 < 0$, and arrive at the conclusion: $1 > 0$; but, by the trichotomy axiom, the situation $1 < 0$ *and* $1 > 0$ is impossible.

1. $1 < 0$	1.
2. $\therefore \bar{1} > 0$	2.
3. $\therefore \bar{1} \cdot \bar{1} > \bar{1} \cdot 0$	3.
4. $\bar{1} \cdot \bar{1} = 1$	4.
5. $\bar{1} \cdot 0 = 0$	5.
6. $\therefore 1 > 0$	6.

Corollary. $\bar{1} < 0$.   (i.e., $-1 < 0$.)

(The proof of the corollary above is left as an exercise for the student.)

Theorem R21. $2 > 1$

PROOF

1. $1 > 0$	1.
2. $\therefore 1 + 1 > 1 + 0$	2.
3. $1 + 1 = 2$	3.
4. $1 + 0 = 1$	4.
5. $\therefore 2 > 1$	5.

Corollary. $2 > 0$.

(The proof of the corollary above is left as an exercise for the student.)

Theorems R20 and R21, and the corollary to Theorem R21 show that the natural numbers 1 and 2 are both positive, and set up an order relation between 1 and 2. Similarly, it may be shown that all the natural numbers are positive, and an order relation may be established between any pair of natural numbers.

We note that since $2 > 1$, it is permissible to write: $1 < 2$, $2 \geqslant 1$, $1 \leqslant 2$; in fact, it is also correct to write: $1 \leqslant 1$, $1 \geqslant 1$, $2 \leqslant 2$, $2 \geqslant 2$.

We now consider several theorems which are useful in working with inequalities:

Theorem R22.   "Like" inequalities may be added.

This theorem has many cases. For illustrative purposes, we shall prove only one: If a, b, x, y are real numbers such that

$$a < x$$

and

$$b < y$$

then

$$a + b < x + y$$

PROOF

1. $a < x, b < y$ 1.
2. $\therefore a + b < x + b, x + b < x + y$ 2.
3. $\therefore a + b < x + y$ 3.

Theorem R23. Among *positive* real numbers, like inequalities may be multiplied.

We prove only this case: If a, b, x, y are positive real numbers such that

$$a < x$$

and

$$b < y$$

then

$$ab < xy$$

PROOF

1. $a < x, b < y$ 1.
2. $\therefore ab < xb, xb < xy$ 2.
3. $\therefore ab < xy$ 3.

Theorem R24. Multiplying both sides of an inequality by a negative real number reverses the symbol of inequality.

We prove this case: If a, b, c are real numbers such that $a < b$ and $c < 0$, then $ac > bc$.

PROOF

1. $a < b, c < 0$ 1.
2. $\therefore -c > 0$ 2.
3. $\therefore (a)(-c) < (b)(-c)$ 3.
4. $-ac < -bc$ 4.
5. $\therefore -(-ac) > -(-bc)$ 5.
6.   i.e., $ac > bc$ 6.

Theorem R25. (i) If a is a positive real number, then so is $1/a$.
(ii) If a is a negative real number, then so is $1/a$.

PROOF OF (i) By the trichotomy axiom, it will follow that $1/a$ is positive if we can show that $1/a$ cannot be zero or negative.

We therefore consider two cases:

Case 1. We assume that $1/a = 0$ and show that this leads to the conclusion $1 = 0$; but this is impossible, by Axiom F5.

Case 2. We assume that $1/a < 0$ and show that this leads to the conclusion $1 < 0$; but this is impossible, since we have proved $1 > 0$ (Theorem R20), and the trichotomy axiom does not permit both statements to be true.

Case 1. 1. $\dfrac{1}{a} = 0$ 1.

2. ∴ $1 = 0$ 2. Problem 14, Exercise 18

Case 2. 1. $\dfrac{1}{a} < 0, a > 0$ 1.

2. ∴ $a \cdot \dfrac{1}{a} < a \cdot 0$ 2.

3. $a \cdot \dfrac{1}{a} = 1$ 3. Problem ?, Exercise 18

4. $a \cdot 0 = 0$ 4.

5.   5.

[The proof of (ii) is left as an exercise for the student.]

We are now in a position to define exactly what we mean by "betweenness" among the real numbers:

Definition R7. If a, b, c are real numbers, then b is said to be *between* a and c (or between c and a) if:

$$a \leqslant b \quad \text{and} \quad b \leqslant c \text{ (written: } a \leqslant b \leqslant c\text{)}$$

or if:

$$a \geqslant b \quad \text{and} \quad b \geqslant c \text{ (written: } a \geqslant b \geqslant c\text{)}$$

Thus, the real numbers between 2 and 4 include, according to our definition, 2, 3, 3.7, and 4, and, of course, many other real numbers.

▶ **EXERCISE 20**

1. Complete the proof of, or prove:

*(a) Theorem R16.   (b) Theorem R18, (ii).

(c) Corollary, Theorem R18.   (d) Corollary, Theorem R20.

(e) Corollary, Theorem R21.   (f) Theorem R25, (ii).

2. Prove:

(a) $3 > 2$ (b) $4 > 2$ (c) $2 \neq 0$

(d) $3 \neq 0$ (e) $4 \neq 0$

3. Prove:

(a) $2' \cdot \bar{4} = \bar{2}$ (restate this result)   (b) $\frac{1}{2} = \frac{3}{6}$

(c) $\frac{1}{3} = \frac{2}{6}$ (d) $\frac{1}{2} + \frac{1}{3} = \frac{5}{6}$

4. Prove:

(a) If a, p are real numbers and p is positive, then $a + p > a$.

(b) If a, n are real numbers and n is negative, then $a + n < a$.

(c) If a is a positive real number, then $a < 1 \Rightarrow a^2 < a$.

(d) If a is a positive real number, then $a > 1 \Rightarrow a^2 > a$.

(e) If a and b are positive real numbers, then:

$$a < b \Rightarrow \dfrac{1}{a} > \dfrac{1}{b}$$

(In fact, among positive real numbers, taking the reciprocal of both sides of any inequality reverses the symbol of inequality.)

5. State more precisely and prove:

(a) The sum of a pair of positive real numbers is positive.

(b) The sum of a pair of negative real numbers is negative.

(c) The product of a pair of positive real numbers is positive.

(d) The product of a pair of negative real numbers is positive.

(e) The product of a negative real number and a positive real number is negative.

(f) The square of a real number is never negative (i.e., always what?)

(g) The product of a pair of non-negative real numbers is non-negative.

6. Make and prove statements concerning quotients analogous to 5c, (d), and (e).

*7. Prove: If a and b are real numbers, then:

(i) $ab > 0 \Leftrightarrow a > 0$ and $b > 0$, or $a < 0$ and $b < 0$.

(ii) $ab < 0 \Leftrightarrow a > 0$ and $b < 0$, or $a < 0$ and $b > 0$.

*8 (a). Following Problem 3, Exercise 14, how would you define a^n in terms of a^{n-1}, where a is a real number and n a natural number?

(b) Prove: If a and b are real numbers and n is a natural number, then:

$$a = b \Rightarrow a^n = b^n$$

(*Hint:* The process of Problem 3a, Exercise 14, may be continued indefinitely.)

(c) Prove: If a and b are positive real numbers and n is a natural number, then:

$$a < b \Rightarrow a^n < b^n$$

(*Hint:* Multiply both sides of $a < b$ first by a and then by b and then conclude: $a^2 < b^2$; then derive $a^3 < b^3$ in somewhat similar fashion. The process may be continued indefinitely.)

(d) Prove: If a and b are positive real numbers and n is a natural number, then:

$$a^n = b^n \Rightarrow a = b$$

(*Hint:* By the trichotomy axiom, one of the following three must be true: $a = b$, $a < b$, $a > b$; prove each of the latter two impossible in this situation.)

(e) Prove: If a and b are positive real numbers and n is a natural number, then:

$$a^n > b^n \Rightarrow a > b$$

(f) Prove: If r is a real number and n is a natural number, then:

$$r > 0 \Rightarrow r^n > 0$$

*9. Assuming x and k are real numbers and k is positive, prove:

(a) $x^2 < k^2$ if and only if $-k < x < k$.

(b) $x^2 > k^2$ if and only if $x > k$ or $x < -k$.

*10. Prove that, if a and b are real numbers and $a < b$, then:

$$a < \frac{a+b}{2} < b$$

*11. Prove that, if a and b are real numbers such that $a \leqslant b$ and $b \leqslant a$, then $a = b$.

*12. State more precisely and prove a case of Theorem R17 not proved in the text.

*13. In this problem we reintroduce the absolute value function, whose definition is given in Problem 13 of Exercise 9: If x is a real number and $x \geqslant 0$, then $|x| = x$; if $x < 0$, then $|x| = -x$.

The following important and useful properties of absolute value may be proved, assuming that a and b are real numbers:

(1) $|a| \geqslant 0$.

(2) $a = 0 \Leftrightarrow |a| = 0$.

(3) $a \neq 0 \Leftrightarrow |a| > 0$.

(4) $|a|^2 = a^2$.

(5) $|a| = |-a|$.

(6) $a \leqslant |a|$.

(7) $a \geqslant -|a|$.

(8) $|a| \, |b| = |ab|$.

(9) $-b < a < b \Leftrightarrow |a| < b$.

(10) $|a + b| \leqslant |a| + |b|$.

(11) $|a| - |b| \leqslant |a - b|$.

(12) If $b \neq 0$, then $\left|\dfrac{a}{b}\right| = \dfrac{|a|}{|b|}$.

(13) $|a - b| = a - b$ or $b - a$, whichever is non-negative.

We shall find it convenient to utilize less formal proofs as we go on, as illustrated by the following.

The student may answer the following questions and supply the proofs or parts of proofs which have been omitted:

PROOFS

(1) *Case* 1. $a \geqslant 0$. Then $|a| = a$ (why?). Hence (substituting equals for equals in an inequality), $|a| \geqslant 0$, Q.E.D.

Case 2. $a < 0$. Then $|a| = -a$ (why?). Also, $-a > 0$ (why?). Hence $|a| > 0$ (why?) and therefore $|a| \geqslant 0$ (why?), Q.E.D.

(2) ($\Rightarrow$): If $a = 0$, then $a \geqslant 0$, and $|a| = a$ (why?), Q.E.D.

($\Leftarrow$): We use the indirect method. Suppose $a \neq 0$, then $a < 0$ or

$a > 0$ (why?). If $a < 0$, then $|a| = -a > 0$ (why?), which together with the hypothesis $|a| = 0$ contradicts what axiom? Similarly, $a > 0$ leads to a contradiction (show this). Therefore $a \neq 0$ is false, i.e., $a = 0$ is true, Q.E.D.

(3) This can be proved as a corollary to (1) and (2).

(4) *Hint:* $|a| = \pm a$.

(5) *Hint:* Consider cases as in 1.

(8) *Hint:* Consider four cases: $a \geqslant 0$, $b \geqslant 0$; $a \geqslant 0$, $b < 0$; $a < 0$, $b \geqslant 0$; $a < 0$, $b < 0$.

(9) This theorem has a nice geometric interpretation. On a scale line, $|a|$ may be thought of as the distance from the point labeled a to the origin:

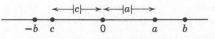

[*Hint for proof:* Consider cases for proof of $\Rightarrow$, and use (6), (7) for proof of $\Leftarrow$.]

(10) *Hint:* By (9), it will be sufficient to prove:
$$-(|a| + |b|) \leqslant a + b \leqslant |a| + |b|$$

(11) *Hint:* Restate (10): If x and y are real numbers, then $|x + y| \leqslant |x| + |y|$. Then let $x = a - b$, $y = b$.

*4.15 THE AXIOM OF DEDEKIND

First of all, we introduce several definitions.

Definition. Suppose A and B are non-null sets of real numbers such that the following is true:
$$a \in A, \quad b \in B \Rightarrow a < b$$
(i.e., such that whenever a is an element of A and b is an element of B, then $a < b$).

Then we shall call the ordered pair of sets (A, B) a *tandem pair*.

EXAMPLES OF TANDEM PAIRS (A, B): (It will help to picture these sets on a scaled line.)

1. $A =$ the set of all negative real numbers.
   $B =$ the set of all positive real numbers.
2. $A = \{2 \dashrightarrow 4\}$.
   $B = \{6 \dashrightarrow 7\}$.
3. $A = \{1, 2, 3\}$.
   $B = \{7, 11\}$.
4. $A =$ the set of all positive rational numbers whose squares are less than 2.

B = the set of all positive rational numbers whose squares are greater than 2.

Definition. A real number x is said to be *between* the sets A, B of a tandem pair (A, B) if the following is true:

$$a \in A, \quad b \in B \Rightarrow a \leqslant x \leqslant b \qquad \text{(i.e. ?)}$$

EXAMPLES OF REAL NUMBERS BETWEEN THE SETS OF A TANDEM PAIR:

1. In Example 1 above, 0 is between A and B.
2. In Example 2 above, $\sqrt{23}$ is between A and B.
3. In Example 3 above, 3 is between A and B.
4. In Example 4 above, $\sqrt{2}$ is between A and B.

We have introduced the notions above first of all in order to make it possible to describe, in simple terms, a deep-lying deficiency of the rational number system—one which, for example, makes the rational numbers unsuitable for the development of the very important branch of mathematics known as calculus.

The deficiency to which we refer is the following: There exist tandem pairs of sets of rational numbers with no rational number whatever between them.

This is intuitively evident in Example 4 above. For between all positive rational numbers whose squares are less than 2 and all positive rational numbers whose squares are greater than 2, one would expect to find only a number whose square is equal to 2. But we have proved (see Section 3.3) that *no* rational number has a square equal to 2.

We feel, however, that such a gap between tandem sets could not exist in the real number system. The real number $\sqrt{2}$, for example, repairs the gap in the preceding example. Again, thinking pictorially of a pair of tandem sets as they appear on a scaled line, we feel that between a pair of tandem sets of real numbers there must always be at least one point, i.e., at least one real number.

We are led, therefore, to include the following in our sets of axioms characterizing real numbers:

Axiom of Dedekind. Between the sets of every tandem pair of sets of real numbers, there is at least one real number.

We shall now put the axiom of Dedekind to work in the proof of the following important theorem:

Theorem. There is a unique positive real number whose square is 2.

PROOF: Let A be the set of all positive real numbers whose squares are less than 2, B the set of all positive real numbers whose squares are greater than 2.

It is left to the student to verify that the ordered pair (A, B) is a tandem pair.

At this point we introduce a lemma:

Lemma 1. There is a unique real number between the sets A, B defined above.

PROOF OF LEMMA 1. We know that there is a real number between A and B by the axiom of Dedekind.

To show that it is unique, we suppose that there are two different real numbers between A and B, and arrive at a contradiction.

By the trichotomy axiom, one of these real numbers (call it u) must be less than the other (call it v).

Let $x = (u + v)/2$ and $y = (x + v)/2$. Then by Problem 10, Exercise 20,

$$u < x < y < v$$

Now if a and b are (respectively) any elements of A and B whatever, we have, since u and v are between A and B:

$$a \leqslant u < x < y < v \leqslant b$$

This means that x and y are positive real numbers which are members of neither A nor B; i.e., we have that x^2 is neither less than nor greater than 2, and y^2 is neither less than nor greater than 2.

Hence, by the axiom of trichotomy, $x^2 = 2$ and $y^2 = 2$, from which follows: $x^2 = y^2$.

But then: $x = y$ (by Problem 8d of Exercise 20.)

We now have: $x = y$ and $x < y$, which, in the light of the trichotomy axiom, is a contradictory situation.

This completes the proof of Lemma 1.

We now introduce a second lemma:

Lemma 2. If $a \in A$, then $\dfrac{2}{a} \in B$, and if $b \in B$, then $\dfrac{2}{b} \in A$.

PROOF OF LEMMA 2. Suppose $a \in A$. Then $a^2 < 2$ (why?). Hence $\dfrac{2}{a^2} > 1$ (why?), from which follows: $\dfrac{4}{a^2} > 2$ (why?), i.e., $\left(\dfrac{2}{a}\right)^2 > 2$, i.e., $\dfrac{2}{a} \in B$.

The proof of the other part of the lemma is similar, and is left as an exercise for the student.

Now we are ready to complete the proof of the theorem.

Let p be that unique real number between sets A and B whose existence is guaranteed by Lemma 1. Clearly p is positive, for since A is non-null, we know that there exists a positive real number q in A, and by the definition of p, $p \geqslant q$. Since $q > 0$, it follows that $p > 0$, i.e., p is positive.

Now suppose that a is any element of A and b is any element of B. Then by Lemma 2, $\frac{2}{b} \in A$ and $\frac{2}{a} \in B$. Therefore, since p is between the sets A and B:

$$\frac{2}{b} \leqslant p \leqslant \frac{2}{a}$$

and dividing through by 2:

$$\frac{1}{b} \leqslant \frac{p}{2} \leqslant \frac{1}{a}$$

Hence (by Problem 4e of Exercise 20):

$$b \geqslant \frac{2}{p} \geqslant a$$

i.e.,

$$a \leqslant \frac{2}{p} \leqslant b$$

Thus, $2/p$ is also between the sets A and B. Therefore, by Lemma 1, $p = 2/p$, i.e., $p^2 = 2$.

We have now shown that there is a positive real number whose square is 2. That this positive real number is unique follows from Problem 8d of Exercise 20; and the proof of our theorem is now complete.

▶ *EXERCISE 21

1. Supply suggested details and answer questions posed in Section 4.15.
2. Prove the following:

Theorem. If r is a positive real number, then there exists a unique positive real number p such that $p^2 = r$.

Hints:

(1) Follow, but with appropriate changes, the proof of the theorem of Section 4.15.

(2) How should A and B be defined now?

(3) To prove A and B non-null, consider the cases $r = 1$, $r < 1$, $r > 1$. Problems 4c and d of Exercise 20 will be found useful.

The unique positive real number whose square is the positive real number r is, of course, denoted $\sqrt{r}$.

3. Prove the following:

Theorem. If r is a positive real number, then there exists a unique positive real number p such that $p^3 = r$.

Hints:

(1) Follow, but with appropriate changes, the proof of the theorem of Problem 2.

(2) How should A and B be defined now?

(3) In proving A and B non-null, the following lemma will be found useful:

Lemma. If r is a positive real number such that $r < 1$, then $r^3 < r$ and $1^3 > r$; and if r is a positive real number such that $r > 1$, then $1^3 < r$ and $r^3 > r$.

(4) As an analog of Lemma 2, prove the following:

Lemma. If $a \in A$, then $\sqrt{\dfrac{r}{a}} \in B$, and if $b \in B$, then $\sqrt{\dfrac{r}{b}} \in A$.

The process illustrated by the preceding two theorems may be continued, and, in fact, we may prove that for *any* given natural number n, if r is a positive real number, then there is a unique positive real number p such that $p^n = r$; and this unique positive real number p is, of course, denoted $\sqrt[n]{r}$.

In the case $n = 4$, the preceding lemma is changed to:

Lemma: If $a \in A$, then $\sqrt[3]{\dfrac{r}{a}} \in B$, etc.; and so on for $n \geqslant 5$.

4. Prove: Zero is the only real number whose nth power is zero (assuming n to be a natural number).

Hence we define: $\sqrt[n]{0} = 0$.

*4.16 THE NATURAL NUMBERS DEFINED

We now consider a definition of the natural numbers within the logical framework of the real number system.

Two very important characteristics of the set of natural numbers are that it contains 1 and that it is closed under the operation of adding 1 to each member of the set. But there are other sets which exhibit this property: Adding 1 to any real number, for example, yields again a real number; adding 1 to any integer produces once more an integer; and 1 belongs to both of these sets.

We therefore make a preliminary definition.

Definition. An *inductive set S* is a set of real numbers with the properties:

(i) $1 \in S$.

(ii) $s \in S \Rightarrow s + 1 \in S$.

Examples, then, of inductive sets are the set of all real numbers, the set of all integers, and the set of all natural numbers.

We feel, however, that the natural numbers are in a sense the *smallest* of all inductive sets. The sense in which we mean "smallest" here is that *every* inductive set must contain at least the natural numbers as a subset. For by (i), an inductive set S must include the number 1. And by (ii), the fact that 1 belongs to S implies that $1 + 1$, or 2 belongs to S; and again by (ii), since 2 belongs to S, it follows that $2 + 1$ or 3 belongs to S; and so on. And the numbers 1, 2, 3, $\cdots$ are, of course, those which we think of as the natural numbers.

Since we feel that the natural numbers are precisely those which are "common" to all inductive sets, we are led to the following definition (see Section 1.6).

Definition. The set of *natural numbers* is the intersection of all inductive sets of real numbers.

Since the intersection of sets is always contained within each of the original sets, there follows immediately:

Corollary. Every inductive set contains all the natural numbers.

*4.17 THE PRINCIPLE OF MATHEMATICAL INDUCTION

A row of dominoes may be toppled by knocking down only the first if the dominoes are close enough together; and one may be sure of being able to reach *any* rung of an upright ladder, knowing that the first rung is within reach, and that one can span the distance from any rung to the next.

These examples illustrate the intuitive background of the so-called "Principle of Mathematical Induction:"

Principle of Mathematical Induction: A set S contains all the natural numbers if S satisfies the following two conditions:

(i) $1 \in S$.
(ii) $s \in S \Rightarrow s + 1 \in S$.

This principle, in fact, is nothing more than a restatement of the preceding corollary.

The Principle of Mathematical Induction finds its use in proving theorems about natural numbers. It is especially useful in rigorizing proofs of the "and so on" type. In Section 4.14, for example, beginning with Theorem R20, we proved that the numbers 1 and 2 are positive, and we stated that "similarly" one may prove that all the other natural numbers are positive. But now, as an example of the application of the Principle of Mathematical Induction, we rigorously prove this:

Theorem. All the natural numbers are positive.

PROOF: Let S be the set of all *positive* natural numbers. We wish to show that actually *all* the natural numbers belong to S. By the Principle of Mathematical Induction, our goal will be achieved as soon as we have proved (i) and (ii) above.

Proof of (i): That 1 is positive has been proved in Section 4.14, Theorem R20. Therefore $1 \in S$, Q.E.D.

Proof of (ii): Suppose $s \in S$. Then s is positive; i.e., $s > 0$. Adding 1 to both sides of this inequality: $s + 1 > 1$. But as we have just noted, $1 > 0$. Therefore (why?), $s + 1 > 0$; therefore (why?), $s + 1 \in S$, Q.E.D.

One may also prove by mathematical induction that 1 is the "least" natural number:

Theorem. If n is any natural number, then $1 \leqslant n$. (The proof of this theorem is left as an exercise for the student.)

We see another application of the principle of mathematical induction in the proof of the following theorem:

Theorem. If n is any natural number, then $n < 2^n$.

PROOF: Let S be the set of natural numbers for which this theorem is true. We wish to show that *all* natural numbers belong to S. We shall show this by proving (i) and (ii) of the Principle of Mathematical Induction.

Proof of (i): For $n = 1$, the theorem states: $1 < 2$, which *is* true (how do we know that?)

Proof of (ii): Suppose $s \in S$. Then:

$$(1) \qquad\qquad s < 2^s \quad \text{(why?)}$$

We wish to show that there follows now that $s + 1 \in S$, i.e., $s + 1 < 2^{s+1}$. But from (1) we have:

$$(2) \qquad\qquad 2s < 2^{s+1} \quad \text{(why?)}$$

Our desired result would now follow if we knew that $s + 1 \leqslant 2s$ (why?); but $s + 1 \leqslant 2s$ is equivalent to $1 \leqslant s$, which *is* true by the preceding theorem.

The proof of the theorem is now complete.

A classical application of the method of mathematical induction is to problems involving summation of sets of numbers:

Theorem. The sum of the first n odd natural numbers is n^2; i.e.:

$$(3) \qquad 1 + 3 + \cdots + (2n - 3) + (2n - 1) = n^2$$

PROOF. Let S be the set of all natural numbers n for which (3) is true.

We prove the theorem by proving (i) and (ii) of the principle of mathematical induction.

Proof of (i): For $n = 1$, the theorem states: $1 = 1$, which is true (why?). (Note that the sum of the elements of a set which contains only one element is defined to be simply that element.)

Proof of (ii): Suppose $s \in S$.   Then:

(4) $$1 + 3 + \cdots + (2s - 3) + (2s - 1) = s^2$$

We wish to show that $s + 1 \in S$, i.e.,
$$1 + 3 + \cdots + [2(s + 1) - 3] + [2(s + 1) - 1] = (s + 1)^2$$
or, in other words,
$$1 + 3 + \cdots + (2s - 1) + (2s + 1) = (s + 1)^2.$$
But from (4): $1 + 3 + \cdots + (2s - 1) + (2s + 1) = s^2 + (2s + 1) = (s + 1)^2$, Q.E.D.

REMARK.   The name "mathematical induction" is a historical misnomer; proof by mathematical induction is actually a *deductive* proof. In fact, many results which are discovered inductively are then proved deductively by means of mathematical induction.   A case in point is the statement that the sum of the first n odd numbers is n^2, which we approached inductively in Section 3.6 and which we proved deductively, by means of mathematical induction, in this section.

*4.18 BOUNDS

Definition.   An *upper bound* for a set of real numbers is a real number which is greater than or equal to each element of the set, and a *lower bound* for a set of real numbers is a real number which is less than or equal to each element of the set.

Examples.

1. Suppose $S = \{4, 5, 6\}$.   Then 1 and $\sqrt{2}$ and π and 4 are lower bounds for S, and, in fact, any real number $\leqslant 4$ is a lower bound for S; and 6 and 7.11 and π^2 are upper bounds for S, and, in fact, any real number $\geqslant 6$ is an upper bound for S.

2. Suppose S is the set of all real numbers between 7 and 11, excluding 11.   (The symbol [7, 11) is often used to denote this set; cf. page 224). Then 7 is a lower bound for S; 11 is an upper bound for S; any real number $\leqslant 7$ is a lower bound for S; any real number $\geqslant 11$ is an upper bound for S.

Bounds for a set may or may not belong to the set, as Example 2 shows.

This leads us to distinguish between maxima and upper bounds, and between minima and lower bounds:

Definition. A *maximum* or *greatest* element of a set of real numbers is an upper bound for that set which belongs to that set; and a *minimum* or *least* element of a set of real numbers is a lower bound for that set which belongs to that set.

(In other words, a greatest element of a set is an element of that set which is $\geqslant$ each element of that set, and a least element of a set is an element of that set which is $\leqslant$ each element of that set.)

Examples. In Example 1 above, 4 is a minimum and 6 a maximum element. In Example 2 above, 7 is a minimum; it can be proved, however, that in this case there is no maximum element (the proof is left as an exercise for the student).

In Example 2 above it is clear that among all the upper bounds for S, 11 is the least. In other words, 11 is the *least upper bound* (abbreviated "lub," which is pronounced as spelled) for S. In the same example, we see that 7 is the *greatest lower bound* (abbreviated "glb," which is pronounced as best you can) for S. Thus, while S in this case has no maximum element to mark its upper boundary, it *does* have a lub which serves that purpose. This is a special case of the following theorem.

Completeness Theorem.

(*a*) Every non-null set of real numbers which has an upper bound has a lub.

(*b*) Every non-null set of real numbers which has a lower bound has a glb.

We first prove:

Lemma:

(i) If a set of real numbers has a maximum element, then that maximum is a lub for the set.

(ii) If a set of real numbers has a minimum element, then that minimum is a glb for the set.

PROOF OF (i): Suppose m is a maximum element of a set S. Then by definition, m is an upper bound for S. Now suppose b is *any* upper bound for S. Then, since $m \in S$, $m \leqslant b$. Hence m is an upper bound for S which is $\leqslant$ each upper bound for S; i.e., m is a lub for S, Q.E.D.

PROOF OF (ii): (Left as exercise for student.)

PROOF OF (*a*): *Case* 1. S is a non-null set of real numbers which has a maximum element. Then the lemma above takes care of this case.

Case 2. *S* is a non-null set of real numbers which has an upper bound but no maximum element.

Then let *U* be the set of all upper bounds for *S*.

It is left to the student to show that (S, U) is a tandem pair of sets of real numbers.

There exists, therefore, by the Axiom of Dedekind, a real number *b* between *S* and *U* so that, if *s* is any element of *S* and *u* is any upper bound for *S*:

$$s \leqslant b \leqslant u$$

Hence *b* is an upper bound for *S* which is $\leqslant$ each upper bound for *S*, i.e., *b* is a lub for *S*, and the existence of *b* proves (*a*) of our theorem.

PROOF OF (b): (Left as exercise for student.)

Assuming all the other axioms we have given for the real numbers, the Axiom of Dedekind and the Completeness Theorem may, in fact, be proved to be equivalent; and both, therefore, are said to embody the "completeness" property of real numbers. What we mean by "completeness" here is roughly the same as what we meant in Section 2.6; namely, a process (which process?) which could not always be carried through in a restricted set (which set?) becomes always possible in an extended set (which set?).

*4.19 ARCHIMEDEAN ORDER

An obvious example of a set of real numbers which has no upper bound is the set of all natural numbers. We prove this:

Theorem. The set of all natural numbers has no upper bound.

PROOF. We point out first that it is an immediate consequence of the definition of natural numbers (see Section 4.16) that, if *n* is a natural number, then $n + 1$ is a natural number also.

Now suppose that the set of all natural numbers *does* have an upper bound *u*. We shall show that this leads to a contradiction.

By the Completeness Theorem, if the set of all natural numbers has an upper bound *u*, it must have a lub *b*. Then since $b - 1 < b$, $b - 1$ cannot be an upper bound for the set of all natural numbers. Therefore there exists a natural number *n* such that $n > b - 1$; hence $n + 1 > b$. But $n + 1$ is a natural number; hence $n + 1 < b$. But now we have a contradiction of the Trichotomy Axiom. This contradiction proves our theorem.

Corollary. (*Archimedean Order Theorem.*) If a and b are any positive real numbers, then there exists a natural number n such that $na > b$.

PROOF: (Left as exercise, with this hint: Consider the real number $\dfrac{b}{a}$. Can it be an upper bound for the set of all natural numbers? What then?)

In geometric terms, the Archimedean Order Theorem states that given any pair of line segments, by laying out either, end to end along a straight line a sufficient natural number of times, one may arrive at a line segment which exceeds the other in length. This is the way Archimedes (287–212 B.C.), the greatest of ancient mathematicians, thought of this theorem; that is to say, in geometric terms.

Both the Archimedean Order Theorem and the Completeness Theorem play outstanding roles in further developments of the theory of real numbers, especially in careful developments of "calculus"; and for this reason, in addition to the fact that they embody important characteristic properties of the real number system, these theorems have been included here.

▶ ***EXERCISE 22**

1. Give several examples of inductive sets different from those mentioned in the text.

2. Answer the questions posed in Section 4.17.

3. Prove the theorem: If n is any natural number, then $1 \leqslant n$.

4. Prove that, if n is any natural number, then:

(a) $n + 1 \leqslant 2^n$.

(b) $n^2 < 3^n$.

(c) $(x - y) \mid (x^n - y^n)$.

5. Prove that, if n is any natural number, then:

(a) $1 + 2 + \cdots + n = \dfrac{n(n + 1)}{2}$.

(b) $1^2 + 2^2 + \cdots + n^2 = \dfrac{n(n + 1)(2n + 1)}{6}$.

(c) $1^3 + 2^3 + \cdots + n^3 = \dfrac{n^2(n + 1)^2}{4}$.

6. Can you give an example to illustrate each case? A set has:

(a) An upper bound but no lower bound.

(b) A lower bound but no upper bound.

(c) An upper bound and a lower bound.

(d) Neither an upper nor a lower bound.

(e) A maximum but no minimum.

(f) A minimum but no maximum.

(*g*) A minimum and a maximum.

(*h*) Neither a minimum nor a maximum.

(*i*) An upper bound but no maximum.

(*j*) A maximum but no upper bound.

7. In each example you have given in Problem 6, name the lub and the glb and the "max" and the "min," so far as they exist.

8. Answer the questions posed in Section 4.18.

9. Construct the proofs left as exercises in Sections 4.18 and 4.19.

10 (*a*). Prove that, if a non-null set of real numbers has a maximum, it is unique.

(*b*) What about a minimum? Prove.

(*c*) What about a lub? Prove.

(*d*) What about a glb? Prove.

11. Prove that, if a is any positive real number, then there exists a natural number n such that $\dfrac{1}{n} < a$.

5 COMPLEX NUMBERS AND THE UNARY OPERATION $\sqrt{}$

5.1 COMPLEX NUMBERS

It is, of course, well known that, if a real number is either positive or negative, then its square is positive; and if a real number is 0, then its square is 0.   The square of a real number, then, is *never* negative.

As a consequence, so long as only real numbers are known, there will be some real numbers whose square roots do not exist; namely, the negative real numbers.

The deficiency is a serious one.   It means, among other things, that so long as it exists, some algebraic equations, as for example the equation $x^2 = -7$, can have no solutions.

Just as it occurred historically that the system of natural numbers was enlarged to become the system of common fractions in order to make the operation of division complete—and just as the number system has after that been extended again and again in order to make various other operations complete—so we now extend the real number system in order to make the (unary) operation $\sqrt{}$ complete.   The larger system of numbers that results is called the *complex number system*.

One of the basic deficiencies of the real number system is that it lacks a square root of -1.   Very well; let us repair this defect by inventing a new number "i" which shall have the defining property:

$$i^2 = -1$$

so that i will be a square root of -1.   This is not as daring as it may seem; it is very much like what is done when the number -1 is invented with the defining property that it shall be a number whose addition to 1 yields 0.

132

Now we "adjoin" i to our real number system. But this involves more than just the inclusion of one more number in our system. Among other things, we wish to be able to multiply i by any real number, and we wish to be able to add any real number to the result.

In other words, if a and b are any real numbers, we would like a number $a + bi$ to exist.

The process of extending the real number system to a larger system, having the useful "field" properties (see Section 4.3) and containing a square root of -1, will be carried out in the next (optional) section; here we shall only state the final result:

The set of real numbers may be enlarged, and the relation $=$ and the operations $+$ and $\cdot$ may be extended to apply to the enlarged set, to arrive at a *field* (whose elements are called "complex numbers") which contains not only the field of real numbers but also an element i such that $i^2 = -1$. Furthermore, every complex number is uniquely expressible in the form $a + bi$, where a and b are real numbers.

Examples of complex numbers are: $2 + 3i$, $3 + i$, $\sqrt{7} + \pi i$, $7i$, 7, $\sqrt{7}$, 0.

We classify complex numbers $a + bi$ as: real (if $b = 0$); imaginary (if $b \neq 0$); pure imaginary (if $a = 0$, $b \neq 0$).

Examples of operations on complex numbers:

$$(2 + 3i) + (3 + i) = 5 + 4i$$

$$(2 + 3i)(3 + i) = 6 + 11i + 3i^2 = 6 + 11i - 3 = 3 + 11i$$

$$(2 + 3i) \div (3 + i) = \frac{2 + 3i}{3 + i} = \frac{2 + 3i}{3 + i} \cdot \frac{3 - i}{3 - i} = \frac{9 + 7i}{10} = \frac{9}{10} + \frac{7}{10}i$$

Note that in carrying out the division, we have used the trick of multiplying numerator and denominator by the "conjugate" of the denominator. (If a and b are real numbers, the *conjugate* of $a + bi$ is defined to be $a - bi$.)

Note also that in carrying out these operations, liberal use of such field axioms as distributivity, associativity, etc., has been made, and we have also used such field definitions and theorems as Definition R3 and Problem 5 of Exercise 18. This is an example of the economy of the abstract approach. The definitions we have made and the theorems we have proved for the *field* of real numbers apply immediately to any field without any further work; for if the complex numbers, for example, satisfy the six field axioms, as they do (replacing "real number" in these axioms by "complex number"), they must satisfy the consequences of these axioms also (replacing "real number" in these consequences by "complex number").

Although the complex numbers satisfy all the field axioms, it is easy to show that they cannot be made to satisfy all the order axioms. That is to say, it is impossible to introduce a relation $<$ into the system of complex numbers which satisfies the three order postulates.

For we have shown that it is a consequence of these postulates that the square of an element of the field is never negative (Exercise 20, Problem 5f). In the field of complex numbers there is, however, an element whose square is negative, namely i (see the corollary to Theorem R20). Therefore the postulates of order could not apply to the complex numbers. As a consequence, when dealing with inequality relations, we shall restrict ourselves to the real number system.

We remark, finally, that the names "imaginary" and "real" as they apply to numbers reflect only early attitudes toward these numbers. In the light of their definition in terms of simpler numbers and their practical applications, "imaginary" numbers are just as real as "real" numbers.

*5.2 COMPLEX NUMBERS DEFINED AS ORDERED PAIRS OF REAL NUMBERS

In this section, borrowing from knowledge of properties we would *like* complex numbers to have, we shall arrive at a clear-cut definition of what we mean by a complex number as well as by equality, addition, and multiplication of complex numbers; and then these definitions will enable us to show that the complex numbers do indeed have all the properties we would like them to have.

We have seen above that we would like every complex number to be expressible in the form $a + bi$, where a and b are real numbers. Note, then, that a complex number should be determined as soon as we know what "a" and "b" are. This suggests an alternate notation: We may agree to use the ordered pair (a, b) to mean the complex number $a + bi$. Thus, for our present purposes, $(7, 11)$ is simply another way of writing $7 + 11i$. It becomes possible, then, to write every complex number as an ordered pair of real numbers. Indeed, we are now led to make the following definition:

Definition. A complex number is an ordered pair of real numbers.

Since equality of ordered pairs has already been defined (Exercise 2, Problem 13), we automatically have at hand a definition of equality of complex numbers: If a, b, c, d are real numbers, the complex numbers (a, b) and (c, d) are equal [written $(a, b) = (c, d)$] if and only if $a = c$ and $b = d$.

Now we tackle the question of defining addition of complex numbers. That is to say, if (a, b) and (c, d) are complex numbers, what shall we mean by $(a, b) + (c, d)$? Again we borrow from the way we would like things to turn out. In writing $(a, b) + (c, d)$, we have in mind the sum $a + bi + c + di$, which we would like to be equal to $(a + c) + (b + d)i$, which in our alternate notation would be written: $(a + c, b + d)$. Therefore we make the following definition:

Definition. If a, b, c, d are real numbers, we define the sum of the complex numbers (a, b) and (c, d) as follows:

$$(a, b) + (c, d) = (a + c, b + d)$$

Similarly, in the case of multiplication we would like to have:
$$
\begin{aligned}
(a, b)(c, d) &= (a + bi)(c + di) \\
&= ac + adi + bci + bdi^2 \\
&= (ac - bd) + (ad + bc)i \\
&= (ac - bd, \ ad + bc)
\end{aligned}
$$
Therefore we make the following definition:

Definition. If a, b, c, d are real numbers, we define the product of the complex numbers (a, b) and (c, d) as follows:

$$(a, b)(c, d) = (ac - bd, ad + bc)$$

It is not difficult now, but a lengthy task, to verify that the complex numbers, with the above definitions of equality, addition, and multiplication, satisfy all six of the field axioms. (This verification we shall leave as an exercise for the student.)

We shall soon show that the complex numbers we have just defined actually conform to patterns that may be more familiar to the student. But first it is worth pointing out that the definitions above should serve to strip the last vestige of mystery from the complex numbers. For if they are labeled by pairs of real numbers, they are no more mysterious than rational numbers, which are, of course, labeled by pairs of numbers also (integers, as it happens).

Now it turns out that within the set of complex numbers there is a subset that behaves "just like" the set of real numbers. Indeed, the complex number $(a, 0)$ is a number that we would like to turn out to be equal to the real number $a + 0i$, i.e., the real number a; and according to the definitions we have made:

      (i) $(a, 0) = (b, 0)$ if and only if $a = b$.

      (ii) $(a, 0) + (b, 0) = (a + b, 0)$.

     (iii) $(a, 0)(b, 0) = (ab, 0)$.

Note that statements (i), (ii), and (iii) would continue to be true statements if all commas, parentheses, and zeros were deleted. The force of this remark is that, so far as the field of complex numbers is concerned, no harm will be done if the real number a and the complex number $(a, 0)$ are considered to be equal. For example, the correct sum and product of $(7, 0)$ and $(11, 0)$ are $(18, 0)$ and $(77, 0)$ respectively. If we considered $(7, 0)$ to be equal to 7 and $(11, 0)$ to be equal to 11, and found the sum and product of 7 and 11 instead, these would, of course, be equal to 18 and 77 respectively. But still assuming $a = (a, 0)$, we have $18 = (18, 0)$ and $77 = (77, 0)$, so that our final results remain consistent with our former results.

In effect, then, complex numbers of the form $(a, 0)$ will be, from now on, what we shall mean when we say "real numbers"; and if a is a real number, we shall use the symbols "a" and "$(a, 0)$" interchangeably, and we shall write: $a = (a, 0)$.

[As a matter of fact, the student has already done essentially the same thing in cartesian coordinate systems. Points on the X-axis originally labeled by real numbers are also labeled by ordered pairs of real numbers, with second element zero. For example, the point on the X-axis originally labeled "7," may also be labeled "$(7, 0)$."]

A principal objective of the construction of the complex number system is to arrive at a number whose square is -1. Again referring to things we would like to be true, $i = 0 + 1i = (0, 1)$ ought to be such a number. But by the definition of multiplication of complex numbers: $(0, 1)(0, 1) = (-1, 0)$, and by our convention regarding the equality of real and complex numbers, $(-1, 0) = -1$. Hence $(0, 1)^2 = -1$, and if we now *define* the symbol "i" to denote the complex number $(0, 1)$, we finally arrive at the familiar statement: $i^2 = -1$:

Definition. $i = (0, 1)$.

Corollary. $i^2 = -1$.

Now suppose b is any real number. It is easy to show that $bi = (0, b)$, for $bi = (b, 0)(0, 1) = (b \cdot 0 - 0 \cdot 1, b \cdot 1 + 0 \cdot 0) = (0, b)$.

Using this fact, consider the complex number (a, b). We have: $(a, b) = (a, 0) + (0, b) = a + bi$; and we have finally arrived at the traditional or "standard" representation for any complex number!

5.3 VECTORS

The physicist finds one very practical use for complex numbers in connection with what are called *vector* concepts, that is to say, concepts like velocity, acceleration, and force, for which a magnitude and a direction are the determining characteristics.

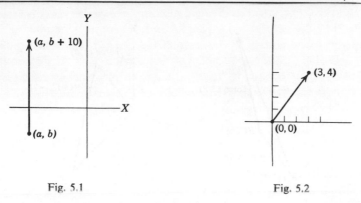

Fig. 5.1   Fig. 5.2

For example, when we say that we are exerting a push of 10 *pounds* in the direction *north*, we are defining a particular force. The physicist uses an arrow (called a *vector*) to describe a force: An arrow of length 10 units drawn in a northerly direction would be a symbol for the force we have just defined. Supposing that the positive Y-axis of a cc plane points north, the arrow whose tail is at $(0, 0)$ and whose point is at $(0, 10)$, and the arrow whose tail is at $(2, -3)$ and whose point is at $(2, 7)$, and many other arrows represent that same force. In fact any arrow whose tail is at any point (a, b), and whose point is at $(a, b + 10)$ may be used to represent that force (Fig. 5.1).

We may identify the force of Fig. 5.1 by the ordered pair $(0, 10)$. [It is the ordered pair $(0, 10)$ which, to the mathematician, is the *vector*.] In general, we shall understand by a force (r, s), where r, s are real numbers, a force represented by an arrow whose tail is at any point (a, b) and whose point is at $(a + r, b + s)$. For example, the force $(3, 4)$ might be represented by an arrow drawn from $(0, 0)$ to $(3, 4)$ (Fig. 5.2); by the Pythagorean theorem we discover that the length of that arrow is 5. Assuming our unit of magnitude of force to be the pound, this force would be one of 5 lb, whose direction of exertion would be given by the direction of the arrow.

Now it is a physical fact that given two forces (called *component* forces) acting at a point on a body, there is always a single force (called the *resultant* force) that would have the same effect, if exerted at that point, as the original separate component forces acting together. It is also a fact that the resultant force may be computed in the following way: If one of the component forces is represented by an arrow drawn with tail at A and point at B (Fig. 5.3), and the other component force by an arrow with tail at B and point at C, then the resultant force is represented by an arrow with tail at A and point at C.

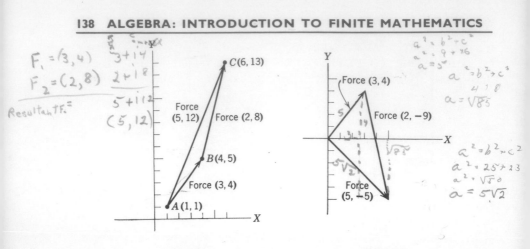

Fig. 5.3   Fig. 5.4

In Fig. 5.3, the component forces we have drawn are, in the symbolism we have suggested, the forces (3, 4) and (2, 8). Note that the resultant force is the force (5, 12). Indeed, it may be verified that in all possible cases, the "sum" (i.e., the resultant) of forces (a, b) and (c, d) is the force $(a + c, b + d)$.

At this point we may begin to see a connection with the complex numbers; for a convenient shorthand symbol for the complex number $a + bi$ is the ordered pair (a, b) (see Section 5.2). Thus, when we refer to the complex number (a, b), we mean the complex number otherwise written as $a + bi$. In that case, what must $(a, b) + (c, d)$ be? We compute:

$$(a, b) + (c, d) = a + bi + c + di = (a + c) + (b + d)i = (a + c, b + d)$$

Thus, forces may be identified by complex numbers, and added by adding their identifying complex numbers. In doing so, we shall find it most convenient to use the ordered pair (a, b) notation for complex numbers rather than the $a + bi$ notation. Note that, by the Pythagorean theorem, the magnitude of the force (a, b) is $\sqrt{a^2 + b^2}$.

Illustrative Example. Find the resultant of forces (3, 4) and (2, −9). Find the magnitude of each of these forces, and draw a diagram to illustrate.

SOLUTION. The resultant of the forces (3, 4) and (2, −9) is the force (5, −5). The magnitudes of forces (3, 4), (2, −9), and (5, −5) are (if the pound is the unit of force), 5 lb, $\sqrt{85}$ lb, and $5\sqrt{2}$ lb respectively. The forces are pictured in Fig. 5.4. [Note that the first force may be drawn from any point whatever. We have chosen to draw it from (0, 0) to (0 + 3, 0 + 4), or (3, 4). But having drawn the first force, we have, in our method, no choice as to drawing the second.   It must be drawn from (3, 4) to ((3 + 2, 4 + (−9)), or (5, −5).   The resultant must then be drawn from the first point (0, 0) to the last point (5, −5), and is, of course, the force (5 − 0, −5 − 0), or (5, −5).]

5.4 THE UNARY OPERATION $\sqrt{\ }$

Up until now we have dealt informally with the unary operation $\sqrt{\ }$ (see Section 2.5, Note 2, and Section 3.3), and later on (in Exercise 21, Problems 2 and 4), we gave a precise definition of the unary operation $\sqrt{\ }$ in the set of all non-negative real numbers.

We have seen that a number may have more than one square root. For example, the real number 9 has the square roots 3 and −3.   The symbol "$\sqrt{9}$" is intended to represent just one of these square roots, namely 3.   In general, since the symbol $\sqrt{\ }$ will always indicate just one among possibly several square roots, we shall be careful from now on to read this symbol as "the *principal* square root of."

Now that we have complex numbers at our disposal, we are prepared to extend the domain of the unary operation $\sqrt{\ }$ to include *all* real numbers.

Problems 2 and 4 of Exercise 21 guarantee that, given any non-negative real number r, there is a unique non-negative real number whose square is r.   This makes possible the following definition:

Definition A.   If r is a non-negative real number, $\sqrt{r}$ is defined to be the unique non-negative real number whose square is r.

Directly from this definition, it follows that, if r is a non-negative real number, then:

(1) $$(\sqrt{r})^2 = r$$

There is still left to us, now, the task of defining $\sqrt{-p}$, where p is any positive real number.

What we seek is a number whose square is $-p$.   But a fairly obvious choice for such a number is $i\sqrt{p}$.   For:

$$(i\sqrt{p})^2 = (i\sqrt{p})(i\sqrt{p}) = (i)^2(\sqrt{p})^2 = (-1)(p) = -p$$

Therefore we make the following definition:

Definition B.   If $-p$ is a negative real number, $\sqrt{-p}$ is defined to equal $i\sqrt{p}$.

Directly from this definition, there follows that, if $-p$ is a negative real number, then:

(2) $$(\sqrt{-p})^2 = -p$$

Thus, from (1) and (2) above, we have the following important fact:

(i) If r is any real number, then $(\sqrt{r})^2 = r$.

It is necessary to distinguish carefully between $(\sqrt{r})^2$ and $\sqrt{r^2}$, where r is a real number; for example, suppose $r = -2$. Then by (i) above:

$$(\sqrt{-2})^2 = -2$$

But:

$$\sqrt{(-2)^2} = \sqrt{4} = 2$$

And we see that $\sqrt{r^2}$ is not always r! However, using the notation of absolute value (see Exercise 9, Problem 13), we can state the situation precisely:

(ii) If r is any real number, then $\sqrt{r^2} = |r|$.

PROOF OF (ii): By Problem 5f of Exercise 20, r^2 is a non-negative real number. Therefore, Definition A applies and, to prove (ii), we need merely show that $|r|$ is a non-negative real number and that its square is r^2. But $|r|$ is non-negative by the definition of absolute value; and, since always $|r| = \pm r$, it follows that $(|r|)^2 = r^2$.

A third important property of the unary operation $\sqrt{}$ follows:

(iii) If r, s are any non-negative real numbers, then $\sqrt{r} \cdot \sqrt{s} = \sqrt{rs}$.

PROOF OF (iii): First of all, by Exercise 20, Problem 5g, if r and s are non-negative real numbers, then rs is a non-negative real number. Now to prove that a given real number is $\sqrt{rs}$, our definition of $\sqrt{}$ requires us to show that the given real number is non-negative, and that its square is rs.

But we know (again by our definition of $\sqrt{}$) that $\sqrt{r}$ and $\sqrt{s}$ are non-negative. Therefore, again by Exercise 20, Problem 5g, $\sqrt{r} \cdot \sqrt{s}$ is non-negative.

Furthermore: $(\sqrt{r} \cdot \sqrt{s})^2 = (\sqrt{r} \cdot \sqrt{s})(\sqrt{r} \cdot \sqrt{s}) = (\sqrt{r})^2(\sqrt{s})^2 = rs$.

Therefore both conditions for $\sqrt{r} \cdot \sqrt{s}$ to be principal square root of rs have been satisfied, so that the theorem is proved.

NOTE. Actually, we are now able to find a simple expression for the product of $\sqrt{r}$ and $\sqrt{s}$ even when r or s, or both, are negative, *if we first convert the product into a form in which (iii) is applicable.* For example:

$$\sqrt{2} \cdot \sqrt{-3} = \sqrt{2} \cdot i \cdot \sqrt{3} = i\sqrt{2} \cdot \sqrt{3} = i\sqrt{6}$$
$$\sqrt{-2} \cdot \sqrt{-3} = i\sqrt{2} \cdot i\sqrt{3} = i^2\sqrt{2} \cdot \sqrt{3} = -1 \cdot \sqrt{6} = -\sqrt{6}$$

Illustrative Example 1. Express each of the following complex numbers in the form $a + bi$, where a and b are real:

(a) 7   (b) $2i$ (c) $\sqrt{-3}$

(d) $\dfrac{1 + \sqrt{-3}}{2}$ (e) $(3 + 2i)(3 - 2i)$ (f) $\dfrac{1 + i}{1 - i}$

SOLUTION.

(a) $7 = 7 + 0i$ $(a = 7, b = 0)$

(b) $2i = 0 + 2i$ $(a = 0, b = 2)$

(c) $\sqrt{-3} = i\sqrt{3}$ (by Definition B)

         $= 0 + \sqrt{3}i$ $(a = 0, b = \sqrt{3})$

(d) $\dfrac{1 + \sqrt{-3}}{2} = \dfrac{1 + i\sqrt{3}}{2} = \dfrac{1}{2} + \dfrac{\sqrt{3}}{2}i$ $\left(a = \dfrac{1}{2}, b = \dfrac{\sqrt{3}}{2}\right)$

(e) $(3 + 2i)(3 - 2i) = 9 - 4i^2 = 9 + 4 = 13 = 13 + 0i$

                                         $(a = 13, b = 0)$

(f) $\dfrac{1 + i}{1 - i} = \dfrac{1 + i}{1 - i} \cdot \dfrac{1 + i}{1 + i} = \dfrac{1 + 2i + i^2}{1 - i^2} = \dfrac{1 + 2i - 1}{1 + 1}$

       $= \dfrac{2i}{2} = i = 0 + 1i$ $(a = 0, b = 1)$

Illustrative Example 2. Classify the complex numbers (a) through (f) of Illustrative Example 1 according to type.

SOLUTION.   Real: (a), (e), since $b = 0$ in these cases.

Imaginary: (b), (c), (d), (f), since $b \neq 0$ in these cases.

Pure imaginary: (b), (c), (f), since $a = 0$, $b \neq 0$ in these cases.

Illustrative Example 3. Solve the equation: $x + yi = 2 + 3i$, under the condition that x and y must be real.

SOLUTION.   The unique expressibility of a complex number in the form $a + bi$, where a and b are real, means that the only solution of the given equation is $x = 2$, $y = 3$.

Illustrative Example 4. "Simplify" $\dfrac{2}{\sqrt{2}}$, $\frac{1}{2}\sqrt{2}$, $\sqrt{\frac{3}{8}}$, $\sqrt{0.02}$, $\dfrac{3 + 2\sqrt{2}}{3 - 2\sqrt{2}}$.

SOLUTION.   The word "simplify" is ambiguous. A representation that is convenient in one application may be awkward in another. In adding fractions, it is convenient to have simple denominators; in that situation, therefore, we often "rationalize" denominators. Sometimes, however, it helps to rationalize numerators rather than denominators. Below we indicate methods by which either may be accomplished in certain typical cases:

$$\frac{2}{\sqrt{2}} = \frac{\sqrt{2}\sqrt{2}}{1\sqrt{2}} = \sqrt{2}; \text{ or alternatively: } \frac{2}{\sqrt{2}} = \frac{2\sqrt{2}}{\sqrt{2}\sqrt{2}} = \frac{2\sqrt{2}}{2} = \sqrt{2}.$$

$$\tfrac{1}{2}\sqrt{2} = \frac{\sqrt{2}}{2} = \frac{1\sqrt{2}}{\sqrt{2}\sqrt{2}} = \frac{1}{\sqrt{2}};$$

$$\text{or alternatively: } \tfrac{1}{2}\sqrt{2} = \frac{\sqrt{2}}{2} = \frac{\sqrt{2}\sqrt{2}}{2\sqrt{2}} = \frac{2}{2\sqrt{2}} = \frac{1}{\sqrt{2}}.$$

$$\sqrt{\tfrac{3}{8}} = \sqrt{\tfrac{6}{16}} = \frac{\sqrt{6}}{\sqrt{16}} = \frac{\sqrt{6}}{4} \text{ (Note the use of Problem } 5a \text{ of the next}$$

exercise.)

$$\sqrt{0.02} = \sqrt{0.01}\,\sqrt{2} = 0.1\sqrt{2}.$$

$$\frac{3 + 2\sqrt{2}}{3 - 2\sqrt{2}} = \frac{3 + 2\sqrt{2}}{3 - 2\sqrt{2}} \cdot \frac{3 + 2\sqrt{2}}{3 + 2\sqrt{2}} = \frac{17 + 12\sqrt{2}}{1} = 17 + 12\sqrt{2} \quad \text{(In}$$

this case we have rationalized the denominator by multiplying the fraction by $\frac{k}{k}$, where k is the "conjugate" of the denominator.)

Illustrative Example 5. What can be said about the value of $\dfrac{\sqrt{1 + h} - 1}{h}$, when h is a number very close to zero?

SOLUTION. (This type of problem is very important in courses in calculus, where the question is phrased: "What is the *limit* of $\dfrac{\sqrt{1 + h} - 1}{h}$ as h approaches zero?" A precise definition of the idea of a "limit" exists, and a somewhat extensive consideration of this definition and its consequences is necessary in any serious study of calculus. Here we shall content ourselves with the rough formulation of the question given above.)

We note first that we can get no help from substituting $h = 0$ itself into the original expression, for then the result is $0/0$, which is, of course, undefined.

This is a case where rationalizing the *numerator* is helpful:

$$\frac{\sqrt{1 + h} - 1}{h} \cdot \frac{\sqrt{1 + h} + 1}{\sqrt{1 + h} + 1} = \frac{h}{h(\sqrt{1 + h} + 1)} = \frac{1}{\sqrt{1 + h} + 1}$$

In the latter form, it is easy to see that, for h close to zero, the given expression is close to $\dfrac{1}{\sqrt{1} + 1}$ or $\tfrac{1}{2}$.

▶ **EXERCISE 23**

1. Express in the form $a + bi$, where a and b are real numbers, each of the following complex numbers, and tell what type of complex number each is:

(a) 0   (b) 1

(c) $2i$ (d) 2

(e) $(2 - 3i)^2$ (f) $(2 - 3i)(2 + 3i)$

(g) $(2 - 3i) + (2 + 3i)$ (h) $(3 - 4i)(3 + 4i)$

(i) $(3 - 4i) + (3 + 4i)$ (j) $(2 + 3i)(3 + 4i)$

(k) $(2 + 3i) - (3 + 4i)$ (l) $(7 + 11i) - (7 - 11i)$

(m) $\dfrac{1 + 5i}{2}$ (n) $\dfrac{1 - i}{1 + i}$

(o) $\dfrac{2 + 4i}{3 + 2i}$

2.(a) What can always be said about the sum and product of conjugate complex numbers?

(b) Prove the statement you have made in answer to (a).

(c) What type of reasoning led to your statement made in answer to (a)? Explain.

(d) What type of reasoning did you use in (b)? Explain.

3. Where is the flaw in reasoning in the following paradox?

(1) $\sqrt{-1} \cdot \sqrt{-1} = \sqrt{(-1)(-1)} = \sqrt{1} = 1$

(2) $\sqrt{-1} \cdot \sqrt{-1} = i \cdot i = i^2 = -1$

(3) $\therefore 1 = -1$!

4. In what sense do the complex numbers "complete" the set of all real numbers? That is to say, what is it which is not always possible within the set of all real numbers before the set of all complex numbers is known, but which becomes possible once the set of all complex numbers is available?

5.(a) Prove that, if r, s are both positive real numbers, $\sqrt{\dfrac{r}{s}} = \dfrac{\sqrt{r}}{\sqrt{s}}$.

(b) For what other types of real numbers r, s is it true that $\sqrt{\dfrac{r}{s}} = \dfrac{\sqrt{r}}{\sqrt{s}}$?

(c) For what types of real numbers r, s is it false that $\sqrt{\dfrac{r}{s}} = \dfrac{\sqrt{r}}{\sqrt{s}}$?

(d) We have proved above that, if r, s are both non-negative real numbers, then $\sqrt{r}\sqrt{s} = \sqrt{rs}$. For what other real numbers r, s is this equation true? For what real numbers r, s is it false?

(e) Find the limit as h approaches zero of:

(i) $\dfrac{\sqrt{4 + h} - 2}{h}$ (ii) $\dfrac{\sqrt{9 + h} - 3}{h}$

(iii) $\dfrac{\sqrt{x + h} - \sqrt{x}}{h}$, where x is any positive real number.

6. Simplify:

(a) $\sqrt{3}\sqrt{12}$ (b) $(\sqrt{8})^3$ (c) $(\sqrt{-3})^2$ (d) $\sqrt{(-3)^2}$

(e) $\sqrt{-2}\sqrt{8}$ (f) $\sqrt{-2}\sqrt{-8}$ (g) $\sqrt{8}$ (h) $\sqrt{-8}$

(i) $\sqrt{8}\sqrt{-8}$ (j) $\sqrt{-8}\sqrt{-8}$ (k) $\sqrt{6}\sqrt{8}$ (l) $\sqrt{-6}\sqrt{8}$

(m) $\sqrt{-6}\sqrt{-8}$ (n) $(\sqrt{-2})^3$ (o) $\sqrt{(-2)^3}$ (p) $\sqrt{3^2 + 4^2}$

(q) $\sqrt{1/3}$ (r) $1/\sqrt{3}$ (s) $3/\sqrt{3}$ (t) $(1/5)\sqrt{5}$

(u) $\sqrt{-1/32}$ (v) $\sqrt{18} - 3\sqrt{8} + 3\sqrt{2}$

(w) $3\sqrt{1/2} - \sqrt{2}$ (x) $i + (1/i)$

(y) $(\sqrt{3} + \sqrt{2})(\sqrt{3} - \sqrt{2})$ (z) $(\sqrt{3} + \sqrt{2})/(\sqrt{3} - \sqrt{2})$

(a') $(\sqrt{2} + 1)/(\sqrt{2} - 1)$ (b') $(\sqrt{2} - 1)/(\sqrt{2} + 1)$

7. Given: $\sqrt{2} \doteq 1.41$ ($\doteq$ is read: "is approximately equal to"), $\sqrt{3} \doteq 1.73$, $\sqrt{5} \doteq 2.24$, find approximations for the following. (Note that results should not be given to a greater degree of accuracy than given information.)

(a) $\sqrt{6}$ (b) $\sqrt{8}$ (c) $\sqrt{10}$ (d) $\sqrt{12}$

(e) $\sqrt{15}$ (f) $\sqrt{18}$ (g) $\sqrt{20}$ (h) $\sqrt{24}$

(i) $1/\sqrt{2}$ (j) $1/\sqrt{3}$ (k) $\sqrt{2/3}$ (l) $\sqrt{3/2}$

(m) $\sqrt{3/8}$ (n) $\sqrt{0.02}$ (o) $\sqrt{1/32}$ (p) $\sqrt{0.18}$

8. Using (ii) above, we may simplify $\sqrt{x^2 + 2x + 1}$, where x is a real number, as follows: $\sqrt{x^2 + 2x + 1} = \sqrt{(x + 1)^2} = |x + 1|$. Given that x is a real number, simplify the following:

(a) $\sqrt{x^2}$ (b) $\sqrt{4x^2}$

(c) $\sqrt{-4x^2}$ (d) $\sqrt{(-3)^2}$

(e) $(\sqrt{-3})^2$ (f) $\sqrt{x^2 - 2x + 1}$

(g) $\sqrt{x^2 - 6x + 9}$ (h) $\sqrt{x^2 + 4x + 4}$

(i) $\sqrt{6x - x^2 - 9}$ (j) $\sqrt{x}\sqrt{1/x}$

9. Illustrate by means of an Euler diagram the inclusion relationships among the following sets: complex numbers, integers, natural numbers, rational numbers, real numbers.

10. In each of the following cases, find the resultant of the given forces, and the magnitude of each of the given forces and of their resultant

(assuming the unit of force to be the pound), and draw a diagram to illustrate:

(a) (3, 4), (4, 3)   (b) (10, 0), (0, 10)
(c) (3, 4), (4, −3)   (d) (3, 4), (3, 4)
(e) (3, 4), (−3, −4)   (f) (10, 0), (−5, 0)
(g) (2, 3), (3, 4), (0, 5)   (h) (2, 3), (3, 4), (−5, −7)

11.(a) Suppose a force (a, b) is applied to a body. What force applied to the body at the same point will cancel the effect of the force (a, b)? Why?

(b) In a three-way tug-of-war, two boys are pulling on ropes at right angles to each other with forces of 75 and 100 lb. Their father tugs in an opposite direction at a third rope knotted to the first two at the vertex of the right angle. What force must Dad exert to hold his own? Draw a diagram to illustrate.

12. Velocity is a vector concept also. For example, a velocity of 10 miles per hour north may be represented by the vector (0, 10), in a cc system in which the positive Y-axis is labeled "north." An airplane traveling east at 240 miles per hour [i.e., with velocity (240, 0)], and subjected to a gale wind that blows it south with a velocity of 70 miles per hour [i.e., with velocity (0, −70)], actually travels a southeasterly path described by the velocity (240, 0) + (0, −70), i.e., (240, −70). The actual air speed of the plane will be $\sqrt{(240)^2 + (-70)^2}$, or $\sqrt{62,500}$, or 250 miles per hour (see Fig. 5.5).

(a) A boat heads straight across a river at a speed of 20 miles per hour. A current sweeps it down stream at a speed of 5 miles per hour. Draw a diagram to show the direction of the path the boat actually follows, and find the actual speed of the boat along that path.

(b) A bird flying south at a speed of 30 miles per hour is blown west by the wind at a speed of 10 miles per hour. Draw a diagram to show the direction of the path the bird actually follows, and find the actual speed of the bird along that path.

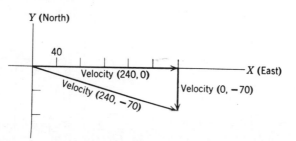

Fig. 5.5

13. Is the operation of adding forces complete? closed? associative? commutative? Justify your answers, and illustrate the questions of associativity and commutativity by vector diagrams.

14. Draw the graph of the function f whose mapping is given by $f(x) = \sqrt{x}$, and whose domain is the set of all numbers x for which $\sqrt{x}$ is defined and real; do the same for $f(x) = -\sqrt{x}$; how are the two graphs related?

15. Restricting the operations $+$, $\cdot$, as they are defined in the set of complex numbers to the following subsets, which are fields? (i.e., which satisfy the six field axioms?) Which are ordered fields (i.e., which may be made to satisfy the six field axioms and the three order axioms)? Justify your answers.

(a) All natural numbers.

(b) All integers.

(c) All rational numbers.

(d) All positive rational numbers.

(e) All rational numbers with odd denominators.

(f) All complex numbers $a + bi$ such that a, b are rational numbers.

16. On the face of a clock, if we "add" 3 to 11, the result is 2. We may think of this result as having been attained by identifying 12 with 0: $3 + 11 = 14 = 12 + 2 = 0 + 2 = 2$. This suggests a number of new operations, for which we shall, as a matter of convenience and because no ambiguity is caused thereby, continue to use the old symbols $+$ and $\cdot$.

One is called "addition mod 12." It is defined on the set $S = \{0, 1, \cdots, 11\}$ as follows: If $a \in S$ and $b \in S$, $a + b$ is defined to be the remainder that results when, in the system of integers, the sum of a and b is divided by 12. Similarly, we may define multiplication mod 12 on the same set S as follows: If $a \in S$ and $b \in S$, $a \cdot b$ is defined to be the remainder that results when, in the system of integers, the product of a and b is divided by 12; more generally and similarly, one may define, for any positive integer n, addition and multiplication mod n in the set $\{0, \cdots, n - 1\}$.

For example, here are addition and multiplication tables for addition mod 3:

+	0	1	2			0	1	2
0	0	1	2		0	0	0	0
1	1	2	0		1	0	1	2
2	2	0	1		2	0	2	1

(a) Define addition mod n and multiplication mod n, for any positive integer n.

(b) In each of the following cases, construct addition and multiplication tables, mod n, and tell whether the set $\{0, \cdots, n-1\}$ under $+$ and $\cdot$ mod n is a field and, if so, whether it can be made into an ordered field.   Justify your answers.

(i) $n = 1$ (ii) $n = 2$ (iii) $n = 3$ (iv) $n = 4$

(v) $n = 5$ (vi) $n = 6$ (vii) $n = 7$ (viii) $n = 12$

(c) What type of number must n be in order for the set $\{0, \cdots, n-1\}$, under addition and multiplication mod n, to be a field?

*5.5 ROOTS OF COMPLEX NUMBERS: DEMOIVRE'S THEOREM

Since the domain of the unary operation $\sqrt{\ }$ has been defined to be the set of all real numbers, it would be meaningless at this point to speak, for example, of $\sqrt{i}$.   We might, of course, extend the domain of the operation $\sqrt{\ }$ so that $\sqrt{i}$ (the "principal" square root of i) became meaningful, but actually we shall have little use for such an extended definition.   Nevertheless, we shall wish to speak of square roots and even other roots of complex numbers, whether they are real or not.   We shall do so, but for the reason just given, we shall not single out any one nth root to be called the *principal* nth root.

Definition.   Given a natural number n, a number a is called an *nth root* of a number b if $a^n = b$.   (In the cases $n = 2, 3$ the nth roots are called square and cube roots respectively.)

The question now arises: Given any natural number n, does every complex number have an nth root?   The answer is "yes"; in fact, every complex number (except 0) has n distinct nth roots, as we shall proceed to show.   (Zero, of course, has only one nth root, namely itself.   Why?) Our demonstration will make use of trigonometry, so that what follows in this section will require some knowledge of that subject.

First of all, we recall the well-known facts that, if $u = \cos \theta$ and $v = \sin \theta$, then u and v are real numbers whose absolute values are less than or equal to 1, and $u^2 + v^2 = 1$.   Conversely, it is also true that, if u and v are real numbers whose absolute values are less than or equal to 1, then there exists a real number θ such that $u = \cos \theta$, $v = \sin \theta$.   (Of course, before the real number θ can be determined, we must specify whether the trigonometric functions we are dealing with are defined in degree or in radian measure.   For convenience, we shall use degree measure throughout this section.)

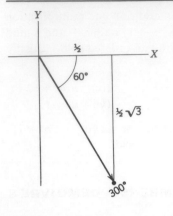

Fig. 5.6

For example, suppose $u = \frac{1}{2}$, $v = -\frac{1}{2}\sqrt{3}$. Then it is easily verified that u and v have absolute values not exceeding 1, and that $u^2 + v^2 = 1$. Therefore there exists a real number θ such that $\cos \theta = \frac{1}{2}$, $\sin \theta = -\frac{1}{2}\sqrt{3}$. For these values of u and v, θ is rather easily determined by drawing a vector (whose length $r = \sqrt{u^2 + v^2} = 1$) from the origin to the point (u, v)—a standard method in trigonometry courses (see Fig. 5.6).

The vector points in the 300° direction; $\theta = 300°$. (The value 300° is not, of course, unique; $\theta = -60°$, for example, also satisfies the conditions $\cos \theta = \frac{1}{2}$, $\sin \theta = -\frac{1}{2}\sqrt{3}$.)

Now suppose we are given a complex number $a + bi$. Our next goal will be to show that, if r represents the magnitude of the vector (a, b), i.e., $r = \sqrt{a^2 + b^2}$, and if $r \neq 0$, then the real numbers $\dfrac{a}{r}$ and $\dfrac{b}{r}$ have absolute values $\leqslant 1$:

For suppose $\left|\dfrac{a}{r}\right| > 1$. Then $\dfrac{|a|}{|r|} > 1$, $|a| > |r|$, $|a|^2 > |r|^2$, i.e., $a^2 > r^2$, $a^2 > a^2 + b^2$, $0 > b^2$. But since b is a real number, $b^2 \geqslant 0$. The last two inequalities contradict the trichotomy axiom; therefore $\left|\dfrac{a}{r}\right| > 1$ is impossible. Therefore, by the trichotomy axiom, $\left|\dfrac{a}{r}\right| \leqslant 1$. Similarly, $\left|\dfrac{b}{r}\right| \leqslant 1$.

Thus, there exists a real number θ such that $\cos \theta = \dfrac{a}{r}$, $\sin \theta = \dfrac{b}{r}$, and we may express $a + bi$ as follows:

$$a + bi = r\left(\frac{a}{r} + \frac{b}{r}i\right) = r(\cos \theta + i \sin \theta)$$

The form $r(\cos \theta + i \sin \theta)$ for a complex number is called the *trigonometric* or *polar form* (the latter from its close connection with the "polar coordinate" system for locating points in a plane, encountered in analytic geometry). We shall abbreviate $r(\cos \theta + i \sin \theta)$: $r \operatorname{cis} \theta$. [Note that the polar form is applicable even if $r = 0$. For if $r = 0$, then $a^2 + b^2 = 0$, and this can happen for real numbers a, b only if $a = 0$, $b = 0$. Hence

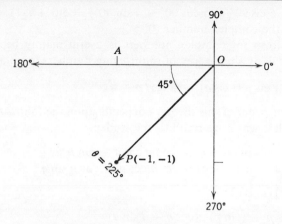

Fig. 5.7

$a + bi = 0$, and this complex number can be represented as $0(\cos 0 + i \sin 0)$. This representation is, of course, not unique.]

The real number $r = \sqrt{a^2 + b^2}$ is called the *magnitude* or *absolute value* or *modulus* of the complex number $a + bi$, and, if $\cos \theta - \dfrac{a}{r}$ and $\sin \theta - \dfrac{b}{r}$, then θ is called the *amplitude* or *argument*, or simply the *angle* of $a + bi$.

Illustrative Example 1. Express the following complex numbers in polar form: (a) $-1 - i$; (b) 1.

SOLUTION. (a) $a = -1$, $b = -1$, $r = \sqrt{(-1)^2 + (-1)^2} = \sqrt{2}$. In finding θ, it is helpful to draw the vector (a, b), in this case $(-1, -1)$, from the origin to the point (a, b) (Fig. 5.7).
Clearly $\measuredangle AOP = 45°$, so that $\theta = 180° + 45° = 225°$. Hence $-1 - i = \sqrt{2} \operatorname{cis} 225°$.

(b) Since $1 = 1 + 0i$: $a = 1$, $b = 0$, $r = \sqrt{1^2 + 0^2} = 1$. From Fig. 5.8, $\theta = 0°$. Hence $1 = 1 \operatorname{cis} 0°$.

Illustrative Example 2. Express in another simple form, the complex number $5 \operatorname{cis} 90°$.

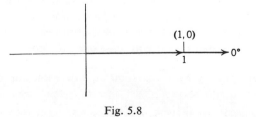

Fig. 5.8

SOLUTION. $5 \operatorname{cis} 90° = 5(\cos 90° + i \sin 90°) = 5(0 + i \cdot 1) = 5i$. [Or alternatively, the complex number $(0, 5)$.]

The polar form for complex numbers is useful mainly because there exists a particularly simple way of multiplying numbers in polar form:

Theorem. $(r \operatorname{cis} p)(s \operatorname{cis} q) = rs \operatorname{cis}(p + q)$.

PROOF. The proof of this theorem depends upon the following trigonometric formulas, which we recall to the student:

(1) $$\cos(p + q) = \cos p \cos q - \sin p \sin q$$
(2) $$\sin(p + q) = \sin p \cos q + \cos p \sin q$$

Now: $(r \operatorname{cis} p)(s \operatorname{cis} q)$

$$= r(\cos p + i \sin p) \cdot s(\cos q + i \sin q)$$
$$= rs[(\cos p \cos q - \sin p \sin q) + i(\sin p \cos q + \cos p \sin q)]$$
$$= rs[\cos(p + q) + \sin(p + q)]$$
$$= rs \operatorname{cis}(p + q) \quad \text{Q.E.D.}$$

Repeated applications of the theorem yield the following corollary:

Corollary 1.

$$(r_1 \operatorname{cis} \theta_1)(r_2 \operatorname{cis} \theta_2)(r_3 \operatorname{cis} \theta_3) \cdots (r_n \operatorname{cis} \theta_n)$$
$$= r_1 r_2 \cdots r_n \operatorname{cis}(\theta_1 + \theta_2 + \cdots + \theta_n)$$

for any natural number n.

If $r_1 = r_2 = \cdots = r_n = r$ and $\theta_1 = \theta_2 = \cdots = \theta_n = \theta$, we derive from Corollary 1 the following famous result (named after and known to a mathematician who was born in France in 1667, but lived most of his life in England, where he became a close friend of Isaac Newton.)

DeMoivre's Theorem. If n is a natural number, $(r \operatorname{cis} \theta)^n = r^n \operatorname{cis} n\theta$.

Illustrative Example 3. Find $(1 + i)^{10}$.

SOLUTION. In polar form, $1 + i = \sqrt{2} \operatorname{cis} 45°$. Therefore $(1 + i)^{10} = (\sqrt{2} \operatorname{cis} 45°)^{10}$. By DeMoivre's theorem, $(\sqrt{2} \operatorname{cis} 45°)^{10} = (\sqrt{2})^{10} \operatorname{cis} 450° = 32 \operatorname{cis} 90° = 32(\cos 90° + i \sin 90°) = 32(0 + i \cdot 1) = 32i$. Thus, $(1 + i)^{10} = 32i$.

Using DeMoivre's theorem, we now find ourselves able to justify our earlier assertion about nth roots of complex numbers.

First of all, supposing that $r \operatorname{cis} \theta$ is a complex number, and n is a natural number, we shall produce at least one nth root of $r \operatorname{cis} \theta$. In fact, it is easy to see that $\sqrt[n]{r} \operatorname{cis} \dfrac{\theta}{n}$ is such an nth root, for by DeMoivre's theorem $\left(\sqrt[n]{r} \operatorname{cis} \dfrac{\theta}{n}\right)^n = (\sqrt[n]{r})^n \operatorname{cis} n \cdot \dfrac{\theta}{n} = r \operatorname{cis} \theta$.

Secondly, we note that, if k is any integer, $\sqrt[n]{r}$ cis $\left(\dfrac{\theta}{n} + k \cdot \dfrac{360°}{n}\right)$ is also an nth root of r cis θ, for $\left[\sqrt[n]{r}\text{ cis }\left(\dfrac{\theta}{n} + k \cdot \dfrac{360°}{n}\right)\right]^{n} = r$ cis $(\theta + k \cdot 360°) = r$ cis θ.

Indeed, it follows from properties of the sine and cosine functions that, if $r \neq 0$ and $k = 0, 1, \cdots, n - 1$, then these n nth roots are all distinct; and it follows from the fact that all the nth roots of a complex number c satisfy the equation $x^{n} = c$, which we shall later show can have no more than n complex roots, that no more than n complex nth roots of a given complex number can exist. Therefore we may state the following theorem:

Theorem. If r cis θ is a complex number in polar form with $r \neq 0$, and n is a natural number, there exist exactly n complex nth roots of r cis θ. They are the n complex numbers:

$$\sqrt[n]{r}\text{ cis }\left(\dfrac{\theta}{n} + k \cdot \dfrac{360°}{n}\right)$$

(In other words, one nth root of r cis θ is $\sqrt[n]{r}$ cis $\dfrac{\theta}{n}$, and the others may be obtained by successive additions of $\dfrac{360°}{n}$ to the amplitude of this first nth root, until n nth roots are obtained.)

Illustrative Example 4. Find all complex cube roots of -1.

SOLUTION. We first express $-1 = -1 + 0i$ in polar form: $-1 = 1$ cis $180°$. Here $n = 3$, $\sqrt[n]{r} = \sqrt[3]{1} = 1$, $\theta = 180°$, $\dfrac{\theta}{n} = 60°$, $\dfrac{360°}{n} = 120°$. The required cube roots are 1 cis $60°$, 1 cis $180°$, 1 cis $300°$, i.e.,
$$\tfrac{1}{2} + (\tfrac{1}{2}\sqrt{3})i, \ -1, \ \tfrac{1}{2} - (\tfrac{1}{2}\sqrt{3})i.$$

After we have studied the subject of algebraic equations, we shall return to the question of finding roots of complex numbers, but by non-trigonometric means.

▶ ***EXERCISE 24**

1. Draw a vector to represent each of the following complex numbers, and represent each complex number in polar form:

(a) 2 (b) $2i$ (c) -2 (d) $-2i$
(e) $2 + 2i$ (f) $-2 + 2i$ (g) $-2 - 2i$ (h) $2 - 2i$
(i) $\sqrt{3} + i$ (j) $-\sqrt{3} + i$ (k) $-\sqrt{3} - i$ (l) $\sqrt{3} - i$
(m) $1 + i\sqrt{3}$ (n) $-1 + i\sqrt{3}$ (o) $-1 - i\sqrt{3}$ (p) $1 - i\sqrt{3}$

2. Give several different polar representations for the complex number 0. What is the most general polar representation of the number 0? Do the same for the complex number 1, and, finally, for the complex number r cis θ.

3. Draw a vector to represent each of the following complex numbers, and also represent each in nontrigonometric form:

(a) 10 cis 30°   (b) 10 cis 45°   (c) 10 cis 60°   (d) cis 0°
(e) cis 360°   (f) cis 90°   (g) cis 180°   (h) cis 270°
(i) 4 cis 120°   (j) 4 cis 135°   (k) 4 cis 150°   (l) −4 cis 150°
(m) 10 cis 210°   (n) 10 cis 225°   (o) 10 cis 240°   (p) 10 cis 600°
(q) cis 300°   (r) cis 315°   (s) cis 330°   (t) cis (−30°)

4. Express each of the following complex numbers in the standard $a + bi$ form:

(a) $(1 + i)^8$ (b) $(1 - i)^8$ (c) $(\sqrt{3} + i)^{10}$
(d) $(\sqrt{3} - i)^{10}$ (e) $(-1 + i)^8$ (f) $(1 + i\sqrt{3})^3$
(g) $(1 - i\sqrt{3})^3$ (h) i^{100} (i) $(-i)^{50}$

5. Find, and represent as vectors drawn from the origin of a cc system, all complex:

(a) Square roots of i (b) Cube roots of 1
(c) Square roots of $1 + i\sqrt{3}$ (d) Square roots of $1 - i\sqrt{3}$
(e) Fourth roots of 1   (f) Fifth roots of 1
(g) Sixth roots of 1   (h) Cube roots of i
(i) Fourth roots of −1   (j) Eighth roots of 1

6. Suppose $(a_1, b_1), (a_2, b_2), \cdots, (a_n, b_n)$ are the n complex nth roots of 1, where $n > 2$. Describe the geometric pattern formed by the *points* $(a_1, b_1), (a_2, b_2), \cdots, (a_n, b_n)$ in a cc system. Generalize to the n complex nth roots of the complex number (a, b).

7.(a) Show that either of the imaginary cube roots of 1 is both the conjugate and the square of the other; hence that if ω represents either imaginary cube root of 1, then the set of all complex cube roots of 1 is the set of powers of ω: $\{\omega, \omega^2, \omega^3\}$.

8. A primitive nth root of 1 is defined to be a complex number ω such that $\{\omega, \omega^2, \cdots, \omega^n\}$ constitutes the set of all complex nth roots of 1. (We then say that ω *generates* the set of all complex nth roots of 1.) We have seen in Problem 7 that either imaginary cube root of 1 is a primitive nth root of 1. For each of the following values of n, find all primitive nth roots of 1.

(a) 2   (b) 4   (c) 6   (d) 8

Which nth roots of 1 will always be primitive nth roots?

9.(a) Show that the conjugate of the complex number r cis θ is r cis $(-\theta)$.

(b) Suppose we let c^* represent the conjugate of the complex number c. Show that $(c^n)^* = (c^*)^n$, where n is any natural number.

6 EXPONENTIAL AND LOGARITHMIC FUNCTIONS

6.1 INTRODUCTION

Up until now we have made use of expressions of the form x^n to only a limited extent. (We recall to the student that in the expression x^n, n is called the *exponent* that is applied to the *base* x, and x^n is called the nth *power* of x.) In this chapter we shall consider in some detail exponents of various sorts, and functions defined by means of exponents.

6.2 NATURAL NUMBER EXPONENTS

Suppose a is a complex number. (Our statements about a will then apply if a is a real number, since every real number is also a complex number.) Then if n is a nn, we define a^n to be a if $n = 1$, and to be the product of n factors, each equal to a if $n > 1$. That is:

$$a^1 = a$$
$$a^2 = a \cdot a$$
$$a^3 = a \cdot a \cdot a, \text{ etc.}$$

If a, b are complex numbers and m, n are nn, it is not hard to see that the following familiar statements hold true as a consequence of the preceding definition:

1: $\qquad a^m a^n = a^{m+n}$

2: $\qquad (a^m)^n = a^{mn}$

3: $\qquad (ab)^m = a^m b^m$

4: $$\left(\frac{a}{b}\right)^m = \frac{a^m}{b^m} \quad (\text{where } b \neq 0)$$

5a: $$\frac{a^m}{a^n} = a^{m-n} \quad (\text{where } a \neq 0 \text{ and } m > n)$$

5b: $$\frac{a^m}{a^n} = \frac{1}{a^{n-m}} \quad (\text{where } a \neq 0 \text{ and } m < n)$$

Statements 1 through 5b may be proved rigorously by means of the Principle of Mathematical Induction [see Exercise 25, Problem 18]. At this point we shall content ourselves with the following somewhat informal demonstrations of their validity:

1: Since $a^m = \overbrace{a \cdot a \cdot a \cdots a}^{m \text{ factors}}$, and $a^n = \overbrace{a \cdot a \cdot a \cdots a}^{n \text{ factors}}$,

$$a^m \cdot a^n = \underbrace{\overbrace{a \cdot a \cdot a \cdots a}^{m \text{ factors}} \cdot \overbrace{a \cdot a \cdot a \cdots a}^{n \text{ factors}}}_{m+n \text{ factors}} = a^{m+n}$$

We now make repeated use of statement 1 to prove statement 2.

2: $(a^m)^n = \overbrace{a^m \cdot a^m \cdot a^m \cdots a^m}^{n \text{ factors, each} = a^m} = \overbrace{a^{m+m+m+\cdots+m}}^{n \text{ terms}} = a^{mn}.$

The proof of statement 3 makes use of both the commutativity and the associativity of multiplication (see Exercise 14, Problem 4).

3: $(ab)^m = \overbrace{(ab)(ab)(ab)\cdots(ab)}^{m \text{ factors, each} = ab} = \overbrace{(a \cdot a \cdot a \cdots a)}^{m \text{ factors}} \cdot \overbrace{(b \cdot b \cdot b \cdots b)}^{m \text{ factors}} = a^m b^m.$

4: Follows from the rule for the multiplication of fractions (see Exercise 18, Problem 5).

5a: If m, n are natural numbers such that $m > n$, it may be proved that $m - n$ is a nn; therefore, by our definition of natural number exponents, a^{m-n} exists, and by statement 1, $a^{m-n} \cdot a^n = a^{m-n+n} = a^{m-n+n} = a^m$. Hence:

$$\frac{a^m}{a^n} = \frac{a^{m-n} \cdot a^n}{a^n} = a^{m-n} \quad (\text{see Exercise 18, Problem } 2i)$$

5b: (Left as an exercise for the student.)

Illustrative Examples:

$2^5 = 2 \cdot 2 \cdot 2 \cdot 2 \cdot 2 = 32$

$2^{10} = 2^5 \cdot 2^5 = 32 \cdot 32 = 1024 \quad [\text{or: } 2^{10} = (2^5)^2 = (32)^2 = 1024]$

$2 \cdot 5^2 = 2 \cdot 25 = 50$

$(2 \cdot 5)^2 = (10)^2 = 100$

$3^2 + 4^2 = 9 + 16 = 25$

$(3 + 4)^2 = 7^2 = 49$

$\left(\dfrac{6}{\sqrt{3}}\right)^2 = \dfrac{6^2}{(\sqrt{3})^2} = \dfrac{36}{3} = 12$

$\dfrac{100^3}{10^3} = \left(\dfrac{100}{10}\right)^3 = 10^3 = 1000$

$\dfrac{a^5}{a^2} = a^{5-2} = a^3$ (if a is any nonzero complex number)

$\dfrac{a^2}{a^5} = \dfrac{1}{a^{5-2}} = \dfrac{1}{a^3}$ (if a is any nonzero complex number)

$\dfrac{a^5}{a^5} = 1$ (if a is any nonzero complex number; see Exercise 18, Problem 4c)

$1^n = 1$ (if n is any positive integer)

6.3 INTEGER EXPONENTS

In simplifying the expression a^5/a^3, where a is a non-zero complex number, statement 5a permits us to proceed as follows:

$$\frac{a^5}{a^3} = a^{5-3} = a^2$$

But in simplifying the expression a^3/a^5, again for a nonzero complex number a, statement 5a does not apply, for in this case $m = 3, n = 5$, and the condition $m > n$ demanded by the statement is not satisfied. That the condition $m > n$ is necessary in statement 5a may be seen from the fact that otherwise we would be led to an exponent (namely, $m - n$) which is *not* a nn, and the only exponents we have as yet defined are nn exponents.

It would seem, then, that it might be useful to extend our definition of exponents to include all integers rather than just the nn; we shall find that statement 5a suggests a reasonable definition for a^k, in case k is an integer other than a nn; i.e., in case $k = 0$ or k is a negative integer.

First, supposing that a is a nonzero complex number; we may consider the expression: a^2/a^2. On the one hand, we know: $a^2/a^2 = 1$. On the other hand, *if statement 5a did apply*, $a^2/a^2 = a^{2-2} = a^0$. This suggests the following definition:

If a is a nonzero complex number, a^0 is defined to equal 1. (*Note:* Later on, in Chapter 7, we shall find it useful to define $0^0 = 1$ also.)

Again, supposing that a is a nonzero complex number, we may consider the expression: a^3/a^5. On the one hand, we know (by statement 5b) that

$a^3/a^5 = 1/a^2$. On the other hand, *if statement 5a did apply,* $a^3/a^5 = a^{-2}$. This suggests that we define $a^{-2} = 1/a^2$ and, in general, that we make the following definition:

If a is a nonzero complex number and n is a nn, then a^{-n} *is defined to equal* $1/a^n$.

These definitions turn out to have been well chosen. For it may be proved that, if a and b are *nonzero* complex numbers and m, n are integers, all of the statements 1 through 5b continue to hold true, even with the parenthetical conditions in 4 through 5b deleted.

We proceed to prove that statements 1 through 5b so modified continue to hold true. In order to do so, we first prove several preliminary statements.

6: *For any nonzero complex number a and any integer n,* $a^{-n} = 1/a^n$.

PROOF OF 6: By our definition of integer, n must be either a nn, or the negative of a nn, or zero. If n is a nn, then $a^{-n} = 1/a^n$ by the preceding definition. If n is the negative of a nn, then $n = -m$, where m is a nn; in that case, $a^{-n} = a^{-(-m)} = a^m$, and $1/a^n = 1/(1/a^m) = a^m$ also, so that again $a^{-n} = 1/a^n$. Finally, if $n = 0$, then $a^{-n} = a^{-0} = a^0 = 1$, and $1/a^n = 1/a^0 = 1/1 = 1$, so that once more $a^{-n} = 1/a^n$; thus in all cases, the statement is true.

(a) *For any nonzero complex number a and any integers m, n,* $a^{m-n} = 1/a^{n-m}$.

Proof of (a): Since $m - n = -(n - m)$, we have: $a^{m-n} = a^{-(n-m)} = 1/a^{n-m}$ (by statement 6 above).

(b) *For any nonzero complex number a and any natural numbers m and n,* $a^m/a^n = a^{m-n}$.

Proof of (b): In case $m > n$ or $m < n$, (b) follows immediately from statements 5a, 5b and (a). There remains to consider only the case $m = n$. But in that case, $a^m/a^n = a^n/a^n = 1$, and $a^{m-n} = a^{n-n} = a^0 = 1$; so that $a^m/a^n = a^{m-n}$, Q.E.D.

We are now ready to prove statement 1 in the modified form for integer exponents: If $m = 0$ or $n = 0$, then the proof of statement 1 is easy, and is left as an exercise for the student.

If m and n are both nn, statement 1 has already been shown to hold true.

If m and n are both negative, then $m = -r$, $n = -s$, where r, s are nn. In that case $a^m \cdot a^n = a^{-r} \cdot a^{-s} = (1/a^r)(1/a^s) = 1/a^{r+s}$, and $a^{m+n} = a^{-r+(-s)} = a^{-(r+s)} = 1/a^{r+s}$ also, so that here too $a^m a^n = a^{m+n}$.

If m is a nn and n is negative, then $n = -p$, where p is a nn. In that case $a^m \cdot a^n = a^m \cdot a^{-p} = (a^m)(1/a^p) = a^m/a^p = a^{m-p}$ [by (b) above], and $a^{m+n} = a^{m+(-p)} = a^{m-p}$ also, so that again $a^m a^n = a^{m+n}$.

There remains to consider only the case where m is negative and n is a nn. But then $a^m a^n = a^n a^m$, and, by the preceding case, $a^n a^m = a^{n+m} = a^{m+n}$. Hence $a^m a^n = a^{m+n}$ in this final case also, and our proof is complete.

The proofs of statements 2 through 5b in the modified form for integers are similar and are, therefore, left as exercises for the student.

The following theorems and corollary will be found useful in computation:

Theorem. If n is any integer, $1^n = 1$.

(The proof is left as an exercise, with this hint: Consider the cases n a positive integer, $n = 0$, n a negative integer.)

Theorem. If n is an odd integer, $(-1)^n = -1$, and if n is an even integer, $(-1)^n = 1$.

PROOF. If n is an odd integer, then there exists an integer k such that $n = 2k - 1$. Thus $(-1)^n = (-1)^{2k-1} = (-1)^{2k}(-1)^{-1} = (-1)^{2k}(-1) = [(-1)^2]^k(-1) = 1^k(-1) = 1(-1) = -1$, Q.E.D.

The proof of the second part of the theorem is left as an exercise for the student.

Corollary. If a is any nonzero complex number and n any integer, then $(-a)^n = -a^n$ if n is odd and $(-a)^n = a^n$ if n is even.

[The proof is left as an exercise with this hint: $-a = (-1) \cdot a$.]

Illustrative Examples:

$$-2^4 = -(2 \cdot 2 \cdot 2 \cdot 2) = -16$$

$$(-2)^4 = 2^4 = 16$$

$$(-2)^5 = -2^5 = -32$$

$$-2^{-2} = -\frac{1}{2^2} = -\tfrac{1}{4}$$

$$(-2)^{-2} = \frac{1}{(-2)^2} = \tfrac{1}{4}$$

$$2^{-2} \cdot 5^{-2} = (2 \cdot 5)^{-2} = 10^{-2} = 0.01$$

$$\left(\frac{a}{b}\right)^{-1} = \frac{1}{(a/b)} = \frac{b}{a} \quad \text{(if } a \text{ and } b \text{ are nonzero complex numbers)}$$

$$\left(\frac{1}{a}\right)^{-1} = \frac{a}{1} = a \quad \text{(if } a \text{ is ?)}$$

$$\left(\frac{a}{b}\right)^{-n} = \left[\left(\frac{a}{b}\right)^{-1}\right]^n = \left(\frac{b}{a}\right)^n \quad \text{(if } a \text{ and } b \text{ are nonzero complex numbers and } n \text{ is any integer)}$$

$$\left(\frac{1}{a}\right)^{-n} = \left(\frac{a}{1}\right)^n = a^n \quad \text{(if } a \text{ is ? and if } n \text{ is ?)}$$

$$\left(\frac{1}{2}\right)^{-3} = 2^3 = 8$$

$$\left(-\frac{2}{3}\right)^{-3} = -\left(\frac{2}{3}\right)^{-3} = -\left(\frac{3}{2}\right)^3 = -\frac{27}{8}$$

$$(a^{-2})^3(a^{-3})^{-2} = a^{-6}a^6 = a^0 = 1 \quad \text{(if } a \text{ is ?)}$$

$$\frac{a^{-m}}{b^{-n}} = \frac{1/a^m}{1/b^n} = \frac{b^n}{a^m} \quad \text{(conditions on } a, b, m, n \text{ ?)}$$

$$\frac{a^{-2}b^{-2}}{a^{-1}b^{-1}} = \frac{a^{-2}}{a^{-1}} \cdot \frac{b^{-2}}{b^{-1}} = \frac{a}{a^2} \cdot \frac{b}{b^2} = \frac{1}{ab}$$

$$\frac{a^{-2}b^{-2}}{a^{-1}b^{-1}} = a^{-2-(-1)}b^{-2-(-1)} = a^{-1}b^{-1} = \frac{1}{ab}$$

(conditions on a, b ?)

$$\frac{a^{-2} + b^{-2}}{a^{-1}b^{-1}} = \frac{a^{-2} + b^{-2}}{a^{-1}b^{-1}} \cdot \frac{a^2b^2}{a^2b^2} = \frac{a^0b^2 + a^2b^0}{ab} = \frac{a^2 + b^2}{ab}$$

(conditions on a, b ?)

6.4 RATIONAL EXPONENTS

Having enlarged our definition of exponent to apply not only to the set of all nn but also to the more inclusive set of all integers, we now take the next natural step—that of extending our definition of exponent to the set of all rational numbers.

Again, it will be a statement which does not yet apply which will suggest a reasonable definition; in this case, statement 2.

Suppose r is any rational number. Then r may be written in the form p/q, where q is a positive integer and p is an integer that may be positive, or negative, or zero. Suppose now that a is a *positive real number*. Then *if statement 2 did apply*:

$$(a^{p/q})^q = a^p$$

However, if a is positive, it easily follows that a^p is positive. In a manner similar to that in which we proved that 2 has a unique positive square root (see Section 4.15), it may be proved that, if q is a nn, then any positive real number r has a unique positive real qth root, denoted $\sqrt[q]{r}$, with the defining property that $(\sqrt[q]{r})^q = r$.

If $(a^{p/q})^q = a^p$, then $a^{p/q}$ must be a qth root of a^p. This suggests the following definition:

If a is a positive real number, p/q a rational number in which q is a positive integer, we define $a^{p/q}$ to equal $\sqrt[q]{a^p}$, so that $(a^{p/q})^q = a^p$.

Since it may be proved that in this case: $\sqrt[q]{a^p} = (\sqrt[q]{a})^p$, we have, with the above conditions on a, p, q:

$$a^{p/q} = \sqrt[q]{a^p} = (\sqrt[q]{a})^p$$

A direct proof of the preceding statement follows:

If q is a nn, and x, y are positive real numbers, then to prove that $x = \sqrt[q]{y}$, is sufficient to show that $x^q = y$.

Thus, to show that $(\sqrt[q]{a})^p = \sqrt[q]{a^p}$ (where a is a positive real number, q a nn, p an integer), it is sufficient to note that $(\sqrt[q]{a})^p$ and a^p are positive real numbers and to show that $[(\sqrt[q]{a})^p]^q = a^p$.

But $[(\sqrt[q]{a})^p]^q = (\sqrt[q]{a})^{pq} = (\sqrt[q]{a})^{qp} = [(\sqrt[q]{a})^q]^p = a^p$, which completes the proof.

Again our definition turns out to have been well chosen, for it may be proved that, if a and b are positive real numbers, and m, n are rational numbers, statements 1 through 6 continue to hold true. (The parenthetical conditions in statements 4 through 5b may be deleted in this case also.) The following lemma is useful in the proof:

Lemma. If a and b are positive real numbers, and p is an integer, and q is a positive integer, then:

$$b = a^{p/q} \Leftrightarrow b^q = a^p$$

PROOF OF LEMMA: On the one hand, if $b = a^{p/q}$, then $b^q = (a^{p/q})^q = a^p$; conversely, if $b^q = a^p$, then $b = \sqrt[q]{a^p} = a^{p/q}$, so that both implications of the lemma are true.

We now use this lemma to prove statement 1, as it applies to rational exponents; that is, assuming that a and b are positive real numbers, and that $m = p/q$ and $n = r/s$, where p, r are integers and q, s are positive integers:

By the lemma, to prove that $a^{p/q}a^{r/s} = a^{(p/q)+(r/s)} = a^{(ps+qr)/qs}$, it is sufficient to show that $(a^{p/q}a^{r/s})^{qs} = a^{ps+qr}$. But using our preceding results on integer exponents: $(a^{p/q}a^{r/s})^{qs} = (a^{p/q})^{qs}(a^{r/s})^{qs} = (a^{p/q})^{qs}(a^{r/s})^{sq} = [(a^{p/q})^q]^s [(a^{r/s})^s]^q = a^{ps}a^{rq} = a^{ps+qr}$, Q.E.D.

The proofs of statements 2 through 6 follow similarly from the lemma and from properties of integer exponents, and will be left as exercises for the student.

From statement 2, it follows that $a^{p/q} = a^{(1/q)p} = (\sqrt[q]{a})^p$. Thus $a^{p/q}$ is equal to $(\sqrt[q]{a})^p$ as well as $\sqrt[q]{a^p}$. Generally it is the form $(\sqrt[q]{a})^p$ which lends itself better to computation when evaluating $a^{p/q}$ for a particular value of a. For example, $16^{\frac{3}{4}} = (\sqrt[4]{16})^3 = 2^3 = 8$ is easier to carry through than $16^{\frac{3}{4}} = \sqrt[4]{16^3} = \sqrt[4]{4096} = 8$.

It will be noted that although we have now extended our definition of exponent to include all rational numbers, we have lost something: with this type of exponent our base a is restricted to being a positive real number rather than any nonzero complex number. This restriction was forced upon us because, at this point, we have information at hand only about qth roots of positive real numbers. A study of the situation with respect to qth roots of complex numbers would be necessary before an extension of the present base to a complex number, or even to a negative real number, could be considered. Such a study is beyond the scope of this course, but is included in courses in "Functions of a Complex Variable."

In any case it turns out that an extension of the concept of rational exponents to apply even to negative real bases has some built-in deficiencies; for example, the important statement 3 above cannot be made to hold true (see Problem 3, Exercise 23).

At this point we do, however, make two further extensions in agreement with traditional usage: If a is a negative real number and p is an odd integer, we define $a^{p/2} = (\sqrt{a})^p$. [For example, $(-2)^{\frac{3}{2}} = (\sqrt{-2})^3 = (i\sqrt{2})^3 = -2i\sqrt{2}$.] Finally, if q is an odd natural number and p is an integer, we define $a^{p/q}$ for any negative real number a, to be equal to $(\sqrt[q]{a})^p$. [For example, $(-27)^{\frac{2}{3}} = (\sqrt[3]{-27})^2 = (-3)^2 = 9$.] It may be proved that statements 1 through 6 continue to be valid in all cases so far defined, except in some of those involving square roots and negative real bases. {For example, $(-8)^{\frac{1}{3}}(-8)^{\frac{1}{3}} = (-8)^{\frac{2}{3}}$ and $(-1)^{\frac{1}{2}}(-1)^{\frac{1}{2}} = -1$, but $(-1)^{\frac{1}{3}}(-2)^{\frac{1}{2}} \neq 2^{\frac{1}{2}}$ and $[(-8)^{\frac{2}{3}}]^{\frac{1}{2}} \neq (-8)^{\frac{1}{3}}$.}

Illustrative Examples:

$$8^{\frac{2}{3}} = (\sqrt[3]{8})^2 = 2^2 = 4$$

$$8^{-\frac{2}{3}} = \frac{1}{8^{\frac{2}{3}}} = \tfrac{1}{4}$$

$$(-8)^{\frac{2}{3}} = (\sqrt[3]{-8})^2 = (-2)^2 = 4$$

$$(a^{-\frac{3}{4}}b^2)^{-4} = (a^{-\frac{3}{4}})^{-4}(b^2)^{-4} = a^3 b^{-8} = \frac{a^3}{b^8} \quad \text{(if } a \text{ is any positive real number and } b \text{ is any nonzero complex number)}$$

$$\frac{a^{\frac{2}{3}}b^{-\frac{1}{3}}}{a^{-\frac{1}{3}}b^{\frac{2}{3}}} = \frac{a^{\frac{2}{3}}a^{\frac{1}{3}}}{b^{\frac{1}{3}}b^{\frac{2}{3}}} = \frac{a}{b} \quad \text{(if } a \text{ and } b \text{ are any nonzero real numbers)}$$

$$\frac{a^{-\frac{1}{3}} + a^{\frac{2}{3}}}{a^{\frac{5}{3}}} = \frac{a^{-\frac{1}{3}} + a^{\frac{2}{3}}}{a^{\frac{5}{3}}} \cdot \frac{a^{\frac{1}{3}}}{a^{\frac{1}{3}}} = \frac{1 + a}{a^2} \quad \text{(if } a \text{ is ?)}$$

6.5 RADICALS

Radicals are expressions of the form $\sqrt[n]{a}$. When problems involve radicals other than square roots, we generally find it helpful to replace radical by exponential notation.

Illustrative Examples:

$$\sqrt{2} \cdot \sqrt{6} = \sqrt{12} = \sqrt{4}\sqrt{3} = 2\sqrt{3} \quad \text{(see Section 5.4)}$$

But:

$$\sqrt{2} \cdot \sqrt[4]{4} = 2^{\frac{1}{2}} \cdot 4^{\frac{1}{4}} = 2^{\frac{1}{2}} \cdot (2^2)^{\frac{1}{4}} = 2^{\frac{1}{2}} \cdot 2^{\frac{1}{2}} = 2$$

$$\sqrt[3]{16} = (2^4)^{\frac{1}{3}} = 2^{\frac{4}{3}} = 2^1 \cdot 2^{\frac{1}{3}} = 2\sqrt[3]{2}$$

$$\frac{\sqrt[3]{-8ab^2}}{\sqrt[6]{a^2b^4}} = \frac{(-8)^{\frac{1}{3}}a^{\frac{1}{3}}b^{\frac{2}{3}}}{a^{\frac{2}{6}}b^{\frac{4}{6}}} = -2 \quad \text{(if } a \text{ and } b \text{ are positive real numbers)}$$

The following expression occurs in working out a problem of calculus:

$$\frac{(1 + x^2)^{\frac{2}{3}} - x(\frac{2}{3})(1 + x^2)^{-\frac{1}{3}}(2x)}{(1 + x^2)^{\frac{4}{3}}}$$

We simplify this expression by multiplying numerator and denominator by $3(1 + x^2)^{\frac{1}{3}}$ and arrive at:

$$\frac{3(1 + x^2) - x(2)(1 + x^2)^0(2x)}{3(1 + x^2)^{\frac{5}{3}}} = \frac{3(1 + x^2) - 4x^2}{3(1 + x^2)^{\frac{5}{3}}} = \frac{3 - x^2}{3(1 + x^2)^{\frac{5}{3}}}$$

For many purposes, this expression is sufficiently simple. We might, however, arrive at alternative simple forms of the expression by multiplying numerator and denominator by $(1 + x^2)^{\frac{1}{3}}$, arriving at

$$\frac{(3 - x^2)(1 + x^2)^{\frac{1}{3}}}{3(1 + x^2)^2} = \frac{(3 - x^2)\sqrt[3]{1 + x^2}}{3(1 + x^2)^2}$$

(The simplifications are valid for any real number x.)

6.6 REAL EXPONENTS

What shall we mean, now, by an expression like $2^{\sqrt{2}}$?

We approach this problem by means of approximations. We know that $\sqrt{2}$ lies between 1.4 and 1.5. Since 1.4 and 1.5 are rational numbers, our preceding section guarantees that $2^{1.4}$ and $2^{1.5}$ exist and are real numbers. Any number between $2^{1.4}$ and $2^{1.5}$, for example, $2^{1.4}$ itself, might therefore naturally serve as a first approximation to $2^{\sqrt{2}}$.

But $\sqrt{2}$ may be more narrowly pinched down between 1.41 and 1.42. A better approximation for $2^{\sqrt{2}}$ would therefore seem to be a number lying in the narrower range between $2^{1.41}$ and $2^{1.42}$, for example, $2^{1.41}$ itself, and so on.

In fact it may be proved that this process "pinches down on" a unique real number which we define to be $2^{\sqrt{2}}$.

If a is any positive real number unequal to 1, and r is any real number at all, we similarly define a^r by means of successive approximations.

The intuitive treatment sketched above may be rigorized by means of the following:

Theorem and Definition.   Suppose $a \neq 1$ is a positive real number and r is any real number.

Let A be the set of all real numbers a^x, where x may be any positive *rational* number less than r.

Let B be the set of all real numbers a^y, where y may be any positive *rational* number greater than r.

Then there is a unique real number between A and B which we define to be a^r.

It is worth noting that this new definition is consistent with the old; that is to say, if r happens to be rational, the preceding definition of a^r leads to the same result as the definition of Section 6.4.

Since all rational powers of 1 are equal to 1, we are led to define, for each real number r, $1^r = 1$.

Once more, it turns out that statements 1 through 6 continue to hold true, this time for a, b any positive real numbers, and m, n any real numbers.

Finally, since all positive integer powers and roots of 0 are equal to 0, we define, for each positive real number r, $0^r = 0$.

Summary: We have defined the expression a^m for a complex number a and a real number m, subject to the following restrictions:

If exponent is:	Base must be:
Not positive	Not zero
Not an integer	Real
Not rational, or rational with even denominator other than 2	Positive real

Statements 1 through 6 are valid (even with parenthetical conditions in 5a and 5b deleted) in all the cases in which we have defined exponents, except in some of those involving square roots and negative real bases.

▶ **EXERCISE 25**

1. Evaluate, or identify as not yet defined:

(a) 2^9	(b) -2^9	(c) $(-2)^9$
(d) -2^{-9}	(e) 2^8	(f) -2^8
(g) $(-2)^8$	(h) -2^{-8}	(i) 3^4
(j) 3^{-4}	(k) -3^4	(l) $(-3)^4$
(m) $2 \cdot 3^4$	(n) $2^3 \cdot 2^4$	(o) $(2^3)^4$
(p) 1^0	(q) 0^1	(r) 0^0
(s) 0^{-2}	(t) 1^1	(u) 1^{23}
(v) $(-1)^{23}$	(w) $(-1)^{24}$	(x) -1^{24}
(y) $2 \cdot 5^3$	(z) $2^3 \cdot 5^3$	(a') $2 \cdot 5^{-3}$
(b') $2^{-3} \cdot 5^{-3}$	(c') $3^2 + 7^2$	(d') $(3 + 7)^2$
(e') $\left(\dfrac{1}{\sqrt{2}}\right)^2$	(f') $\left(\dfrac{2}{\sqrt{2}}\right)^2$	(g') $\left(-\dfrac{1}{\sqrt{3}}\right)^2$
(h') $\left(-\dfrac{3}{\sqrt{3}}\right)^2$	(i') 10^{-1}	(j') 10^{-2}
(k') $(2^2)^{-3}$	(l') $(2^3)^{-2}$	(m') $3^2 \cdot 3^3$
(n') $(3^2)^3$	(o') $(2^2)^3$	(p') $2^2 \cdot 2^3$
(q') $4^{\frac{1}{2}}$	(r') $(-4)^{\frac{1}{2}}$	(s') $\left(\dfrac{1}{3}\right)^{-4}$
(t') $\left(-\dfrac{1}{8}\right)^{\frac{2}{3}}$	(u') $\left(-\dfrac{4}{9}\right)^2$	(v') $\left(-\dfrac{4}{9}\right)^{-2}$
(w') $\left(\dfrac{4}{9}\right)^{\frac{1}{2}}$	(x') $\left(-\dfrac{4}{9}\right)^{\frac{1}{2}}$	(y') $\left(-\dfrac{4}{9}\right)^{-\frac{1}{2}}$
(z') $(-1)^{\frac{1}{4}}$		

2. Express in simple form without using negative or fractional exponents, and in each case state conditions on a and b under which the two expressions are equal:

(a) a^{-2}	(b) $a^{\frac{1}{2}}$	(c) $a^{-\frac{1}{2}}$
(d) $\dfrac{a^6}{a^3}$	(e) $\dfrac{a^3}{a^6}$	(f) $\dfrac{a^3}{a^3}$
(g) $\left(\dfrac{1}{a+b}\right)^{-1}$	(h) $\left(\dfrac{1}{a+b}\right)^{-2}$	(i) ab^{-1}
(j) $(ab)^{-1}$	(k) $\dfrac{11}{a^{-1}}$	(l) $\dfrac{a^{-1}}{11}$
(m) $\left(\dfrac{a^{-1}}{2}\right)^{-1}$	(n) $a \cdot 10^{-2}$	(o) $a^{-1} + b^{-1}$
(p) $(a + b)^{-1}$	(q) $\dfrac{a^{-1}}{b^{-1}}$	(r) $\dfrac{a}{b^{-1}}$
(s) $a^{-1}a^{-2}$	(t) $(a^{-1})^{-2}$	(u) $\dfrac{a^{-1} + b^{-1}}{a^{-1}b^{-1}}$

(v) $\dfrac{a^{-1}b^2}{ab^{-2}}$ (w) $(a^{-2})^{-3}a^4$ (x) $\dfrac{(a^2)^{-3}}{a^4}$

(y) $(a^{-\frac{1}{3}})^6$ (z) $\dfrac{a^{-\frac{3}{2}}}{a^{-\frac{1}{3}}}$ (a') $a^{-\frac{3}{2}}a^{-\frac{1}{3}}$

(b') $(a^{-\frac{3}{2}})^{-\frac{1}{3}}$ (c') $a^{\frac{6}{5}}$ (d') $a^{\frac{2}{6}}$

(e') $\dfrac{a^{-\frac{1}{2}}}{b^{-\frac{1}{2}}}$ (f') $a^{-\frac{1}{2}}b^{\frac{1}{2}}$ (g') $\dfrac{a^{-\frac{1}{3}}b}{ab^{-\frac{1}{3}}}$

(h') $\dfrac{a^{\frac{1}{2}} + a^{-\frac{1}{2}}}{a^{-\frac{1}{2}}}$ (i') $\left(\dfrac{a^{\frac{1}{2}}b^{-\frac{1}{2}}}{ab}\right)^2$ (j') $(a + b)^{-\frac{1}{2}}$

(k') $a^{-\frac{1}{2}} + b^{-\frac{1}{2}}$ (l') $a^{-\frac{1}{2}}b^{-\frac{1}{2}}$ (m') $\dfrac{a^{-\frac{1}{2}}b}{b^{-\frac{1}{2}}a}$

(n') $(a - b)^{-\frac{2}{3}}$

3. Express in simple form using negative and fractional exponents and, where appropriate, state conditions on a and b under which the two expressions are equal:

(a) $\dfrac{1}{a}$ (b) $\sqrt{a}$ (c) $\dfrac{a}{b}$

(d) $\sqrt[3]{a}$ (e) $\sqrt{a + b}$ (f) $\dfrac{2}{\sqrt{a + b}}$

(g) $\dfrac{1}{a^3}$ (h) $\sqrt[3]{a^2}$ (i) $\sqrt[4]{a^3}$

(j) $\dfrac{1}{\sqrt[3]{a^3}}$ (k) $\dfrac{1}{\sqrt[3]{a}}$ (l) $\left(\dfrac{1}{\sqrt[3]{a}}\right)^6$

(m) $(\sqrt[3]{a^2})^{\frac{1}{2}}$ (n) $(\sqrt{a^3})^4$ (o) $(\sqrt{a^4})^3$

(p) $\sqrt{a}\sqrt[3]{a}$ (q) $\dfrac{1}{\sqrt{a}}$ (r) $\dfrac{2}{\sqrt{ab}}$

(s) $\dfrac{3}{10}$ (t) 0.02 (u) $\dfrac{a}{b^2}$

(v) $\dfrac{1}{a} + \dfrac{1}{b}$ (w) $\dfrac{1}{a + b}$ (x) $\dfrac{1}{ab}$

4. Simplify and state the types of numbers for which your simplification is valid:

(a) $a^2 \cdot a^5$ (b) $\dfrac{a^5}{a^2}$ (c) $\dfrac{a^2}{a^5}$

(d) $a^{-2}a^5$ (e) $\dfrac{a^5}{a^{-2}}$ (f) $(a^2)^5$

(g) $a^{-2} + a^{-5}$ (h) $(ab^2c^3)^4$ (i) $\dfrac{ab^2c^3}{a^3b^2c}$

(j) $\left(\dfrac{a^{-2}}{a^{-5}}\right)^{\frac{2}{3}}$ (k) $(-2ab^2)^2$ (l) $-2(ab^2)^2$

(m) $(2a^2b)(3ab^2)^2$ (n) $\dfrac{(-2ab)^2}{2(ab)^2}$ (o) $\dfrac{a^{\frac{1}{3}}b^{\frac{2}{3}}}{a^{-\frac{2}{3}}b^{-\frac{1}{3}}}$

(p) $\left(\dfrac{3a^2}{-b}\right)^3\left(\dfrac{b^3}{-a}\right)^2$ (q) $\dfrac{(2a^4b^5)^2}{(ab^2)^3(2ab)^2}$ (r) $(a^2b^2)^{\frac{1}{2}}$

(s) $\sqrt[4]{16a^5}$ (t) $\sqrt{10a}\,\sqrt[3]{10a}$ (u) $\sqrt[3]{4a}\,\sqrt[3]{16a^2}$

(v) $\sqrt[3]{16a^5}$ (w) $\sqrt{6ab}\,\sqrt[3]{12a^2b^2}$ (x) $\dfrac{\sqrt[3]{12a^2b^2}}{\sqrt{6ab}}$

(y) $\dfrac{(x^2+1)^{\frac{1}{2}} - x(\frac{1}{2})(x^2+1)^{-\frac{1}{2}}(2x)}{x^2+1}$

(z) $\dfrac{(x^2+1)^{\frac{1}{3}} - x(\frac{1}{3})(x^2+1)^{-\frac{2}{3}}(2x)}{(x^2+1)^{\frac{2}{3}}}$

5. Recalling that $i^2 = -1$, express each of the following, using no power of i higher than the first:

(a) i^3 (Hint: $i^3 = i^2 \cdot i$)

(b) i^4 (c) i^5 (d) i^6 (e) i^7

(f) i^8 (g) i^9 (h) i^{10} (i) i^{11}

(j) i^{20} (k) i^{25} (l) i^{50} (m) i^{101}

(n) i^{-1} (Hint: $i^{-1} = i^{-1} \cdot 1 = i^{-1} \cdot i^4 = i^3$)

(o) i^{-2} (p) i^{-3} (q) i^{-4} (r) i^{-101}

6.(a) Devise a rule for evaluating i^n, for any positive integer n.

(b) Extend the rule so that it applies to any integer n.

7. Every positive real number may be written in the form $a \cdot 10^b$, where $1 \leqslant a < 10$, and b is an integer. This form is called the *scientific notation* for positive real numbers. In each of the following cases, transform from scientific to ordinary decimal notation, or vice versa:

(a) $2 \cdot 10^2$ (b) 3000 (c) $3 \cdot 10^{-2}$

(d) 0.02 (e) 0.025 (f) 1

(g) 10 (h) 100 (i) 25

(j) $186,000$ (k) $93,000,000$ (l) $2.837 \cdot 10^{-6}$

(m) $6.78 \cdot 10^0$ (n) 0.0000567 (o) 12.04

8. Calculate by writing each number in scientific notation:

(a) $\dfrac{123,000 \times 0.0002}{0.0246}$ (b) $\dfrac{5000 \times 0.002}{2,000,000 \times 0.0005}$

9.(a) Under certain standard conditions of temperature and pressure, 1 cubic centimeter of any gas contains 2.69×10^{19} molecules (see in chemistry texts, "Avogadro's hypothesis"). If one hydrogen molecule weighs $3.32 \cdot 10^{-24}$ gram, find the weight of 1 cubic centimeter of hydrogen.

(b) One cubic yard is equal to 7.646×10^5 cubic centimeters. One gram is equal to $3.53 \cdot 10^{-2}$ oz. Find the weight in ounces of 1 cubic yard of hydrogen.

(c) If it were possible to count 10 molecules in a second, how many years would it take to count all the molecules in 1 cubic centimeter of a gas (under standard conditions)?

10.(a) The distance from the earth to the sun is about $9.3 \cdot 10^7$ miles. Light travels at about 1.86×10^5 miles per second. How long does it take light from the sun to reach the earth?

(b) The very large unit of distance called the "light-year" is the distance traveled by light in a year, and is equal to 5.88×10^{12} miles. The bright star Betelgeuse is at a distance of 300 light years from the earth. If a person on earth sights the star on January 1, 1975, on what date, approximately, did the light observed leave Betelgeuse?

11. A function f whose mapping is given by an equation $f(x) = a^x$ is called an *exponential function with base a*. Following traditional practice, we shall speak of "the function a^x" when we mean the function f whose mapping is given by $f(x) = a^x$, and whose domain (unless otherwise mentioned) is *maximal*; i.e., whose domain is the set of *all* real numbers for which a^x is defined.

Sketch a representative portion of the graph of each of the following functions, and in each case state the range of the given function, and whether it is one-one or many-one:

(a) 2^x (b) 3^x

(c) 4^x (Use some nonintegral values of x, i.e., values other than integers, in your table of values.)

(d) 8^x (Use some nonintegral values of x in your table of values.)

(e) $\left(\frac{1}{2}\right)^x$ (f) $\left(\frac{1}{3}\right)^x$

(g) $\left(\frac{1}{4}\right)^x$

(h) $\left(\frac{1}{8}\right)^x$ } (Use some nonintegral values of x in your table of values.)

(i) 2^{-x} (j) 3^{-x}

12. Use your results in Problem 11 to induce the answers to the following questions:

(a) If a is a real number such that $a > 1$, describe the graph of the function a^x.

(b) If a is a positive real number such that $a < 1$, describe the graph of the function a^x.

(c) What may be said about the range of any exponential function a^x if a is real and positive but $\neq 1$? Will this function a^x be always one-one, always many-one, or sometimes one and sometimes the other?

(d) Describe the relation between the graph of a^x and the graph of a^{-x}.

13. Sketch a representative portion of the graph of each of the following

functions, and in each case state the range of the given function, and whether it is one-one or many-one:

(a) $2 \cdot 2^z$

(b) $2 \cdot 2^{-z}$

(c) $-3 \cdot 2^z$

(d) 2^{z^2} [This means $2^{(z^2)}$]

(e) 2^{-z^2} ("Bell" curve)

(f) $2^z + 2^{-z}$

(g) $2^z - 2^{-z}$

14. Describe the relation between the graph of $c \cdot a^z$ and the graph of a^z, where c is a nonzero real number.

15. Suppose $f(x) = 2^z + 2^{-z}$, $g(x) = 2^z - 2^{-z}$. Find:

(a) $f(x) + g(x)$

(b) $f(x) - g(x)$

(c) $f(x) \cdot g(x)$

(d) $[f(x)]^2$

(e) $[g(x)]^2$

(f) $[f(x)]^2 + [g(x)]^2$

(g) $[f(x)]^2 - [g(x)]^2$

*16. Describe the graph of the exponential function $(-2)^z$.

*17. Write out one or more of the proofs in the preceding section that have been left as exercises for the student.

*18. Suppose we define natural number exponentiation as follows: $a^1 = a$; $a^{k+1} = a^k \cdot a$, for each nn k. (Such a definition, which enables us to compute successive results from earlier results is called a *recursive* definition; see Exercise 14, Problem 3.) Using this definition and the Principle of Mathematical Induction, prove that, if a, b are complex numbers, m, n nn, then:

(a) $a^m a^n = a^{m+n}$ [*Hint:* Use "induction on n," i.e., prove that if a and b are given complex numbers, and m is a given nn, then the set S of all nn n for which (a) is true contains all nn.]

(b) $(a^m)^n = a^{mn}$

(c) $(ab)^m = a^m b^m$

6.7 NEW FUNCTIONS FROM OLD: INVERSES AND COMPOSITES

At this point we introduce two very general methods which may often be used to derive new functions from given functions. In the next section we shall use one of these methods to derive from the exponential type of function another well-known class of functions of great importance in both pure and applied mathematics.

First of all, we point out that, whenever we have given a one-one function, it is possible to define another function called its *inverse*, simply by interchanging the domain and range of the given function and "reversing" its mapping. If the original function is denoted f, then its inverse is denoted f^{-1} (read: "f inverse").

For example, suppose f is a function whose domain is the set of names

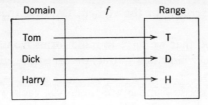

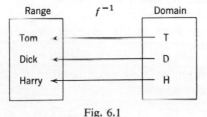

Fig. 6.1

{Tom, Dick, Harry}, and whose mapping assigns to each name its initial letter. Then in Fig. 6.1 we see a diagram of the function f, and then, derived from it, a diagram of the function f^{-1}.

Now we can see the motivation for the use of a double arrow in diagramming one-to-one correspondences: It is simply to indicate the two one-one functions, each other's inverses, which are associated with every one-to-one correspondence.

In fact, one-to-one correspondences and one-one functions are essentially the same: Whenever A and B are sets which are in one-to-one correspondence, then a one-one function exists with domain A and range B, and vice versa.

Now we frame a formal definition for the inverse of a given one-one function f:

Let f be a one-one function with range B.

Then we define the function f^{-1} (called "the inverse of f"; read: "f inverse") in the following way:

(i) f^{-1} has domain B;

(ii) if b is a member of B, we define $f^{-1}(b)$ to be the unique pre-image of b under the function f.

Thus $\qquad f(a) = b \quad$ if and only if $\quad f^{-1}(b) = a$

That is, $\qquad a \xrightarrow{f} b \quad$ if and only if $\quad a \xleftarrow{f^{-1}} b$

It is left as an exercise for the student to prove that f^{-1} must also be one-one.

The other method that we have in mind forms from an ordered pair of functions (f, g) in certain cases a function called the *composite* of f and g, and denoted fg.

For example, suppose f and g are functions, each with domain the set of all complex numbers and with mappings given by: $f(x) = x^2$, $g(x) = x + 1$.

Then in this situation f and g may "operate" or "work" sequentially on any complex number; that is, we may first allow g to work on a given number and then f to work on the result, or vice versa, as follows:

$$f[g(3)] = f(4) = 16 \qquad g[f(3)] = g(9) = 10$$

In fact, we may compute in advance the effect of either of these sequential operations on any number x:

$$f[g(x)] = f(x + 1) = (x + 1)^2 \qquad g[f(x)] = g(x^2) = x^2 + 1$$

Thus: $f[g(3)] = (3 + 1)^2 = 16$, and $g[f(3)] = 3^2 + 1 = 10$, agreeing, of course, with our previous results.

Now the new function fg that we have in mind would be, in the example we are considering, the function whose domain is the set of all complex numbers, and whose mapping is given by: $fg(x) = f[g(x)]$ that is to say, $fg(x) = (x + 1)^2$; and gf would be the function whose domain is the set of all complex numbers, and whose mapping is given by: $gf(x) = g[f(x)]$ that is to say, $gf(x) = x^2 + 1$.

More generally, given any two functions f, g, we define their composite fg to be the function whose mapping is given by $fg(x) = f[g(x)]$, and whose domain is the set of all x such that $f[g(x)]$ is defined [i.e., the set of all x such that x is in the domain of g and $g(x)$ is in the domain of f].

*In certain special cases, the situation becomes simpler. For example, suppose the range of g happens to be a subset of the domain of f. Then, of course, for *all* x in the domain of g, $g(x)$ is in the domain of f. In this case, therefore, the domain of fg is simply the domain of g. We state this important result formally, using the notation $D(f)$, $R(f)$ to denote the domain and range, respectively, of a function f.

*Theorem. If f and g are functions such that $R(g) \subset D(f)$, then $D(fg) = D(g)$.

▶ **EXERCISE 26**

1. Referring to Exercise 4, Problem 10, find:

(a) $f[g(3)]$ (b) $g[f(3)]$ (c) $f[g(x)]$

(d) $g[f(x)]$ (e) $f[g(5)]$ (f) $g[f(5)]$

(g) $g[h(3)]$ (h) $h[g(3)]$ (i) $g[h(x)]$
(j) $h[g(x)]$ (k) $h[g(5)]$ (l) $g[h(5)]$

2. Suppose: $f(x) = 2^x$, the domain of f is the set of all real numbers, $g(x) = 2x - 3$, and the domain of g is the set of all complex numbers.

(a) Find $fg(1)$, $gf(1)$.

(b) Find $fg(x)$, $gf(x)$.

(c) What is the domain of fg? of gf?

3. In Exercise 4, Problem 11, in the case of each function f that has an inverse:

(a) Write a table of values for f^{-1}.

(b) On the same ccs, draw the graphs of f and f^{-1} in different colors.

(c) How are the graphs of f and f^{-1} always related?

*4. Prove that, if f is a one-one function, its inverse, f^{-1} must also be one-one. [*Hint:* See the discussion in reduced print preceding Section 2.2; let $k = f^{-1}(a) - f^{-1}(b)$.]

*5.(a) Which of the functions of Exercise 4, Problem 10, have inverses?

(b) Find the inverse of each of the functions you have named in (a). [We offer one solution as an illustration: f is one of the functions named that has an inverse. f^{-1} has as domain the set of all odd nn. Mapping: $f^{-1}(x) = (x + 1)/2.$]

*6.(a) The most important fact about inverse functions is that, when a function and its inverse are applied sequentially to an element, they leave the element unchanged.

More precisely· If b is an element of the range of a one-one function f, then $f[f^{-1}(b)] = b$; and if a is an element of the domain of f, then $f^{-1}[f(a)] = a$.

Show that this is so.

(b) An important function defined on a set S is the function that maps each element of S to itself. This function, which we shall denote I_S, is called the *identity function on S*. Thus, I_S has domain S, and if a is any element of S, then $I_S(a) = a$.

Suppose f is a one-one function with domain D and range R. Prove this sharper statement of (a):

$$ff^{-1} = I_R \qquad f^{-1}f = I_D$$

(*Hint:* Use Section 2.3 and the theorem preceding Exercise 26.)

(c) Show that the inverse of the inverse of a function is equal to the function itself; i.e., show that if $g = f^{-1}$, then $g^{-1} = f$.

(d) Prove that, if f is a function with domain D and range R, then $fI_D = f$, and $I_R f = f$.

(e) Prove that for functions whose domain and range are the same set S, composition of functions is associative. {*Hint:* Show first that, if

f, g, h are functions with domain S and range S, then fg, gh, $(fg)h$, and $f(gh)$ each have domain S; next, assuming $s \in S$, $h(s) = t$, $g(t) = u$, and $f(u) = v$, find $gh(s)$, $fg(t)$, $[(fg)h](s)$, and $[f(gh)](s)$.}

(f) Prove that the composite of one-one functions is one-one. (*Hint:* See the discussion in reduced print preceding Section 2.2.)

6.8 THE LOGARITHMIC FUNCTION

If a is a positive real number, and $a \neq 1$, the graph of the exponential function with base a indicates, (see Exercise 25, Problem 12 and Fig. 6.2), and it may be rigorously proved, that this function is one-one, that its (maximal) domain is the set of all real numbers, and that its corresponding range is the set of all positive real numbers. (From now on we shall assume that the base a of each function a^x that we shall consider is a positive real number and is $\neq 1$.)

We abbreviate "the exponential function with base a" to "$\exp_a$," and we shall make use of this abbreviation as follows:

Just as we call the image that a function f assigns to x, $f(x)$, so we call the image that the function $\exp_a$ assigns to x, $\exp_a x$ (read: "exponent to the base a of x"). Thus:

(1) $$\exp_a x = a^x \qquad x \xrightarrow{\exp_a} a^x$$

For example, $\exp_2 3 = 2^3 = 8$, $\exp_{10} 2 = 10^2 = 100$.

In fact, in most cases we dispense with the expression "$\exp_a x$," using in its place its synonym "a^x". However, we shall find the notation "$\exp_a x$" useful in defining the "logarithmic function with base a".

Since the function $\exp_a$ is one-one, it has an inverse (see Section 6.7) which we call the *logarithmic function with base a*, abbreviated: $\log_a$.

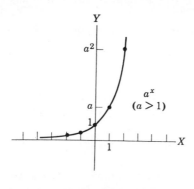

Fig. 6.2

Since $\exp_a$ and $\log_a$ are each other's inverses, (1) above is equivalent to:

(2) $$\log_a (a^x) = x \qquad x \xleftarrow{\log_a} a^x$$

For example, the statements $\exp_2 3 = 8$ and $\exp_{10} 2 = 100$ are respectively equivalent to $\log_2 8 = 3$ and $\log_{10} 100 = 2$.

In fact: $\exp_a x = N$ and $\log_a N = x$ are equivalent statements; and since $\exp_a x = a^x$, we have the following important relation which enables us to transform exponential to logarithmic expressions, and vice versa:

$$a^x = N \Leftrightarrow \log_a N = x$$

Immediate consequence: $a^{\log_a N} = N$.

This equation brings us to the well-known description of a logarithm as an exponent. In fact $\log_a N$ is equal to the (*unique*) exponent that when applied to the base a yields the number N. Hence, the fact that $2^3 = 8$, i.e., the fact that 3 is the exponent that when applied to 2 yields 8, tells us that $\log_2 8 = 3$; and to find, for example, $\log_{10} 100$, we ask: What exponent applied to the base 10 yields the number 100? The answer, of course, is 2. Therefore $\log_{10} 100 = 2$.

The same reasoning, or the use of the equation $\log_a (a^x) = x$, enables us to say immediately, for example: $\log_{10} (10^2) = 2$, $\log_7 (7^{11}) = 11$, $\log_{10} (10^{1.1}) = 1.1$, $\log_2 (2^{\sqrt{2}}) = \sqrt{2}$.

Since $\log_a$ and $\exp_a$ are each other's inverses, (p, q) will be a point on the graph of $\exp_a$ if and only if (q, p) is a point on the graph of $\log_a$. This information enables us to derive the graph of the function $\log_a x$ quite easily from the graph of the function $\exp_a x$ (see Fig. 6.3). In fact, it may be proved that the graphs of any pair of inverse functions are symmetric with respect to the straight line l whose equation is $y = x$; that is to say, if the line l were a mirror, the graphs would be each other's reflections in l; or alternatively expressed, if the paper on which the graphs are drawn

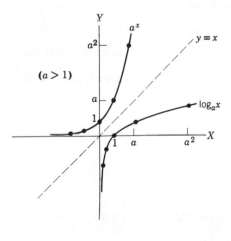

Fig. 6.3

were folded over and creased on l, the graphs of inverse functions would coincide (see Exercise 26, Problem 3c).

Note that the function $\log_a$, being the inverse of a one-one function, must be a one-one function also.

▶ **EXERCISE 27**

1. Find:

(a) $\log_2 (\frac{1}{8})$ (b) $\log_2 (\frac{1}{4})$ (c) $\log_2 (\frac{1}{2})$

(d) $\log_2 (1)$ (e) $\log_2 (2)$ (f) $\log_2 (4)$

(g) $\log_2 (8)$ (h) $\log_2 (0)$ (i) $\log_2 (-1)$

(j) $\log_{10} (0.001)$ (k) $\log_{10} (0.01)$ (l) $\log_{10} (0.1)$

(m) $\log_{10} (1)$ (n) $\log_{10} (10)$ (o) $\log_{10} (100)$

(p) $\log_{10} (1000)$ (q) $\log_{10} (0)$ (r) $\log_{10} (-1)$

2. Translate into logarithmic statements:

(a) $10^z = 5$ (b) $2^{10} = 1024$

(c) $10^{0.3010} \doteq 2$ (d) $2^{0.5000} \doteq 1.414$

3. Translate into exponential statements:

(a) $\log_{10} 3 \doteq 0.4771$ (b) $\log_{10} 5 \doteq 0.6990$

(c) $\log_{10} x = y$ (d) $\log_2 x = y$

4. Draw the graphs of each pair of functions on the same cc system:

(a) 2^z and $\log_2 x$ (b) 10^z and $\log_{10} x$

5. Draw the graphs of the following functions:

(a) $3 \log_2 x$ (b) $0.1 \log_{10} x$

(c) $\log_2 \left(\frac{x}{3}\right)$ (d) $\log_{10} (5x)$

*6. Describe the graph of the function $\log_a x$, when $a < 1$.

*7. Prove: $(\log_a b)(\log_b a) = 1$. (*Hint:* Let $\log_a b = x$, $\log_b a = y$, so that $a^x = b$, $b^y = a$.)

*8. Prove:

$$\log_b N = \frac{\log_a N}{\log_a b}$$

*9. What property of the function $\exp_a$ justifies our statement that the exponent whose application to the base a results in the number N is *unique*?

*10. Name the domain and the range of $\exp_a$; of $\log_a$.

6.9 LOGARITHMIC COMPUTATION

Consider the table of values:

x	2^x
-3	$\frac{1}{8}$
-2	$\frac{1}{4}$
-1	$\frac{1}{2}$
0	1
1	2
2	4
3	8
4	16
5	32
6	64
7	128
8	256
9	512
10	1024

First of all we note that, in this table of values, each number on the left is the $\log_2$ of the number on its right; for example: $\log_2\left(\frac{1}{4}\right) = -2$.

Next, observe what happens when two numbers on the right are multiplied. For example, when we multiply 4 (whose $\log_2$ is 2) by 8 (whose $\log_2$ is 3), the result is 32 (whose $\log_2$ is 5).

In fact, the student may verify that, whenever we multiply two numbers on the right, the corresponding numbers on the left, i.e., the corresponding logarithms, are added.

This may be used to reduce the labor involved in multiplying numbers on the right. For example, to multiply 16 by 32, we add their logarithms in the table above: $4 + 5 = 9$, and find the product $16 \cdot 32$ opposite 9: $16 \cdot 32 = 512$.

Our use of logarithms has converted a multiplication problem into an easier addition problem. Of course, our miniature table will not permit us to do too much of this sort of thing, but we will shortly make use of a considerably more detailed table.

We should not be surprised to discover that (roughly speaking) multiplying numbers implies adding their logarithms; for logarithms may be thought of as exponents and (again roughly speaking), when we multiply numbers with the same base, we add exponents. We would expect, then, that to divide numbers (still roughly speaking) we should subtract exponents.

In the table above, for example, to divide 512 by 16, we find the difference of their corresponding logarithms: $9 - 4 = 5$; the result opposite 5 is 32 and, indeed, $512 \div 16 = 32$.

The following theorems now make precise what we have been saying.

Log Theorem 1. If p, q are positive real numbers, then:

$$\log_a (pq) = \log_a p + \log_a q$$

PROOF. Let $x = \log_a p$, $y = \log_a q$, $z = \log_a (pq)$.
Then

$$a^x = p \qquad a^y = q \qquad a^z = pq$$

$$\therefore \; a^z = a^x \cdot a^y = a^{x+y}$$

But since the exponential function with base a is one-one, $z = x + y$; i.e., $\log_a (pq) = \log_a p + \log_a q$, Q.E.D.

Log Theorem 2. If p, q are positive real numbers, then:

$$\log_a \left(\frac{p}{q}\right) = \log_a p - \log_a q$$

PROOF. Left as an exercise.

Two other theorems which also follow from the relations between logarithms and exponents, and which are useful in computation, are the following (proofs are left as exercises):

Log Theorem 3. If p is a positive real number and r is any real number whatever, then:

$$\log_a (p^r) = r \cdot \log_a p$$

Log Theorem 4. If p is a positive real number and n is a nn, then:

$$\log_a \sqrt[n]{p} = (\log_a p) \div n$$

(*Note.* Log Theorem 4 may be proved as a corollary of Log Theorem 3.) Now we shall apply these log theorems to problems of computation.

In order to do so, we shall make use of a table of logarithms. Actually, tables of logarithms are generally available only for the base $a = 10$ and for another base called "e". The latter is a number which is approximately 2.7; its use in the calculus simplifies many formulas.

From this point on, we shall restrict ourselves, unless otherwise noted, to the base 10 in working with logarithms. In fact, from now on we shall omit the base designation when we wish to indicate a logarithm to the base 10; i.e., $\log x$ will mean $\log_{10} x$.

In computing with the help of logarithms, our first task is to learn the use of the table.

The table we shall use actually gives logarithms of numbers between 1 and 10; the student may imagine a decimal point placed after the first digit of each entry in the column headed N; and to the right of N, a second decimal place may be found.

For example, to find log 1.23, we run down the N column until we come to 12, and then we run across the page to the reading in the column headed 3. There we discover the reading 0899. Here a decimal point has actually been omitted, for obvious reasons. All readings within the body of the table are to be understood as being prefixed by a decimal point. Finally, then:

$$\log 1.23 = .0899$$

But a word of caution: all values in the table, with the exception of one (which one?), are approximations, correct to four decimal places, and not exact. It would be better to write $\log 1.23 \doteq .0899$, but the traditional usage will lead to no trouble if one keeps in mind that the equality here is only approximate.

Now what about numbers not between 1 and 10? Their logarithms may easily be derived from the ones we have available, using the obvious facts that $\log 100 = 2$, $\log 1000 = 3$, $\log 0.1 = -1$, $\log 0.01 = -2$, etc.

For example:

$$\begin{aligned}
\log 12.3 &= \log (10 \cdot 1.23) \\
&= \log 10 + \log 1.23 \text{ (by Log Theorem 1)} \\
&= 1 + .0899 \\
&= 1.0899 \\
\log 123 &= \log (100 \cdot 1.23) \\
&= \log 100 + \log 1.23 \\
&= 2 + .0899 \\
&= 2.0899 \\
\log 1230 &= \log (1000 \cdot 1.23) \\
&= \log 1000 + \log 1.23 \\
&= 3 + .0899 \\
&= 3.0899 \\
\log 0.123 &= \log \left(\frac{1.23}{10}\right) \\
&= \log 1.23 - \log 10 \text{ (by Log Theorem 2)} \\
&= .0899 - 1 \\
&= -.9101
\end{aligned}$$

In the following we shall find that we rarely want to carry out the computation of a logarithm to an ultimate negative result, as in this last case. The reason is that such a value cannot be found in our table of logarithms which contains only *positive* real numbers. Unless some good reason exists for doing otherwise, then, we shall stop short at:

$$\log 0.123 = .0899 - 1$$

A last example:

$$\log 0.0123 = \log \left(\frac{1.23}{100}\right)$$
$$= \log 1.23 - \log 100$$
$$= .0899 - 2$$

In general, we may write all logarithms in the form $k + m$, where k is an integer and m is a decimal between 0 and 1; k is called the *characteristic* of the logarithm, m the *mantissa*.

For example, log 1.23 has a characteristic of 0 and a mantissa equal to .0899; log 123 has a characteristic of 2 and a mantissa of .0899; log 0.123 has a characteristic of -1 and a mantissa of .0899.

It is easy to see that when decimal numbers differ only in the position of their decimal points, all the logarithms of these numbers have the same mantissa. We may find the mantissa of the logarithm of a decimal number, then, simply by disregarding the decimal point and using the table of logarithms (which might more accurately be called a table of mantissas).

A short-cut rule for finding the characteristic of the logarithm of a number in decimal form is easy to derive. From the examples given, it may be seen that the following rule holds.

To find the characteristic of the logarithm of a positive decimal, place an arrow to the right of the first nonzero digit; count the number of digits from arrow to decimal point; $+$, if to the right and $-$, if to the left. The result is the characteristic of the logarithm of the positive decimal.

For example, the characteristic of log 0.01$\overset{\uparrow}{2}$3 is -2. Therefore log 0.0123 = .0899 $- 2$; the characteristic of log 1$\overset{\uparrow}{2}$30 is 3. Therefore log 1230 = 3.0899.

Note that it would lead to an incorrect result to write a negative characteristic immediately before the mantissa, as we may do in the case of a positive characteristic. In the case of log 0.123, for example, this would lead to the number -1.0899, whereas we have seen that $-.9101$ is correct. We shall therefore always write negative characteristics *following* the mantissa.

What about finding something like log 12.34? There is no trouble about the characteristic, which we know to be 1. We may even go further: Since 12.34 lies between 12.3 and 12.4, log 12.34 must lie between log 12.3

and log 12.4 (i.e., the logarithmic function " preserves order "—a fact we shall use, but not prove).   Thus, using our table of logarithms, we know that the mantissa of log 12.34 lies between .0899 and .0934.   But how far between?   We use the method of *linear interpolation* to arrive at an approximation to the correct answer.

The method of linear interpolation assumes that the values in both domain and range of a (real-real) function change proportionately; that is to say, if a, b, c are numbers in the domain with respective images, a', b', c', and b is some fraction of the way between a and c, then b' will be the same fraction of the way between a' and c'.

For example, 12.34 is .4 of the way between 12.3 and 12.4.   The mantissa we seek, by the method of linear interpolation, should be .4 of the way between .0899 and .0934.   The "way between" the mantissas is their difference .0035; .4 of the way between is .4 (.0035), or .0014.   The mantissa we seek is therefore .0014 further than .0899, i.e., .0899 + .0014, or .0913.   Therefore log 12.34 = 1.0913.

The work may be arranged as follows, although with a little practice all or most of it, can be done mentally:

	Number	Mantissa of Log
	12.40	.0934
.10 [.04 [12.34	x] d] .0035
	12.30	.0899

$$\frac{.04}{.10} = .4; \quad d = .4(.0035) = .0014; \quad x = .0899 + .0014 = .0913.$$

The method of linear interpolation is so called because it actually assumes that, if the three entries in question were graphed, the corresponding points would lie on a straight line.   For most tables of values, this, of course, is not the case.   However, for most tables of values, very small sections of the graph do approximate a straight-line segment, and that is why linear interpolation is useful.   Remember, however, that its results are not guaranteed, but generally are more and more trustworthy as the numbers we work with come closer and closer together.

(The student will find it interesting to check the accuracy of some of his interpolations with a five-place table, especially those in that part of the table where gaps are largest.)

In finding something like log 12.347, there is no point in interpolating .47 of the way between log 12.3 and log 12.4, since this would impute an accuracy to the method of linear interpolation which it just does not have.

In cases like this (with our table), we would round off to four digits and find log 12.35 by interpolation.

NOTE: It is assumed that the student is familiar with the "rounding-off" process by which a decimal is replaced by one with fewer decimal places. We round off, for example, 1.23, when we require the best possible one-decimal place approximation, to 1.2; and with the same requirement we round off 2.351 to 2.4, since 2.351 is between 2.3 and 2.4, but nearer 2.4.

But what shall we do with a number like 2.45, when we seek a one-decimal place approximation? The number 2.45 is exactly mid-way between 2.4 and 2.5. In such cases, mainly for the sake of uniformity, we agree always to choose that possibility which makes the last digit an *even* digit. Thus we shall round off 2.45 to 2.4, and 2.35 to 2.4 also.

Now we are ready to compute logarithmically.

Illustrative Example 1:

To compute: $(24.67)(0.0183)$ (let P represent this product).

SOLUTION. $\log 24.67 = 1.3922$

$\log 0.0183 = .2625 - 2$

Note. Set down characteristics before looking up mantissas.

$\log P \quad = 1.6547 - 2$ (by Log Theorem 1)

$\quad\quad\quad = .6547 - 1$

$\therefore P \quad\quad = .4516$

.6547 is located between .6542 and .6551 in table of mantissas; then we interpolate between 451 and 452 to find P. Finally, the decimal point in P is determined by the characteristic –1.

Illustrative Example 2:

To compute: $\dfrac{24.67}{0.0183}$ (let Q represent this quotient).

SOLUTION. $\log 24.67 = 1.3922$

$\log 0.0183 = .2625 - 2$

$\log Q \quad = 1.1297 + 2$ (by Log Theorem 2)

$\quad\quad\quad = 3.1297$

$\therefore Q \quad\quad = 1348$

Illustrative Example 3:

To compute: $\dfrac{0.0183}{24.67}$ (let Q represent this quotient).

SOLUTION. $\log 0.0183 = .2625 - 2$
$\log 24.67 = 1.3922$

But here, if we subtract as things stand, we will not immediately arrive at the mantissa we seek. The trouble is that the positive number to be subtracted is larger than the positive number from which it is to be subtracted. This may easily be remedied by expressing the characteristic -2 of $\log 0.0183$ differently; $2 - 4$, for example, will do:

$$\log 0.0183 = 2.2625 - 4$$
$$\log 24.67 = 1.3922$$
$$\log Q = .8703 - 4$$
$$\therefore Q = 0.0007418$$
$$\uparrow$$

Illustrative Example 4:
To compute: 2^{50}.

SOLUTION. $\log 2 = .3010$
$\log 2^{50} = 50 \log 2 = 15.0500$ (by Log Theorem 3)

Counting off 15 places, however, would result in a number of awkward length. We, therefore, express the result as $10^{15} \cdot N$, where $\log N = .0500$. Hence:

$$2^{50} = 1.122 \cdot 10^{15}$$

(This method may be justified as follows: If $\log 2^{50} = 15.0500$, then $2^{50} = 10^{15.0500} = (10^{15})(10^{.0500}) = 10^{15} \cdot N$, where $\log N = .0500$.)

Illustrative Example 5:
To compute: $\sqrt[3]{0.0183}$ (let N represent this number).

SOLUTION. $\log 0.0183 = .2625 - 2 = 1.2625 - 3$

(Here we have expressed the characteristic -2 as $1 - 3$, in order to make it possible to divide the negative part of the logarithm easily by 3.)

$$\log N = \dfrac{1.2625 - 3}{3} = .4208 - 1 \quad \text{(by Log Theorem 4)}$$
$$\therefore N = 0.2635$$

Illustrative Example 6:

To compute: $N = \sqrt[3]{\dfrac{(1.23)(0.456)^2}{\sqrt[5]{0.987}}}$.

SOLUTION.

$$\log 1.23 = .0899 \qquad \log 0.456 = .6590 - 1$$

$$\log (0.456)^2 = 1.3180 - 2$$

$$\overline{1.4079 - 2} = \text{log of numerator within cube root}$$

$$\log 0.987 = 4.9943 - 5$$

$$\log \sqrt[5]{0.987} = .9989 - 1 = \text{log of denominator within cube root}$$

$$\left. \begin{array}{l} 1.4079 - 2 \\ .9989 - 1 \end{array} \right\} \text{subtract}$$

$$\overline{.4090 - 1} = \text{log of expression within cube root}$$

$$\log N = \frac{2.4090 - 3}{3} = .8030 - 1$$

$$\therefore N = 0.6353$$

▶ **EXERCISE 28**

1. Prove Log Theorems: (*a*) 2; (*b*) 3; (*c*) 4.

2. Use the table at the beginning of Section 6.9 to compute:

(*a*) $16 \cdot 64$ (*b*) $32 \div 256$ (*c*) 4^5 (*d*) $\sqrt[10]{1024}$

3. Check the accuracy of the logarithmically computed results of Illustrative Examples 1, 2, and 3. If a result is inaccurate, how do you explain the inaccuracy?

4. Compute by means of logarithms:

(*a*) $(83.4)(0.2176)$ (*b*) 2^{20} (*c*) $\sqrt{2}$

(*d*) $0.162 \div 8735$ (*e*) 2^{40} (*f*) $\sqrt[3]{4}$

(*g*) $(3.142)(87.3)^2$ (*h*) 3^{10} (*i*) $\sqrt{3}$

(*j*) $\dfrac{(1.73)(2^{0.3})}{78.2}$ (*k*) $300(1.06)^{20}$ (*l*) $\sqrt[3]{5}$

(*m*) $\dfrac{2478\sqrt[3]{0.298}}{(12.46)^2}$ (*n*) $2(3.14)\sqrt{\dfrac{5}{32}}$ (*o*) $\sqrt{5}$

(*p*) $\sqrt[3]{\dfrac{17.6\sqrt{5}}{0.298}}$ (*q*) $10^{\frac{2}{3}}$ (*r*) $\sqrt[3]{6}$

(*s*) $\sqrt{(1.234)^2 + (5.678)^2}$ (*t*) $\sqrt{0.1}$ (*u*) $\sqrt[3]{0.1}$

(*v*) $\sqrt[3]{\dfrac{(-1.41)(89.76)}{(-24.7)^4}}$

(*Hint:* We cannot find the logarithms of negative numbers; but in cases like this we may determine the sign of the answer first, and then neglect all negative signs.)

7 POLYNOMIALS AND FRACTIONAL EXPRESSIONS

7.1 POLYNOMIALS

Among the most important algebraic sums are those we call *polynomials*. Examples of polynomials are: $x^2 + 2x - 1$ (a "polynomial in one variable, x"); $y + 10y^3$ (a "polynomial in one variable, y"); $2x + y$ (a "polynomial in two variables, x and y"). Before we define the term *polynomial*, we shall find it convenient to make two preliminary definitions. First we once more extend our definition of exponent, this time to include the case 0^0, which we now define to be equal to 1; then we define the term *monomial* as follows:

Definition. A *monomial in one variable x over the complex numbers* is a one-term algebraic sum that is equal, for each complex number x, to kx^n, where k is any complex number and n is any non-negative integer.

(For example 0, 7, x are monomials in x over the complex numbers, since $0 = 0x^0$, $7 = 7x^0$, $x = 1x^1$; $\sqrt{2}x^4$ and $0.7x^{10}$ are, of course, also monomials in x over the complex numbers, as are x^2, $2x$, and -1; y and $10y^3$ are monomials in y. All of these are also monomials over the *real* numbers, since in each of these cases k is a real number.)

The *degree* in x of a monomial equal to the aforesaid kx^n is undefined if $k = 0$, and it is equal to n if $k \neq 0$.

Thus no degree at all is assigned to 0, but the degree (in x) of 7 is 0 (since $7 = 7x^0$), the degree in x of $2x$ is 1 (since $2x = 2x^1$), and the degrees in x of x^2, $\sqrt{2} x^4$, $0.7x^{10}$ are 2, 4, 10 respectively. Similarly the degree in y of y is 1, and the degree in y of $10y^3$ is 3.

A *monomial in two variables x and y over the complex numbers* is a one-term algebraic sum that is equal, for each pair of complex numbers

183

x and y, to $kx^m y^n$, where k is a complex number, and m, n are non-negative integers.

(For example, $0, 7, x, 2y$ are monomials in x and y over the complex numbers, since $0 = 0x^0 y^0$, $7 = x^0 y^0$, $x = 1x^1 y^0$, $2y = 2x^0 y^1$; $\sqrt{3}x^2 y^3$ and $0.7xy$ are, of course, also monomials in x and y over the complex numbers, as well as over the real numbers.)

Given a monomial equal to the aforesaid $kx^m y^n$, no *degree* is defined for it if $k = 0$; but if $k \neq 0$, its *degree in* x is defined to be m, its degree in y, n, and its degree in x and y, $m + n$.

For example, $3xy^2$ is of degree 1 in x, 2 in y, 3 in x and y; 3 is of degree 0 in x, 0 in y, 0 in x and y; x is of degree 1 in x, 0 in y, 1 in x and y; 0 has no degree.

Similarly, we may define monomials in x, y, z, etc., and their degrees.

In each of these defined monomials, k is called the *coefficient* of the monomial; monomials are called *like* or *alike*, if they are exactly the same or if they differ only in their coefficients. (Thus, $2xy^2$, $3xy^2$, $-2xy^2$, and $2xy^2$ are like polynomials in x and y with coefficients 2, 3, -2, and 2 respectively.)

A *polynomial in one variable x over the complex numbers* is an algebraic sum, each term of which is equal to a monomial in x over the complex numbers; similarly, for polynomials in x and y, etc. (See examples in first paragraph of this section.)

The *degree in* x of a polynomial is undefined if the polynomial is equal to 0; otherwise it is the largest degree in x exhibited by any of its monomial terms (assuming that no two of its terms are alike). Similarly, the degree in x and y of a nonzero polynomial is the largest degree in x and y exhibited by any of its terms (assuming that no two of its terms are alike); etc.

For example, the terms of the polynomial $x^2 + 2x - 1$ have degrees 2, 1, 0 respectively in x. The largest of these is 2. Therefore the degree in x of the polynomial $x^2 + 2x - 1$ is 2. In the case of the polynomial $xy + x + y$, its terms have degrees 1, 1, 0 in x; 1, 0, 1 in y; and 2, 1, 1 in x and y respectively. Therefore the polynomial $xy + x + y$ is of degree 1 in x; 1 in y; and 2 in x and y. But note that before we can discuss the degree of the polynomial $x^2 y + xy - x^2 y$, we must write a polynomial equal to it in which no two terms are alike, namely: xy.

Polynomials of degrees 0, 1, 2, 3, 4, 5 are called *constant, linear, quadratic, cubic, quartic*, and *quintic* polynomials respectively. When we write a nonzero polynomial in one variable, say x, in " descending powers of x" (i.e., the terms of the polynomial diminish in degree as we read from left to right), with the coefficient of the highest degree term unequal to zero, and with each of the lower degree terms and their coefficients written (whether equal to zero or not), then we say that the polynomial is in "standard form." ("0," of course, will be defined to be the standard form for a zero polynomial.) Standard forms for polynomials in x, over the real numbers, of undefined degree or of degrees $\leqslant 3$ are:

$$\begin{aligned}
&\text{Constant:} && a \text{ or } 0 \\
&\text{Linear:} && ax + b \\
&\text{Quadratic:} && ax^2 + bx + c \\
&\text{Cubic:} && ax^3 + bx^2 + cx + d
\end{aligned}$$

where a, b, c, d are real numbers and $a \neq 0$.

When more than one variable is involved, we define the standard form similarly; however, rather than require that successive terms (in x and y, say) decrease in degree, we require that successive terms be unlike and never increase in degree. Standard forms for polynomials in x and y, over the real numbers, of undefined degree or of degrees $\leqslant 2$ are:

Constant: A or 0 (where A is a real number which is unequal to 0).

Linear: $Ax + By + C$ (where A, B, C are real numbers and A, B are not both equal to 0).

Quadratic: $Ax^2 + Bxy + Cy^2 + Dx + Ey + F$ (where A, $\cdots$, F are real numbers, and A, B, C are not all equal to 0).

(The use of capital letters for the coefficients above is simply traditional and has no special significance.)

In our study of algebraic sums, we have already carried out a number of operations with polynomials. We now look further into this question, especially from the point of view of simplifying the mechanical labor involved.

In adding polynomials, for example, an arrangement of the polynomials into rows, with like terms in the same column, may introduce a helpful orderly element into the work, especially if the number of polynomials and terms is large. For example, if we were asked to find the sum of the polynomials in Exercise 19, Problems $7u$ through z, we might do so as follows:

$$\begin{array}{r}
x^3 - x^2 + x - 1 \\
x^3 \quad\quad\quad + 1 \\
x^3 \quad\quad\quad - 1 \\
8x^3 \quad\quad\quad\quad - 27y^3 \\
8x^3 \quad\quad\quad\quad + 27y^3 \\
x^4 \quad\quad + 8x^2 \quad + 16 \\
\hline
x^4 + 19x^3 + 7x^2 + x + 15
\end{array}$$

It should not be overlooked, however, that the use of this arrangement is simply an application of associative and commutative laws of numbers.

In multiplying polynomials, the following way of applying distributive, associative, and commutative laws is familiar:

$$
\begin{array}{r}
3x^2 - 2x + 1 \\
x + 2 \\
\hline
3x^3 - 2x^2 + x \\
+ 6x^2 - 4x + 2 \\
\hline
3x^3 + 4x^2 - 3x + 2
\end{array}
$$

In subtracting polynomials, the content of Section 4.11 will be found applicable.

Finally, in the case of division, it turns out that a division algorithm theorem very much like that for integers (see Section 4.12) holds true for polynomials. We shall devote the next section to this important algorithm.

To free us from tedious repetition, from now on, unless otherwise mentioned, all polynomials in this text will be understood to be over the complex numbers.

▶ **EXERCISE 29**

1. In each of the following cases, state the degree (if any) of the given polynomial in x, and also state the name that applies to each polynomial because of its degree (or lack of it).

(a) 0	(b) 7
(c) $-\sqrt{2}$	(d) x
(e) x^2	(f) x^3
(g) $2x - x - x$	(h) x^4
(i) $1 - x$	(j) $2x^2$
(k) $-2x^2$	(l) $-x^3$
(m) $x^2 - x + 5$	(n) $2x + 1 - x^2$
(o) $x^3 - x^2 - x^3$	(p) $(x - 1)(x + 4)$
(q) $x^2(x - 3)$	(r) $(x^3 + 1)^2$
(s) $x^2 + x - x^3 + 1$	(t) $x^3 - x^2 + x - 1$
(u) $x^4 - x^2$	(v) $x^2 - x^4$
(w) $(x + 1)(x + 2)(x - 2)$	(x) $x^3 - (x + 1)(x + 2)(x + 3)$
(y) $(x + 1)^2 - (x - 1)^2$	(z) $x(x + 1) - x(x - 1)$

2. Write out standard forms for quartic and quintic polynomials in x.

3. A single standard form which includes the forms 0, a, $ax + b$, $ax^2 + bx + c$, etc., as special cases is the following:

$$
a_0 x^n + a_1 x^{n-1} + \cdots + a_{n-1} x + a_n
$$

where n is a non-negative integer.

For $n = 0$, this form is understood to represent simply $a_0 x^0$ or a_0.   For $n = 1$: $a_0 x + a_1$; for $n = 2$: $a_0 x^2 + a_1 x + a_2$.

(*a'*) Write out the polynomials represented by this form for $n = 3$ and $n = 4$.

(*a*) through (*z*) In the case of each of the polynomials of Problem 1, identify n and $a_0, \cdots, a_n$, so that this new form expresses the given polynomial.

4.(*a*) Write out a standard form for a cubic polynomial in x and y.

(*b*) What is a polynomial in x and y?

(*c*) Write out definitions for a monomial in x, y, and z, and for its degree; also for a polynomial in x, y, and z, and for its degree.

(*d*) Write out a standard form for a linear polynomial in x, y, and z.

(*e*) Write out a standard form for a quadratic polynomial in x, y, and z.

5. In each of the following cases, state the degree (if any) of the given polynomials in x and y, and also state the name that applies to each polynomial because of its degree (or lack of it).

(*a*) 0

(*b*) x

(*c*) y

(*d*) 7

(*e*) $-\sqrt{2}$

(*f*) $x + y - 7$

(*g*) xy

(*h*) $xy + x - y + 7$

(*i*) $3x^2 - y + y - 3x^2$

(*j*) $x^2 - y^2$

(*k*) $x^2 + 2xy + y^2$

(*l*) $2x^2 - xy + 3y^2 + x + y + 7$

(*m*) $x^3 - xy + 1$

(*n*) $x^4 + x^2 y^3 + y^4 - 1$

(*o*) $(x - y)(x + y)$

(*p*) x^2

(*q*) $1 - xy + x$

(*r*) $(1 + x)(x + y)$

(*s*) $x^3 + y^3 + 1$

(*t*) $xy - (x + 1)(y + 1)$

(*u*) $(x + y - 1)^2$

(*v*) $(x + y)^3$

(*w*) $(x + y)^2 - (x - y)^2 - 4xy$

(*x*) $x(y - 1) - y(x - 1)$

(*y*) $(x - y)^3$

(*z*) $x(x + y)^2 - y(x - y)^2$

6. Find the sum (in simple form) of the polynomials referred to:

(*a*) Problem 1*a* through 1*f*

(*b*) Problem 1*g* through 1*n*

(*c*) Problem 1*o* through 1*t*

(*d*) Problem 1*u* through 1*z*

(*e*) Problem 5*a* through 5*f*

(*f*) Problem 5*g* through 5*n*

(*g*) Problem 5*o* through 5*t*

(*h*) Problem 5*u* through 5*z*

7. Find, in simple form, the sum, differences, and product of each of the following pairs of polynomials:

(*a*) $x + y$, $x - y$

(*b*) $x + y + 1$, $x - y + 1$

(*c*) $x^2 - x + 2$, $x^2 + 2x - 1$

(*d*) $\dfrac{x}{\sqrt{2}} + \dfrac{y}{\sqrt{2}} - 1$, $\dfrac{x}{\sqrt{2}} - \dfrac{y}{\sqrt{2}} + 1$

(*e*) $x^2 + xy + y^2$, $x - y$

(*f*) $x^2 - xy + y^2$, $x + y$

(*g*) $x^3 + x^2 + x + 1$, $x - 1$

(*h*) $x^3 - x^2 + x - 1$, $x + 1$

8.(a) A function f is called a *polynomial* function if its mapping may be given by an equation $f(x) = p$, where p is a polynomial in x. We shall follow the general practice of referring, for example, to a function $x^2 + 1$ when we mean a function f whose mapping is given by $f(x) = x^2 + 1$. In discussing the graph of a polynomial function (sometimes referred to simply as a polynomial), we assume that its domain is the set of all real numbers unless otherwise mentioned.

Draw a representative portion of the graph of f, given that $f(x) =$:

(i) x (ii) x^2 (iii) x^3 (iv) 1
(v) $2x$ (vi) $2x^2$ (vii) $x^3 - 4x$ (viii) 0
(ix) $x + 1$ (x) $x^2 + 1$ (xi) $x^2 - 1$ (xii) $x^2 + x$
(xiii) $2x + 1$ (xiv) $2x - 1$ (xv) $-x + 2$ (xvi) 2

(b) From your results in (a) induce a general statement about the graph of a constant polynomial; linear polynomial; quadratic polynomial.

7.2 THE DIVISION ALGORITHM FOR POLYNOMIALS

Up until now we have defined no degree for the polynomial 0. In this section we shall find it convenient to assign a degree to 0, less than the degree of any other polynomial. We shall now therefore define the degree of 0 to be -1.

We shall also find it convenient to use the abbreviation deg p for the degree of a polynomial p.

Division Algorithm Theorem for Polynomials. Suppose $d \neq 0$, D are polynomials in x. Then there exist unique polynomials q, r in x such that:

$$D = dq + r \quad \text{and} \quad \deg r < \deg d$$

For example, suppose $D = 3x^2 + 1$, $d = 2x + 1$. Then we can verify that, if $q = \frac{3}{2}x - \frac{3}{4}$ and $r = \frac{7}{4}$, then $D = dq + r$, and the degree of r (namely 0) is less than the degree of d (namely 1). But how did we discover that the required "quotient" q and "remainder" r were $\frac{3}{2}x - \frac{3}{4}$ and $\frac{7}{4}$ respectively? There is a procedure called the *division algorithm for polynomials*, for computing the q and r whose existence is guaranteed by the preceding theorem.

We shall now describe this procedure and, incidentally, in doing so prove an important part of the preceding theorem.

If deg $D <$ deg d, then our goal is easily attained, for letting $q = 0$, $r = D$, we have $dq + r = d \cdot 0 + D = D$, and deg $r =$ deg $D <$ deg d, satisfying the requirements of the theorem.

Suppose, then, that deg $D \geqslant$ deg d, and that D, d have nonzero coefficient highest degree terms (so-called leading terms), ax^n, bx^m respectively, so that deg $D = n$, deg $d = m$. In that case, let $q_1 = \dfrac{ax^n}{bx^m} = \dfrac{a}{b}x^{n-m}$. Since

$\deg D \geqslant \deg d$, we have $n \geqslant m$, $n - m \geqslant 0$, so that q_1 is a monomial in x. In the preceding example, for instance, we have $q_1 = \frac{3}{2}x$.

Next we multiply d by q_1. The product of the leading term in d by q_1 is

$$(bx^m)\left(\frac{a}{b}x^{n-m}\right) = ax^n,$$ so that the leading term in dq_1 is ax^n. Now if we

subtract dq_1 from D we must have $\deg (D - dq_1) < \deg D$, since in the subtraction the leading term ax^n of D will be canceled out. (Thus, in the preceding example, $dq_1 = (2x + 1)(\frac{3}{2}x) = 3x^2 + \frac{3}{2}x$, $D - dq_1 = 3x^2 + 1 - 3x^2 - \frac{3}{2}x = -\frac{3}{2}x + 1$.)

Now if $\deg (D - dq_1) < d$, we are all done, since the theorem may be satisfied by letting $q = q_1$, $r = D - dq_1$; for then $dq + r = dq_1 + D - dq_1 = D$, and $\deg r < \deg d$, as required by the theorem.

If $\deg (D - dq_1) \geqslant \deg d$, we repeat the preceding process, with $D - dq_1$ in place of D, arriving at a polynomial q_2, such that $\deg (D - dq_1 - dq_2) < \deg (D - dq_1)$. [In the preceding example, $q_2 = -\frac{3}{2}/2 = -\frac{3}{4}$; $dq_2 = (2x + 1)(-\frac{3}{4}) = -\frac{3}{2}x - \frac{3}{4}$; $D - dq_1 - dq_2 = -\frac{3}{2}x + 1 + \frac{3}{2}x + \frac{3}{4} = \frac{7}{4}$.]

If $\deg (D - dq_1 - dq_2) < \deg d$, then the theorem may be satisfied by letting $q = q_1 + q_2$, $r = D - dq_1 - dq_2$. (This is the case in the preceding example.) For then $dq + r = dq_1 + dq_2 + D - dq_1 - dq_2 = D$, and $\deg r < \deg d$, as required by the theorem.

If $\deg (D - dq_1 - dq_2) \geqslant \deg d$, we repeat the process of the preceding step once more, this time with $D - dq_1 - dq_2$ in place of $D - dq_1$; and so on. But since $\deg D > \deg (D - dq_1) > \deg (D - dq_1 - dq_2) > \cdots$, the process must eventually produce a $D - dq_1 - dq_2 - \cdots$ that is lower in degree than d. At that stage, if we define $q = q_1 + q_2 + \cdots$, and $r = D - dq_1 - dq_2 - \cdots$, the theorem will be satisfied, for then $dq + r = dq_1 + dq_2 + \cdots + D - dq_1 - dq_2 - \cdots = D$, and $\deg r < \deg d$, as required by the theorem.

We have now actually proved part of the above division algorithm theorem, namely, the part that states that there exist a quotient q and a remainder r satisfying the conditions of the theorem. The proof that q and r are unique is left as an optional exercise for the student.

We recall to the student the following pattern for carrying out efficiently the steps of the above division algorithm:

$$
\begin{array}{r}
\frac{3}{2}x \quad - \frac{3}{4} \\
2x + 1 \overline{\smash{\big)}\, 3x^2 \qquad\quad + 1} \\
3x^2 + \frac{3}{2}x \\
-\frac{3}{2}x + 1 \\
-\frac{3}{2}x - \frac{3}{4} \\
\frac{7}{4}
\end{array}
$$

7.3 SYNTHETIC DIVISION

If the divisor d is of the special form $x - k$, we may streamline the polynomial division algorithm even more. Consider what happens when $D = ax^3 + bx^2 + cx + e$, and $d = x - k$:

$$
\begin{array}{r}
ax^2 + (ak + b)x + (ak^2 + bk + c) \\
x - k\,\overline{)\,ax^3 + \quad\quad bx^2 + \quad\quad\quad\quad\quad\quad cx + e} \\
ax^3 - \quad akx^2 \quad\quad\quad\quad\quad\quad\quad\quad\quad\quad \\
\hline
(ak + b)x^2 + \quad\quad\quad\quad\quad cx \\
(ak + b)x^2 - \quad (ak^2 + bk)x \quad\quad\quad \\
\hline
(ak^2 + bk + c)x + e \\
(ak^2 + bk + c)x - (ak^3 + bk^2 + ck) \\
\hline
ak^3 + bk^2 + ck + e
\end{array}
$$

Note that each coefficient of the quotient q, after the first, may be derived by multiplying the preceding coefficient of q by k, and adding the corresponding coefficient of the "dividend" D. This suggests a refinement of the polynomial division algorithm called *synthetic division*, which applies only when $d = x - k$, and in which we list only coefficients and carry out the observation of the preceding sentence. The preceding algorithm, for example, may be carried through by making use of the following pattern:

a	b	c	e	$\lfloor k$
	ak	$ak^2 + bk$	$ak^3 + bk^2 + ck$	
a	$ak + b$	$ak^2 + bk + c$	$ak^3 + bk^2 + ck + e$	

Note that in the above pattern:

1. The first line displays the coefficients of the dividend D in the order in which they appear in D, assuming that D is in standard form (see Section 7.1). (To achieve this, it may in some cases be necessary to insert 0 coefficients to mark "missing" terms.) To the right of the coefficients of D, the number k is displayed in a box.

2. The first entry in line 3 is the same as the first entry in line 1. This entry is multiplied by k, and the result placed in the next column, in line 2. The entries in lines 1 and 2 of that column are then added, and the result entered in line 3 of the same column. The process is repeated continually: Each entry in line 3 is multiplied by k and the result entered in line 2 of the next column. Lines 1 and 2 of a column are always added to arrive at the entry in line 3 of that column.

3. Our result is then read as follows: The last entry in line 3 is the remainder r. The other entries are the coefficients of the quotient q,

written in standard form. The degree of the quotient q is 1 less than the degree of the dividend, D. [For example, in the synthetic division carried out above, the degree of the quotient is 2. The first term of the quotient is therefore ax^2; the quotient is therefore $ax^2 + (ak + b)x + (ak^2 + bk + c)$.]

Illustrative Example I. Using synthetic division, we divide $x - 1$ into $x^4 + x^2 + 1$:

$$
\begin{array}{rrrrr|r}
1 & 0 & 1 & 0 & 1 & \underline{1} \\
  & 1 & 1 & 2 & 2 & \\
\hline
1 & 1 & 2 & 2 & 3 &
\end{array}
$$

Quotient: $x^3 + x^2 + 2x + 2$
Remainder: 3
That is to say: $x^4 + x^2 + 1 = (x - 1)(x^3 + x^2 + 2x + 2) + 3$

Illustrative Example 2. Using synthetic division, we divide $x + 2$ into $x^3 + 8$:
Note that the divisor is in the form $x - k$, with $k = -2$, for $x - (-2) = x + 2$.

$$
\begin{array}{rrrr|r}
1 & 0 & 0 & 8 & \underline{-2} \\
  & -2 & 4 & -8 & \\
\hline
1 & -2 & 4 & 0 &
\end{array}
$$

Quotient: $x^2 - 2x + 4$
Remainder: 0
That is to say: $x^3 + 8 = (x + 2)(x^2 - 2x + 4)$

In fact, it is clear that in all cases, the remainder is zero if and only if the divisor is a factor of the dividend.

It is interesting to note that, when we divided $D = ax^3 + bx^2 + cx + e$ above by $x - k$, the remainder turned out to be the polynomial D, with x replaced by k. Functional notation will help us to state this more simply: If f is a function, and if $f(x) = ax^3 + bx^2 + cx + e$, then, upon dividing the polynomial $f(x)$ by $x - k$, the remainder will be $f(k)$.

The observation we have just made about cubic polynomials may, of course, be carried further. Our discussion leading to the synthetic division process, as a matter of fact, yields the following more general result:

Remainder theorem. If a polynomial $f(x)$ is divided by a linear polynomial $x - k$, the remainder will be equal to the number $f(k)$.

The remainder theorem may also be proved directly from the division algorithm theorem for polynomials: For, from that theorem, for each complex number x, $f(x) = (x - k)q(x) + r(x)$, where $q(x)$ and $r(x)$ are polynomials in x, and deg $r(x) < $ deg $(x - k) = 1$. But if deg $r(x) < 1$, $r(x)$ must be of degree 0 or -1, i.e., the remainder $r(x)$ must be equal to a complex number, say c.

Thus $f(x) = (x - k)q(x) + c$, so that $f(k) = (k - k)q(k) + c = 0 \cdot q(k) + c = 0 + c = c$, i.e., the remainder c is equal to $f(k)$, Q.E.D.

The student may object that for $x = k$ the divisor $x - k = 0$, which seems to contradict our agreement that division by 0 is to be prohibited! He has a valid objection, but it is to our nomenclature rather than to our mathematics. First of all, properly speaking, the d of the division algorithm theorem should not be called a "divisor" unless $r = 0$; secondly, although it is correct to say $x - k \neq 0$ (since it is *not* true for each complex number x that $x - k = 0$), our proof has shown the equation of the division algorithm theorem to be true for each real number x, even those that make our so-called divisor equal to zero. It would help, probably, to use other terms in place of "divisor" and "division algorithm" in this context, but we bow to tradition and common usage in continuing to employ them here.

Illustrative Example 3. What is the remainder when: (i) $x - 1$ is divided into $x^4 + x^2 + 1$? (ii) $x + 2$ is divided into $x^3 + 8$?

SOLUTION. (i) Letting $f(x) = x^4 + x^2 + 1$, by the remainder theorem the remainder $r = f(1) = 1 + 1 + 1 = 3$.

(ii) Letting $f(x) = x^3 + 8$, by the remainder theorem the remainder $r = f(-2) = -8 + 8 = 0$.

Both of these results agree, of course, with the results of Illustrative Examples 1 and 2 above.

Very often we wish to find the value of a polynomial $f(x)$ for a real value of x, i.e., we wish to "substitute" a given real number for x in a polynomial $f(x)$. Phrased still differently, given a real number k and a polynomial $f(x)$ we wish to find the real number $f(k)$ in simple form.

In such cases we may simply reverse the process of Illustrative Examples 2 and 3. There we substituted directly to find the remainder. But if it were easier to find the remainder in some other fashion, that remainder would be equal to the result of direct substitution. By the remainder theorem, $f(k)$ is the remainder when the polynomial $f(x)$ is divided by $x - k$. This remainder may be found by means of the synthetic division process, an approach that is often easier to carry through than direct substitution.

Illustrative Example 4. Find the value of $2x^3 + 3x^2 + 17x$ when $x = -7$.

SOLUTION. We divide $f(x) = 2x^3 + 3x^2 + 17x$ synthetically by $x + 7$.

According to the remainder theorem, the remainder will be the required $f(-7)$:

$$
\begin{array}{rrr|rr}
2 & 3 & 17 & 0 & \underline{\;-7\;} \\
 & -14 & 77 & -658 & \\
\hline
2 & -11 & 94 & -658 &
\end{array}
$$

The required $f(-7) = -658$.

When we compute $f(k)$ as in this example, the process is called *synthetic substitution*. Note that, to find $f(k)$ by synthetic substitution [where $f(x)$ is a polynomial over the real numbers and k is a real number], the pattern is the same as that for synthetic division; but k itself is in the box to the right of the first line of the pattern, and the required $f(k)$ is the last entry in line 3 of the pattern.

The following theorem is an immediate corollary of the remainder theorem.

Factor Theorem. A linear polynomial $x - k$ is a factor of a polynomial $f(x)$ if and only if k is a "root" of the equation $f(x) = 0$ [i.e., if and only if $f(k) = 0$].

PROOF. If $(x - k) \mid f(x)$, then $f(x) = (x - k)q(x)$, where $q(x)$ is a polynomial. Therefore $f(k) = (k - k) \cdot q(k) = 0 \cdot q(k) = 0$, Q.E.D.

Conversely, suppose $f(k) = 0$. By the division algorithm theorem, there exist polynomials q, r such that $f(x) = (x - k)q + r$. But by the remainder theorem, $r = f(k)$, and by hypothesis $f(k) = 0$. Therefore, $r = 0$ and $f(x) = (x - k)q$, i.e., $(x - k) \mid f(x)$, Q.E.D.

▶ **EXERCISE 30**

1. In each of the following cases, use the ("long") division algorithm for polynomials to find the quotient q and the remainder r when the dividend D is divided by the divisor d, and verify that the division algorithm theorem is satisfied.

(a) $D = x^2 - 3x + 2$, $d = x + 2$
(b) $D = x^2 + 1$, $d = x + 1$
−(c) $D = 2x^3 - 3x^2 + 7$, $d = x - 2$
(d) $D = x^3 + x + 1$, $d = x^2 + x + 1$
−(e) $D = 2x^4 - 3x^3 + x^2 + x + 1$, $d = x^2 + 1$
(f) $D = x^3 + 8$, $d = x + 2$
−(g) $D = x^3 - 8$, $d = x - 2$
(h) $D = x^3 + a^3$, $d = x + a$
−(i) $D = x^3 - a^3$, $d = x - a$
(j) $D = x^4 + a^4$, $d = x + a$
(k) $D = x^4 - a^4$, $d = x - a$
(l) $D = x^2 + 3xy + y^2 + x + y$, $d = x + y$

[*Hint:* express D as a polynomial in x, with coefficients that are polynomials in y: $D = x^2 + (3y + 1)x + (y^2 + y)$.]

(*m*) $D = 2x^2y^2 - 3xy^2 - 6x^3y + 2x^4 + y^3 + x^2y, \; d = y + 2x^2$

2. Do by synthetic division each of the cases of Problem 1 that can be done by synthetic division.

3. By dividing both sides of the division algorithm equation by d, we arrive at: $\dfrac{D}{d} = q + \dfrac{r}{d}$, (for each value of x such that $d \neq 0$).

This result is often used to express an "improper" fraction whose numerator and denominator are polynomials, as the sum of a polynomial and a "proper" fraction. (A fraction whose numerator and denominator are polynomials in one variable of degree at least 1 is called *proper* if the numerator is lower in degree than the denominator, *improper* otherwise.)

For example, $\dfrac{x^2 + 1}{x + 1}$ is an improper fraction. Dividing $x + 1$ into $x^2 + 1$, we find the quotient to be $x - 1$, the remainder 2. Therefore, since we have seen above that $\dfrac{D}{d} = q + \dfrac{r}{d}$, we have:

$$\frac{x^2 + 1}{x + 1} = x - 1 + \frac{2}{x + 1} \quad \text{(for each complex number } x \text{ except } x = -1)$$

In each of the following cases, express the given improper fraction as the sum of a polynomial and a proper fraction, noting the numbers for which the equality holds.

(*a*) $\dfrac{x^2 + x + 1}{x - 1}$

(*b*) $\dfrac{x + 1}{x - 1}$

(*c*) $\dfrac{y^4 + 1}{y^2 + 1}$

(*d*) $\dfrac{x^2 + 2x + 3}{x^2 - 2x + 1}$

4. In each of the cases of Problem 1 to which the remainder theorem applies, use the remainder theorem to find the remainder when D is divided by d.

5. In each of the following cases use the synthetic substitution process to find $f(4), f(-4), f(\frac{1}{2}), f(-\frac{1}{2})$, given that $f(x) =:$

(*a*) $2x^3 - 3x^2 + 3x + 4$

(*b*) $2x^4 - 4x^2 + 1$

(*c*) $4x^4 - 2x^3 - 6x^2$

(*d*) $x^5 - x^4 + 2x^3 - 2x^2 + x - 1$

6.(*a*) In Problem 5c, show that -1 and 0 are roots of $f(x) = 0$. Then use the factor theorem to find factors of $f(x)$. Factor $f(x)$ as completely as you can, and find all roots of $f(x) = 0$.

(*b*) In Problem 5d, show that 1 is a root of $f(x) = 0$. Then use the factor theorem to find a factor of $f(x)$. Factor $f(x)$ as completely as you can, and find all roots of $f(x) = 0$.

*7.(*a*) Suppose $f(x)$ and $g(x)$ are nonzero polynomials of degrees m, n. What must be the degree of $f(x)g(x)$?

(b) Suppose $f(x)$ and $g(x)$ are polynomials. What relation must exist between deg $[f(x) + g(x)]$ and the maximum m of the pair of numbers $[\deg f(x), \deg g(x)]$? between deg $[f(x) - g(x)]$ and m? between deg $g(x)$ and deg $[-g(x)]$?

(c) Using statements you have made in (a) and (b), prove the uniqueness part of the division algorithm theorem; i.e., prove that, if $D = dq_1 + r_1 = dq_2 + r_2$, and deg $r_1, r_2 < \deg d$, then $q_1 = q_2$ and $r_1 = r_2$. [*Hint:* We must have $d(q_1 - q_2) = r_2 - r_1$. Now suppose $q_1 \neq q_2$, and arrive at the contradiction deg $(r_2 - r_1) \geqslant \deg d$, deg $(r_2 - r_1) < \deg d$. Hence $q_1 = q_2$, from which it easily follows that $r_1 = r_2$.]

7.4 FRACTIONAL EXPRESSIONS

An expression in the form $\dfrac{a}{b}$ or a/b is, of course, called a *fractional expression*, or a *fraction*, with *numerator a* and *denominator b*. In Section 4.12 and Exercise 18 are to be found the principal statements that are used in operating with fractions. We now proceed to consider substantial simplifications that may be effected in these operations, through the application of facts about factoring and division that we have developed in Sections 4.13 and 7.2.

Illustrative Example 1   Simply: $\dfrac{x^2 - 1}{x - 1}$.

SOLUTION: $\dfrac{x^2 - 1}{x - 1} = \dfrac{(x + 1)(x - 1)}{(x - 1)} = x + 1$ if $x \neq 1$

by Exercise 18, Problem 4a.

Illustrative Example 2. $\frac{5}{6} + \frac{7}{8} = ?$

SOLUTION: We might use Exercise 18, Problems 6 and 7 directly:

$$\frac{5}{6} + \frac{7}{8} = \frac{40}{48} + \frac{42}{48} = \frac{82}{48} = \frac{41 \cdot 2}{24 \cdot 2} = \frac{41}{24}$$

Simplifying further:

$$\frac{41}{24} = \frac{24 + 17}{24} = \frac{24}{24} + \frac{17}{24} = 1 + \frac{17}{24} = 1\frac{17}{24}$$

(What statements justify this last sequence of equations?)

Alternatively, we might attempt to make the numbers we are dealing with less awkwardly large by means of the "least common denominator" technique. A "least common denominator" is a special case of what is called a *least common multiple*. We therefore first define the latter. Our definition, it will be noted, is not in terms of size but in terms of divisibility; that is because we would like the definition to apply to any set in which multiplication is defined, regardless of whether or not an order relation is defined in the set.

Definitions. In any set in which multiplication is defined, c is said to be a *common multiple* of a and b, if $a \mid c$ and $b \mid c$.

If, furthermore, the common multiple c is a divisor of each common multiple of a and b, then c is called a *least common multiple* of a and b.

For example, in the set of integers, 300 is a common multiple of 20 and 15 since $20 \mid 300$ and $15 \mid 300$; so is 60; indeed 60 is a least common multiple of 20 and 15. And in the set of polynomials in x, $x(x + 1)(x - 1)$ is a least common multiple of $x^2 + x$ and $x^2 - x$. We now give (without proof) a technique for finding least common multiples.

The technique requires factorization into primes. (A prime nn may be thought of as a nn that is not equal to 1 and that cannot be expressed as a product of smaller nn; a prime polynomial is a polynomial of degree at least 1 that cannot be expressed as a product of polynomials of lower degree than itself.)

Now suppose a and b are two nn unequal to 1 (or two polynomials of degree at least 1). A least common multiple of a and b will be the product $p^r q^s \cdots$, where $p, q, \cdots$ are all the primes that divide a or b, and $p^r, q^s \cdots$ are respectively the highest powers of $p, q, \cdots$ that divide a or b.

For example, $20 = 2^2 \cdot 5$, and $15 = 3 \cdot 5$ are factorizations of 20 and 15 into products of primes. The primes that appear in this factorization are 2, 3, 5; 3 and 5 appear with maximum exponent 1, 2 with maximum exponent 2. Therefore a least common multiple of 20 and 15 is $2^2 \cdot 3 \cdot 5$, or 60.

Similarly, $x^2 + x = x(x + 1)$, $x^2 - x = x(x - 1)$, and a least common multiple of $x^2 + x$ and $x^2 - x$ is $x(x + 1)(x - 1)$.

Illustrative Example 3. $\frac{5}{6} + \frac{7}{8} = ?$

SOLUTION: This time we make use of a least common denominator (i.e., a least common multiple of the denominators), which is 24 (since $6 = 2 \cdot 3$, $8 = 2^3$, a least common denominator is $2^3 \cdot 3$).

$$\tfrac{5}{6} + \tfrac{7}{8} = \tfrac{20}{24} + \tfrac{21}{24} = \tfrac{41}{24} = 1\tfrac{17}{24}$$

Illustrative Example 4. $\dfrac{x - 1}{x^2 + x} - \dfrac{x + 1}{x^2 - x} = ?$

SOLUTION: Here a least common denominator is $x(x + 1)(x - 1)$. The factor by which both numerator and denominator of an original fraction is to be multiplied is obtained, of course, by dividing the original denominator into the least common denominator:

$$\frac{x-1}{x^2+x} - \frac{x+1}{x^2-x} = \frac{x-1}{x(x+1)} - \frac{x+1}{x(x-1)}$$

$$= \frac{(x-1)(x-1)}{x(x+1)(x-1)} - \frac{(x+1)(x+1)}{x(x+1)(x-1)}$$

$$= \frac{x^2-2x+1-x^2-2x-1}{x(x+1)(x-1)}$$

$$= \frac{-4}{(x+1)(x-1)} \quad (\text{if } x \neq 0, \pm 1)$$

The meaning of our result is that, for any number x other than 0, -1, and 1, the original expression defines the same number as the final expression. As a check upon our work, we might verify that this is indeed true for some particular value of x. For example, for $x = 2$:

$$\frac{x-1}{x^2+x} - \frac{x+1}{x^2-x} = \frac{1}{6} - \frac{3}{2} = \frac{1}{6} - \frac{9}{6} = -\frac{8}{6} = -\frac{4}{3}$$

$$\frac{-4}{(x+1)(x-1)} = \frac{-4}{3\cdot 1} = -\frac{4}{3}$$

Note, however, that our check only indicates the likelihood, not the certainty, that our result is correct. It is quite possible for two expressions to define the same number for some, but not all, complex numbers x, in which case it would be incorrect to write the two expressions as equal.

Illustrative Example 5. $\dfrac{1}{6x^3-6x^2} - \dfrac{1}{8x^2-8} + \dfrac{1}{10x^3+10x^2} = ?$

SOLUTION: The least common denominator technique applies to more than two denominators. Since the respective denominators are equal to $2\cdot 3\cdot x^2(x-1)$, $2^3(x+1)(x-1)$, and $2\cdot 5\cdot x^2(x+1)$, a least common denominator is $2^3\cdot 3\cdot 5\cdot x^2(x+1)(x-1)$, and the given expression (we abbreviate the work) is equal to:

$$\frac{1[2^2\cdot 5\cdot (x+1)] - 1(3\cdot 5\cdot x^2) + 1[2^2\cdot 3\cdot (x-1)]}{120x^2(x+1)(x-1)}$$

$$= \frac{20x+20-15x^2+12x-12}{120x^2(x+1)(x-1)}$$

$$= \frac{-15x^2+32x+8}{120x^2(x+1)(x-1)} \quad (\text{which, by Exercise 18, Problem 13})$$

$$= -\frac{15x^2-32x-8}{120x^2(x+1)(x-1)} \quad (\text{if } x \neq 0, \pm 1)$$

Check: For $x = 2$, the original is equal to: $\frac{1}{24} - \frac{1}{24} + \frac{1}{120} = \frac{1}{120}$; and our final result is equal to $-\dfrac{-12}{120 \cdot 4 \cdot 3 \cdot 1} = \dfrac{1}{120}$ (see Exercise 18, Problem 13).

Illustrative Example 6. $\dfrac{x^2 - 9}{x^2 - 4x + 4} \cdot \dfrac{4 - x^2}{x - 3} = ?$

SOLUTION.   The given expression is equal to:

$$\frac{(x + 3)(x - 3)(2 + x)(2 - x)}{(x - 2)(x - 2)(x - 3)} \quad \text{(see Exercise 18, Problem 5)}$$

$$= \frac{(x + 3)(x + 2)(-1)}{x - 2} \quad \text{(see Theorem R12)}$$

$$= -\frac{(x + 3)(x + 2)}{x - 2} \quad \text{(if } x \neq 2, 3)$$

For many purposes, the result may be left in this form.   Sometimes, however, it is useful to apply the technique of Exercise 30, Problem 3:

Dividing $x^2 + 5x + 6$ by $x - 2$, we arrive at a quotient of $x + 7$ and a remainder of 20.   Therefore our original expression is equal to:

$$- (x + 7) - \frac{20}{x - 2}, \text{ if } x \neq 2, 3.$$

Illustrative Example 7. $\dfrac{4x^2 - 9}{2x + 1} \div \dfrac{2x - 3}{4x^2 - 1} = ?$

SOLUTION: The given expression is equal to:

$$\frac{4x^2 - 9}{2x + 1} \cdot \frac{4x^2 - 1}{2x - 3} \quad \text{(see Exercise 18, Problem 10)}$$

$$= \frac{(2x + 3)(2x - 3)(2x + 1)(2x - 1)}{(2x + 1)(2x - 3)}$$

$$= (2x + 3)(2x - 1) \quad \text{(if } x \neq \pm\tfrac{1}{2}, \tfrac{3}{2})$$

Illustrative Example 8. $\dfrac{\dfrac{1}{x - 1} - \dfrac{1}{x + 1}}{1 + \dfrac{1}{x^2 - 1}} = ?$

SOLUTION: A useful technique here is to find the least common denominator for the denominators $x - 1$, $x + 1$, and $x^2 - 1$, namely $x^2 - 1$, and use it as follows:

$$\frac{\dfrac{1}{x-1} - \dfrac{1}{x+1}}{1 + \dfrac{1}{x^2-1}} = \frac{\left(\dfrac{1}{x-1} - \dfrac{1}{x+1}\right)(x^2-1)}{\left(1 + \dfrac{1}{x^2-1}\right)(x^2-1)}$$

$$= \frac{(x+1)-(x-1)}{(x^2-1)+1} = \frac{2}{x^2} \quad (\text{if } x \ne \pm 1, 0)$$

Alternative method:

$$\frac{\dfrac{1}{x-1} - \dfrac{1}{x+1}}{1 + \dfrac{1}{x^2-1}} = \frac{\dfrac{(x+1)-(x-1)}{x^2-1}}{\dfrac{(x^2-1)+1}{x^2-1}}$$

$$= \frac{\dfrac{2}{x^2-1}}{\dfrac{x^2}{x^2-1}} = \frac{2}{x^2-1} \cdot \frac{x^2-1}{x^2} = \frac{2}{x^2} \quad (\text{if } x \ne \pm 1, 0)$$

▶ **EXERCISE 31**

Simplify:

1. $\dfrac{-30}{45}$

2. $\dfrac{-225}{-150}$

3. $\dfrac{64}{-1024}$

4. $\dfrac{-14x^2yz}{28xy}$

5. $\dfrac{a-b}{b-a}$

6. $\dfrac{a^2-b^2}{a-b}$

7. $\dfrac{a^2-b^2}{b-a}$

8. $\dfrac{a^2-b^2}{(a-b)^2}$

9. $\dfrac{ax-ay}{by-bx}$

10. $\dfrac{2a^2+2b^2}{4a+8b}$

11. $\dfrac{4a^2-b^2}{2a-b}$

12. $\dfrac{(a-b)-(a+b)}{(a^2-b^2)-(a^2+b^2)}$

13. $\dfrac{x^2-2xy-3y^2}{x^2-5xy+6y^2}$

14. $\dfrac{x^2-3x+2}{2-3x+x^2}$

15. $\dfrac{x^2-x-6}{x-3}$

16. $\dfrac{x^2-x-6}{3-x}$

17. $\dfrac{ab^2+a^2b}{ab^2-a^2b}$

18. $\dfrac{a^2-(b-c)^2}{(a-b)^2-c^2}$

19. $\dfrac{a^{-1}b}{a^{-1} + 1}$

20. $\dfrac{1}{x - 1} \cdot \dfrac{1}{x + 1}$

21. $\dfrac{1}{x - 1} \div \dfrac{1}{x + 1}$

22. $\dfrac{1}{x - 1} + \dfrac{1}{x + 1}$

23. $\dfrac{1}{x - 1} - \dfrac{1}{x + 1}$

24. $\dfrac{14}{25} \cdot \dfrac{15}{28}$

25. $\dfrac{x - y}{a^2} \cdot \dfrac{3a}{2x - 2y}$

26. $\dfrac{y^3 - 27}{y^2 - 9} \cdot \dfrac{3y + 9}{y^2 + 3y + 9}$

27. $\dfrac{y^2}{4} \cdot \dfrac{8}{y(x^2 - 4)} \div \dfrac{2}{x - 2}$

28. $\dfrac{x^2 - 4}{y - 2} \cdot \dfrac{y^2 + 4}{x + 2} \cdot \dfrac{x - 1}{x^2 - 3x + 2}$

29. $\dfrac{-8ab^2}{9a^2b} \cdot \dfrac{6a}{4b}$

30. $\dfrac{-8ab^2}{9a^2b} \cdot \dfrac{6a + b}{4b + a}$

31. $\dfrac{2a + 6}{3a^2 - 27} \cdot \dfrac{3a - 9}{(a + 3)^2}$

32. $\dfrac{x^2 + 2xy + y^2}{x + y} \cdot \dfrac{x - y}{x^2 - y^2}$

33. $\dfrac{ax + ay}{4x^2} \div \dfrac{2x + 2y}{4xy}$

34. $\left(a - \dfrac{1}{4}\right) \div \left(\dfrac{2}{a} - 8\right)$

35. $\dfrac{2a^3 - 16b^3}{a - 2b} \div a^2 + 2ab + 4b^2$

36. $\dfrac{6x^2 - 5x - 6}{6x^2 - x - 2} \div \dfrac{9x^2 - 4}{4x^2 + 8x + 3}$

37. $\dfrac{5}{6} + \dfrac{7}{8} - \dfrac{8}{9}$

38. $\dfrac{1}{(x + 1)^2} - \dfrac{1}{x^2 - 1}$

39. $\dfrac{2x}{x^2 - 1} + \dfrac{1}{1 - x}$

40. $\dfrac{x}{y^2 - xy} + \dfrac{x}{x^2 - y^2}$

41. $\dfrac{x - 3}{x + 3} - \dfrac{x + 3}{x - 3}$

42. $\dfrac{1}{x^3 - y^3} + \dfrac{1}{x^2 - y^2}$

43. $\dfrac{x - 3}{x^2 - x - 2} + \dfrac{2x - 1}{x^2 - 3x + 2}$

44. $\dfrac{a}{a - b} - \dfrac{ab + b^2}{a^2 - b^2}$

45. $\dfrac{1}{x + 1} - \dfrac{1}{x - 1} + \dfrac{1}{x^2 - 1}$

46. $\dfrac{2b}{a - b} + \dfrac{2a}{b - a} + \dfrac{1}{a^2 - b^2}$

47. $\dfrac{a + b}{(c - a)(b - c)} + \dfrac{b + c}{(a - b)(c - a)} + \dfrac{a + c}{(b - c)(a - b)}$

48. $\dfrac{b - (1/a)}{1/a}$

49. $\dfrac{(x/y) + (y/x)}{1/xy}$

50. $\dfrac{1 - (1/a)}{1 + (1/a)}$

51. $\dfrac{(s^2/r) - (r^2/s)}{(s/r) - (r/s)}$

52. $\dfrac{(s^2/r^2) - (r^2/s^2)}{(s/r) - (r/s)}$

53. $\dfrac{1 - \dfrac{1}{1 + x}}{1 + \dfrac{1}{x - 1}}$

7.5 THE BINOMIAL THEOREM

It may be verified directly from the definition of a natural number exponent that, if x, y are complex numbers, then:

$$(x + y)^0 = 1$$
$$(x + y)^1 = x + y$$
$$(x + y)^2 = x^2 + 2xy + y^2$$
$$(x + y)^3 = x^3 + 3x^2y + 3xy^2 + y^3$$
$$(x + y)^4 = x^4 + 4x^3y + 6x^2y^2 + 4xy^3 + y^4$$

One may induce that, if n is any nn (x, y as above), then:

(i) $(x + y)^n$ is equal to a sum [called the "binomial expansion" of $(x + y)^n$] of $n + 1$ terms of the form kx^uy^v, where k is a nn, and u, v are non-negative integers such that $u + v = n$.

From now on we shall assume that the terms of this binomial expansion are written so that the exponents of x occur, as above, in decreasing order.

(ii) In the binomial expansion of $(x + y)^n$, the first and last coefficients (i.e., the coefficients of x^n and y^n) are each 1; the coefficients form a symmetric array about the middle; the second coefficient, from either end, is n.

In fact, one may display the coefficients of successive expansions in the following pattern, called the "Pascal triangle":

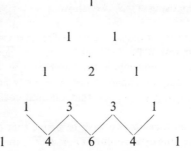

It is interesting to note that, in this pattern, between the 1's which occur at the ends of a row, each number is the sum of the two numbers in the row above it between which it falls.

Thus, the successive coefficients in the expansion of $(F + S)^5$ are: 1, 5, 10, 10, 5, 1. This information enables us to write:

$$(x + y)^5 = x^5 + 5x^4y + 10x^3y^2 + 10x^2y^3 + 5xy^4 + y^5$$

(iii) If ax^uy^v and $bx^{u-1}y^{v+1}$ are successive terms in the expansion of $(x + y)^n$, then:

$$b = \frac{au}{v + 1}$$

Thus, having found the coefficient of one term, one may find the coefficient of the next by multiplying the coefficient of the first of these terms by the exponent of x in that term, and dividing by one more than the exponent of y in that term.

The student should verify, in the examples given above, i.e., where $n = 1, 2, 3, 4, 5$, that this statement is true.

This process leads to the following formula:

$$(x + y)^n = x^n + nx^{n-1}y + \frac{n(n-1)}{2} x^{n-2}y^2$$

$$+ \frac{n(n-1)(n-2)}{2 \cdot 3} x^{n-3}y^3 + \cdots + y^n$$

The statement that this formula is true for all complex numbers x, y and all natural numbers n is known as the "binomial theorem."

A *proof* of the binomial theorem, by means of mathematical induction (see Section 4.17), follows:

Let S be the set of all nn for which the preceding formula is true. We prove that S contains all the nn by proving (i) and (ii) of the Principle of Mathematical Induction.

PROOF OF (i): That $1 \in S$ is trivial, since for $n = 1$ the preceding formula reduces to: $(x + y)^1 = x + y$.

PROOF OF (ii): Supposing $s \in S$, we show $s + 1 \in S$. That is to say, we assume that the method which led to the preceding formula is correct for $n = s$, and prove that then it must be correct for $n = s + 1$.

But a binomial expansion for $(x + y)^{s+1}$ may be derived from a binomial expansion for $(x + y)^s$ by multiplying the latter by $x + y$.

Clearly, the first term in this expansion of $(x + y)^{s+1}$ arises, in this multiplication, only from multiplying x by x^s, so that the first coefficient is 1, as we wish it to be.

Now for the other coefficients, we wish to prove that if ax^uy^v and $bx^{u-1}y^{v+1}$ are successive terms in this expansion of $(x + y)^{s+1}$; then:

$$b = \frac{au}{v + 1}$$

But in our multiplication these terms arise only from multiplying the terms: $cx^uy^{v-1} + dx^{u-1}y^v + ex^{u-2}y^{v+1}$, in the expansion of $(x + y)^s$, by $x + y$. (If $v = 0$, omit the first term; if $u = 1$, omit the last. The student may complete the proof in these two special cases.) In fact, upon multiplying, we see that:

$$a = c + d \qquad b = d + e$$

Also, from the inductive assumption, i.e., that our formula holds for $n = s$, we have:

$$d = \frac{cu}{v} \qquad e = \frac{d(u-1)}{v+1}$$

Hence:

$$b = d + \frac{d(u - 1)}{v + 1} = \frac{dv + du}{v + 1} = \frac{cu + du}{v + 1} = \frac{(c + d)u}{v + 1} = \frac{au}{v + 1}, \text{ Q.E.D.}$$

Illustrative Example I. We expand: $(2x - 3y)^4$.

$$(2x - 3y)^4 = (2x)^4 + 4(2x)^3(-3y) + 6(2x)^2(-3y)^2$$
$$+ 4(2x)(-3y)^3 + (-3y)^4$$
$$= 16x^4 - 96x^3y + 216x^2y^2 - 216xy^3 + 81y^4$$

The coefficients in this example may be derived from the Pascal triangle or from the rule which derives each coefficient (after the first) from the preceding. In the latter case, because of the symmetric array of co-efficients, it is necessary to compute only the first three coefficients.

Note that, in an expansion of the form $(x - y)^n$, the signs of the terms finally alternate.

An interesting and useful extension of the binomial theorem leads to certain approximation formulas. For example, suppose we attempt the following expansion, proceeding by our expansion rule:

$$(1) \qquad (1 + x)^{\frac{1}{2}} = 1^{\frac{1}{2}} + \tfrac{1}{2}(1)^{-\frac{1}{2}}(x) + \frac{(\frac{1}{2})(-\frac{1}{2})}{2}(1)^{-\frac{3}{2}}(x)^2 + \ldots$$

Now we know nothing of the truth of this statement since we have proved the binomial theorem only for nn exponents. In fact, the statement is meaningless, for the process never terminates and we have an infinite progression of terms on the right. But meaning may be given to this expansion, as the student will discover in later courses, when he encounters "infinite series." For the present, we state, without proof, that for certain values of x, in this case $-1 \leqslant x \leqslant 1$, the above equality is approximate if the expansion is terminated at any point, and the more terms we include in our sum on the right, the better the approximation.

For example:

$$(1 + x)^{\frac{1}{2}} \doteq 1 + \tfrac{1}{2}x - \tfrac{1}{8}x^2$$

is an approximation arrived at by terminating the expansion (1) above after three terms. Thus:

$$\sqrt{2} = (1 + 1)^{\frac{1}{2}} \doteq 1 + \tfrac{1}{2} - \tfrac{1}{8} = \tfrac{11}{8} \doteq 1.4$$

$$\sqrt{10} \doteq \sqrt{(9)(1.11)} = 3(1 + 0.11)^{\frac{1}{2}} \doteq 3\left(1 + \frac{0.11}{2}\right) = 3(1.055) \doteq 3.16$$

In approximating $\sqrt{10}$, we used only two terms of our expansion. Three terms would have led to a better result.

▶ **EXERCISE 32**

1. Extend the Pascal triangle to find the coefficients in the expansions of $(x + y)^6$ and $(x + y)^7$.

2. Expand:

(a) $(a - b)^3$	(b) $(2a - b)^3$	(c) $(3a + 2b)^3$
(d) $(1 + x)^3$	(e) $(1 - x)^3$	(f) $(a - b)^4$
(g) $(2a + b)^4$	(h) $(3a - 2b)^4$	(i) $(1 + x)^4$
(j) $(1 - x)^4$	(k) $(a - b)^5$	(l) $(2a - b)^5$
(m) $(3a + 2b)^5$	(n) $(1 + x)^5$	(o) $(1 - x)^5$

3. Approximate $(1.01)^{100}$ by using only the first four terms of the expansion of $(1 + 0.01)^{100}$. Why does this yield a feasible approximation?

*4. Find three-term polynomial approximations for:

(a) $\sqrt[3]{1 + x}$ $\qquad$ (b) $\sqrt[3]{1 - x}$ $\qquad$ (c) $1/\sqrt{1 + x}$

*5. Use the results of Problem 4 to approximate:

(a) $\sqrt[3]{1.1}$ $\qquad$ (b) $\sqrt[3]{0.9}$ $\qquad$ (c) $1/\sqrt{1.1}$ $\qquad$ (d) $\sqrt[3]{10}$

*6. The binomial theorem, as we have stated and proved it, implies that the coefficient k of $x^u y^v$ in the expansion of $(x + y)^n$ is given by:

$$k = \frac{(n)(n - 1) \cdots (n - v + 1)}{(1) \quad (2) \quad \cdots \quad (v)}$$

We use the notation $v!$ (read "v factorial") to represent the product of all nn ⩽ the nn v.

Thus:

$$k = \frac{(n)(n - 1) \cdots (n - v + 1)}{v!}$$

Show, using the fact that $u + v = n$, that:

$$k = \frac{n!}{u! \, v!}$$

Use this fact to prove the symmetric property of the coefficients in the binomial expansion of $(x + y)^n$; i.e., that the coefficient of $x^u y^v$ is equal to the coefficient of $x^v y^u$.

8 EQUATIONS AND INEQUALITIES

8.1 INTRODUCTION

"$1 + 1 = 2$" is a *true* statement.

"$3 + 1 = 2$" is a *false* statement.

But what shall we say of the statement "$x + 1 = 2$?" Neither the word "true" nor the word "false" seems to apply. Indeed, we shall regard this statement as a *meaningless* or "*open*" statement, one which takes on meaning only when x is replaced by a number. When x is replaced by 3, the statement $x + 1 = 2$ becomes meaningful but false; when x is replaced by 1, the statement $x + 1 = 2$ becomes meaningful and true. We then say: "$x = 1$ is a solution (or root) of the equation $x + 1 = 2$" or "the solution set of the equation $x + 1 = 2$ is $\{1\}$." In this instance, "x" is called an "unknown" or "variable," and $x + 1 = 2$ is called an "equation in x."

Thus, <u>solving an equation in x simply means finding each of the numbers which, when it replaces the variables in the equation, converts the equation into a meaningful and true statement</u>. ✳

Something must be said about what we mean here by "numbers": in this text, in solving equations, we shall mean "complex numbers." It is customary, in solving equations, to name a *universal set* from which solutions are to be drawn. In our work, unless otherwise noted, the universal set for the solution of equations will be the set of all complex numbers. (The concept of a universal set is useful in many other situations in which we wish to restrict our discussion to a particular set.)

The introduction of the "set-builder" notation will, perhaps, help us to make clearer statements about equations (and about other relations as well). The notation $\{x \mid \quad \}$ is read "the set of all x such that." (As often happens, we find the symbol $\mid$ doing double duty; the student will recall that it may also be used to mean "divides." However, in actual practice, the meaning should always be clear from the context.) Thus, $\{x \mid 2x = 5\}$ is read "the set of all x such that $2x = 5$." The use of the set-builder notation always requires a prior agreement as to the universal set of which the set being built is to be a subset. Thus, if the universal set is the set of all rational numbers, $\{x \mid 2x = 5\} = \{\frac{5}{2}\}$. But if the universal set is the set of all integers, $\{x \mid 2x = 5\} = \{\ \}$, the null set.

Using this notation, we may say that solving the equation $f(x) = 0$ means finding $\{x \mid f(x) = 0\}$, where the universal set, unless otherwise mentioned, is the set of all complex numbers. Again by way of example: $\{x \mid x^2 = 9, x < 0\} = \{-3\}$. (Note that the preceding comma may be read "and".)

In this chapter we first consider the problem of solving certain equations, and then of solving certain "inequalities," both of types that occur most often in practical applications of mathematics.

We shall depart in our presentation, however, from the coldly formal and relentlessly logical style emphasized in Chapter 4, for example. For mathematics has great variety in its aspects and, in order to develop a feeling for what the subject is like and what it is all about, more than one of the many sides of mathematics must be seen.

The deductive presentation of Chapter 4 indicates something of an ideal towards which all mathematics bends. But that ideal is the end result of a long process of mathematical creation involving intuition and imagination and often a great deal of interplay with physical situations and practical problems. To neglect either the deductive or the intuitive sides of mathematics, or the give-and-take between mathematics and its applications, is to arrive at an incomplete and distorted picture of mathematics.

But there are still other aspects of mathematics that should not be overlooked: It has to do with people and it has a history. Not only does mathematics serve humanity; it is indeed created by human beings, and exists neither in a vacuum nor in an ivory tower but in societies and civilizations which leave their indelible impressions on the mathematicians and on the mathematics of their times, and which throughout the breadth of their cultures—in science, in art, in philosophy, in literature, and even in music and in poetry—reflect the converse influence of mathematics.

We shall therefore attempt, in this chapter, to present something of the human and historical side of mathematics; and, together with material which for the sake of complete clarity has been formulated in rigorous, deductive fashion, there will also be included some material justified here only by intuition.

That which has to do with people and history lends itself to being told as a story; and nowhere in mathematics, nor probably even in all the annals of science, is there a better story to be found than that which has to do with the apparently mundane subject of algebraic equations.

8.2 THE STORY OF THE ALGEBRAIC EQUATION IN ONE UNKNOWN

Some 4000 years ago, in the Biblical times of Abraham, Isaac, and Jacob, there flourished the two earliest of Western civilizations: the Egyptian, on the banks of the Nile in Northern Africa, and the Babylonian, between the Tigris and Euphrates Rivers—legendary site of both the Garden of Eden and the Arabian Nights' adventures—in Western Asia.

Many records of these nations have come down to us; the Babylonians wrote on durable baked clay tablets, and the Egyptians on a paperlike material called "papyrus," preserved by the dry Egyptian climate. The records show remarkable progress in many fields, but at the moment our interest is in mathematics and, in particular, in the algebraic equation. We note particularly, therefore, this translation of a line from an ancient Egyptian papyrus:

A quantity whose fourth part is added to it becomes 15 . . .

There is a problem implied here, of course, namely, to find the quantity. In modern notation, we would say the problem is to solve the equation:

$$x + \frac{x}{4} = 15$$

The Egyptians did not, of course, write the problem in this way. Nevertheless, they were able not only to state but also to solve the problem in verbal terms. But it is interesting that there has not yet been found anything very much more complicated than this in the records that have been discovered so far of the work done by Egyptians on algebraic equations.

We may say, then, that the ancient Egyptians knew how to solve the simple type of algebraic equation that we call the "linear" or "first-degree" equation in one "unknown."

On the other hand, the Babylonians seem to have been much further advanced in the field of algebraic equations. They could solve "quadratic" or "second-degree" equations in one unknown like:

$$x^2 - 3x + 2 = 0$$

For example, here is a problem taken from a tablet of about the time of King Hammurabi that leads to such an equation (Hammurabi, c. 1800

B.C., is famous as the king whose name is affixed to recorded history's first codified body of law):

Two bur is the area; the length exceeded the width by 126 gar. What are the length and width?

A rectangle may be assumed to be the figure to which the problem refers. In order to solve the problem, it is necessary to know further that a "bur" is the area of a rectangle whose length is 60 "gar" and whose width is 30 "gar."

(The solution of this problem is left as an exercise for the student.)

Now, before we can go on with our story, we shall find it necessary to define with greater precision some of the terms we have been using.

First of all, we introduce the following nomenclature:

The equation $ax + b = 0$ is called a *general algebraic equation of the first degree in x.*

Particular first-degree equations in x may be derived from this general equation by substituting numbers for a and b, with the stipulation that the number 0 shall *never* be substituted for a; having made such a substitution, we say that we have an equation in the "form" $ax + b = 0$. Furthermore, any equation which may be transformed into this form by certain operations on equations with which we are familiar (and which we shall presently discuss) is also called an equation of the first degree in x.

For example, by adding -5 to both its sides, the equation $4x - 3 = 5$ is transformed into $4x - 8 = 0$, which may be derived from the general equation $ax + b = 0$ by the substitution: $a = 4$, $b = -8$. Therefore, $4x - 3 = 5$ is an equation of the first degree in x.

Similarly, the equation $ax^2 + bx + c = 0$ is called a *general algebraic equation of the second degree in x.*

Particular second-degree equations in x may be derived from this general equation by substituting numbers for a, b, and c, but again we stipulate: $a \neq 0$. As in the preceding case, equations that may by certain legal methods be transformed into the form $ax^2 + bx + c = 0$ are also called equations of the second degree in x.

For example, the equation $x^2 - 3x + 2 = 0$ is already in the form $ax^2 + bx + c = 0$, for it may be derived from the general equation by the substitution: $a = 1$, $b = -3$, $c = 2$. Therefore $x^2 - 3x + 2 = 0$ is an equation of the second degree in x.

Similar remarks hold for the following general algebraic equations:

"Cubic" or "third degree": $ax^3 + bx^2 + cx + d = 0$ $(a \neq 0)$

"Quartic" or "fourth degree": $ax^4 + bx^3 + cx^2 + dx + e = 0$ $(a \neq 0)$

"Quintic" or "fifth degree": $ax^5 + bx^4 + cx^3 + dx^2 + ex + f = 0$

$(a \neq 0)$, etc.

In the equations above, a, b, c, etc., are called the "coefficients" of their respective equations.

From now on, unless otherwise noted, we shall use the term "algebraic equation" to mean an algebraic equation of any positive degree in x or in y, or in any other single "unknown," such that all of its coefficients are complex numbers. (Note that every algebraic equation may be written as a polynomial set equal to zero. For that reason, algebraic equations are also called *polynomial equations*. Note also that the nomenclature of polynomials has been carried over to polynomial equations.)

Now we consider the general problem of solving algebraic equations by means of formulas.

The linear equation is very easy to dispose of. The same method that enables us to solve particular linear equations enables us also to solve the general equation $ax + b = 0$. The solution, of course, is: $x = -b/a$. This last may be considered as a formula which once and for all gives the solution to any linear equation, once its coefficients a and b are known. For example, by this formula, the solution to $4x - 8 = 0$ would be:

$$x = \frac{-(-8)}{4} = \frac{8}{4} = 2$$

The student will recall that there is a formula also for the solution of quadratic equations in terms of their coefficients, the famous "quadratic formula":

$$x = \frac{-b \pm \sqrt{b^2 - 4ac}}{2a}$$

For example, applying this formula to the solution of the equation

$$x^2 - 3x + 2 = 0$$

the general equation $ax^2 + bx + c = 0$ may be transformed into our particular case by the replacements: $a = 1$, $b = -3$, $c = 2$. Therefore, by the quadratic formula:

$$x = \frac{-(-3) \pm \sqrt{(-3)^2 - 4 \cdot 1 \cdot 2}}{2 \cdot 1} = \frac{3 \pm \sqrt{9 - 8}}{2} = \frac{3 \pm 1}{2} = 2 \quad \text{or} \quad 1$$

The student may now easily verify that the numbers 1 and 2 are both solutions of the equation $x^2 - 3x + 2 = 0$, and, using the quadratic formula, he should now be able to solve the Babylonian problem above. As a matter of fact, the quadratic formula, not of course in modern notation but in terms of indicated steps of procedure, was known to the Babylonians of 4000 years ago!

At this point we begin to recognize the outlines of a very general problem: Formulas exist which in terms of the operations of addition, subtraction, multiplication, division, and the extraction of roots, all working on the coefficients of the equations, enable us to solve any linear or quadratic equation in a finite number of steps. Do similar formulas exist for the solution of cubics and quartics, and, in fact, for algebraic equations of any degree whatever?

Since the linear and quadratic formulas were already known as early as 2000 B.C., it comes as something of a surprise to learn that a cubic formula was not discovered until about A.D. 1535. During the 3500 years or so that separated these discoveries, there flourished the glorious civilization of Greece, with its incomparable array of magnificent minds, as well as Indian and Arabic civilizations of considerable intellectual accomplishment. Many brilliant mathematicians must have tried and failed to find the elusive formula. But it was not until Renaissance times, almost half a century after Columbus discovered America, that the problem was solved.

The times were turbulent and the actors in the drama not in the highest degree scrupulous. Versions of how the solution was attained, therefore, differ somewhat. One which is generally accepted is incorporated into the following account.

In histories of medicine we learn that Jerome Cardan of Italy, who lived during that period of brilliant cultural achievement in Europe known as the Renaissance, was one of the leading physicians of the early sixteenth century. It was the era of such universal geniuses as Michelangelo, Cellini, and Leonardo da Vinci, so that we are not overly surprised to learn that Cardan's reputation as a mathematician was greater even than his reputation in medicine. Indeed, the formula for the solution of cubic equations, with which we are at the moment concerned, appears in many present-day mathematics texts under the name "Cardan's formula." But Cardan did *not* discover the formula, nor did he even claim to have done so!

Actually it was Tartaglia (whose name was not Tartaglia) who discovered "Cardan's formula."

In Italian, *tartaglia* means "stammerer." In the year 1512, politically dismembered Italy found itself torn by bloody wars. The disorderly period left its lifelong mark on a twelve-year-old boy, called Nicolo Fontana, when a soldier gashed the child's mouth with his sword in an attempted massacre of the inhabitants of Brescia. The injury impeded his speech, and Nicolo became known as "Tartaglia."

Poverty-stricken Tartaglia enjoyed no education but that which he gave himself. Too poor to afford paper, he pursued his studies in cemeteries, writing on tombstones with pieces of charcoal. And one day he found the answer to a riddle which had evaded solution for almost 4000 years. He found a method for solving *any* cubic equation.

Learning of the discovery, the great Cardan persuaded Tartaglia to reveal it to him, but under a strict oath of secrecy. The reason for the oath of secrecy? It was due to the fact that the tradition of a free exchange of ideas among scholars did not exist at the time of the Renaissance. Learning, in those days, was a highly competitive field of endeavor. Indeed, the reputation and, hence, the very livelihood of Renaissance mathematicians might depend upon their performance in public contests of mathematical skill. These contests often took the form of an exchange of problems, each mathematician attempting to confound his opponent. Popular among the posers of Tartaglia's day was one particular cubic equation or another which the proposer had already managed to solve by some special method. A general formula solving *any* cubic equation would be a valuable commodity to a mathematician who engaged in these contests; good reason, certainly, for keeping such a formula secret.

But when Cardan published a monumental treatise on mathematics in 1545, Tartaglia's formula, credited to Tartaglia, but nevertheless no longer secret, was included; that publication accounts for the name " Cardan's formula," which, as we have noted, persists up to this very day.

The student may now be curious to see this famous formula. It is, as one might guess, considerably more complicated than the quadratic formula. Even worse, it often presents comparatively simple solutions in a form in which square roots of negative numbers—then considered to be totally fantastic—are inextricably involved. Nevertheless, to satisfy the student's curiosity at least partially, we present a streamlined version of how the formula operates to give one root of the cubic equation whose general form was given above.

Beginning with the given values of the coefficients a, b, c, d, we compute successively:

$$p = \frac{3ac - b^2}{3a^2} \quad q = \frac{2b^3 - 9abc + 27a^2d}{27a^3} \quad r = \sqrt{q^2 + \frac{4p^3}{27}}$$

$$s = \sqrt[3]{\frac{r - q}{2}} \quad t = \sqrt[3]{\frac{r + q}{2}}$$

Now a solution of our cubic equation will be: $x = s - t - (b/3)$.

For example, consider the equation $4x^3 - 3x + 1 = 0$. Here $a = 4$, $b = 0$, $c = -3$, $d = 1$. Then $p = -\frac{3}{4}$, $q = \frac{1}{4}$, $r = 0$, $s = -\frac{1}{2}$, $t = \frac{1}{2}$, and finally $x = -1$, all of which the student should verify, as well as the fact that $x = -1$ is a root of the given equation.

With the cubic equation conquered, mathematicians naturally turned their attention to the problem of finding a similar formula for the solution of quartic equations. Here success came relatively quickly. Only 5 years or so after Tartaglia found a cubic formula, a pupil of Cardan's, named Ferrari, found and gave his name to a quartic formula.

We pause for a moment to remark upon the dramatic lives of Renaissance scholars. We have encountered three great names among the sixteenth-century mathematicians: Ferrari, Tartaglia, and Cardan. Ferrari was poisoned by his sister; of Tartaglia's life we have already spoken; and as to Cardan—he was an immoderate gambler, a man of furious temper who cut off his son's ears in a fit of rage, who spent time in prison, whose son was hanged for murder, and who himself committed suicide in order to make his own prophecy of the date of his death come true.

But to get on with our story: Ferrari's formula, though even more complicated than Tartaglia's, amounts to nothing more than a clever trick which reduces the solution of a quartic to a problem involving the solution of a cubic. Nothing would be gained by considering Ferrari's formula here, and for that very good reason we omit it.

If the student begins to grow weary of a seemingly endless progression of equations and their solutions, we have at this point a word of reassurance. The next case, that of the quintic equation, is the most interesting of all, and for a reason soon to be revealed, the last which we shall want to discuss.

As time goes on, the Renaissance fades into history and century follows century, but still the quintic equation remains an "enigma wrapped in a mystery." Giants of mathematics live and die; seventeenth-century England produces Newton and eighteenth-century Germany, Gauss, two who rank among the very greatest mathematicians of all time. But still the quintic resists every attack, and the inductive suspicion begins to grow that the search for a formula which solves the quintic and which involves nothing more complicated than radicals (i.e., square roots, cube roots, etc.) is a search for something which does not exist.

To another Italian physician, Paolo Ruffini, belongs the honor of being the first to prove that no such formula exists for equations of degree higher than 4. He first attempted to prove that fact in 1799, but it was not until 1813 that he completed his proof. Eleven years later, in 1824, another completely independent proof was constructed by the Norwegian Niels Henrik Abel. Only 22 when he wrote this paper, only 27 when he died of poverty and tuberculosis, Abel is one of the immortals of mathematics.

But in the work which they did on equations, Ruffini and Abel are both eclipsed by the incomparable genius of Evariste Galois, who was killed in a duel at the age of *twenty*! The story loses nothing from an investigation of the cause of his death: *Cherchez la femme*! He died, in his own words, "the victim of an infamous coquette."

When Galois was born, in 1811, Napoleon was emperor of France; but still fresh in the minds of the French nation was the memory of the Revolution of 1789 and the brief period afterward when France had been a republic. Throughout Galois' short life France remained a monarchy, but in the face of continual republic opposition. Galois threw himself heart and soul into the most extreme faction of the republicans. The details of the duel in which he died are lost to us, but despite the evidence of his quoted statement, it is likely that the primary reason for the challenge was not romantic but political in nature. In and out of jail, he was a thorn in the flesh of the monarchists. A duel would seem to have been a convenient device for putting him out of the way, and a coquettish woman may well have served the purpose of arranging a situation of "honor."

What do we have of Galois' work? Only several manuscripts and the contents of a letter written to a friend on the eve of his death. Here is what two present-day mathematicians have to say about Galois:

This letter, if judged by the novelty and profundity of ideas it contains, is perhaps the most substantial piece of writing in the whole literature of mankind.

HERMANN WEYL: *Symmetry*

All night . . . he had spent the fleeting hours feverishly dashing off his scientific last will and testament, writing against time to glean a few of the great things in his teeming mind before the death which he foresaw could overtake him. Time after time he broke off to scribble in the margin "I have not time; I have not time," and passed on to the next frantically scrawled outline. What he wrote in those desperate last hours before the dawn will keep generations of mathematicians busy for hundreds of years. He had found, once and for all, the true solution of a riddle which had tormented mathematicians for centuries: under what conditions can an equation be solved? But this was only one thing of many. In this great work, Galois used the theory of groups with brilliant success. Galois was indeed one of the great pioneers in this abstract theory, today of fundamental importance in all mathematics. . . .

He was buried in the common ditch of the South Cemetery, so that today there remains no trace of the grave of Evariste Galois. His enduring monument is his collected works. They fill sixty pages.

E. T. BELL: *Men of Mathematics*[1]

Often the question is raised as to who was the greatest mathematician who ever lived. It is a difficult question to answer; usually the three

[1] Copyright 1937 by E. T. Bell. By permission of Simon and Schuster, Inc.

greatest are named (Archimedes, Gauss, and Newton) rather than just one. But it is not unlikely that, if Galois had lived only a few years longer, his name would have served to answer the question unequivocally. Certainly no mathematician has ever done more before he was 21.

▶ **EXERCISE 33**

1. Suppose f and g are functions and we are given the equation: $f(x) = g(x)$. Explain verbally and by means of symbols exactly what is meant when we say: "The number r is a solution (or 'root') of the equation $f(x) = g(x)$."

2. Solve the Egyptian problem of this section.

3. Solve the Babylonian problem of this section.

4. What is the reason for the stipulation "$a \neq 0$" in our definitions of algebraic equations of various degrees?

5. An artistic tradition, which it has been said goes back to Greek times, claims that a rectangle is most pleasing to the eye when it has the following property:

If two squares are constructed with the length and width respectively of the given rectangle as sides, then the difference between the areas of the two squares will be equal to the area of the given rectangle. (This is the so-called golden rectangle.)

Assuming that a golden rectangle has width 1 unit and length x units, where $x > 1$, express its defining property as a quadratic equation in x and solve for x. Obtain a rational approximation to your answer by using the approximation 2.2 for $\sqrt{5}$. Examine several actual rectangles to see how close they come to being golden rectangles (i.e., find the ratio between their length and width and compare with your solution for x).

6. With the aid of formulas, solve for x, and where feasible, verify that your solutions are correct:

(a) $2x - 14 = 0$ (b) $x - 7 = 7 - x$

(c) $x^2 - 1 = x$ (d) $6x^2 - 13x + 6 = 0$

(e) $2x^2 + 3x - 2 = 0$ (f) $2x^2 + 3x + 2 = 0$

(g) $x^2 - 1 = 0$ (h) $x^2 = 0$

(i) $x^2 + x = 0$ (j) $a^2x^2 - 5ax + 4 = 0$

(k) $x^2 + x + 1 = 0$ (l) $x^2 + (p^2 + 1)x + 1 = 0$

★(m) $x^3 + 3x^2 + 3x + 1 = 0$ ★(n) $x^3 + 3x^2 + 9x + 5 = 0$

★(o) $x^3 - 6x^2 - 4 = 0$ ★(p) $x^3 + 63x = 316$

★(q) $x^3 - 9x + 8 = 0$ ★(r) $x^3 - 63x = 162$

★7. Find, by trial, integer solutions of equations (q) and (r) above.

8. Write a simpler expression for each of the following sets, assuming

that the universal set is: (i) the set of all real numbers; (ii) the set of all positive integers.

(a) $\{x \mid x^2 = 9\}$ (b) $\{x \mid x^2 = 9, x + 1 = 4\}$

(c) $\{x \mid -1 \leqslant x \leqslant 3\}$ (d) $\{x \mid x^2 = -1\}$

(e) $\{x \mid x \leqslant 7\} \cap \{x \mid x \geqslant 2\}$

8.3 ON THE SOLUTION OF EQUATIONS: THE "CANDIDATE" POINT OF VIEW

In this section we shall consider a very general approach to the problem of solving equations.

We apply the point of view we have in mind to the solution of the equation:

$$2x + 4 = 0$$

In solving this equation, we may reason as follows:

Let us suppose for the moment that there *is* a solution of this equation, i.e., there is a number x such that $2x + 4 = 0$.

Then, adding -4 to both sides of this equation, it must be true (why?) that $2x = -4$.

Now, dividing both sides of the preceding equation by 2, it must be true (why?) that $x = -2$.

Our conclusion, then, is that, *if* there is a number x such that $2x + 4 = 0$, then there is only one such, and it is -2. In other words, we have shown that the only *possibility* for a solution is -2, but we have not proved that this possibility actually *is* a solution. That, however, is easily done; for substituting -2 for x in the given equation:

$$2(-2) + 4 = -4 + 4 = 0$$

This is a true statement; and since a solution of the equation $2x + 4 = 0$ is simply a number which yields a true statement when substituted for x in the equation, it follows that -2 *is* a solution of the given equation.

Now, by way of contrast, consider the equation:

$$x + 1 = x + 2$$

Here ordinary methods lead to no solution; for subtracting x from both sides, we arrive at: $1 = 2$. This is a very peculiar statement and, in any case, suggests no solution for x.

Let us attempt, then, something out of the ordinary. We multiply both sides by $x - 1$. Then

$$x^2 - 1 = x^2 + x - 2$$
$$x = 1$$

But substituting $x = 1$ in the original equation leads to: $1 + 1 = 1 + 2$, or $2 = 3$, which is, of course, not true; hence, 1 is *not* a solution of the given equation.

With regard to this paradoxical situation, the facts are actually as follows: First of all, *if* there were a number x such that $x + 1 = x + 2$, *then* by subtracting x from both sides, we would be able to conclude that $1 = 2$. Since this conclusion is absurd (i.e., contradictory; see Theorem R21 and the trichotomy axiom), our hypothesis, which states that there is such a number x, must be false. A correct conclusion, then, is this: The equation $x + 1 = x + 2$ has no solution.

Secondly, we point out that our method in deriving the result $x = 1$ directly above is perfectly valid, but again, it is based upon the assumption that the equation $x + 1 = x + 2$ has a solution. What we have shown is that, *if* the given equation has a solution, *then* a solution is $x = 1$. But actually the equation has no solution and the *possibility* $x = 1$ must be discarded.

Now we turn our attention to the solution of quadratic equations in x; we consider, in particular, the equation:

$$x^2 - 3x + 2 = 0$$

Again, we suppose to begin with that there *is* a number x such that $x^2 - 3x + 2 = 0$. But if x is any real number, then $x^2 - 3x + 2 = (x - 1)(x - 2)$. Therefore:

$$(x - 1)(x - 2) = 0$$

Now (by Theorem R9 of Section 4.8), if the product of the numbers $x - 1$ and $x - 2$ is 0, then

$$x - 1 = 0 \quad \text{or} \quad x - 2 = 0$$

Furthermore, if $x - 1 = 0$, then $x = 1$; and if $x - 2 = 0$, then $x = 2$.

We conclude, then, that, *if* the equation $x^2 - 3x + 2 = 0$ has a solution, that solution must be 1 or 2. Our process of reasoning has not yet justified our saying that either of these numbers *is* a solution of the given equation, but only that there are *no other* solutions possible; our method, so to speak, has given us the only possible "candidates" for the position of solution to the given equation, but the candidates have not yet been elected—we must substitute into the original equation to see which, if any, of the possible solutions are actual solutions:

Substituting 1 for x: $1^2 - 3 \cdot 1 + 2 = 1 - 3 + 2 = 0$.

Substituting 2 for x: $2^2 - 3 \cdot 2 + 2 = 4 - 6 + 2 = 0$.

Both candidates have been elected; now we may say that the roots of the given equation are $x = 1$ and $x = 2$.

Finally, we consider a third equation, one involving a square root:

$$x + \sqrt{x} = 6$$

Remember that complex roots are what we seek; but in this case we must further restrict ourselves to *real* complex numbers since the symbol $\sqrt{}$ has been defined only for real numbers.

Our reasoning in solving the above equation might go as follows:

If x is a real number such that

$$x + \sqrt{x} = 6$$

then

$$\sqrt{x} = 6 - x$$

and squaring both sides

$$x = 36 - 12x + x^2$$

Working with this quadratic equation as in the preceding case, we conclude that the only possible candidates for a solution to the given equation are $x = 4$ and $x = 9$. Now let us see whether either, or both, or neither are solutions.

Checking 4: $4 + \sqrt{4} = 4 + 2 = 6$.

Checking 9: $9 + \sqrt{9} = 9 + 3 = 12 \neq 6$. (Remember that $\sqrt{9}$ means: the non-negative square root of 9!)

Our final conclusion, then, is that $x = 4$ is the only solution of the equation $x + \sqrt{x} = 6$.

(Values like $x = 9$ in the preceding case, which are suggested by certain methods of solving equations, but which turn out *not* to be roots, are unfortunately sometimes called "extraneous roots." It has been said of the Holy Roman Empire that it was neither holy, nor Roman, nor an empire. It may be remarked that extraneous roots are roots in the same sense that the Holy Roman Empire was an empire.)

8.4 QUADRATIC EQUATIONS

One of the techniques which we shall have to employ frequently in the mathematics which follows is that for solving quadratic equations. The student will therefore find it greatly to his advantage to make sure that he is competent in this technique. Toward this end, we shall review certain methods, commonly presented in high-school algebra, for the solution of quadratic equations.

We note that, as a last resort, the quadratic formula may be used to solve *any* quadratic equation in one unknown. In this section we shall be concerned, however, with methods which, when they are applicable, are simpler than the formula method.

Illustrative Example 1. Solve: $3 - 2x = x^2$.

SOLUTION. We add -3 and $2x$ to both sides and reverse the equality to arrive at the equation:

$$x^2 + 2x - 3 = 0$$

Factoring: $(x + 3)(x - 1) = 0$

By Theorem R9: $x + 3 = 0$ or $x - 1 = 0$

Therefore: $x = -3$ or $x = 1$

From what we have said so far, it would appear that all we can say at this point is that -3 and 1 are the only *candidates* for solutions to the given equation.

In the particular case of algebraic equations, however, it can easily be seen (and will be even more evident after reading the next section) that candidates for roots arrived at by the method of factoring, and by the use of Theorem R9, will always be successful candidates.

In such a case, if we check to see that our candidates satisfy the given equation, we do so only to make sure that we have not made an error in the process of solution.

The student may verify that no error has been made in this case by substituting -3 and 1 for x in the given equation and arriving at true statements.

Illustrative Example 2. Solve: $4x^2 = 8x$.

SOLUTION: The temptation to divide both sides by $4x$ to arrive at $x = 2$ should be avoided. For, although 2 actually *is* a root, there happens to be another root which has been lost in this process.

When solving equations, avoid, if possible, multiplying or dividing by anything but nonzero numbers.

In this case, there is no harm in dividing both sides by the number 4:

$$x^2 = 2x$$

But then, in order to take advantage of Theorem R9, we add $-2x$ to both sides, to arrive at:

$$x^2 - 2x = 0$$

Factoring: $x(x - 2) = 0$

Therefore: $x = 0$ and $x = 2$ are the solutions.

Illustrative Example 3. Solve: $x^2 - 2x = 8$.

SOLUTION: Here the trap to be avoided is to imagine that, since the equation may be written $x(x - 2) = 1 \cdot 8$, equating the factors: $x = 1$, $x - 2 = 8$, will yield solutions. It is easy to verify that neither 1 nor 10 are solutions of the given equation, and, indeed, there is no reason why they should be. *The method of factoring and the use of Theorem R9 require that one side of the equation be 0.*

We therefore proceed in this fashion:

$$x^2 - 2x - 8 = 0$$
$$(x - 4)(x + 2) = 0$$

$x = 4$ and $x = -2$ are the solutions.

▶ EXERCISE 34

1. Solve, without using formulas:

(a) $x^2 - 4 = 0$

(b) $x^2 - x = 0$

(c) $x^2 - x = 6$

(d) $4x^2 - 9 = 0$

(e) $4x^2 - 9x = 0$

(f) $4x^2 - 9x = -5$

(g) $x^2 - 5x + 6 = 0$

(h) $5x = 6x^2 + 1$

(i) $5x + 2 = 1 - 6x^2$

(j) $6x^2 + 5x = 6$

(k) $x^2 = 0$

(l) $x^2 = 2x$

(m) $x^3 = 0$

(n) $x^2 - 2 = (x - 1)(x + 1)$

★(o) $x^4 - 12x^2 + 27 = 0$

★(p) $x^3 - x^2 - x + 1 = 0$

2. Solve:

(a) $x - \sqrt{x} = 2$

(b) $x + \sqrt{x - 2} = 8$

(c) $3x + \sqrt{1 + x} = 7$

(d) $9x - 3\sqrt{x} = 2$

(e) $1 + x = 2\sqrt{x}$

(f) $1 + x = \sqrt{2x}$

(g) $\sqrt{x} + \sqrt{4x} = 2$

(h) $\sqrt{x} + \sqrt{2x} = \sqrt{3x}$

(i) $\sqrt{x^2} = -1$

(j) $(\sqrt{x})^2 = -1$

(k) $\sqrt{x + 6} + \sqrt{x - 6} = 10$

(l) $2\sqrt{x} + \sqrt{10 + 4x} = 5$

8.5 ON THE SOLUTION OF RELATIONS: THE "EQUIVALENCE" POINT OF VIEW

We return to the equation: $2x + 4 = 0$.

In our preceding treatment, we derived from this equation, by adding -4 to both sides, the equation: $2x = -4$; and we may say the following about the relation between these equations:

If x is a complex number such that $2x + 4 = 0$, then $2x = -4$. That is to say, any complex number which satisfies the equation $2x + 4 = 0$ must also satisfy the equation $2x = -4$.

But now suppose a complex number satisfies the *second* of these two equations, namely: $2x = -4$. Then by adding 4 to both sides, we would have: $2x + 4 = 0$. In other words, any complex number which satisfies the equation $2x = -4$ must also satisfy the equation $2x + 4 = 0$.

We have shown that any complex number which satisfies *either* of these two equations satisfies the other. Thus, to solve one, we may, if we wish, solve the other. In practice, in our particular case, we now forget about the equation $2x + 4 = 0$ and make our new problem that of solving the equation $2x = -4$.

Recalling that the set of all solutions of an equation is called the *solution set* of the equation, we are led to make the following definition:

Definition. Two equations are *equivalent* if their solution sets are the same.

Inequalities may be similarly treated. As in the case of equations in x, a solution of an inequality in x is simply a number, which, when it replaces x in the inequality, converts the inequality into a meaningful and true statement. However, in dealing with inequalities, our universal set (unless otherwise mentioned) will be the set of all real numbers rather than the set of all complex numbers, since the relations $<$, $>$, $\leqslant$, $\geqslant$ are not defined for any but *real* complex numbers (see page 134).

Definition. Two inequalities are *equivalent* if their solution sets are the same.

Now in solving an equation, or an inequality, or indeed any relation, if we proceed from our first step to our final solution by a sequence of *equivalent* relations, then there can be no "extraneous" numbers creeping in; our results *must* be solutions.

To analyze all the circumstances under which derived equations or inequalities would be equivalent to the original would be tedious. We shall, however, consider several of the most useful of these. The student will recognize them as the processes used most often in the solution of equations.

First of all, we may add to (hence, of course, also subtract from) both sides of an equation any complex number, and the result will be an equivalent equation. The reason for this was brought out in our examination of the relation between the equations $2x + 4 = 0$ and $2x = -4$.

An analogous statement may be made about inequalities. For example (by Theorem R17) the inequality $2x + 4 > 0$ may be shown to be equivalent to $2x > -4$.

The statements made in the following two tables may be similarly justified.

I. SOME PROCESSES WHICH TRANSFORM EQUATIONS INTO EQUIVALENT EQUATIONS

(i) Adding to (or subtracting from) both sides, equal complex numbers.

(ii) Multiplying (or dividing) both sides by equal *nonzero* complex numbers.

(iii) Substitution of equals for equals (see below).

(iv) "Transposition." [That is, the equation $a(x) + b(x) = c(x)$ is equivalent to $a(x) = c(x) - b(x)$.]

II. SOME PROCESSES WHICH TRANSFORM INEQUALITIES INTO EQUIVALENT INEQUALITIES

(a) Adding to (or subtracting from) both sides, equal real numbers.

(b) Multiplying (or dividing) both sides by equal *positive* real numbers.

(c) Multiplying (or dividing) both sides by equal negative real numbers, *and at the same time reversing the sign of inequality.*

(d) Substitution of equals for equals (see below).

(e) "Transposition." (In Table I, item (iv), replace = by any one of the inequality relations.)

A word as to (iii) and (d) above: By " substitution of equals for equals," we mean, first of all, that in both equalities and inequalities a number may be replaced by an equal number. One may, for example, replace $\frac{4}{2}$ by 2; or, if a and b are numbers, one may replace $(a - b)(a + b)$ by $a^2 - b^2$; both replacements would transform a given equation or inequality only into an equivalent equation or inequality.

Secondly, suppose f and g are equal functions; in the case of equations, both with domain *all* complex numbers; in the case of inequalities both with domain *all* real numbers. Then, in solving for x, $f(x)$ may be replaced by $g(x)$, and the result will be an equivalent equation or inequality. For example, in solving the equation $x^2 - 3x + 2 = 0$, one may replace $x^2 - 3x + 2$ by $(x - 1)(x - 2)$ to arrive at the equivalent equation: $(x - 1)(x - 2) = 0$.

*REMARK. This last paragraph may be sharpened, but we shall find no need to frame a more general statement here. Note that the substitution of 0 for $(1/x) - (1/x)$ does not fall within our set of allowable substitutions, for $(1/x) - (1/x)$ is defined neither for all real nor for all complex numbers. Why not?

We shall now prove a lemma, and use it, together with the principles of Table 1, to derive the formula for the solution of a quadratic equation.

Lemma. The equation $[f(x)]^2 = [g(x)]^2$ is equivalent to the pair of equations: $f(x) = \pm g(x)$.

PROOF: We must prove: (a) that, if a number p is a root of $[f(x)]^2 = [g(x)]^2$, then p is a root of $f(x) = \pm g(x)$; and (b) conversely.

*Proof of (a). We are given that p is a complex number such that: $[f(p)]^2 = [g(p)]^2$. Then $[f(p)]^2 - [g(p)]^2 = 0$, so that $[f(p) - g(p)][f(p) + g(p)] = 0$. Therefore (by Theorem R9), $f(p) - g(p) = 0$ or $f(p) + g(p) = 0$, i.e., $f(p) = g(p)$ or $f(p) = -g(p)$. But this means that p is a root of $f(x) = g(x)$ or of $f(x) = -g(x)$, Q.E.D.

Proof of (b). We are given that p is a complex number such that: $f(p) = g(p)$ or $f(p) = -g(p)$. By the axiom of "product substitution," and in the second case by the law for multiplying opposites, $[f(p)]^2 = [g(p)]^2$. But this means that p is a root of $[f(x)]^2 = [g(x)]^2$, Q.E.D.

The derivation of the quadratic formula utilizes a trick called "completing the square," which is useful in a number of other applications also:

Suppose we wish to add a real number to the expression $x^2 + 6x$ so that the resulting expression shall be a "perfect square"; that is to say, suppose we wish to replace the question marks in the following equation by numbers so that the resulting statement will be true for any number x:

$$x^2 + 6x + ? = (x + ?)^2$$

But if x and a are any real numbers:

$$x^2 + 2ax + a^2 = (x + a)^2$$

Comparing equations, we see that we seek a value of a such that $2a = 6$, i.e., such that $a = \frac{6}{2} = 3$. In that case, a^2 must be 9. And indeed, letting $a = 3$ in the preceding equation:

$$x^2 + 6x + 9 = (x + 3)^2$$

so that the addition of $(\frac{6}{2})^2$ to $x^2 + 6x$ transforms the expression into a perfect square.

In general, it is easily verified that

$$x^2 + kx + \left(\frac{k}{2}\right)^2 = \left(x + \frac{k}{2}\right)^2$$

so that adding to $x^2 + kx$ the expression $(k/2)^2$ will always result in a perfect square.

Now we derive the quadratic formula by successively transforming the original equation

$$ax^2 + bx + c = 0$$

(where a, b, c are complex numbers and $a \neq 0$) into equivalent equations. The student is expected to fill in one of the numbers (i) through (iv) of Table I or the preceding lemma to the right of each of the following equations, as a reason for that equation being equivalent to its predecessor.

1. $x^2 + \dfrac{b}{a}x + \dfrac{c}{a} = 0$ 1.

2. $x^2 + \dfrac{b}{a}x = -\dfrac{c}{a}$ 2.

3. $x^2 + \dfrac{b}{a}x + \left(\dfrac{b}{2a}\right)^2 = \left(\dfrac{b}{2a}\right)^2 - \dfrac{c}{a}$ 3.

4. $\left(x + \dfrac{b}{2a}\right)^2 = \dfrac{b^2 - 4ac}{4a^2}$ 4.

5. $\left(x + \dfrac{b}{2a}\right)^2 = \left(\dfrac{\sqrt{b^2 - 4ac}}{2a}\right)^2$ 5.

6. $x + \dfrac{b}{2a} = \pm \dfrac{\sqrt{b^2 - 4ac}}{2a}$ 6.

7. $x = -\dfrac{b}{2a} \pm \dfrac{\sqrt{b^2 - 4ac}}{2a}$ 7.

8. $x = \dfrac{-b \pm \sqrt{b^2 - 4ac}}{2a}$ 8.

Now we turn our attention to the solution of an *in*equality; in particular, the inequality: $2x - 4 < 10$. The student is asked to justify each of the following steps by a number chosen from Table II and written in the appropriate place:

1. $2x < 14$ 1.
2. $x < 7$ 2.

As another illustrative example, we solve: $4 - 2x < 11$:

1. $-2x < 7$ 1.
2. $2x > -7$ 2.
3. $x > -3.5$ 3.

Finally, we solve the "simultaneous" inequalities: $6 \leqslant 4 - 2x < 16$ (read: "$4 - 2x$ is greater than or equal to 6 and less than 16"):

1. $2 \leqslant -2x < 12$ 1.
2. $-2 \geqslant 2x > -12$ 2.
3. $-1 \geqslant x > -6$ 3.

Our result means that a real number will satisfy the given conditions (i.e., it will belong to the solution set of the given simultaneous inequalities) if and only if it lies between -6 and -1) but is not equal to -6. It is customary to denote this "interval" of numbers $(-6, -1]$. In fact we shall now adopt the following standard nomenclature and notation, given real numbers a, b such that $a < b$.

$[a, b]$ (closed interval): the set of all real numbers between and including a and b; denoted earlier in the text: $\{a \cdot \cdot b\}$. Diagram:

(a, b) (open interval): the set of all real numbers between a and b, excluding both a and b. Diagram:

[a, b) (half-open interval—closed on the left, open on the right): the set of all real numbers between a and b, including a, but excluding b. Diagram:

(a, b] (description left to student).

[a, ∞) (closed ray): the set of all real numbers greater than or equal to a. (*Note*: "∞" is read: "infinity.") Diagram:

(a, ∞), (−∞, a], (−∞, a) (descriptions left to student).

The notation for intervals conflicts with other notation [what else, for example, may (a, b) represent?], but again, the context in which the notation is used should prevent ambiguity.

Using this notation, we may compactly express the preceding three solutions as follows: The solution set of $2x - 4 < 10$ is $(-\infty, 7)$; of $4 - 2x < 11$, $(-3.5, \infty)$; of $6 \leqslant 4 - 2x < 16$, $(-6, -1]$.

Before terminating this section, we note several processes that are useful in solving equations but do *not* always lead to equivalent equations.

We have encountered such processes already: In Section 8.3, for example, multiplying both sides of the equation $x + 1 = x + 2$ by $x - 1$ led to an equation of which 1 was a root, although 1 is not a root of the original equation.

Later on in Section 8.3, we squared both sides of the equation $\sqrt{x} = 6 - x$ to arrive at an equation of which 9 is a root, although it is not a root of the original equation.

We concluded, then, that multiplication by anything other than nonzero numbers and squaring both sides of an equation are processes which may lead to a new equation which is not equivalent to the original.

▶ **EXERCISE 35**

1.(a) Given real numbers $a < b$, define, name, and illustrate by means of a diagram each of the intervals (a, b], (a, ∞), (−∞, a], (−∞, a).

(b) Given real numbers $a < b$, (a, b] may be defined as follows: $(a, b] = \{x \mid a < x \leqslant b\}$. Similarly, use the set-builder notation to define each of the other types of intervals defined above.

2. Find (and diagram) the solution set in each case:

(a) $2x + 3 > 5$ (b) $3x + 2 < 5$
(c) $3 - 2x \leqslant 5 + 3x$ (d) $1 \leqslant 2x + 3 < 1$
(e) $-5 \leqslant 3 - 2x < 5$ (f) $-2 \leqslant -x < 3$

(g) $1 < 2 - x < -1$ (h) $1 \leqslant 5 - x \leqslant 1$

(i) $7 \leqslant 4 - 3x < 10$ (j) $8 < 4 - 4x \leqslant 16$

3. Solve the following inequalities; draw diagrams to illustrate intervals of solution.

(a) $x^2 < 4$.   (*Solution:* By Problem 9 of Exercise 20, the solution is: $-2 < x < 2$.)

(b) $x^2 < 9$ (c) $x^2 > 9$

(d) $x^2 > 5$ (e) $x^2 < 5$

(f) $x^2 > 0$ (g) $x^2 < 0$

(h) $x^2 - 4x + 1 < 0$.   (*Solution:* This is equivalent to: $x^2 - 4x < -1$; then complete the square by adding 4 to both sides: $x^2 - 4x + 4 < 3$. Thus: $(x - 2)^2 < 3$. By Problem 9 of Exercise 20: $-\sqrt{3} < x - 2 < \sqrt{3}$; finally: $2 - \sqrt{3} < x < 2 + \sqrt{3}$.)

(i) $x^2 + 2x < \cdot 3$ (j) $x^2 < 2x$

(k) $x^2 + 3x - 4 < 0$ (l) $x^2 + 2x > 3$

(m) $x^2 > 2x$ (n) $x^2 + 3x - 4 > 0$

(o) $2x^2 + 3x - 2 < 0$ (p) $x^2 + 1 > 0$

(q) $x^2 + 1 < 0$ (r) $x^2 - 1 \leqslant 0$

4. Solve the following equations or inequalities:

(a) $|x + 1| = 5$. Solution: From the definition of absolute value (Problem 13, Exercise 9), this equation is equivalent to: $x + 1 = \pm 5$. Therefore our solution is $x = 4$ or -6.

(b) $|2x + 3| = 7$ (c) $|2x - 3| = 7$

(d) $|3 - 2x| = 7$

(e) $|x + 1| < 5$ (*Hint:* By Problem 13, part 9, of Exercise 20, this inequality is equivalent to: $-5 < x + 1 < 5$.)

(f) $|x + 1| > 5$ (g) $|x + 1| \leqslant 5$

★(h) $|x^2 - 4| < 0.1$ (Find endpoints of intervals of solution correct to two decimal places.)

5. A stone is thrown downward from the top of a building. The height s (in feet above the ground) of the stone, t seconds after it is thrown, is given by the formula, $s = 960 - 64t - 16t^2$.

(a) When does the stone reach the ground? (*Hint:* Solve the equation $960 - 64t - 16t^2 = 0$.)

(b) During what interval of time will the stone be more than 768 ft above the ground? (*Hint:* Solve the inequality $960 - 64t - 16t^2 > 768$.)

(c) During what interval of time will the stone be less than 768 ft but more than 240 ft above the ground?

(d) How tall is the building?

6. Show by means of an example that *division* of both sides of an equation by something other than a number may lead to an equation not equivalent to the original.

*7. Is the equation $\sqrt{x^2 + 1} = 5$ equivalent to the equation $x^2 + 1 = 25$? Justify your answer.
How about the equations $\sqrt{x^2 + y^2} = 5$ and $x^2 + y^2 = 25$?

*8. Are equivalences of equations and inequalities equivalence relationships? (See Section 2.14.) Justify your answer.

8.6 RATIONAL ROOTS

A type of algebraic equation encountered frequently is one in which all coefficients are integers. In solving algebraic equations of this type, rational roots, when they exist, are generally the easiest roots to find. A method for finding them is given by the following theorem.

Theorem on Rational Roots. Suppose N/D is a rational root in lowest terms of the algebraic equation $a_0 x^n + a_1 x^{n-1} + \cdots + a_{n-1} x + a_n = 0$, where $a_0, \cdots, a_n$ are integers, $a_0 \neq 0$, and $a_n \neq 0$.
Then $N \mid a_n$ and $D \mid a_0$.

PROOF. We note first of all that to say that N/D is rational and in lowest terms means that N and D are integers with no common prime factor, and that $D \neq 0$.

Secondly, we note that $N \neq 0$. For if $N = 0$, then $N/D = 0$ is a root of the given equation, and substituting we have $a_n = 0$, contrary to hypothesis.

Now since N/D is a root of the given equation:

$$a_0 \frac{N^n}{D^n} + a_1 \frac{N^{n-1}}{D^{n-1}} + \cdots + a_{n-1} \frac{N}{D} + a_n = 0$$

and multiplying by D^n:

$$a_0 N^n + a_1 N^{n-1} D + \cdots + a_{n-1} N D^{n-1} + a_n D^n = 0$$

from which follows:

(1) $$a_n D^n = NI$$

where I is an integer.

(It is left to the student to write out the expression for I in terms of N, D, etc., and to explain why I is an integer.)

Now N, being a nonzero integer, is equal to $\pm M$, where M is a natural number. If $M = 1$, then $N = \pm 1$. In this case, certainly $N \mid a_n$, since 1 divides any integer, and so does -1.

Otherwise, by the Fundamental Theorem of Arithmetic (Exercise 2, Problem 5), M is equal to a unique (except possibly for order) product of primes $p_1 \cdots p_r$. Hence $N = \pm p_1 \cdots p_r$. Similarly, a_n, D, and I are equal either to ± 1, or to $\pm$ unique products of primes. Substituting these unique expressions into (1), we have unique decompositions of the equal numbers $a_n D^n$ and NI. But $p_1, \ldots, p_r$ appear in the decomposition of NI. By the uniqueness of our decompositions, $p_1, \ldots, p_r$ must appear in $a_n D^n$. However, since N, D can have no common prime factor (see above), none of the primes $p_1, \ldots, p_r$ appear in the decomposition of D, hence not in D^n either. Thus $p_1, \ldots, p_r$ must appear in the decomposition of a_n, i.e., $a_n = p_1 \cdots p_r q$, where q is some integer. Hence $a_n = (\pm N)q = N(\pm q)$; i.e., $N \mid a_n$.

The proof that $D \mid a_0$ is similar, and is left as an exercise for the student.

Illustrative Example I. Solve:

$$p(x) = 6x^4 + 7x^3 + 5x^2 - x - 2 = 0$$

SOLUTION. Since all coefficients are integers, and $a_0 = 6 \neq 0$, and $a_n = -2 \neq 0$, our theorem on rational roots applies, and tells us that, for a rational root of $p(x) = 0$, the only possible numerators are the integer divisors of -2: ± 1, ± 2, and the only possible denominators are the integer divisors of 6: ± 1, ± 2, ± 3, ± 6.

Therefore the only possible rational roots of $p(x) = 0$ are ± 1, ± 2, $\pm \frac{1}{2}$, $\pm \frac{1}{3}$, $\pm \frac{2}{3}$, $\pm \frac{1}{6}$.

It is rather easy to compute $p(1)$ and even $p(-1)$ by direct substitution $[p(1) = 15$, $p(-1) = 6 - 7 + 5 + 1 - 2 = 3]$, and thus to see that neither 1 nor -1 is a root. But to test the other possible rational roots, there is no question but that the method of synthetic substitution (see Section 7.3) is easier. Thus, to test the possibility $\frac{1}{2}$:

6	7	5	-1	-2	$\lfloor \frac{1}{2}$
	3	5	5	2	
6	10	10	4	0	

We see that $p(\frac{1}{2}) = 0$, or in other words, $\frac{1}{2}$ is a root of the given equation. Furthermore, since our computation is the same as that which would be used (in the process called synthetic division) to divide $p(x)$ by $x - \frac{1}{2}$, we know that:

(1) $$p(x) = (x - \tfrac{1}{2})(6x^3 + 10x^2 + 10x + 4)$$

Now a product of complex numbers is equal to zero if and only if at least one factor is equal to zero. Thus the equation $p(x) = 0$ is equivalent to $x - \frac{1}{2} = 0$ or $6x^3 + 10x^2 + 10x + 4 = 0$. The first leads to the root $\frac{1}{2}$ that we already know about. The second equation needs now to be investigated. It is, of course, equivalent to:

$$3x^3 + 5x^2 + 5x + 2 = 0$$

Applying our theorem on rational roots again, we see that of the original possibilities, $\pm\frac{1}{2}$ and $\pm\frac{1}{6}$ may now be rejected (since the possible denominators now are only ±1, ±3). Further trials show that $-\frac{2}{3}$ is another rational root:

$$
\begin{array}{cccc|c}
3 & 5 & 5 & 2 & \underline{\quad -\frac{2}{3}} \\
 & -2 & -2 & -2 & \\
\hline
3 & 3 & 3 & 0 &
\end{array}
$$

And as before, we now know that:
$$3x^3 + 5x^2 + 5x + 2 = (x + \tfrac{2}{3})(3x^2 + 3x + 3) = (x + \tfrac{2}{3})(x^2 + x + 1)(3)$$
Multiplying by 2:

(2) $\qquad 6x^3 + 10x^2 + 10x + 4 = (x + \tfrac{2}{3})(x^2 + x + 1)(6)$

Now substituting (2) into (1):

(3) $\qquad p(x) = (x - \tfrac{1}{2})(x + \tfrac{2}{3})(x^2 + x + 1)(6)$

Clearly, further roots of $p(x) = 0$ can only be roots of $x^2 + x + 1 = 0$. But now that we have "depressed" the original fourth-degree equation to a quadratic equation, the task that remains is routine. A quadratic equation can always be solved; in this case the quadratic formula will do the trick. The solution set of the original equation is $\{\tfrac{1}{2}, -\tfrac{2}{3}, (-1 \pm i\sqrt{3})/2\}$

Illustrative Example 2. Solve: $4x^5 + 4x^4 - 3x^3 - 4x^2 - x = 0$.

SOLUTION. Note that $a_n = 0$, so that our theorem on rational roots does not immediately apply. (Actually, the theorem may be proved to apply even in this case, but as we shall see in a moment, we have no need for the generalization.) But the given equation is equivalent to $x(4x^4 + 4x^3 - 3x^2 - 4x - 1) = 0$. Then $x = 0$ is a solution, and the other solutions are the roots of the depressed equation: $4x^4 + 4x^3 - 3x^2 - 4x - 1 = 0$. We proceed to solve this equation as in Illustrative Example 1, but with less verbiage:

For rational roots, possible numerators are: ±1; possible denominators are ±1, ±2, ±4. Possible rational roots are: ±1, $\pm\frac{1}{2}$, $\pm\frac{1}{4}$.

In order to bring out a point, we try $-\frac{1}{2}$ first:

$$
\begin{array}{ccccc|c}
4 & 4 & -3 & -4 & -1 & \underline{\quad -\frac{1}{2}} \\
 & -2 & -1 & 2 & 1 & \\
\hline
4 & 2 & -4 & -2 & 0 &
\end{array}
$$

The depressed equation may be divided by 2. Then, disregarding the fact that $-\frac{1}{2}$ has already been tried, and since it is still a possible root of the depressed equation, we try $-\frac{1}{2}$ again:

2	1	-2		-1	$\lfloor -\frac{1}{2}$
	-1	0		1	
2	0	-2		0	

Again dividing the depressed equation by 2, we arrive at the equation $x^2 - 1 = 0$, whose roots are, of course, ± 1. Solution set of original equation: $\{0, -\frac{1}{2}, -\frac{1}{2}, \pm 1\}$. (We write $-\frac{1}{2}$ twice in the solution set to indicate that it derives from two linear factors of $4x^5 + 4x^4 - 3x^3 - 4x^2 - x$. In fact, following the analysis of Illustrative Example 1: $4x^5 + 4x^4 - 3x^3 - 4x^2 - x = x(x + \frac{1}{2})(x + \frac{1}{2})(x - 1)(x + 1)(4)$; $-\frac{1}{2}$ is called a *double* root of the original equation.)

▶ **EXERCISE 36**

1. Solve the equation $p(x) = 0$, where $p(x) =$
(a) $9x^3 + 18x^2 - x - 2$ (b) $2x^4 - x^3 - 6x^2 + 7x - 2$
(c) $6x^4 + 7x^3 - 22x^2 - 7x + 6$ (d) $4x^4 + 4x^0 - 7x^2 - 8x - 2$
(e) $4x^4 - 12x^3 - x^2 + 3x$ (f) $4x^4 - 17x^2 + 4$

(g) $x^4 - \frac{1}{6}x^3 + \frac{11}{6}x^2 - \frac{1}{3}x - \frac{1}{3}$ (h) $x^2 + x + \dfrac{1}{x} + \dfrac{1}{x^2}$

2.(a) through (g). The polynomial $p(x) = 6x^4 + 7x^3 + 5x^2 - x - 2$ may be factored into the product of linear and quadratic polynomials, all of whose coefficients are integers by solving the equation $p(x) = 0$, and deriving the factorization: $p(x) = (x - \frac{1}{2})(x + \frac{2}{3})(x^2 + x + 1)(6)$ as in Illustrative Example 1 of the preceding section. Then
$$p(x) = (x - \tfrac{1}{2})(x + \tfrac{2}{3})(x^2 + x + 1)(2)(3)$$
$$= (2)(x - \tfrac{1}{2})(3)(x + \tfrac{2}{3})(x^2 + x + 1)$$
$$= (2x - 1)(3x + 2)(x^2 + x + 1), \text{ which is the de-}$$
sired factorization. Use this technique to factor the polynomials of Problem 1a through 1g into the product of linear and quadratic polynomials, all of whose coefficients are integers.

3.(a) Prove that $\sqrt{2}$ is irrational by proving that $x^2 - 2 = 0$ has no rational roots.

(b) Prove that $\sqrt{3}$, $\sqrt{\frac{2}{3}}$, $\sqrt[3]{2}$ and $\sqrt[4]{10}$ are irrational.

4. Complete the parts of the proof of the theorem on rational roots that were left to the student.

5. Prove that if $a_0 = 1$, then the algebraic equation $a_0 x^n + \cdots + a_n = 0$, with integer coefficients, can have no rational roots but integers that divide a_n.

6. Use the technique of the last section to find all the cube roots of 1 and -1. (Note that Section 5.5 offers another way of solving this problem.)

8.7 THE NUMBER OF ROOTS OF AN ALGEBRAIC EQUATION

What can we say about the number of roots of an algebraic equation? Indeed, we have seen that, for equations of degree greater than 4, there is no general formula for a solution like those existing for equations of lower degree. Is it possible, then, that some algebraic equations with complex coefficients have no roots at all?

The answer to the last question is given by the so-called "Fundamental Theorem of Algebra," first proved (in his doctoral dissertation) by the German mathematician, Carl Friedrich Gauss (1777–1855). The theorem states one of the most important of all the properties of the complex number system.

Fundamental Theorem of Algebra. Every algebraic equation whose coefficients are complex numbers has a solution which is a complex number.

(The proof of this theorem is omitted since it requires a great deal of mathematics not yet at our disposal.)

Real numbers are, of course, special cases of complex numbers. Hence algebraic equations whose coefficients are real numbers are included among algebraic equations whose coefficients are complex numbers. Thus by the fundamental theorem of algebra, we can always be sure that an algebraic equation with real coefficients will have a complex root, even if it has no real roots. It is essentially for this reason that it is more natural to work with the larger set of complex numbers, when we seek roots of an algebraic equation with real coefficients, rather than with the restricted set of real numbers.

Now, in order to answer our original question, we first prove a preliminary theorem:

Theorem on Polynomial Factorization. If $p(x)$ is a polynomial over the complex numbers, of degree $n \geqslant 1$, then $p(x)$ is equal to the product of n linear polynomials over the complex numbers.

PROOF. Consider the algebraic equation $p(x) = 0$. By the Fundamental Theorem of Algebra, this equation has at least one complex root, r_1. Then by the factor theorem, $(x - r_1) \mid p(x)$, so that $p(x) = (x - r_1)p_1(x)$, where $p_1(x)$ is a polynomial over the complex numbers of degree $n - 1$.

If $p_1(x)$ is a complex number, we terminate the process at this point. Otherwise, $p_1(x)$ must be of degree at least 1, and, as before, a complex root r_2 of the equation $p(x) = 0$ must exist, and $p_1(x) = (x - r_2)p_2(x)$, where $p_2(x)$ is a polynomial over the complex numbers of degree one less than the degree of $p_1(x)$; that is to say, of degree $n - 2$.

Now we have $p(x) = (x - r_1)p_1(x) = (x - r_1)(x - r_2)p_2(x)$.

The process may be continued until we have:

$$p(x) = (x - r_1)(x - r_2) \cdots (x - r_n)p_n(x)$$

for $p_n(x)$ will be of degree $n - n = 0$, so that $p_n(x)$ is some nonzero complex number c. Therefore:

$$
\begin{aligned}
(1) \qquad p(x) &= (x - r_1)(x - r_2) \cdots (x - r_n)c \\
&= (cx - cr_1)(x - r_2) \cdots (x - r_n), \text{ Q.E.D.}
\end{aligned}
$$

Note that the final factor c must be equal to the coefficient of x^n in $p(x)$; for in the successive steps of the synthetic division process, the first coefficient does not change.

Definition. In the factorization (1) above, if the total number of times that $x - r$ occurs as a factor is m, then r is called a root of $p(x) = 0$ of multiplicity m.

Theorem on Number of Roots. An algebraic equation of degree n has at most n distinct roots; the sum of the multiplicities of the distinct roots is n.

PROOF: By the preceding theorem, an algebraic equation $p(x) = 0$ of degree n is equivalent to an equation:

$$c(x - r_1) \cdots (x - r_n) = 0$$

where $c \neq 0$, $r_1, \cdots, r_n$ are complex numbers. Clearly $r_1, \cdots, r_n$ are roots of this equation and, since in order for a product of complex numbers to be zero, at least one factor must be zero, there are no other roots. If $r_1, \cdots, r_n$ are all different, we have n roots. If some are equal to each other, we have fewer than n roots, but if each distinct root is counted a number of times equal to its multiplicity, the total of these multiplicities will be n.

NOTE. It is traditional to say that "an algebraic equation of degree n has n roots." This statement is correct, with the understanding that each root of multiplicity m is counted m times.

8.8 CONJUGATE ROOTS

Consider the function k (the "conjugacy" function) defined as follows:

Domain of k: Set of all complex numbers.
Mapping of k: $k(a + bi) = a - bi$ (the "conjugate" of $a + bi$), where a, b are any real numbers.

Thus:
$$k(2 + 3i) = 2 - 3i$$
$$k(3 - 4i) = k[3 + (-4)i] = 3 - (-4)i = 3 + 4i$$
$$k(7i) = k(0 + 7i) = 0 - 7i = -7i$$
$$k(2) = k(2 + 0i) = 2 - 0i = 2$$

In fact, generalizing from the last statement:

1. If a is a real number, then $k(a) = a$.

[The (easy) proof of statement 1 is left to the student.]
Further interesting properties of the function k are the following.

2. If u, v are complex numbers, then $k(uv) = k(u) \cdot k(v)$.

PROOF OF STATEMENT 2: Suppose $u = a + bi$, $v = c + di$, where a, b, c, d are real numbers. Then:

$$k(uv) = k[(a + bi)(c + di)] = k[ac + (ad + bc)i + bdi^2]$$
$$= k[(ac - bd) + (ad + bc)i]$$
$$= (ac - bd) - (ad + bc)i$$

while

$$k(u) \cdot k(v) = k(a + bi) \cdot k(c + di) = (a - bi)(c - di)$$
$$= ac - adi - bci + bdi^2$$
$$= (ac - bd) - (ad + bc)i$$

Thus, $k(uv) = k(u) \cdot k(v)$, Q.E.D.
As a corollary to statement 2, we may prove:

3. If $u_1, \cdots, u_n$ are complex numbers, then:
$$k(u_1 u_2 u_3 \cdots u_n) = k(u_1) \cdot k(u_2) \cdot k(u_3) \cdot \cdots \cdot k(u_n)$$

PROOF OF STATEMENT 3:

$$k(u_1 u_2 u_3 \cdots u_n) = k[(u_1)(u_2 u_3 \cdots u_n)]$$
$$= k(u_1) \cdot k(u_2 u_3 \cdots u_n) \quad \text{(by statement 2)}$$
$$= k(u_1) \cdot k[(u_2)(u_3 \cdots u_n)]$$
$$= k(u_1) \cdot k(u_2) \cdot k(u_3 \cdots u_n) \quad \text{(by statement 2)}$$
$$\vdots$$
$$= k(u_1) \cdot k(u_2) \cdot k(u_3) \cdot \cdots \cdot k(u_n) \quad \text{(by successive applications of statement 2)}$$

As an immediate consequence of statement 3, we have:

4. If u is a complex number, and n is any positive integer, then $k(u^n) = [k(u)]^n$. ("k of the nth power of u is equal to the nth power of k of u.")

PROOF OF STATEMENT 4: Let $u_1 = u$, $u_2 = u$, $\cdots$, $u_n = u$. Then:

$$k(u^n) = k(u_1 u_2 \cdots u_n)$$
$$= k(u_1) \cdot k(u_2) \cdot \cdots \cdot k(u_n) \quad \text{(by statement 3)}$$
$$= [k(u)]^n, \text{ Q.E.D.}$$

The proof of the next statement, being very much like the proof of statement 2, is left to the student:

5. If u, v are complex numbers, then $k(u + v) = k(u) + k(v)$.

[Another way of expressing statements 2 and 5 is to say that "the function k preserves multiplication and addition in the set of complex numbers."]

It is also left to the student to show that in almost the same way that statement 3 followed from statement 2 statement 6 follows from statement 5.

6. If u_1, $\cdots$, u_n are complex numbers, then:

$$k(u_1 + u_2 + u_3 + \cdots + u_n) = k(u_1) + k(u_2) + k(u_3) + \cdots + k(u_n)$$

Now we shall put our conjugacy function k to work in proving an important theorem about imaginary roots. The student may have noticed in solving quadratic equations with real coefficients that imaginary roots always come in conjugate pairs; that when, for example, $2 + 3i$ was a root of such an equation, then $2 - 3i$ turned out to be a root also. This was a special case of the following theorem.

Theorem on Conjugate Roots. If all of the coefficients of an algebraic equation are real numbers, and if u is a root of the algebraic equation, then so is the conjugate of u.

In order to prove this theorem, we first prove the following Lemma.

Lemma. Suppose $p(x) = a_0 x^n + a_1 x^{n-1} + \cdots + a_{n-1} x + a_n$ is a polynomial in x of positive degree, in which a_0, $\cdots$, a_n are real numbers, and suppose that u is any complex number. Then $k[p(u)] = p[k(u)]$.

PROOF OF LEMMA: $p(u) = a_0 u^n + a_1 u^{n-1} + \cdots + a_{n-1} u + a_n$. Therefore:

$$k[p(u)] = k[a_0 u^n + a_1 u^{n-1} + \cdots + a_{n-1} u + a_n]$$
$$= k(a_0 u^n) + k(a_1 u^{n-1}) + \cdots + k(a_{n-1} u) + k(a_n)$$

(by statement 6)

$$= k(a_0)k(u)^n + k(a_1)k(u^{n-1}) + \cdots + k(a_{n-1})k(u) + k(a_n)$$

(by statement 2)

$$= a_0 k(u^n) + a_1 k(u^{n-1}) + \cdots + a_{n-1}k(u) + a_n \quad \text{(by statement 1)}$$

$$= a_0[k(u)]^n + a_1[k(u)]^{n-1} + \cdots + a_{n-1}[k(u)] + a_n$$

(by statement 4)

$$= p[k(u)], \text{ Q.E.D.}$$

PROOF OF THEOREM ON CONJUGATE ROOTS. We wish to prove that, if $p(x)$ is as in the lemma above, and if u is a root of $p(x) = 0$, then so is $k(u)$; i.e., we wish to prove that, if $p(u) = 0$, then $p[k(u)] = 0$ also. But if $p(u) = 0$,

$$\begin{aligned} p[k(u)] &= k[p(u)] \quad \text{(by the lemma)} \\ &= k(0) \quad \text{(by hypothesis)} \\ &= 0 \quad \text{(by statement 1)} \end{aligned}$$

Therefore,

$$p[k(u)] = 0, \text{ Q.E.D.}$$

*REMARK. Among the most important functions of modern algebra are those that are called "isomorphisms." An *isomorphism of a field S onto itself* is a function f such that: S is both the domain and range of f, f is one-one, and f preserves addition and multiplication in S. Actually, the function k defined above is an isomorphism of the field of all complex numbers onto itself. Below we complete the proof of this statement.

*7. f is a one-one function.

*PROOF OF STATEMENT 7: To show that k is one-one, we must show that if $u, v \in$ domain of k and $k(u) = k(v)$, then $u = v$. Suppose, then, that $u = a + bi$, $v = c + di$, where a, b, c, d are real numbers, and that $k(u) = k(v)$, i.e., $a - bi = c - di$. Then by the unique expressibility property of complex numbers, $a = c$ and $-b = -d$, so that $b = d$. But if $a = c$ and $b = d$, then $u = a + bi = c + di = v$, Q.E.D.

*8. The range R of k is the set of all complex numbers C.

*PROOF OF STATEMENT 8: By the definition of k, $R \subset C$. Our statement will be proved if we can show that $C \subset R$, i.e., each complex number $p + qi$ is an element of the range of k. But consider the complex number $p - qi$: $k(p - qi) = p - (-q)i = p + qi$, so that $p + qi$, being the image of $p - qi$, is an element of the range of k, Q.E.D.

▶ **EXERCISE 37**

1. Prove the following statements of Section 8.8.

(a) Statement 1   (b) Statement 5   (c) Statement 6

2. Suppose u, v are conjugate imaginary numbers (i.e., $u = a + bi$, $v = a - bi$; a, b are real numbers, $b \neq 0$). Show that $(x - u)(x - v)$ is equal to a quadratic polynomial with real coefficients. (There follows from this statement and the theorems on polynomial factorization and conjugate roots:—*Theorem:* Every polynomial $p(x)$ of positive degree in x, with all coefficients real, is a product of linear and quadratic polynomials in x, with all coefficients real.)

3. Justify the following statement: Every algebraic equation with real coefficients has an even number of imaginary roots, and, if its degree is odd, it has at least one real root.

4. Prove that if $p(x) = a_0 x^n + \cdots + a_n$ is a polynomial in x with complex coefficients and $n \geqslant 1$, and $p(x) = 0$ has more than n distinct roots, then each coefficient of $p(x)$ must be equal to 0. [*Hint:* If $a_0 \neq 0$, then $p(x) = 0$ would have $\leqslant n$ distinct roots. (Why?) Therefore, $a_0 = 0$, etc.]

There follows:—*Theorem:* If two polynomials in x are equal, then they must have the same degree and corresponding coefficients must be equal. [For the difference $d(x)$ of the two polynomials would have to equal zero for *all* complex values of x; i.e., any complex number is a root of $d(x) = 0$. Hence for each pair of corresponding coefficients a_i, b_i: $a_i - b_i = 0$, so that $a_i = b_i$, Q.E.D.]

5. Suppose u, v are complex numbers. Prove that u, v are the roots of $x^2 - Sx + P = 0$ if and only if $S = u + v$, $P = uv$. [*Hint:* Suppose u, v are the roots of $x^2 - Sx + P = 0$. Then by the theorem on polynomial factorization, $x^2 - Sx + P = (x - u)(x - v)(1)$. Multiply out, and use the theorem of Problem 4. Conversely, if $S = u + v$, $P = uv$ show that $x^2 - Sx + P = (x - u)(x - v)$, etc.]

6. Find an algebraic equation with integer coefficients of minimal degree of which the following are roots: (*Hint:* Use Problem 5, when it applies.)

(*a*) 1   (*b*) 1, 2   (*c*) 1, 2, 3
(*d*) $\frac{1}{2}$ (*e*) $\frac{1}{2}, \frac{1}{3}$ (*f*) $1 + i, 1 - i$
(*g*) $2 + 3i$ (*h*) $(1 + i)/2$ (*i*) 1, i
(*j*) 0, 1, $-i$ (*k*) $\frac{2}{3}, 3 - 4i$ (*l*) $\frac{2}{3}, 3 + 4i$
(*m*) i (a double root)

*7. Prove that the following functions f, with domain the set of all complex numbers C, are *not* isomorphisms of the field C onto itself:

(*a*) $f(x) = 2x$ (*b*) $f(x) = -x$ (*c*) $f(x) = x^2$

*8.(*a*) It may be proved that, if r is a rational number, then the set of all numbers $a + b\sqrt{r}$, where a, b may be any rational numbers, is a field F containing the field of rational numbers. Prove that, if $\sqrt{r}$ is irrational, then the function f with domain F, such that $f(a + b\sqrt{r}) = a - b\sqrt{r}$, is an isomorphism of F onto itself that maps each rational number to itself.

(*b*) Use (*a*) to prove that, if a, b, r are rational but $\sqrt{r}$ is irrational, and $a + b\sqrt{r}$ is a root of an algebraic equation all of whose coefficients are rational, then $a - b\sqrt{r}$ is a root of that equation also.

(*c*) Find an algebraic equation of minimum degree, of which $1 + i$ and $1 + \sqrt{2}$ are roots, with coefficients: (i) all integers; (ii) all real; (iii) all complex.

8.9 THE GRAPH OF A POLYNOMIAL p(x)

In Sections 2.11 and 2.12 we discussed cartesian coordinate systems and graphs. We remarked there upon the reciprocal role played by functions and their graphs, in that each of these concepts helps us to understand the other better. In this section we shall consider the graph of a polynomial, and we shall find, in particular, that graphs have something to contribute to the problem of solving equations, and, conversely, solving equations may be helpful in drawing a graph.

In this section it will be understood that we are dealing only with polynomial functions all of whose coefficients are real numbers, and that the domain of each such function is the set of all real numbers unless otherwise noted.

We begin by considering the situation in which $p(x)$ is of degree less than 1. Then in this case, $p(x)$ must be equal to a real number. By way of example, suppose $p(x) = 7$. Then $p(0) = 7$ and $p(1) = 7$ and $p(\sqrt{2}) = 7$ and $p(\pi) = 7$, and indeed for each real number r, $p(r) = 7$. The graph of $p(x)$ must then consist of the points $(0, 7)$ and $(1, 7)$ and $(\sqrt{2}, 7)$ and $(\pi, 7)$, and in fact all points of the form $(r, 7)$, where r may be any real number. Clearly, these points constitute a straight line parallel to the X-axis, intersecting the Y-axis at the point labeled 7. (We say the graph has "y-intercept" 7, see (v) below.)

In the same way, it is easy to see that, for each real number k, the graph of $p(x) = k$ is a straight line parallel to the X-axis, with y-intercept k.

Next we consider a polynomial $p(x)$ of degree 1. In this case $p(x) = ax + b$, where $a \neq 0$. We shall omit the proof here (it may be found in analytic geometry texts), but it may be proved that the graph of a first-degree polynomial $p(x)$ is again always a straight line, but parallel to neither the X- nor the Y-axis.

Since two points determine a line, it is easy to draw the graph of a first-degree polynomial function. The graph of $2x - 3$ is a straight line through $(0, -3)$ and $(5, 7)$, for example.

So far as the graphs of quadratic and higher degree functions are concerned, we shall now make several definitions and statements, most of

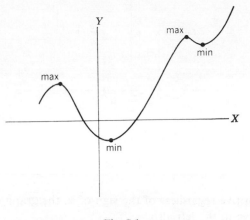

Fig. 8.1

which, although they will be given roughly and intuitively and without proof, will nevertheless turn out to be helpful in drawing these graphs.

(i) A point on a graph that is higher than any "near-by" point is called a *maximum* point; a point on a graph that is lower than any nearby point is called a *minimum* point; an *extremum* is either a maximum or a minimum point.

The graph of a polynomial $p(x)$ of degree n has at most $n - 1$ extrema. Furthermore, the exact number of extrema differs from $n - 1$ by an even number (see Fig. 8.1).

[Thus the graph of a quadratic polynomial $p(x)$ (called a "parabola") must have exactly one extremum, which may of course be a maximum or a minimum.]

(ii) The graph of a polynomial $p(x)$ is always "continuous"; that is to say, there are no "breaks" in the graph.　Graphs of polynomials are also free of sharp points.

[The statements made in (i) and (ii) above are made more precisely and proved in courses such as "calculus" and "functions of a real variable."]

(iii) The term of highest degree in a polynomial $p(x)$ eventually "dominates" the polynomial.　For example, in the polynomial $p(x) = 2x^4 - 7x^3 - x^2 - 2$, the term of highest degree is $2x^4$.　For sufficiently large positive x, $2x^4$ will be very large positively, enough to outweigh the negative effect of the other terms.　Therefore, in this case, after we have gone sufficiently far to the right, the graph simply continually rises.　We say that on the right the graph eventually only rises.　On the left, it is again the term of highest degree, examined this time for large *negative* values of x, which determines the behavior of $p(x)$.　In the case above,

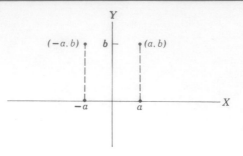

Fig. 8.2

since $2x^4$ is positive regardless of the sign of x, the graph eventually only rises as we move to the left also.

The graph of $-2x^4 + 6x^2 - 7$, however, will eventually only fall on both its left and right; the graph of $x^3 - 999$ will eventually rise on the right and fall on the left; and the graph of $-2x^3 + 999$ will fall on the right and rise on the left.

(iv) Consider the polynomial: $p(x) = x^4 + x^2$. It happens that $(2, 20)$ is a point of the graph of $p(x)$. It follows, without further computation, that $(-2, 20)$ is a point of this graph also. For since only even exponents occur in $p(x)$, $p(-2)$ must have the same value as $p(2)$.

Thus, whenever (a, b) is a point on the graph of $x^4 + x^2$, then so is $(-a, b)$.

But if the Y-axis were a mirror, the points (a, b) and $(-a, b)$ would be each other's images (Fig. 8.2). For this reason, the points (a, b) and $(-a, b)$ are said to be *symmetric with respect to the Y-axis*; and when it is true that for each point (a, b) on a graph, $(-a, b)$ is on the graph also, then we say that the graph is symmetric to the Y-axis. What we have remarked, then, is that the graph of $x^4 + x^2$ is symmetric to the Y-axis. And in fact:

If each term of a polynomial $p(x)$ is of even degree, then the graph of $p(x)$ is symmetric to the Y-axis.

(Note that a nonzero constant term is of even degree, for it is of degree 0, and 0 is an even number.)

On the other hand, suppose all the terms of a polynomial $p(x)$ are of odd degree, as for example in the case $p(x) = x^3 + x$. We note that $(1, 2)$ and $(-1, -2)$ are points of the graph of $x^3 + x$, and in fact it may be shown that whenever (a, b) is a point of the graph of $x^3 + x$, then so is $(-a, -b)$.

Points (a, b), $(-a, -b)$ are said to be *symmetric with respect to the*

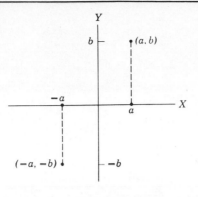

Fig. 8.3

origin (Fig. 8.3); and when it is true that for each point (a, b) on a graph, $(-a, -b)$ is on the graph also, then we say that the graph is symmetric to the origin. Thus the graph of $x^3 + x$ is symmetric to the origin and in fact:

If each term of a polynomial $p(x)$ is of odd degree, then the graph of $p(x)$ is symmetric to the origin.

(v) The x-values of the points in which a graph intersects the X-axis are called the *x-intercepts* of the graph, and the y-values of the points in which a graph intersects the Y-axis are called *y-intercepts* of the graph.

The x-intercepts of the graph of $p(x)$ are the real roots of the equation $p(x) = 0$. [Hence to approximate the real roots of $p(x) = 0$, read, from the graph of $p(x)$, the values of its x-intercepts.] The graph of a polynomial $p(x)$ will always have just one y-intercept, namely $p(0)$.

Illustrative Example I. We sketch the graph G of: $p(x) = x^3 - 8x$.

We note that: G has either 2 or 0 extrema.

On the right, G eventually only rises.

On the left, G eventually only falls.

G is symmetric to the origin.

x-intercepts occur when $x^3 - 8x = 0$.

The solution of this equation is: $x(x^2 - 8) = 0$; $x = 0, \pm 2\sqrt{2}$; or $x = 0, \pm 2.8$, approximately.

The unique y-intercept is $y = p(0)$ or $y = 0$.

Since G is symmetric to the origin and since we already have $p(0)$, only the functional values for positive x had actually to be computed in working out the following table of values (Synthetic substitution is useful in the computation):

x	-3	-2	-1	0	1	2	3
$p(x)$	-3	8	7	0	-7	-8	3

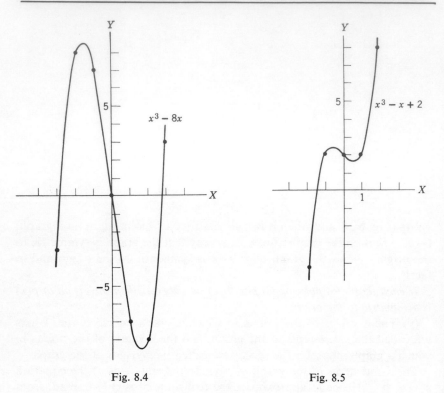

Fig. 8.4   Fig. 8.5

Using this information, we sketch the graph of $x^3 - 8x$ (Fig. 8.4).

Illustrative Example 2.   We sketch the graph G of: $p(x) = x^3 - x + 2$. We note that: G has either 2 or 0 extrema.

G rises as we go far to the right and falls as we go far to the left.

G is symmetric to neither the Y-axis nor to the origin. x-intercepts are not easily computed by solving the equation $p(x) = 0$.   Indeed, here it is more feasible to use the graph to estimate roots of $p(x) = 0$, rather than vice-versa.   From the graph it appears that $x^3 - x + 2$ $= 0$ has only one real root, approximately: -1.5.

y-intercept: $y = p(0) = 2$.

Table of values:

x	-2	-1	0	1	2
$p(x)$	-4	2	2	2	8

The graph of $x^3 - x + 2$ is drawn in Fig. 8.5.

▶ **EXERCISE 38**

1. In each of the following cases state the degree (if any) and the type of the polynomial function $p(x)$ given, and discuss and sketch its graph; also, use the graph to approximate the values of the real, irrational roots of $p(x) = 0$, if any such exist.

(a) 0	(b) 7
(c) $-\pi$	(d) x
(e) x^2	(f) x^3
(g) x^4	(h) $2x$
(i) $1 - x$	(j) $2x^2$
(k) $-2x^2$	(l) $-x^3$
(m) $-x^4$	(n) $x^2 - x + 5$
(o) $-x^2 + 2x + 1$	(p) $x^3 - x^2 - 5$
(q) $(x - 1)(x + 4)$	(r) $x^2(x - 3)$
(s) $-x^3 + x^2 + x + 1$	(t) $(x - 2)(x + 1)(x + 3)$
(u) $x^3 - x^2 - x + 1$	(v) $x^3 - x^2 + x - 1$
(w) $x^4 - x^2$	(x) $x - x^4$

⋆2. Why have we not discussed the symmetry of graphs of functions with respect to the X-axis?

8.10 APPROXIMATING REAL ROOTS

The practical applications of complex numbers are numerous. But more often, when a solution of an algebraic equation is sought, it is actually a *rational* root that is desired or a decimal approximation to a *real* root, correct to a certain number of decimal places.

For example, the exact solution of the equation $x^2 = 2$ is $x = \pm\sqrt{2}$. Approximate solution, correct to one decimal place, $x = \pm 1.4$; to two decimal places, $x = \pm 1.41$; to three decimal places, $x = 1.414$; etc.

Beginning with cubic equations, formula methods for solving algebraic equations are, as we have seen, generally impracticable or even impossible. A great deal of attention has been devoted, therefore, to the problem of finding real roots of equations approximately, since approximate solutions are, after all, all that we usually need in solving practical problems.

There is one very intuitive, simple, versatile, and effective method for attacking this problem that goes all the way back to the Babylonians. It is the method of *linear interpolation*, discussed in Section 6.9.

We now apply the method of linear interpolation to the problem of finding an approximation to $\sqrt{2}$. Actually, what we seek here is a positive real number x such that $x^2 = 2$. We therefore form a table of values:

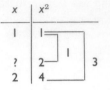

Further progress now depends on the following intuitively plausible theorem. (The proof of this theorem is omitted since it requires a more thorough investigation of real-number and function theory than we have time for in this course.)

Theorem. Suppose $f(x) = k$ is an algebraic equation with real coefficients, and suppose that a and c are real numbers such that: $f(a) < k$, $f(c) > k$.

Then the equation $f(x) = k$ has at least one real root b between a and c.

In the preceding example, $x^2 = 2$ may be thought of as the algebraic equation $f(x) = k$, and 1 and 2 play the role of a and c respectively. Since $f(1) = 1 < 2$ and $f(2) = 4 > 2$, the theorem assures us that there is a real root of the equation $x^2 = 2$ between 1 and 2.

Now the method of linear interpolation offers as a first approximation to $\sqrt{2}$, $1 + \frac{1}{3}$, or approximately 1.3. But squaring 1.3 results in only 1.69, which falls considerably short of the goal 2. Trying 0.1 more: $(1.4)^2 = 1.96$, which still falls short of 2, but this time by very little; and when we square the next natural candidate, 1.5, the result is 2.25, and we have gone right past 2.

However, now we are sure (because of the preceding theorem) that $\sqrt{2}$ is between 1.4 and 1.5, and we interpolate again:

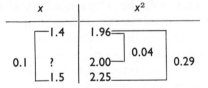

Our next approximation to $\sqrt{2}$ is: $1.4 + \frac{4}{29}(0.1)$, or $1.4 + 0.01$, or 1.41. (We advance only one decimal place at a time.) Squaring, we find: $(1.41)^2 = 1.9881$ and $(1.42)^2 = 2.0164$.

Now we know (again by the preceding theorem) that $\sqrt{2}$ is between 1.41 and 1.42, and, at this point, we may say that correct to one-decimal place, $\sqrt{2}$ is approximately 1.4.

But as a matter of fact, to be able to say that a correct one-decimal place approximation to $\sqrt{2}$ is 1.4, it is only necessary to know that $\sqrt{2}$ is between 1.4 and 1.45. Therefore, if all that we require is a correct one-decimal place approximation to $\sqrt{2}$, we may proceed as follows.

Having determined that $\sqrt{2}$ lies between 1.4 and 1.5, we would see what happens when we square 1.45: $(1.45)^2 = 2.1025$, which is greater than 2. Therefore $\sqrt{2}$ lies between 1.4 and 1.45, which means that correct to one-decimal place $\sqrt{2} \doteq 1.4$.

Note that in approximating $\sqrt{2}$, our second interpolation required less adjustment than our first; this, of course, is due to the fact that in the second interpolation the tabular gaps are smaller.

As a final illustrative example of the use of interpolation in approximating a real root of an algebraic equation, we apply the method to the equation:

$$x^3 - 2x - 1 = 0$$

First of all, we simply guess at an integer value of x, say $x = 1$, and substitute on the left-hand side of the equation, to arrive at the result: -2. Trying the next larger integer value $x = 2$, the left-hand side of the equation becomes 3. Described tabularly:

x	$x^3 - 2x - 1$
1	-2
?	0
2	3

Since 0 lies between -2 and 3, we know that there is a root of this equation between 1 and 2. Interpolation now offers 1.4 as a possible approximation to this root. Substituting 1.4 for x on the left side of our equation (synthetic substitution now begins to be advisable), the result is -1.056, which is not too close to our desired result of 0; but we know now that there must be a root between 1.4 and 2 (why?).

Our next attempt, therefore, is: $x = 1.5$. The result of substitution in this case is -0.625, and now we know that there is a root between 1.5 and 2; the next candidate is $x = 1.6$, whose substitution leads to -0.104. We are now, of course, aiming at a value of x whose substitution will lead to a *non*-negative result, and we seem to be getting there, but we have not yet quite made the grade.

But when we try $x = 1.7$, the result is 0.513. Now we know that there is a root between 1.6 and 1.7, and we are ready for another interpolation:

x	$x^3 - 2x - 1$	
1.6	-0.104	
?	0	$(x \doteq 1.6 + \dfrac{104}{617}(0.1) \doteq 1.62)$
1.7	0.513	

The result of substituting 1.62 for x on the left-hand side of our equation is approximately 0.0115 (which we note is quite close to being the desired result 0). Therefore we now know that a root lies between 1.6 and 1.62 (why?); we also know that correct to one decimal place, a root of this equation is 1.6.

In finding further decimal places, a next step would be to try the value 1.61 for x. It will be left to the student to continue with the goal of finding a root of the given equation correct to *two* decimal places.

The labor involved in the preceding example is admittedly burdensome and tedious. Devices for lightening the task are therefore welcome. It is pleasant to be able to report that much of the mechanical work involved has in recent times been taken over by computing machines. Furthermore, greater theoretical understanding of the properties of equations is very helpful and is, therefore, the subject of study in more advanced courses in mathematics.

One such useful property of equations is the following, which we state without proof:

(*Note:* Suppose $p(x)$ is a polynomial in standard form all of whose coefficients are real. If, omitting zero coefficients, two successive coefficients are of opposite sign, we say that a *variation of sign* occurs. For example, $x^3 - x + 1$ has 2 variations of sign.)

Descartes' Rule of Signs. Suppose $p(x)$ is a polynomial, all of whose coefficients are real, with v variations of sign. Then the number of positive real roots of $p(x) = 0$ is either equal to v or less than v by an even number; furthermore, if $p(-x)$ has v' variations in sign, then the number of negative real roots of $p(x) = 0$ is either equal to v' or is less than v' by an even number.

For example, consider the equation $x^5 + x^2 - 2 = 0$. Here $v = 1$, $v' = 2$. Therefore this equation has exactly one positive root and either 2 or 0 negative roots. Counting multiple roots then, either the equation has 1 positive, 2 negative, and 2 imaginary roots, or 1 positive, 0 negative, and 4 imaginary roots.

8.11 BOUNDS FOR ROOTS

Simple techniques for narrowing the search for roots are given by the following theorems.

Theorem. Suppose that a is a real number, $p(x) = 0$ is an algebraic equation, all of whose coefficients are real, and that in finding $p(a)$ by synthetic substitution, no number in the third line is negative. Then any positive number $b > a$ may be rejected as a possible root of $p(x) = 0$.

PROOF: By hypothesis, $p(x) = (x - a)q(x) + r$, where neither the real number r nor any coefficient of $q(x)$ is negative, and at least one coefficient, the first, must be positive. From this, and the fact that b is positive, it follows that $q(b)$ must be positive. Since $b - a > 0$ also, we have $p(b) = (b - a)q(b) + r > 0$. Hence b cannot be a root of $p(x) = 0$, Q.E.D.

For example, in Illustrative Example 1 of Section 8.6, we see after the first synthetic division that $\frac{1}{2}$ is an "upper bound" for the roots of the given equation; i.e., no number $> \frac{1}{2}$ can be a root of the given equation.

Theorem. Suppose that a is a real number, $p(x)$ is an algebraic equation all of whose coefficients are real, and that in finding $p(a)$ by synthetic substitution, the numbers in the third line alternate in sign. Then any negative number $b < a$ may be rejected as a possible root of $p(x) = 0$.

PROOF: We shall prove the theorem assuming that the coefficient of the highest degree term (the "leading coefficient") of $p(x)$ is positive. [It is left to the student to prove the theorem in the (actually little used) case in which the leading coefficient is negative.]

By hypothesis, $p(x) = (x - a)q(x) + r$, where the coefficients of $q(x)$ and, finally, r alternate in sign, and where the first coefficient is positive. Then, if $q(x)$ is of odd degree, hence with an even number of coefficients, we have $r > 0$; whereas if $q(x)$ is of even degree, then $r < 0$. Furthermore, if $q(x)$ is of odd degree, then $q(b) < 0$, and if $q(x)$ is of even degree, then $q(b) > 0$.

Therefore, if $q(x)$ is of odd degree, $p(b) = (b - a)q(b) + r > 0$, and if $q(x)$ is of even degree, $p(b) = (b - a)q(b) + r < 0$. In no case is $p(b) = 0$, Q.E.D.

As an example of an application of the preceding theorem, consider the equation $x^3 + x^2 + x + 1 = 0$. Substituting $x = -3$:

$$
\begin{array}{rrrr|r}
1 & 1 & 1 & 1 & \underline{-3} \\
  & -3 & 6 & -21 & \\
\hline
1 & -2 & 7 & -20 &
\end{array}
$$

We conclude that -3 is a "lower bound" for the roots of the given equation; i.e., no number < -3 can be a root of the given equation.

We terminate this section with two examples illustrating methods of finding approximate solutions in the case of equations quite different from the algebraic equations with which we have been dealing.

Illustrative Example I. Solve the "exponential" equation: $2^{0.4x} = 7$.

SOLUTION. Equivalent to the given equation is:

$$\log 2^{0.4x} = \log 7$$

or:

$$0.4x \log 2 = \log 7$$

or:

$$x = \frac{\log 7}{0.4 \log 2} = \frac{0.8451}{(0.4)(0.3010)} = \frac{0.8451}{0.1204}$$

Now if we wish we may complete the solution by long division, or by using logarithms again:

$$\log 0.8451 = .9269 - 1$$
$$\log 0.1204 = .0806 - 1$$
$$\overline{}$$
$$\log x \quad\;\; = .8463$$
$$x \quad\;\; = 7.020 \text{ (approximately, of course)}$$

Illustrative Example 2. Find: $\log_2 17$.

SOLUTION. Let $x = \log_2 17$. Then (see page 173), $2^x = 17$. Now proceed as in the preceding example.

(This method may be used to find logarithms to any base when we have available a table of logarithms to a particular base, say the base 10. Note also: A short-cut to the result is given by Problem 8 of Exercise 27.)

▶ **EXERCISE 39**

1. Carry the process of approximating $\sqrt{2}$ one place further than the text does, to arrive at an approximation correct to two decimal places.

2. By linear interpolation, find approximations to the following numbers correct to one decimal place:

(a) $\sqrt{3}$ (b) $\sqrt{5}$ (c) $\sqrt{6}$ (d) $\sqrt{7}$
(e) $\sqrt{8}$ (f) $\sqrt{10}$ (g) $\sqrt[3]{2}$ (h) $\sqrt[3]{3}$
(i) $\sqrt[3]{4}$ (j) $\sqrt[3]{5}$ (k) $\sqrt[3]{6}$ (l) $\sqrt[3]{7}$
(m) $\sqrt[4]{17}$ (n) $(1.1)^{1.1}$ (o) $56/7.5$ (p) $\sqrt{110.5}$

3.(a) Carry the process begun in the text to the point of finding an irrational root of the equation $x^3 - 2x - 1 = 0$, correct to two decimal places.

(b) What does Descartes' rule tell us about the roots of $x^3 - 2x - 1 = 0$?

(c) Find all rational roots of $x^3 - 2x - 1 = 0$.

(d) Find the exact value of each of the roots of $x^3 - 2x - 1 = 0$.

(e) Using a table of logarithms, find $\sqrt{5}$ correct to three decimal places.

(f) Using (d) and (e), find decimal approximations to the irrational roots of $x^3 - 2x - 1 = 0$, correct to two decimal places.

(g) Draw the graph of the function $p(x) = x^3 - 2x - 1$.

*(h) Apply Cardan's formula to the equation $x^3 - 2x - 1 = 0$.

4.(a) Does $x^3 - x - 3 = 0$ have any rational roots?

(b) What does Descartes' rule tell us about the roots of $x^3 - x - 3 = 0$?

(c) Plot the graph of the function $p(x) = x^3 - x - 3$.

(d) Find each real root of $x^3 - x - 3 = 0$ correct to one decimal place.

(e) Find each real root of $x^3 - x - 3 = 0$ correct to two decimal places.

*(f) What does Cardan's formula offer as a root of this equation?

5.(a) through (f). As in Problem 4, but with respect to the equation $x^3 - x - 2 = 0$.

6.(a) through (f). As in Problem 4, but with respect to the equation $x^3 + x - 3 = 0$.

7.(a) Prove the following *Theorem*: If $q(x) = p(-x)$, then a is a root of $p(x)$ if and only if $-a$ is a root of $q(x)$.

(b) Theorem (a) is used to lighten the labor of solving for negative roots. For example, by Theorem (a), the negative roots of $x^3 - 5x - 1 = 0$ are the opposites of the positive roots of $(-x)^3 - 5(-x) - 1 = 0$, i.e., of $-x^3 + 5x - 1 = 0$, which is equivalent to $x^3 - 5x + 1 = 0$. Use this technique to find each negative root of $x^3 - 5x - 1 = 0$ correct to one decimal place.

8.(a) through (f). As in Problem 4, but with respect to the equation $x^3 - 4x^2 + 3x + 1 = 0$.

9. State the information that Descartes' rule gives about each of the following equations, and find upper and lower bounds for the real roots of each equation.

(a) $9x^3 - 9x^2 + 8 = 0$ (b) $x^3 - x^2 - x - 1 = 0$

(c) $2x^3 + x^2 - 5x + 3 = 0$ (d) $3x^3 - 5x^2 + 7 = 0$

(e) $x^4 + 10x + 9 = 0$ (f) $x^4 + 2x^3 - 6x^2 - 20x + 25 = 0$

10. Solve each of the following equations as completely as possible. Find all real, irrational roots correct to one decimal place.

(a) $2x^3 + 3x^2 - 7x - 3 = 0$ (b) $2x^3 + 3x^2 + 3x + 1 = 0$

(c) $3x^4 - 2x^3 - 12x^2 + 5x + 2 = 0$

(d) $2x^4 + 3x^3 - 8x^2 - 10x + 3 = 0$

11. Complete the solution of Illustrative Example 2 of the preceding section.

12. Solve the following exponential equations:

(a) $2^x = 5$ (b) $3(2^x) = 10$ (c) $4(2^{0.5x}) = 25$

13. Find:

(a) $\log_2 10$ (b) $\log_2 3$ (c) $\log_3 2$

8.12 SIMULTANEOUS EQUATIONS

Often, rather than seeking numbers satisfying a given equation, we seek ordered pairs of numbers satisfying two equations, or ordered triples of numbers satisfying three equations (or even ordered m-tuples of numbers satisfying n equations). When we seek a solution that satisfies each of a set of equations, we say that we seek a simultaneous solution of the equations, or that we are solving a set of simultaneous equations.

Illustrative Example I. Solve simultaneously:

$$2x + 3y = 6$$
$$y = -\tfrac{2}{3}x + 2$$

SOLUTION. The problem may be posed as follows:

Find $\{(x, y) \mid 2x + 3y = 6 \text{ and } y = (-2x/3) + 2\}$.

Substituting $-(2x/3) + 2$ for y in the first equation:

$$2x + 3\left(\frac{-2x}{3} + 2\right) = 6$$
$$2x - 2x + 6 = 6$$
$$6 = 6$$

Apparently we have gotten nowhere! The statement $6 = 6$ is eminently true but indicates no solution. Actually, our result shows that no matter what real number x may be chosen, if y is then determined by the second equation, then the first equation will be satisfied; and, of course, since the second equation must be satisfied by any solution, no other kind of ordered pair will be a solution.

That is to say, the solution set is the set of all ordered pairs $\{(k, -\tfrac{2}{3}k + 2)\}$, where k is any complex number. [For example, when $k = 3$, we derive the solution $(3, 0)$, i.e., $x = 3$, $y = 0$.]

Check. $\quad 2k + 3(-\tfrac{2}{3}k + 2) = 6 \qquad -\tfrac{2}{3}k + 2 = -\tfrac{2}{3}k + 2$
$$2k - 2k + 6 = 6$$
$$6 = 6$$

(The student should check all subsequent simultaneous solutions.)

The reason for the peculiar behavior of this pair of equations becomes obvious when we take a closer look at the equation $y = (-2x/3) + 2$. It is equivalent to $3y = -2x + 6$, hence to $2x + 3y = 6$.

In other words, the two given equations are equivalent. If an ordered pair of numbers (x, y) satisfies either, it must satisfy the other.

Illustrative Example 2. Solve the equations $2x + 3y = 6$ and $4x + 6y = 7$ simultaneously.

SOLUTION.

Doubling the first: $\quad 4x + 6y = 12$
Writing the second: $\quad 4x + 6y = 7$
Subtracting: $\qquad\qquad\qquad 0 = 5$

we have an even *more* peculiar result!

Actually, what we have shown in this case is that, if there were a simultaneous solution to the given equations, then 0 would equal 5. But the conclusion is impossible; therefore there can be no simultaneous solution to these two equations, i.e., no ordered pair of complex numbers (x, y) satisfies both of these equations; their solution set is the null set.

Illustrative Example 3. Solve the equations $3x + 2y = 1$ and $5x - 3y = 8$ simultaneously.

SOLUTION.

Multiplying the first by 3: $\qquad 9x + 6y = 3$
The second by 2: $\qquad\qquad 10x - 6y = 16$
Adding: $\qquad\qquad\qquad\qquad 19x = 19$
$\qquad\qquad\qquad\qquad\qquad\quad x = 1$
Substituting $x = 1$ in the first: $\quad 3 + 2y = 1$
$\qquad\qquad\qquad\qquad\qquad\quad 2y = -2$
$\qquad\qquad\qquad\qquad\qquad\quad\ y = -1$

[Alternatively, y might have been found by multiplying the first equation by 5, the second by -3, and adding; and still another path to the solution lies in deriving $y = (1 - 3x)/2$ from the first equation and then proceeding as in Illustrative Example 1.]

In this example, there is a unique solution: The solution set is $\{(1, -1)\}$.

Note that in our solutions, our method is one of successively replacing the original set of equations by equivalent sets of equations. In Illustrative Example 1, for example, the original set of equations is equivalent to the set $\{y = -\frac{2}{3}x + 2, 6 = 6\}$, which is equivalent to $\{y = -\frac{2}{3}x + 2\}$. In Illustrative Example 3, the original set is equivalent to $\{9x + 6y = 3, x = 1\}$, etc.

8.13 FUNCTIONS AND EQUATIONS OF TWO OR MORE VARIABLES

A function whose domain consists of ordered pairs is called a *function of two variables*. For example, the function whose domain consists of all ordered pairs of complex numbers, and which assigns to each ordered pair (x, y) the number $x - y$, is a function of two variables. (The symbols "x" and "y" used in defining the mapping are called the variables.) This particular function assigns to $(3, 2)$ the image 1, to $(2, 3)$ the image -1, to (i, i) the image 0, etc. If f represents a function of two variables, we use the notation $f(x, y)$ (read: "f of x, y") to represent the image of (x, y); thus the mapping of the particular function above may be defined by the equation $f(x, y) = x - y$, and we write the above statements about images: $f(3, 2) = 1, f(2, 3) = -1, f(i, i) = 0$.

If f and g are functions of two variables x, y, then $f(x, y) = g(x, y)$ is called an *equation in two variables* x, y. For example, $x - y = x^2 + y^2$, $x - y = 0$, $xy = x$ are equations in two variables x, y.

Similarly, a function of three variables is one whose domain consists of ordered triples; etc.

We shall conform to the common practice of referring to the function "$f(x, y)$" when we mean the function f; etc.

8.14 GRAPHS OF EQUATIONS

Suppose $f(x, y)$ and $g(x, y)$ are functions whose domains consist of ordered pairs of *real numbers*. Then the cartesian graph of the equation $f(x, y) = g(x, y)$ is defined to be the set of all points in a cc plane whose coordinates satisfy the given equation.

For example, the graph of the equation $x + y = 5$ contains the points $(0, 5), (\frac{1}{2}, \frac{9}{2}), (6, -1), (\sqrt{2}, 5 - \sqrt{2})$, and, of course, infinitely many other points. The set of all of these points is a straight line. In fact, it is easy to prove the following theorem:

Theorem. If $Ax + By + C = 0$ is a linear (or "first-degree") equation in x and y over the real numbers (i.e., if A, B, C are real numbers and either $A \neq 0$ or $B \neq 0$), then the graph of this equation is a straight line.

PROOF. Suppose $B \neq 0$. Then the given equation is equivalent to: $y = (-A/B)x - c$. But the graph of an equation $y = f(x)$ is identical with the graph of the function $f(x)$. Hence the graph of the equation $y = (-A/B)x - c$ is the same as that of the function $(-A/B)x - c$. This function is of degree $\leqslant 1$ in x, and we have already seen that the graph of a function of degree $\leqslant 1$ in x is a straight line. (Note that $c = C/B$.)

On the other hand, suppose $B = 0$. Then by hypothesis $A \neq 0$, and our given equation is equivalent to $x = -C/A$, whose graph is the set of all points at a distance of C/A from the Y-axis, and on the side of the Y-axis containing the point $(-C/A, 0)$; that set of points is a straight line parallel to the Y-axis.

Just as equations in one variable and graphs of functions play a mutually helpful role, so with equations in two variables and their graphs. For example, consider the illustrative examples in the preceding section. In each case a pair of linear equations in x and y is involved; hence, in each case a pair of straight lines, the graphs of these equations, is involved also. What is the graphical interpretation of our algebraic results? It is as follows:

In Illustrative Example 1, the equations are equivalent. Hence their graphs are identical; the pair of straight lines is actually only one straight line.

In Illustrative Example 2, no simultaneous solution exists; i.e., no ordered pair satisfying both equations; hence no point common to both graphs. (It is clear that, when equations have graphs, their real simultaneous solutions are simply the ordered pairs labeling points of intersection of the graphs.) When two straight lines in a plane have no points in common, they must be parallel, and indeed in this case, the graphs of the given equations are parallel straight lines.

In Illustrative Example 3, exactly one simultaneous solution exists. Therefore the graphs of the given linear equations must be straight lines intersecting in exactly one point.

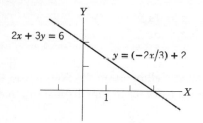

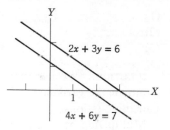

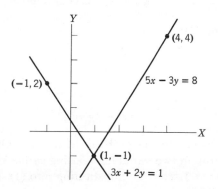

Since a pair of lines in a plane must intersect in 0, 1, or an infinite number of points, we see that a pair of linear equations over the real numbers must have 0, 1, or an infinite number of solutions. In the first case the equations are said to be *inconsistent*, in the last *dependent*.

The graphs associated with Illustrative Examples 1, 2 and 3 are drawn in Fig. 8.6. Note that, to draw the line that is the graph of a linear equation, only two points satisfying the equation are needed. These are easily found. For example, given the equation $2x + 3y = 6$, it is clear that if $x = 0$, then $y = 2$, and if $y = 0$, then $x = 3$. Hence the graph of $2x + 3y = 6$ is a straight line containing the points $(0, 2)$ and $(3, 0)$.

8.15 THREE LINEAR EQUATIONS IN THREE VARIABLES

Given three linear equations in three variables, they also may have exactly one solution, or they may be inconsistent (no solutions) or dependent (an infinite number of solutions).

We illustrate the three possibilities and methods of solution below.

Illustrative Example 1. Solve the set of simultaneous equations:

(1) $$x + 2y + 3z = 14$$
(2) $$2x - y + z = 3$$
(3) $$3x + 4y - z = 8$$

SOLUTION. We use the method called "elimination." We choose to eliminate the variable z. We eliminate z twice, each time from a different pair of equations.

Multiplying by -3, (2) is equivalent to

(4) $$-6x + 3y - 3z = -9$$

Adding (1) and (4):

(5) $$-5x + 5y = 5$$

Adding (2) and (3):

(6) $$5x + 3y = 11$$

Now we have reduced the problem to that of solving two equations, namely (5) and (6), in two variables. Using earlier methods, we see that the solution is $x = 1$, $y = 2$. Substituting into (1), say, we find: $z = 3$. The solution is: $(1, 2, 3)$.

Illustrative Example 2.   Solve the set of simultaneous equations:

(7)
(8)
(9)

$$x + 2y + 3z = 14$$
$$2x - y + z = 3$$
$$3x + y + 4z = 8$$

SOLUTION. y looks like a likely candidate for elimination.   Multiplying (8) by 2 and adding to (7):

(10)
$$5x + 5z = 20$$

And adding (8) and (9):

(11)
$$5x + 5z = 11$$

Subtracting (11) from (10):

(12)
$$0 = 9$$

No solution exists, for the existence of numbers satisfying (7) through (9) implies the contradiction $0 = 9$.   The equations (7) through (9) are inconsistent.

Illustrative Example 3.   Solve the set of simultaneous equations:

(13)
(14)
(15)

$$x + 2y + 3z = 14$$
$$2x - y + z = 3$$
$$7x - y + 6z = 23$$

SOLUTION.   Again y is easily eliminated.   Multiplying (14) by 2 and adding to (13):

(16)
$$5x + 5z = 20$$

Subtracting (14) from (15):

(17)
$$5x + 5z = 20$$

But clearly, (16) and (17) are equivalent.   Hence we need satisfy only one of them.   We may assign any value to x, say $x = k$.   Then from (16), $z = 4 - k$.   Substituting in (14), say, $y = 2x + z - 3 = 2k + 4 - k - 3 = k + 1$.   Solution set: The infinite set of ordered triples $\{(k, k + 1, 4 - k)\}$, where k may be any complex number.   The equations (13) through (15) are dependent.

Graphical interpretations of these illustrative examples exist, but they require a three-dimensional coordinate system; for which reason we shall not pursue this question here.

8.16 LINEAR AND QUADRATIC SIMULTANEOUS EQUA-
TIONS

We consider several cases involving equations of degree higher than 1 in x and y.

Illustrative Example 1. Solve simultaneously:

(1)
$$x + y = 7$$
(2)
$$x^2 + y^2 = 25$$

SOLUTION. From (1), $y = 7 - x$; substituting into (2):

$$x^2 + (7 - x)^2 = 25$$
$$2x^2 - 14x + 49 = 25$$
$$2x^2 - 14x + 24 = 0$$
$$x^2 - 7x + 12 = 0$$
$$(x - 3)(x - 4) = 0 \qquad x = 3, 4$$

If $x = 3$, then $y = 7 - x = 4$; if $x = 4$, then $y = 7 - x = 3$. Solution set: $\{(3, 4), (4, 3)\}$.

The graphical interpretation is as follows: The points of intersection of the graphs of (1) and (2) (see Fig. 8.7) are (3, 4) and (4, 3).

Note that the graph of (2) is a circle; indeed, it may be proved that the graph of an equation $x^2 + y^2 = k$, where k is a positive real number, is a circle with center at (0, 0) and radius $\sqrt{k}$.

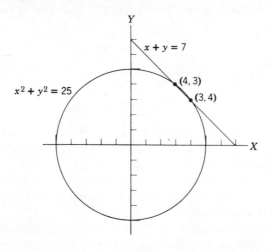

Fig. 8.7

Illustrative Example 2.   Solve simultaneously:

(3) $$y = x^2$$
(4) $$xy = 8$$

SOLUTION.   Substituting $y = x^2$ into (4), we have $x^3 = 8$, hence $x^3 - 8$ $= 0$.   Clearly $x = 2$ is a rational root.   We then use synthetic division to divide $x^3 - 8$ by $x - 2$:

1	0	0	−8	$\underline{2}$
	2	4	8	
1	2	4	0	

Depressed equation: $x^2 + 2x + 4 = 0$; solution (by quadratic formula): $x = -1 \pm i\sqrt{3}$.

For each value of x, $y = x^2$.   Therefore the solution set of (3) and (4) is: $\{(2, 4), (-1 + i\sqrt{3}, -2 - 2i\sqrt{3}), (-1 - i\sqrt{3}, -2 + 2i\sqrt{3})\}$.

Since points on a cc plane must have real coordinates, the only point of intersection of the graphs of (3) and (4) (see Fig. 8.8) is the point (2, 4).

When algebraic solution of simultaneous equations in x and y is difficult, or impossible, solutions in which x, y are both real may often be approximated graphically.   We do not consider the method further here, however, since it requires a more extended study of the graphs of equations than we have undertaken—a study that belongs properly to a course in analytic geometry.

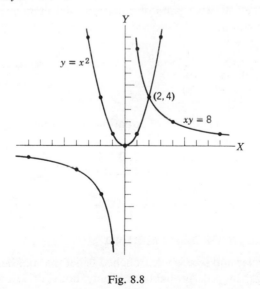

Fig. 8.8

▶ **EXERCISE 40**

1. Find the solution set of each of the following pairs of simultaneous equations, illustrate graphically, and state whether each pair is dependent or inconsistent, or neither.

(a) $3x + 4y = 6$, $x - y = 9$
(b) $2x + y = 13$, $3x - 2y = 6$
(c) $2x + y = 8$, $6x + 3y = 20$
(d) $3x - y = 7$, $39x - 13y = 91$
(e) $2x + 3y = 6$, $3x - 5y + 10 = 0$

2. Find the solution set of each of the following sets of simultaneous equations and state whether the set is dependent or inconsistent, or neither.

(a) $4x + y + z = -17$
$x + 2y + z = -5$
$2x + 7y - z = 53$

(b) $x - y + 2z = 7$
$2x + 2y - z = 11$
$x - 5y + 7z = 10$

(c) $4x + y + z = -17$
$x - y + 2z = 7$
$6x - y + 5z = 5$

(d) $2x - y + 2z = 7$
$4x + 2y + 3z = 3$
$2x - 3y - z = 2$

(e) $3x - 2y + z = 4$
$2x + 4y - 3z = 9$
$x - 8y + 2z = -4$

(f) $4x + 2y - 3z = 10$
$2x - 3y + z = 5$
$8x - 4y - z = 20$

(g) $x + y = z$
$x + z = y$
$y + z = x$

(h) $x + y = z$
$z - y = x$
$z - x = y$

3. Solve the following pairs of equations simultaneously and illustrate by means of graphs.

(a) $y = 3x$, $y = x^2$
(b) $y = 2x + 2$, $x^2 + y^2 = 169$
(c) $y = x^2 + 1$, $xy = 10$
(d) $y = x^2$, $x^2 + y^2 = 20$
(e) $xy = 20$, $x^2 + y^2 = 50$

4. Solve the following sets of equations simultaneously:

(a) $2x + y = 1$, $2x^2 + y^2 = 17$
(b) $2x + 3y = 0$, $x^2 + 2xy + 3 = 0$
(c) $4x^2 + y^2 = 12$, $2x^2 - 3y^2 + 8 = 0$
(d) $y - x = 1$, $x^2 - 2xy = -8$
(e) $(4 - h)^2 + (2 - k)^2 = r^2$, $(3 - h)^2 + (1 - k)^2 = r^2$, $r = |k|$

8.17 LINEAR PROGRAMMING

It is a popular and securely entrenched belief that mathematics is a body of knowledge, indeed, probably the only body of knowledge that has entirely completed its growth. To many people it is inconceivable that the mathematics of today should differ from that of yesterday, or that new mathematics might be created tomorrow. Even those who admit the possibility of something novel under the mathematical sun generally believe that it must be in the stratospheric realm of mathematics, far beyond the level of accessibility of ordinary people.

A case in point, refuting these misapprehensions, is the branch of mathematics called *linear programming*. It is hardly 15 years since mathematicians first began working in this field, and it is today a flourishing area of research. The subject has to do with problems like the following:

Problem. Suppose we have available two types of breakfast cereal, one called "Eggzees," whose price is 1¢ per ounce, and one called "Yums," whose price is 2¢ per ounce. Each proudly proclaims on its box its enrichment with vitamins P and Q. In every ounce Eggzees claims that it contains 1 unit of vitamin P and 2 units of vitamin Q; Yums claims 4 units of vitamin P and 3 units of vitamin Q per ounce. Both boxes agree that a person's minimum daily requirement of vitamin P is 10 units and of vitamin Q, 15 units.

How can a person supply his daily needs for vitamin P and Q, *at least cost*, with the cereals Eggzees and Yums?

DISCUSSION AND SOLUTION. First we tabulate our information:

	PRICE (¢ PER OZ)	VITAMIN P (UNITS PER OZ)	VITAMIN Q (UNITS PER OZ)	NO. OF OZ
Eggzees	1	1	2	x
Yums	2	4	3	y

It is clear that we could satisfy our needs entirely with Eggzees, by using 10 oz of that cereal, at a minimum cost of 10¢ (This would—unavoidably—give us 5 more units of vitamin Q than we really need); or entirely with Yums, by using 5 oz of that cereal, again at a minimum cost of 10¢ (but with what unwanted, but unavoidable, bonus?). However, there is a possibility that some mixture of the cereals might give us our needed vitamins P and Q at less cost. We investigate this possibility, calling the number of ounces of Eggzees and Yums consumed in a day: x, y respectively.

Then our daily consumption of Eggzees and Yums would supply $x + 4y$ units of vitamin P and $2x + 3y$ units of vitamin Q. Our desire is to be supplied with *not less than* 10 units of vitamin P and 15 units of vitamin Q per day, i.e., to satisfy the following conditions:

(1) $$x + 4y \geqslant 10$$
(2) $$2x + 3y \geqslant 15$$

Since, however attractive the prospect, we cannot eat a negative number of ounces of crisp, crunchy, flavorful, vitamin-packed breakfast cereal, we add the conditions:

(3) $$x \geqslant 0$$
(4) $$y \geqslant 0$$

Now we consider the situation graphically. That is to say, we find the points in a cc plane satisfying all of the relations (1) through (4). The set of all points in a cc plane that satisfy a given relation is called the *graph* of the relation. Therefore, what we now seek is the set of all points that lie simultaneously in the graphs of each of the relations (1) through (4); i.e., the *intersection* of these graphs.

We begin with relation (1). First of all, any point satisfying $x + 4y = 10$ satisfies (1). Therefore the graph of $x + 4y = 10$, which is, of course, a straight line, must be at least a part of the graph of $x + 4y \leqslant 10$. We therefore draw this straight line on a cc system (Fig. 8.9).

Now suppose (a, b) is any point on the graph of $x + 4y = 10$. Then it is easy to see that (a, c) is on the graph of $x + 4y > 10$ if and only if

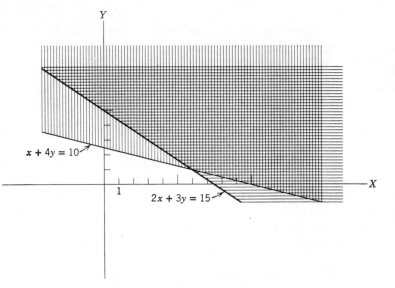

Fig. 8.9

$c > b$. For if $c > b$, then $4c > 4b$, $a + 4c > a + 4b = 10$; conversely, if $a + 4c > 10 = a + 4b$, then $4c > 4b$, $c > b$, Q.E.D. Therefore the graph of $x + 4y > 10$ is the set of all points in the cc plane *above* the graph of $x + 4y = 10$.

The graph of $x + 4y \geqslant 10$, then, is the set of points in a cc plane on or above the graph of $x + 4y = 10$. (The vertical striped region in Fig. 8.9, together with its border.)

Similarly, the graph of (2), $2x + 3y \geqslant 15$, is the horizontal striped region in Fig. 8.9, together with its border. To satisfy conditions (3) and (4), we reject all points with negative x- or y-values, i.e., we restrict ourselves to quadrant I, and its border. The intersection of the graphs of relations (1) through (4) is the shaded region in Fig. 8.10, together with its border. The coordinates of the vertex (6, 1) were found by solving the equations $x + 4y = 10$, $2x + 3y = 15$ simultaneously.

Now we know that the solution (x, y) that we seek to our problem must represent a point in the shaded region in Fig. 8.10 or on its border. (Let us call this region, together with its border, S.) Indeed, we seek a point (x, y) in S such that the cost C in cents of x ounces of Eggzees and y ounces of Yums is a minimum. But referring to the table above:

(5) $$C = x + 2y$$

Let us see whether we could possibly satisfy our demands with the expenditure of only a penny; that is, in such a way that $C = x + 2y = 1$.

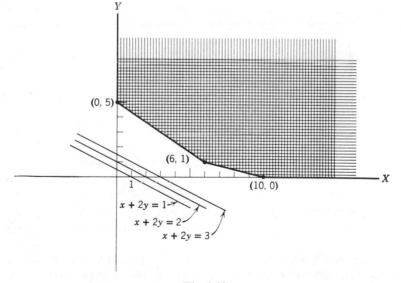

Fig. 8.10

We examine the set of all points (x, y) such that $x + 2y = 1$, i.e., the graph of $x + 2y = 1$, but we discover (see Fig. 8.10) that no point of this line lies in the required set S. We shall have to spend more than a penny.

We therefore, perhaps grudgingly, attempt a solution in which $C = 2$. But the graph of $x + 2y = 2$, although closer to S, still has no point in common with S (see Fig. 8.10); and the graph of $x + 2y = 3$, although even closer to S, succeeds no better in reaching it.

Now we see what needs to be done. We must find the smallest value of C for which the line $x + 2y = C$ intersects S, knowing that, as C becomes larger, the line $x + 2y = C$ moves to the right and approaches S. (Note that the moving line does not change its *direction* as it moves.)

Intuitively, it is clear that as we approach a region, we reach its border before we reach its interior. As a matter of fact, our moving line $x + 2y = k$ must reach a *vertex* of S no later than it reaches any other point of the border of S. For if it is not parallel to an edge of S, the moving line will touch a vertex *before* it touches any other point of the border; and if it is parallel to an edge of S, it will touch all the points of an edge, including a vertex, at the same time.

In our case, we can see from Fig. 8.10 that the vertex $(6, 1)$ is the first point that the moving line $x + 2y = C$ will reach. Indeed the following fundamental theorem can be proved, which will, in subsequent problems, save us a good deal of the preceding analysis.

Theorem. In a cc plane, let S be a region that is the intersection of sides of lines (including their borders). Suppose p is a linear polynomial in x and y with real coefficients.

Then of all points in S, if one point makes p assume a minimum value, it is a vertex point on the border of S.

(Incidentally, if one point makes p assume a maximum value, it is a vertex point on the border of S also.)

Returning to our problem, since the line $x + 2y = C$ that passes through $(6, 1)$ must be satisfied by $(6, 1)$, we have: $6 + 2 \cdot 1 = C$, i.e., $C = 8$. That is the smallest value of C for which our conditions can be met; and $(6, 1)$ is the only point that satisfies $x + 2y = C = 8$ and lies in S also. Therefore $x = 6$, $y = 1$ is the unique solution to our problem: 6 oz of Eggzies and 1 oz of Yums per day will supply us with at least our minimum daily requirement of vitamins P and Q, at a minimum cost of 8¢ per day.

The theorem above would have enabled us to reach this conclusion more quickly. For according to our theorem, the solution must be one of the vertex points $(0, 5)$, $(6, 1)$, or $(10, 0)$. For these three points,

$C = x + 2y = 10, 8, 10$, respectively. The minimum value of C is 8, attained by letting $x = 6$, $y = 1$.

What we have just accomplished in the way of distributing our breakfast between two competing cereals may not seem to be of overwhelming importance; but serious "distribution" problems very much like this actually occur with great frequency in commercial, industrial, and military situations, and, as a consequence, the science of linear programming has found wide practical application.

We conclude this section with an algebraic solution of our cereal problem:

From (5), $x = C - 2y$. Substituting into (1), we have: $C - 2y + 4y \geqslant 10$, i.e.:

$$(6) \qquad C + 2y \geqslant 10$$

Similarly, substituting into (2):

$$(7) \qquad 2C - y \geqslant 15$$

Multiplying (7) by the positive number 2:

$$(8) \qquad 4C - 2y \geqslant 30$$

and adding (6) and (8):

$$5C \geqslant 40$$

from which:

$$(9) \qquad C \geqslant 8$$

Thus, if (1), (2), and (5) are to be satisfied, C can have no value less than 8. The question is, can C have the value 8? If so, it must be the minimum we seek. But if $C = 8$, then from (6): $y \geqslant 1$, and from (7): $1 \geqslant y$. Thus, if $C = 8$, then $y = 1$, and from (5), $x = 6$. It is easy to verify that (6, 1) satisfies conditions (1) through (4), so that (6, 1) is our solution, and 8 is indeed the minimum possible value of C.

▶ **EXERCISE 41**

1. Solve the Eggzee and Yum problem under the following conditions, illustrating graphically:

(a) The same as the text, except that Eggzees cost 1.5¢ per ounce.

(b) The same as the text, except that Yums cost 2.5¢ per ounce.

(c) The same as the text, except that Eggzees cost 2¢, Yums 3¢ per ounce.

(d) The same as the text, except that we now take into account vitamin R also. Eggzees contains 4 units of vitamin R per ounce, Yums 9 units, and the minimum daily requirement of vitamin R is 36 units.

2. A customer who needs 20 large white buttons and 30 small white buttons finds that a store sells white buttons only in cards containing 2 large and 5 small buttons, and boxes containing 10 large and 5 small buttons. How should he make his purchase in order to get the buttons he needs at least cost, if:

(a) The cards cost 10¢, the boxes 25¢ each.

(b) The cards cost 5¢, the boxes 30¢ each.

(c) The cards cost 5¢, the boxes 25¢ each.

3. A man has two machines with which he can manufacture either skate keys or can openers. To manufacture a skate key requires using machine I for 1 minute and machine II for 2 minutes; to manufacture a can opener requires using machine I for 1 minute and machine II for 1 minute. During each hour, machine I cannot be used for more than 50 minutes, machine II for more than 55 minutes. There is a market for as many skate keys and can openers as he can produce. For maximum profit, how many of each should he manufacture per hour if the profit on a skate key is 10¢ and the profit on a can opener is:

(a) 4¢   (b) 5¢   (c) 6¢   (d) 10¢   (e) 11¢

4. Suppose the items in Problem 3 are being manufactured not for profit but for private use. How many of each item should be produced per hour if the following are to be maximized:

(a) Total number of pieces produced.

(b) Total time during which equipment is in use.

5. Each capsule of Dose is required by law to contain at least 8 grains of doo, 20 grains of soo, and 24 grains of foo. A company has supplies of Dis and Dat on hand, from which to manufacture Dose. A gram of Dis contains 1 grain each of doo, soo, and foo. A gram of Dat contains 1 grain of doo, 3 grains of soo, and 4 grains of foo. To minimize cost, how many grams of Dis and how many grams of Dat should each capsule contain, if Dis costs 10¢ per gram and the cost in cents per gram of Dat is:

(a) 5   (b) 10   (c) 20

(d) 30   (e) 35   (f) 40

(g) 45

9 PROGRESSIONS AND THE MATHEMATICS OF FINANCE

9.1 INTRODUCTION

Starting with a number a, repeated multiplication by a number b generates a progression of numbers involving successive powers of b: $a, ab, ab^2, \cdots$; and starting with a number a, repeated addition of a number b generates a progression of numbers involving successive multiples of b: $a, a + b, a + 2b, \cdots$. Both types of progressions are of great importance in pure and applied mathematics. Both arise in the study of a very well-known concept of finance, and we shall take that means of introducing them.

The mathematics of commerce and finance has an ancient origin. In records of the Babylonians and Egyptians dating back as far as 1600 B.C. we find mentioned all sorts of contracts, bills, receipts, promissory notes, accounts, and mortgages. We find also that these ancient peoples were familiar with the concept of *interest*, both simple and compound.

It is to the concept of interest that we now turn our attention.

9.2 SIMPLE INTEREST AND ARITHMETIC PROGRESSIONS

There is an old saying to the effect that everything has its price. It would be appropriate to add: "even money." We do not think it unreasonable, when we rent an automobile, or an apartment, or a book, to pay a sum for its use based upon the time during which it is in our possession, as, for example $20 a day for an automobile, or $100 a month for an apartment, or 3 cents a day for a book.

So, when money was first borrowed, a price called "interest" was paid for its use. To the examples of rental rates we have given above, then, we may add that, when we rent a dollar, we might be asked to pay something like 5 cents a year for its use. We note that 5 cents is $\frac{1}{20}$ of a dollar, a fraction which we term the *interest rate*.

The interest rate, in other words, is the fraction of a sum which we pay for the use of that sum for a stated period of time. It may be expressed as a fraction (e.g., $\frac{1}{20}$) or as a *percentage*, that is, as a numerator of the fraction which represents the interest rate, when that fraction has been converted to one with denominator 100 (e.g., the interest rate $\frac{1}{20}$ may also be expressed as $\frac{5}{100}$ or 5%). Let us consider an example of this so-called simple interest method of paying for a loan. Suppose I were to borrow $100 for which I agree to pay 2% per month simple interest. Then the following table indicates the total interest and the total amount which I would owe the lender at the end of the given period of time:

Number of months	1	2	3	4	5
Total interest due	$2	$4	$6	$8	$10
Total amount owed	$102	$104	$106	$108	$110

In the case of simple interest, it is easy to express the general situation in terms of a formula. Clearly, if the amount borrowed is P (standing for "principal"), and the interest rate is r per time period, then the total interest due at the end of one time period is the product Pr. The total interest due at the end of n time periods must then be the amount Prn. The total amount A owed at the end of n time periods, finally, is the sum of the original principal borrowed, P, and the total interest payment due, Prn.

$$A = P + Prn = P(1 + rn)$$

(Note the use of the distributive law.)

We have not yet extracted all that is interesting from the simple interest situation. Returning to the preceding table, for example, we find in the three rows of the table, three examples of a *sequence*, or *progression*. These are both names for a succession of numbers, written one after the other.

*A sequence has a first element, a second element, a third element, etc. In other words, in a sequence there is an element assigned to the number 1, an element assigned to the number 2, an element assigned to the number 3, etc. That is to say, an (infinite) sequence may be regarded as (in fact, may be defined to be) a function whose domain is the set of all natural numbers. (What would a finite sequence be?)

Sequences are very important in mathematics. They occur in great abundance and differ widely among themselves. The three to which we have just called the student's attention, however, are all of the same type: each may be "generated" by the repeated addition of a number, which we shall denote by d, to the first element or "term" of the sequence, which we shall denote by a. In the three examples we have given, these numbers are respectively: $a = 1, d = 1; a = 2, d = 2; a = 102, d = 2$.

The type of sequence of which these three are examples is called an arithmetic progression. We proceed to define it formally:

> A progression is said to be *arithmetic* if there is a number d with this property: After the first term, any term of the progression may be derived from its predecessor by the addition of d.

Thus, in general, an arithmetic progression with first term a proceeds as follows:

(1) $$a, a + d, a + 2d, a + 3d, a + 4d, \cdots$$

The number d, to which we have not yet given a name, is called the "common difference" of the arithmetic progression since, clearly, it is the difference between any term and its predecessor.

Now in the case of simple interest, we were interested in finding the last term of a certain arithmetic progression (A.P.). This question arises for other A.P.'s as well and, therefore, we derive a general formula to give us the answer.

Suppose our general A.P. has n terms, the last of which we denote by l, Looking back to the A.P. (1) above, we note that, when the A.P. has 3 terms, $l = a + 2d$; when it has 4 terms, $l = a + 3d$; when it has 5 terms, $l = a + 4d$. It is easy to see, then, that for an A.P. with 10 terms. $l = a + 9d$ and, in general, for an A.P. with n terms:

$$l = a + (n - 1)d$$

There are many situations in which we would like to know the sum of all the terms of a given A.P. without going through the labor of writing them all down and adding them all up. Here is an example: A man had a job in which he received a raise of $100 in his annual wage every year. If he earned $2000 during his first year at the job, and if he worked for 21 years before retiring, what was the total of his earnings on his job?

In order to see how to solve this problem, we first consider an easier one of the same nature, namely, to find the sum of all the integers from 1 to 10. There is a trick to this, and the first step is to write the numbers from 1 to 10 *twice*, in two columns next to each other, but so that the numbers run up in one column and down in the other, as shown below. What we do next is to add up all the numbers in both columns, which gives us, of course, just twice the sum we seek. But instead of adding down, we first add across:

$$1 + 10 = 11$$
$$2 + 9 = 11$$
$$3 + 8 = 11$$
$$4 + 7 = 11$$
$$5 + 6 = 11$$
$$6 + 5 = 11$$
$$7 + 4 = 11$$
$$8 + 3 = 11$$
$$9 + 2 = 11$$
$$10 + 1 = 11$$

The result of the additions across is ten 11's. But we know that this is just twice the sum we seek. Therefore, the sum of the numbers from 1 to 10 must be five 11's, or 55.

The student may easily check the answer by adding the numbers directly, and in fact this is so easy that in this case our trick is not very impressive. However, in finding the sum of all the integers from 1 to 1000, let us say, or in solving the preceding wage problem (as we are about to do), the method begins to show real merit.

To find what our worker earned in 21 years, we first compute the number of dollars he earned during the last year of his employment. Since his successive yearly salaries obviously form an A.P.:

$$l = 2000 + (21 - 1)(100) = 2000 + 2000 = 4000$$

Then we follow the method of the last example, but it is unnecessary to write down all 21 salaries:

$$\left.\begin{array}{l} 2000 + 4000 = 6000 \\ 2100 + 3900 = 6000 \\ \cdot \quad \cdot \quad \cdot \quad \cdot \quad \cdot \\ \cdot \quad \cdot \quad \cdot \quad \cdot \quad \cdot \\ 3900 + 2100 = 6000 \\ 4000 + 2000 = 6000 \end{array}\right\} \text{21 rows}$$

His total earnings, then, were: $\dfrac{(21)(6000)}{2} = \$63,000.$

A general formula is now easy to derive:

$$\left.\begin{array}{rl} a \quad + l & = a + l \\ a + d + l - d & = a + l \\ a + 2d + l - 2d & = a + l \\ \cdot \quad \cdot \quad \cdot \quad \cdot \quad \cdot \\ \cdot \quad \cdot \quad \cdot \quad \cdot \quad \cdot \\ \cdot \quad \cdot \quad \cdot \quad \cdot \quad \cdot \\ l - 2d + a + 2d & = a + l \\ l - d + a + d & = a + l \\ l \quad + a \quad & = a + l \end{array}\right\} n \text{ rows}$$

The formula we are led to for the sum S of an A.P. of n terms with first term a and last term l is:

$$S = \frac{n(a + l)}{2} = \frac{n}{2}(a + l)$$

▶ **EXERCISE 42**

1. If \$1200 is loaned at a simple interest rate of 5% per year, how much must be paid back at the end of seven years?

2. If \$225 is loaned at a simple interest rate of $\frac{1}{2}$% per month, how much must be paid back at the end of a year?

3. A man, having borrowed \$125, agrees to pay back \$135 at the end of a year. What is the simple interest rate in this transaction?

4. A man borrows \$175 at simple interest rate of 6%. At the end of what period of time does his debt amount to \$200?

5. Find the last term of an A.P. of 100 terms, if its first term is 7 and its common difference is 11.

6. What is the thousandth odd number?

7. Find the fifty-first term of each A.P. among the following:

(a) 1, 4, 16, $\cdots$ (b) $\frac{1}{2}, \frac{2}{3}, \frac{5}{6}, \cdots$

(c) 1, 0, 1, $\cdots$ (d) $\frac{1}{2}, -\frac{2}{3}, \frac{5}{6}, \cdots$

(e) $-1, 0, 1, \cdots$ (f) $-\frac{1}{2}, \frac{2}{3}, \frac{11}{6}, \cdots$

(g) $-15, -5, 5, \cdots$ (h) $\frac{11}{6}, \frac{2}{3}, -\frac{1}{2}, \cdots$

8. Find the sum of 100 terms of the A.P. of Problem 5.

9.(a) What is the sum of the first 11 odd numbers? of the first 12 odd numbers? of the first 7 odd numbers?

(b) Can you abstract a general theorem from the results of part (a)? Can you prove that your general theorem is true? Discuss the roles played by inductive and deductive reasoning in this problem.

10. Find the sum of 51 terms of each A.P. among those in Problem 7.

11. An economist, knowing that a company spent \$880 for widgets in the first 11 years of its existence, wishes to estimate the portion of that

amount spent during each of the 11 years. He makes two assumptions: first, that annual expenditures for widgets have grown arithmetically (i.e., are in A.P.), and second, that general expenditures having tripled in those 11 years, the amount spent on widgets during the 11th year was three times that spent during the first year.

(a) Under these assumptions, how much did the company spend on widgets during each of the 11 years?

(b) If the company continues buying widgets at the same rate of increase, how much must it plan to spend on widgets during its 25th year of operation? How much, then, will it have spent on widgets during its first 25 years?

12. A man is offered two jobs. Job A pays an initial annual salary of $2000 and offers annual raises of $200. Job B pays an initial semi-annual salary of $1000 and offers semi-annual raises of $50.

(a) If the man plans to work for a year, which is the better job?

(b) If the man plans to work for two years, which is the better job?

(c) If the man plans to work for three years, which is the better job?

(d) Find formulas for the amount the man would earn in n years at each of jobs A and B. Simplify the formulas and compare them to arrive at a conclusion.

9.3 COMPOUND INTEREST

Let us suppose that we have $100 in hand, which we deposit in a bank; and the bank, for the privilege of using this money, is willing to pay us 2% per year simple interest. Then at the end of three years, we would have to our credit in the account: $100[1 + (0.02)(3)], or $106.

As a matter of fact, most banks are more generous than that. They are usually willing to deposit the interest due on an account, periodically to the account, so that the interest itself begins to accumulate interest. Suppose, for example, that the bank in which we deposited our $100 "compounds" annually. Then at the end of one year we would have $100 + $2 = $102 in our account. At the end of the second year we would have to our credit this $102 together with interest amounting to 2% of $102, or a total of: $102 + (0.02)($102) = $102(1 + 0.02) = $102(1.02) = $104.04.

Indeed, if our account begins any year with D dollars, it is easy to see that it ends the year with $D + 0.02D$, or $D(1 + 0.02)$ or $D(1.02)$ dollars. Thus, to find what we have in the account at the end of three years, we compute the product $(104.04)(1.02)$ and discover that compounding 2%

annually will give us $106.12, a clear profit of 12 cents as compared with simple interest.

We shall soon see that, with the passage of time, the gap between compound and simple interest widens greatly.

First, however, let us derive a general formula for the amount A to which a principal P grows in n periods of time, if the interest rate is i per period and if interest is compounded every period.

We note that, if we begin a time period with D dollars in our account, then at the end of that period, i.e., at the beginning of the next period, we have $D + iD$, or $D(1 + i)$ dollars in our account. Thus, the amount of money in an account at the beginning of a period may be derived from the amount in that account at the beginning of the preceding period by multiplying by $1 + i$ (assuming no new deposits have been made).

Thus, tabulating A for the end of several successive periods gives the following results:

PERIODS	1	2	3	4
A	$P(1 + i)$	$P(1 + i)^2$	$P(1 + i)^3$	$P(1 + i)^4$

We see that the exponent applied to $(1 + i)$ is always the same as the number of periods which have elapsed. We are led to the compound interest formula:

$$A = P(1 + i)^n$$

Now, to find from the formula the amount to which our $100 deposit grows in 3 years, we would write: $A = 100(1.02)^3$. But we have, as a matter of fact, essentially computed $(1.02)^3$, and it is equal to almost exactly 1.0612, so that $A = 106.12, as before.

It may be seen that generally the difficult part in finding A will be the computation of $(1 + i)^n$. This is the sort of functional problem in which a table of values worked out in advance is very helpful.

As a historical sidelight, it is interesting to note that the ancient Babylonians delighted in tables of values; hundreds of them have been discovered on their baked clay tablets. They had tables for multiplication and division, for squares, cubes, square roots, and cube roots, and, among many other types, even exponential tables very much like Table II, page 454). Several examples will illustrate the use of this table:

Illustrative Example I. What will $125 amount to 10 years after its deposit in a bank which pays an annual interest rate of 2% and compounds annually?

SOLUTION. $A = 125(1 + 0.02)^{10}$. From Table II: $(1.02)^{10} = 1.21899$. Therefore $A = (125)(1.21899) = \$152.37$.

Illustrative Example 2. What would be the answer to Example 1 if the same bank were to compound semiannually?

SOLUTION. A bank which pays a simple interest rate of 2% annually, pays 1% simple interest semiannually. In this example, therefore, there are 20 time periods, and the interest per period is 1%.

$$A = 125(1 + 0.01)^{20} = 125(1.22019) = \$152.52.$$

Illustrative Example 3. In how many years will money double at an interest rate of 2% per year compounded annually?

SOLUTION. Looking down the 2% column in Table II, we see that the factor $(1 + i)^n$ is very nearly 2 in 35 years. The answer is therefore: a little over 35 years.

Illustrative Example 4. Northampton, Massachusetts, recently celebrated its 300th anniversary. Suppose that one of its citizens, in the year of its founding, deposited \$1 in a bank paying 5% interest per annum compounded annually.

To what approximate amount would his dollar have grown at the time of the anniversary? How much would it have grown to at simple rather than compound interest?

SOLUTION. Referring to Table II, we see that at 5% interest per year, money does a little better than double itself in fifteen years. In 300 years, there are twenty 15-year periods, so the dollar will be doubled 20 times. The student may easily verify that ten doublings will result in a little better than a factor of 1000; another ten will give another factor of more than 1000; the result is more than $\$1 \times 1000 \times 1000$ or more than \$1,000,000! At simple interest, $A = P(1 + rn) = \$1[1 + (0.05)(300)] = \$1(16) =$ only \$16!

▶ **EXERCISE 43**

1. One hundred dollars are invested at 2% per annum compounded annually. What will the investment amount to in 5 years? in 10 years?

2. What is the answer to Problem 1 if compounding is done quarterly?

3. A and B each invest \$100 at 3% interest per annum, but A's interest is simple and B's compound. Compare their investments 10, 20, 30, 40, and 50 years after their initial deposits.

4. A deposits money at 2% per annum compounded quarterly; at what

simple interest rate must B deposit an equal amount of money in order that their investments be equal 20 years from now?

5. A deposits money at 6% per annum simple interest; at approximately what annual compound interest rate must B deposit an equal amount of money in order that their investments be equal at the end of 30 years?

6. When his son Bertrand is born, John Q. Bucks wishes to deposit in a bank which pays 3% interest per annum compounded semiannually, a sum which will amount in 17 years to enough to pay for Bertrand's college education. He estimates the cost of a college education at $8000. How much should he deposit in the bank?

7. About how long does it take for money to double itself at 4% interest per annum compounded annually? Compounded semiannually? How long to triple at the first rate?

8. At what annual compound interest rate does money increase by a third in ten years?

9. Suppose that 20 years from now you become the parent of a son, who, at 40, becomes the proud father of a boy. Suppose also that you have the opportunity now to invest money at a rate of 8% compounded semiannually.

How much would you have to invest now to make your grandson a millionaire at the age of 40?

(We feel it necessary to note here the unhappy fact that there are laws which limit the amount to which a bank account may grow.)

9.4 GEOMETRIC PROGRESSIONS

Just as the concept of simple interest leads naturally into the study of arithmetic progressions, so we are led from compound interest to the consideration of "geometric" progressions (G.P.'s). The table on page 269 suggests the following definition (note the resemblance to the definition of an A.P.):

> A progression is said to be *geometric* if there is a number r with this property: After the first term, any term of the progression may be derived from its predecessor by multiplying by r.

In the table of page 269, of course, $r = 1 + i$. In general, a G.P. with first term a proceeds as follows:

$$a, ar, ar^2, ar^3, ar^4, \cdots$$

The number r is called the "common ratio" since generally it is the *ratio* between any term and its predecessor; in other words, it is the result of *dividing* any term by its predecessor, except when $a = 0$ or $r = 0$.

Noting that the *third* term of the preceding progression is ar^2, the *fourth* ar^3, the fifth ar^4, and so on, we see that, in general, for a G.P. of n terms, first term a, common ratio r, and last term l:

$$l = ar^{n-1}$$

There is also a simple formula for the sum of n terms of a geometric progression:

$$S = \frac{a(r^n - 1)}{r - 1}$$

The derivation of this formula follows:

$$S = a + ar + ar^2 + \cdots + ar^{n-2} + ar^{n-1}$$
$$\therefore rS = \quad ar + ar^2 + \cdots + ar^{n-2} + ar^{n-1} + ar^n$$

Subtracting the second equation from the first:

$$S - rS = a - ar^n$$
$$S(1 - r) = a(1 - r^n)$$
$$S = \frac{a(1 - r^n)}{1 - r} = a\left(\frac{1 - r^n}{1 - r}\right) = a\left(\frac{r^n - 1}{r - 1}\right)$$

(Of the last two forms, the last will be generally more convenient to use when $r > 1$, the next-to-the last, when $r < 1$. When $r = 1$, these formulas clearly fail. Why? In that case, is there a formula for S?)

An interesting situation occurs when r is less than 1 in absolute value, and n is a "large" natural number. For example, suppose $a = 3$, $r = -\frac{1}{2}$, and $n = 10$. Then:

$$S = 3\left[\frac{1 - (-\frac{1}{2})^{10}}{1 - (-\frac{1}{2})}\right]$$

But we note that $(-\frac{1}{2})^{10} = 1/1024$, which in absolute value is quite small as compared with the other terms involved. Therefore, deleting this term will not greatly affect our answer. We may say that, in this case,

$$S \doteq 3\left(\frac{1}{1 + \frac{1}{2}}\right) = 2$$

Of course, it is a difficult thing to say exactly what we mean by n being "large" in comparison with other numbers, or exactly how approximate our approximation for S is. But we do know this: the larger n is, the better will be the approximation for S that we obtain by deleting the term r^n from our formula for S; for when a number is less than 1 in absolute value, as we are assuming r to be, larger and larger powers of the number become smaller and smaller in absolute value.

Deleting the term r^n from our formula for S, we may therefore say:
If $|r| < 1$, then as n becomes larger and larger, $S \doteq a/(1 - r)$.
If $|r| < 1$, the number $a/(1 - r)$ is called "the sum of the infinite G.P. with first term a and ratio r," and denoted S_∞ ("S sub infinity"). Thus:

$$S_\infty = \frac{a}{1 - r}$$

Of course, what is meant is that when $|r| < 1$, S_∞ is a number that is approached more and more nearly by S as n becomes larger and larger. (A more precise formulation of this statement is given by the mathematical theory of "limits.")

Illustrative Example 1.   A certain ball has the property that, when it is dropped from any height h to the ground, it rebounds to the height $\frac{2}{3}h$. Suppose the ball is thrown to a height of 9 ft. How far will it travel before coming to rest?

SOLUTION.   The ball will travel 9 ft up and 9 ft down, then 6 ft up and 6 ft down, then 4 ft up and 4 ft down, and so on.   The distance that it travels is:

$$18 + 12 + 8 + \cdots$$

The successive terms of this sum are terms of a G.P., with $a = 18$, $r = \frac{2}{3}$.   In this case $S_\infty = 18/(1 - \frac{2}{3}) = 54$.   The answer to our problem is: 54 ft.   But of course, no physical ball could bounce forever.   What we mean by this answer is that the longer the ball bounces, the nearer will the total distance it travels approach 54 ft; and indeed, no matter what real number $k \neq 54$ is given, however close to 54, if the ball continues bouncing long enough, the total distance it travels will eventually become and remain closer to 54 ft than it is to k ft.

▶ **EXERCISE 44**

1. Find the tenth term and the sum of the first ten terms of each G.P. among the following:

(a) 1, 2, 4, $\cdots$

(b) $\frac{1}{2}, \frac{1}{4}, \frac{1}{8}, \cdots$

(c) $-2, 4, 8, \cdots$

(d) $\frac{1}{2}, \frac{1}{4}, \frac{1}{6}, \cdots$

(e) 2, -4, 8, $\cdots$

(f) $\frac{1}{16}, \frac{1}{8}, \frac{1}{4}, \cdots$

(g) 4, 2, 1, $\cdots$

(h) $-\frac{1}{2}, 1, 2, \cdots$

2. Suppose that a streptococcus germ splits and forms two germs in 2 minutes.   Starting from a colony of three germs, how many will the colony contain after an hour has passed?

3. An air pump removes half the air in a jar in 5 seconds.   What

fraction of the air will be left in the jar after the pump has been in operation for 1 minute?

4. A certain make of automobile depreciates 20% in value each year. If it cost \$2000 when new, what is its value after 5 years?

5. Derive the following formula for the sum S of n terms of a G.P., with first term a and ratio r: $S = (a - rl)/(1 - r)$.

6.(a) through (h). Use the formula of Problem 5 to compute S in Problems 1a through 1h.

7. For each of the following G.P., find S_∞, and explain the meaning of your result.

(a) $a = 1, r = \frac{1}{2}$ (b) $a = 1, r = -\frac{1}{2}$
(c) $a = 10, r = 0.1$ (d) $a = 10, r = -\frac{1}{2}$
(e) $2, 1, \frac{1}{2}, \cdots$ (f) $8, -6, \cdots$

8.(a) through (f). The concept of a G.P. may be applied to the problem of finding the rational number represented by an infinite repeating decimal. For example, the rational number represented by the infinite decimal $0.711711711 \cdots$ may be regarded as S_∞ for the G.P.: $0.711, 0.000711,$ $0.000000711, \cdots$; in this case $a = 0.711, r = 1/1000$. Hence 0.711711711 $= 0.711/[1 - (1/1000)] = 0.711/(999/1000) = 711/999 = 79/111$.

Use this technique in Exercise 12, Problems 3a through 3f.

9. A certain ball dropped from a height h above the ground will rebound to the height $\frac{1}{2}h$. Suppose this ball is thrown up from the ground to a height of 40 ft. How far will it travel before coming to rest?

10. The same as Problem 9, except that the ball is originally *dropped* from a height of 60 ft.

11. In Problem 9, find *exactly* the distance traveled by the ball after 10 rises and falls. How does your result compare with your answer to Problem 9? Explain.

*9.5 APPLICATIONS OF THE METHOD OF LINEAR INTERPOLATION

Suppose we were to deposit \$100 in a bank which pays $2\frac{1}{2}$% interest per annum, compounded semiannually. How much would our deposit amount to in 5 years?

The problem requires us to find A when $P = $ \$100, $n = 10$, $i = 1\frac{1}{4}$%, but our table has no column for $1\frac{1}{4}$%. The method of *linear interpolation* may be used to arrive at an approximation to the missing value. We review the method below:

Let us copy from the compound interest table the readings for those interest rates which are nearest to $1\frac{1}{4}\%$, leaving a gap for the reading which should correspond to $1\frac{1}{4}\%$ itself:

%	READING WITHIN TABLE
1	1.10462
$1\frac{1}{4}$	
$1\frac{1}{2}$	1.16054

Now since the second value on the left is exactly half-way between the first and third values on the left, the method of linear interpolation fills the gap on the right with a number half-way between the two values on the right.

The distance (i.e., the difference) between the right-hand values is 0.05592. Half that distance is 0.02796. Beginning at 1.10462, then, we travel half-way to the next value in the table by adding 0.02796. The result is 1.13258.

(The answer to our original problem, then, is $A = \$113.25$.)

Again by way of illustration, we present a problem proposed by the Babylonians, and solved by them by the method of linear interpolation.

The problem is this: How long does it take for money to double itself at 20% per annum, compounded annually?

Using the formula $A = P(1 + r)^n$, with $P = 1$ and $A = 2$, we see that the problem is to find an n such that:

$$2 = (1.2)^n$$

By trying several values of n, we will discover that n must lie between 3 and 4:

1.2^n	n
2.0736	4
2.0000	
1.7280	3

Since 2.0000 lies $\dfrac{0.2720}{0.3456}$ or about 0.8 of the way from the number below it to the number above it, we fill the gap on the right with a number 0.8 of the way from 3 to 4. The "way" from 3 to 4 is, of course, 1, and 0.8 of 1 is 0.8. The number we seek, then, is $3 + 0.8$, or 3.8. To the nearest

tenth of a year, this happens to be the correct answer, (as we may determine by the use of logarithms—see Section 8.11, Illustrative Example 1), so that in this case the method of linear interpolation works quite well.

It must be pointed out that our result does *not* mean that, under the conditions of the problem, a bank would pay us double our deposit after 3.8 years; for under these conditions a bank would make no interest payment *during* a year. What would happen in practice is that we would have to wait 4 years to get a little more than double our deposit. If we withdrew our money at any time during the third year, we would get only as much as we had on deposit at the beginning of the third year.

The answer 3.8 years, however, is not entirely devoid of practical meaning. If money doubles in 3.8 years, then in 38 years it doubles ten times, or grows to 1024 times its original value; this last result *is* meaningful in practical terms.

▶ ***EXERCISE 45**

1. How much would a deposit of \$100 at 3% interest per annum compounded quarterly amount to in 10 years?

2. Man A borrows \$100 and agrees to pay back \$103 six months later. What monthly compound interest rate is he paying? What annual rate, compounded monthly, is this equivalent to?

3. Man B borrows \$100 and agrees to pay back \$104 nine months later. Has he made a better or worse bargain than man A?

4. How long will it take for money to quadruple itself at an interest rate of 30% per annum compounded annually?

5. The population of a certain city seems to increase by one-half itself every 30 years. If the population in 1950 was 100,000, when may we expect its population to be 200,000?

*9.6 THE NUMBER e

π and e are two very famous and important numbers in mathematics. Almost everyone has heard of the number π, but e, although its role in mathematics is no less illustrious, is known to very few. The reason is that π is involved in formulas for the circumference and area of a circle, which we learn about even in grade school, but e is usually encountered for the first time only in a college course in the differential calculus.

The number e arises very naturally, however, in the study of compound interest, and we shall take this means of introducing it into our course.

We shall imagine, to begin with, a bank which pays 100% interest per annum, compounded annually. (The interest rate of 100% is not as fantastic as it sounds; if the period were a longer one, it would be quite within the realm of possibility. We have chosen the year as our period only because it is the most familiar of interest periods, but, if the student prefers, he may substitute "decade" or even "century" in this section.)

If we deposited $1 in this bank, then, clearly it would grow to $2 in one year. Now suppose this bank compounded semiannually rather than annually. Then in one year we should have two interest periods, and the interest rate per period would be 50%. Hence $A = \$1(1 + 0.50)^2 = \$1(1.5)^2 = \$2.25$.

Compounding semiannually rather than annually, then, is distinctly to our advantage: we earn $1.25 on our deposit of $1 during the space of a year rather than only $1. Now the question arises: Will we do even better if the bank compounds quarterly? The answer is "yes," of course. The more often the bank compounds, the more our dollar will earn in a year, for compounding often means that interest begins to earn interest more quickly.

Does that mean that, with very rapid compounding, say, every day or every minute, our $1 will earn a huge amount in a year? Let us attempt to answer this question by observing what happens to our dollar as we subdivide the year into smaller and smaller interest periods. Compounding quarterly, for example: $A = \$1(1 + 0.25)^4 = \$(\frac{5}{4})^4 = \$(\frac{625}{256}) = \$2.44$, to the nearest cent. Compounding ten times a year leads to a result which may easily be computed directly, and which is entered in the following table. The other results tabulated below were found with the aid of the compound interest table. The last entry is the result of squaring the value of $(1.01)^{50}$, as found in the compound interest table.

THE AMOUNT (TO THE NEAREST CENT) TO WHICH $1 GROWS IN A YEAR AT 100% INTEREST PER ANNUM COMPOUNDED n TIMES A YEAR

n	1	2	4	10	20	50	100
Amount ($)	2.00	2.25	2.44	2.59	2.65	2.69	2.70

This table is not very encouraging if it was our hope that frequent compounding would make our earnings rise astronomically. Compounding 50 times a year, or about once a week, would make our dollar earn 69 cents more than annual compounding; but compounding twice as often, that is to say a hundred times a year, would then yield only an extra penny.

A decrease in the rate of growth of the numbers in the second row of the table is apparent. As a matter of fact, it may be proved (although the proof is beyond the scope of this course) that no matter how large n is, the amount which corresponds to n will never be as large as 2.72. As the number of interest periods into which our year is divided grows larger and larger, the amount to which our dollar grows will creep closer and closer to a number which the mathematician calls e, and which is just under 2.72. Correct to three decimal places: $e \doteq 2.718$.

Now let us be a bit more precise. The interest rate of 100% per annum which we are considering is equal to the number 1.00, or 1. If interest is compounded n times a year, then the interest rate i for each of these n periods is $1/n$. The number of dollars to which \$1 will grow in one year, if the interest rate is 100% per annum, compounded n times a year [from the formula $A = P(1 + i)^n$] is: $\left(1 + \dfrac{1}{n}\right)^n$.

As the integer n grows larger and larger, the number $\left(1 + \dfrac{1}{n}\right)^n$ grows larger and larger, and approaches, but never reaches, a number called e whose value is approximately 2.718. Here is a picture of what is happening. (The dots represent the successive values of the second row of our table):

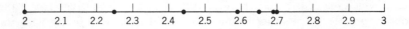

e, then, is the number which is approached by the expression $\left(1 + \dfrac{1}{n}\right)^n$ as the integer n grows larger and larger.

(This last statement, in more advanced courses in mathematics, is the basis for a much more precise definition of the number e. What we lack just now in formulating such a definition are accurate statements of what we mean, for example, by "is approached by" and "grows larger and larger.")

When interest is computed as the limit of interests attained by allowing the compounding interval to approach zero, we say that we *compound continuously*. If it were possible for interest to begin earning interest itself the very instant it was earned, then we would have interest compounded continuously. While most bank tellers would find it difficult to make the necessary entries quickly enough, the concept is nevertheless a useful one. It tells us, to any desired degree of accuracy, the greatest sum to which interest can grow in a given period of time, no matter how often compounded.

The process of compounding continuously leads to the following definition:

> "e" is the number of dollars to which \$1 will grow in one year at 100% interest per annum, compounded continuously.

▶ ***EXERCISE 46**

$e^2 = $ one year @ 200%
$e^3 = $ one year @ 300%

1. Carry out the computation of those values in the preceding table which have not already been computed in the text.

2. How much will \$1 amount to in one year at 100% interest per annum compounded 25 times a year?   40 times a year?

3. Show that, if \$1 is compounded continuously at an interest rate of i, it will amount in one year to e^i dollars, and in y years to e^{iy} dollars.

***9.7 PRESENT VALUE**

Illustrative Example I.   What sum of money, deposited at 3% annual interest compounded annually, would grow in 10 years to \$1?

SOLUTION.   Using the formula $A = P(1 + i)^n$, we have:

$$1 = P(1.03)^{10}$$

where P is the required sum of money, in dollars.

From Table II we find that $(1.03)^{10} = 1.34392$.   Therefore:

$$P = \frac{1}{(1.03)^{10}} = \frac{1}{1.34392} = 0.74 \text{ (approximately)}$$

The answer to the given problem is therefore: \$0.74, approximately.

We call the amount which must be invested at an interest rate of $i\%$ per period, compounded for n periods, to amount to A, the *present value* of A under the given interest conditions.

Thus, in Illustrative Example 1, 74 cents is the present value of \$1 at 3% annual interest, compounded for 10 years.

In the formula $A = P(1 + i)^n$, P represents the present value of A, where the interest rate is $i\%$ per period, compounded for n periods.

Therefore:

$$P = \frac{A}{(1 + i)^n}$$

If $A = 1$:

$$P = \frac{1}{(1 + i)^n}$$

The present value of 1, i.e., $\dfrac{1}{(1+i)^n}$, has been computed and will be found, for various periods and interest rates, in Table III, thus obviating the long division by which we actually obtained the answer to Illustrative Example 1. The student will find in fact, that Table III gives the required present value of 1 as 0.74409.

Now since in general:

$$P = \frac{A}{(1+i)^n} = A \cdot \frac{1}{(1+i)^n}$$

we see that the present value of A may be computed by multiplying the present value of 1 by A.

Illustrative Example 2. What amount of money must be deposited now at 3% annual interest compounded semiannually for 10 years in order to grow to $1200?

SOLUTION. $i = 1\frac{1}{2}\%$; $n = 20$; present value of 1 (from Table III) is 0.74247; present value of $1200 is $(1200)(0.74247), or $890.96.

▶ *EXERCISE 47

1. Using Table III, solve Problems 6 and 9 of Exercise 43.

2. What is the present value of:

(a) $100, if an annual interest rate of 3% is compounded semiannually for 10 years?

(b) $100, if an annual interest rate of 4% is compounded quarterly for 10 years?

(c) $100, if an annual interest rate of 5% is compounded quarterly for 10 years?

3. If an investment pays 4% per annum compounded quarterly, what amount invested $8\frac{1}{2}$ years ago would be worth $1000 today?

4. What sum, invested at 3% interest, will amount to $1000 in 20 years if interest is compounded annually? semiannually?

5. The will of John Smith provides that his son is to receive $10,000 when he reaches the age of 25. If the father dies when his son is 20 years old, how much must the executor of his estate invest in a fund which pays 4% interest per annum compounded quarterly in order to meet this condition of the will?

6. A young man is to inherit $25,000 at the age of 25. He is now 18 and wishes to borrow the present value of his inheritance. How much can he borrow if money is considered worth 3% per year, compounded semiannually?

7. A house is advertised to sell for $4000 down and $6000 three years hence.   If money is worth 5% per year compounded semiannually, what should be the cash price of the house?

8. If money is worth 6% "converted" (i.e., compounded) quarterly, how much must be invested now in order to have $4000 in 6 years 3 months?

*9.8 THE AMOUNT OF AN ANNUITY

A succession of deposits of equal sums of money at equal intervals of time into an interest bearing account is called an *annuity*. We shall consider here only the case in which the interval of compounding is the same as the interval at which money is deposited.   Thus, an example of an annuity of the type we shall consider is one in which $50 is deposited every 3 months for 10 years into an account bearing 4% interest per annum compounded quarterly.

A natural question which arises in this situation concerns the sum which one may expect to have in an account after a certain number of deposits have been made.   That sum, of course, is more than just the sum of the deposits; for the deposits earn interest of varying amounts—more or less depending upon the time which has elapsed since the date on which the deposit was made.

We shall find it convenient to derive a formula for the sum to which an annuity has accrued *just after* the last payment.   This is called the amount of the annuity.

Suppose that a quantity P is deposited into an account regularly for n periods, and that the interest rate for each period is $i\%$, compounded each period.   We shall denote the amount (or "sum") of the annuity by S, and we shall derive a formula for S.

NUMBER OF DEPOSIT	ELAPSED INTEREST PERIODS	AMOUNT TO WHICH P ACCRUES
nth	0	P
$(n-1)$st	1	$P(1+i)$
$(n-2)$nd	2	$P(1+i)^2$
.	.	.
.	.	.
.	.	.
2nd	$n-2$	$P(1+i)^{n-2}$
1st	$n-1$	$P(1+i)^{n-1}$

S will be the sum of the quantities to which each deposit has accrued. The last deposit of P, having had no time to earn interest, will simply contribute P to the sum. The next-to-the-last deposit, having been in the account for one period, will have grown [by the formula $A = P(1 + i)^n$] to the quantity $P(1 + i)$; and so on, as tabulated on previous page.

Therefore:

$$S = P + P(1 + i) + P(1 + i)^2 + \cdots + P(1 + i)^{n-2} + P(1 + i)^{n-1}$$

But the expression on the right above is the sum of the first n terms of a geometric series in which $a = P, r = (1 + i)$. Therefore, by the formula $S = a\left(\dfrac{r^n - 1}{r - 1}\right)$:

(1) $$S = P\left(\frac{(1 + i)^n - 1}{i}\right)$$

If $P = 1$, then $S = \dfrac{(1 + i^n) - 1}{i}$. This is the amount to which an annuity of 1 will grow, and it will be found tabulated, for various values of n and i, in Table IV. Clearly, from (1) above, the amount to which an annuity of P will grow, for a fixed n and i, may be found by multiplying the amount to which an annuity of 1 (with the same n and i) will grow, by P.

Illustrative Example. What will an annuity which consists of payments of $1 every 3 months for 10 years amount to if the interest rate is 4% per annum compounded quarterly? What if the payments were $50 every 3 months?

SOLUTION. Here $i = 1\%, n = 40$. From Table IV, the amount of the annuity of $1 per annum is $48.88. (We choose the lower approximation.) The amount of an annuity of $50 per annum would be $50 (48.8864), or $2,444.32.

▶ ***EXERCISE 48**

1. Find the amount of an annuity which involves payments of $25 every 6 months for 12 years, if the interest rate is 3% per year compounded semiannually.

2. A man deposits $500 at yearly intervals into a fund which pays 3% interest per annum compounded annually. How much does he have to his credit in the fund just after his tenth deposit?

3. A man wants to deposit R dollars into a fund at the end of every month so that at the end of 4 years he will have $15,000. If the fund pays interest at the rate of 6% compounded monthly, find R. [*Hint:* Formula (1) will help make the proper procedure clear.]

4. How much must be deposited into a fund at intervals of 6 months so that after 10 years the deposits will amount to $20,000, if the rate of interest is 3% compounded semiannually?

5.(a) A man buys a boat from Captain Barnacle on the installment plan, paying $200 at the end of every 3 months thereafter for 8 years. As soon as he receives each payment, Captain Barnacle deposits it in a bank which pays 2% interest per year, compounded quarterly. How much does Captain Barnacle have in this account just after he deposits the final payment of $200?

(b) Suppose that the answer to part (a) is S dollars. What sum of money, deposited in the same bank at the time the boat was purchased, would have amounted in 8 years time to S dollars? (i.e., what is the present value of S dollars in 8 years, if the interest rate is 2% per year compounded quarterly?)   The answer to this problem is called the *equivalent cash price* of the boat.

6. A radio is offered on the installment plan, the payments being $20 a month for 12 months, beginning one month after the date of purchase. If money is worth 6% a year compounded monthly, what (see Problem 5) is the equivalent cash price of the radio at the time of purchase?

7. A washing machine is sold on the following installment plan: $50 down and $25 at the end of every succeeding 3 months, for 2 years. If money is worth 6% a year compounded quarterly, what (see Problem 5) is the equivalent cash price of the washing machine at the time it is purchased?

8. At the end of every 6 months a man deposits $100 into an account paying interest at the rate of 6% per annum compounded semiannually. If he does this over a period of 10 years (beginning 6 months before his first deposit), and then stops depositing, how much will he have in the account 5 years after his last deposit?

9. A corporation sets aside $10,000 at the end of each year for depreciation.   If the corporation invests this at 2% per annum, compounded annually, how much is accumulated in the depreciation account just after the twentieth deposit has been made, assuming no withdrawals?

10. A man sets aside $200 at the end of each year towards a fund for his son's college education.   If the money is invested at 4% per year compounded semiannually, how much will be accumulated at the end of 10 years?

11. In order to pay for his son's college education, a man wishes to deposit R dollars every 3 months for 12 years into a fund paying 6% interest per annum compounded quarterly.   If he estimates the cost of a college education to be $8,000, find R.

*9.9 THE PRESENT VALUE OF AN ANNUITY

A common way of providing income after retirement is to "purchase" an annuity. One may, for example, for a certain sum of money called the *present value V* of the annuity, purchase an annuity which provides that each year for 20 years, beginning 1 year from the date of purchase, the purchaser shall be paid $1000. But what should the cost V of such an annuity be?

More generally, suppose an annuity pays a purchaser a quantity R at regular intervals, for n periods, beginning one period after the date of purchase. What should the cost (i.e., the present value V) of such an annuity be?

One may imagine that the purchase price V is deposited in a bank paying $i\%$ interest per period, compounded every period, and that the required payments are periodically withdrawn from the account. V, then, will have to include enough money to take care of each payment. The amount of money necessary to take care of a payment is (see Section 9.7) the present value of that payment. V, therefore, should be equal to the sum of the present values of the n payments. Recalling that each payment is denoted by R, and using the formula $P = \dfrac{A}{(1 + i)^n}$ of Section 9.7 for present value, we have:

$$V = \frac{R}{1 + i} + \frac{R}{(1 + i)^2} + \cdots + \frac{R}{(1 + i)^n}$$

The right side of this equation is the sum of n terms of a geometric series in which $a = \dfrac{R}{1 + i}$ and $r = \dfrac{1}{1 + i}$. Therefore, using the formula $S = a\left(\dfrac{1 - r^n}{1 - r}\right)$ for the sum of n terms of a geometric series:

$$V = \frac{R}{1 + i} \cdot \left[\frac{1 - \dfrac{1}{(1 + i)^n}}{1 - \dfrac{1}{1 + i}}\right] = R\left[\frac{1 - \dfrac{1}{(1 + i)^n}}{i}\right]$$

As before, we see that the present value of R per period may be derived from the present value of 1 per period by multiplying by R. The present value of 1 per period, for various values of n and i, will be found tabulated in Table V.

That is to say, in Table V we find the (approximate) value of

$$\frac{1 - \dfrac{1}{(1 + i)^n}}{i}$$ for various values of n and i.

Illustrative Example 1.   What is the present value of an annuity which pays $1000 at the beginning of each year, beginning one year from now, for 20 years, if money is worth 4% per year compounded annually?

SOLUTION.   From Table V, the present value of 1 per annum, with $n = 20$, $i = 4\%$, is 13.5903.   The answer to the problem is therefore $1000 (13.5903), or $13,590.30.

Illustrative Example 2.   A man has $20,000, with which he wishes to purchase an annual annuity, to begin one year from the date of purchase, and to continue for 25 years.   If money is worth 5% per year compounded annually, what yearly payments can he expect?

SOLUTION.   From Table V, the present value of 1 per annum, with $n = 25$, $i = 5\%$, is 14.0939.

That is to say, a purchase price of $14.0939 will command an annuity of $1 per year.   A purchase price of $20,000 will therefore command an annuity of:

$$\$ \left(\frac{20,000}{14.039}\right)$$

or approximately $1425 a year.

It is interesting to note that the "equivalent cash value" of an item bought on the installment plan (see Problem 5 of the preceding exercise) may be considered to be the present value of an annuity in which the payments are the payments made under the installment plan.   In fact, one may simply regard the installment plan situation as one in which the seller purchases an annuity with an item of a certain cash value, rather than with cash itself.

A proof of the statement of the preceding paragraph follows:

Suppose that an installment plan involves payments of R periodically, for n periods, beginning one period after the date of purchase, and that the interest rate is i per period compounded every period.

Then we have shown [see formula (1) of the preceding section] that the payments will accumulate, just after the last payment, to:

$$R \left[\frac{(1 + i)^n - 1}{i}\right]$$

Now the *equivalent cash price E* is defined to be that sum of money which, if deposited at the time of purchase under the same interest conditions as above, would grow in n periods to the same amount as did the installment payments after n payments.   The amount to which E grows under these conditions is:

$$E(1 + i)^n$$

Therefore:

$$E(1 + i)^n = R \left[\frac{(1 + i)^n - 1}{i} \right]$$

$$E = R \left[\frac{1 - \dfrac{1}{(1 + i)^n}}{i} \right]$$

but this value of E agrees precisely with the value of the present value V derived above, Q.E.D.

We are thus enabled to solve problems involving equivalent cash price more easily than heretofore.

Illustrative Example 3. We turn our attention again to Problem 5 of the preceding section, computing the equivalent cash price directly as the present value of the annuity involved.

SOLUTION. From Table V, with $i = \frac{1}{2}\%$, $n = 32$, the present value of 1 per period is 29.5033. The present value of $200 per period is therefore $200(29.5033), or $5900.66.

An extremely interesting application of the theory of annuities is to the computation of the interest rate involved in certain borrowing or install-ment plan situations.

Illustrative Example 4. A loan company advertises that it will loan $300, to be repaid in 18 "easy" monthly payments of $20. What yearly compound interest is the loan company charging in this transaction?

SOLUTION. The loan of $300 involving payments of $20 is equivalent (so far as interest is concerned) to a loan of $15 involving payments of $1.

From Table V, examining the row for which $n = 18$, we see that the present value of 1 per period is very nearly 15 when $i = 2\%$. Therefore the *monthly* interest rate involved in this transaction is about 2%. The yearly interest rate being charged is therefore about 24%, compounded monthly. (Interpolation may generally be used to arrive at a more accurate answer.)

▶ ***EXERCISE 49**

1. What is the present value of an annuity which pays $2000 at the beginning of each year for 25 years, beginning one year from now, if money is worth 5% per year, compounded annually?

2. Solve Problems 6 and 7 of the preceding section, using Table V.

3. A sum of $4000 is borrowed, to be repaid together with interest at

the rate of 4% per year compounded yearly, in 12 equal annual install-ments.   Find the amount of each payment.

4. How many annual payments of $100 each, plus a final payment of less than $100, will be required to build up a fund of $2500, if interest is earned at the rate of 4% per year compounded annually?   What will be the amount of the final payment?

5. A loan is to be repaid by 20 quarterly payments of $150 each with interest at 6% per year compounded quarterly.   How much was loaned originally?

6. An article whose cash price is $127 can be paid for by 14 "easy monthly payments" of $10 each.   What annual rate of interest is being charged?

7. A man has a choice of any one of the following methods of paying off a certain obligation:

(a) An immediate single payment of $1000.

(b) Ten annual payments of $120 each, beginning one year from the present date.

(c) A single payment of $1500 ten years from the present date.

Arrange these methods in the order best, next best, and worst, from the man's viewpoint, assuming that money is worth 4% per year, compounded annually.

8. A man buys a house for $15,000, for which he pays $3000 down and gives a mortgage for the balance.   The mortgage, including principal and interest at the rate of 6% per annum compounded semiannually, is to be paid in 40 equal semiannual payments, the first payment to be made 6 months hence.

(a) Find the amount of each payment.

(b) After making the first 20 payments on the above contract, find the amount of the single payment with which the purchaser could then cancel the remainder of his debt.

9. If a debt of $90 can be discharged by 10 monthly payments of $10 each, what annual rate of interest is being charged?

10. A television set may be purchased on the installment plan by paying $20 at the end of each month for 15 months.   If the rate of interest being charged is 12% per year compounded monthly, what is the equiva-lent cash price of the television set?

11. A man agrees to buy a house by making yearly payments of $1000 for ten years, beginning one year from the date of purchase.   What is the equivalent cash price for the house, assuming that money is worth 4% per annum, compounded annually?

12. The following are actual loan offers made by several lending institutions.   (Loan Company C specializes in mail-order loans to teachers.)

Rank them in order of interest charged: (Payments are monthly, and begin one month after loan is made.)

	AMOUNT OF LOAN	NUMBER OF PAYMENTS	AMOUNT OF EACH PAYMENT
Loan Company A	$350	12	$32.50
Loan Company B	1530	18	100.00
Loan Company C	100	20	6.75
Bank A	100	15	7.00
Bank B	108	12	10.00

13. Clip one or more loan offer advertisements from a newspaper and compute the annual rate of interest being charged in each case.

10 STATISTICS AND PROBABILITY

10.1 INTRODUCTION

What do statisticians do?

Statisticians (or their assistants) collect "data." They telephone a thousand people, for example, to find out what television program they may be viewing at a certain time; they tabulate the examination grades of a class; they record the results of repeated measurements of the length of a given object; and so on and on.

Statisticians present data. A page on which a thousand examination grades are listed in random order conveys little information. The statistician groups and orders and visually charts his data so that important information about that data is more readily derived. Tables and graphs of varied types are the tools of the statistician in this activity.

Statisticians operate on data. Given a set of data, statisticians compute certain classical numbers that are useful in conveying information about the data. The student is undoubtedly acquainted, for example, with the "average" of a set of grades, as a number which is in some fashion supposed to be typical of the collection of grades. There are many more such descriptive numbers which the statistician associates with sets of data, and which in various ways characterize those sets.

Statisticians infer and predict. This is of course their most important and at the same time their most hazardous function. On the basis of telephone calls to a relatively small number of people, they come to a conclusion as to the *probable* number of people throughout the country who are tuned in on a given program at a given time. On the basis of "public opinion" polls, they predict the results of an election in which very many more people will vote than were polled; on the basis of the lengths of time necessary to burn out 100 light bulbs of a certain brand, they will make statements concerning the longevity of all the bulbs of that brand. The last case is clearly one in which the help of the statistician is necessary. The manufacturer of light bulbs would not care to determine the longevity of each bulb by actual test any more than a manufacturer of chairs would like to determine the maximum weight each chair would support by measuring the exact weight under which each of his chairs collapsed.

Generally speaking, these are the activities of the statistician. In terms of them one may distinguish a number of broad (and often overlapping) areas of the field of statistics. *Sampling theory*, for example, considers especially the problem of choosing "representative" samples (how shall we choose the thousand people we poll in a television poll, or the 25 bulbs we burn out in a test of bulbs?) and the inferences one may draw from knowledge about a sample collection of data. *Design theory* considers the problem of properly designing experiments so that a tentative hypothesis may be confirmed or rejected. How many people should be inoculated with vaccine, how many not inoculated, in what geographical areas, when, etc., etc., in order that one may be fairly certain that the results indicate either an effective or an ineffective vaccine? Clearly, if one person is inoculated and does not fall ill, that is insufficient evidence. His immunity may have been a case of *chance* and not due to the vaccine. Medicine and science in general depend greatly on the statistician for help in such questions.

The barest discussion of statistics inevitably introduces, as we have emphasized by italicizations above, the concepts of *probability* or *chance*. The inference or prediction of the statistician is typically not a statement of certainty, but only a statement that some event is more or less, or comparatively likely or probable. We shall therefore find it eventually necessary, in our study of statistical inference, to examine certain rudiments of probability theory.

10.2 THE PRESENTATION OF DATA

Suppose that the following is a list of grades scored on an examination:

$$64, 77, 80, 61, 76, 82, 64, 80, 72, 90$$
$$65, 71, 85, 73, 67, 30, 53, 86, 80, 88$$

How shall we present this information in better fashion? A first step might be to arrange the grades in order of size, indicating the number of times each grade occurs. The number of times a grade occurs is called the *frequency* of that grade.   A table of the following sort is called a *frequency* table:

GRADE	FREQUENCY
30	1
53	1
61	1
64	2
65	1
67	1
71	1
72	1
73	1
76	1
77	1
80	3
02	1
85	1
86	1
88	1
90	1

20 = Total number of grades

In this array a number of facts fairly well hidden within the original listing come easily to light.   We now see, for example, that the lowest grade is 30, the highest 90, the difference between highest and lowest (called the *range* of the distribution) is 60, and the grade occurring most often (called the *mode* of the distribution) is 80.

The table above presents us with a set of ordered pairs, which may be graphed to arrive at a visual presentation of the data.   When the successive points of the graph are joined by straight line segments, the result is called a *frequency polygon*.   (See Fig. 10.1.)

How many grades occurred that were less than or equal to 60?   An

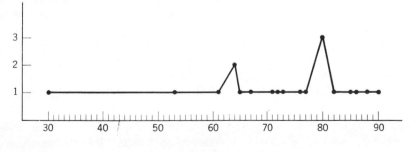

Fig. 10.1

examination of the table reveals that there were 2 such grades.   A question of this sort, however, is more easily answered if a *cumulative frequency* table is prepared.   We define the *cumulative frequency* of a grade to be the number of grades less than or equal to a given grade.   Another question that might arise is one of the sort: What percentage of the grades were less than or equal to 60?   The answer to this particular question is, of course, $\frac{2}{20}$, or 10%, or 0.1.   A *cumulative relative frequency* table is handy to have at hand to take care of questions of this type.   We define the *cumulative relative frequency* of a grade to be the percentage (usually expressed as a decimal) of grades less than or equal to a given grade.

GRADE	FREQUENCY	CUM. FREQUENCY	CUM. REL. FREQUENCY
30	1	1	0.05
53	1	2	0.10
61	1	3	0.15
64	2	5	0.25
65	1	6	0.30
67	1	7	0.35
71	1	8	0.40
72	1	9	0.45
73	1	10	0.50
76	1	11	0.55
77	1	12	0.60
80	3	15	0.75
82	1	16	0.80
85	1	17	0.85
86	1	18	0.90
88	1	19	0.95
90	1	20	1.00

(*Relative frequencies* may of course also be defined and computed, but we shall not find this concept particularly useful in our development.)

The data we have at hand still has the disadvantage of exhibiting many values sprawled over a large range.   A more compact presentation may be achieved by *grouping* the data into convenient non-overlapping "class intervals" whose union covers at least the range of the data.   Convenient intervals in the case we are considering are $20 - 30$, $30 - 40$, etc. Ambiguity arises with respect to the endpoints of these intervals.   In which interval, for example, should the grade 30 fall?   We shall resolve this ambiguity by agreeing that the interval $a - b$ shall include only numbers greater than a and less than or equal to b.   By this agreement, the grade 30 is to be counted as falling within the interval $20 - 30$.

CLASS INTERVALS	FREQUENCY	CUMULATIVE FREQUENCY	CUMULATIVE RELATIVE FREQUENCY
20–30	1	1	0.05
30–40	0	1	0.05
40–50	0	1	0.05
50–60	1	2	0.10
60–70	5	7	0.35
70–80	8	15	0.75
80–90	5	20	1.00

We note that the array of grouped data involves a loss of some detail; we know from the preceding table, for example, that there are 8 grades between 70 and 80, but we cannot tell from this table exactly what those grades are. Generally speaking, this loss of detail becomes less and less important as the mass of data becomes larger and larger.

The grouped data may now be displayed graphically by means of a *frequency histogram* (Fig. 10.2).

A *frequency polygon* for the grouped data may be constructed by joining with line segments the midpoints of the upper sides of the successive rectangles in the histogram. It is customary, furthermore, to extend the class intervals far enough, on both left and right, so that the frequency polygon begins and ends on the horizontal axis (Fig. 10.2).

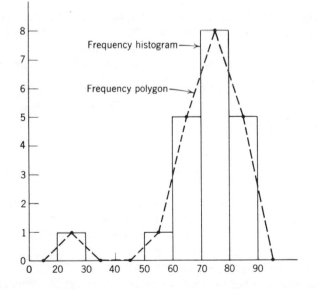

Fig. 10.2

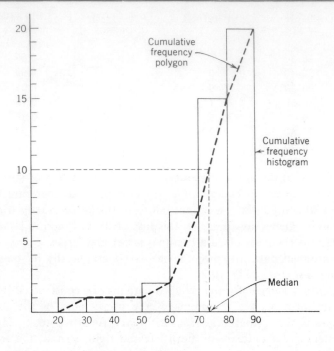

Fig. 10.3

Similarly, a *cumulative* frequency diagram may be constructed for grouped data. In this case, however, the vertices of the polygon are the *upper right hand corners* of the successive rectangles, and the polygon begins, but obviously does not end, on the horizontal axis (Fig. 10.3).

▶ **EXERCISE 50**

Treat the following data as in the preceding section.

1. The grades scored by a class in an examination are: 75, 72, 92, 78, 65, 83, 56, 87, 72, 83, 72, 54.

2. A stone is dropped from the top of a building, and the time of descent determined by means of a stop-watch. The following times (in seconds) were recorded: 5.3, 5.4, 4.9, 5.0, 4.9, 5.1, 4.8, 5.1, 4.7.

3. Count the number of letters in each of the first 30 words of this chapter (beginning with the word "Statistics.")

4. Count the number of words in each of the first 20 sentences of this chapter.

5. Toss 6 coins 25 times and record the number of heads occurring each time.

6. A sample of 20 light bulbs of a certain brand burn for the following number of hours before burning out: 1010, 980, 860, 1300, 1280, 1410, 940, 720, 840, 970, 1120, 980, 1340, 1220, 990, 1130, 1100, 1040, 1120, 980.

7.(a) The scores posted by 15 winning basketball teams in a tournament were: 64, 78, 77, 74, 55, 51, 71, 62, 75, 67, 91, 94, 90, 73, 58.

(b) The corresponding scores posted by the losing teams were: 62, 60, 67, 70, 45, 49, 68, 53, 52, 43, 47, 53, 54, 65, 56.

*8. Throw a single die 30 times and count the number of dots showing on the upper face each time.

*9. Throw a pair of dice 36 times and count the total of the number of dots showing on the upper faces each time.

*10. Explain the reason for the difference in the given techniques for drawing frequency polygons and cumulative frequency polygons for grouped data.

10.3 OPERATING ON DATA: MEASURES OF CENTRAL TENDENCY

In this section we shall consider numbers, called *descriptive statistics*, which are derived from sets of data, and which describe the sets from which they are derived in concise fashion.

The best known of these is commonly called the "average," but named by statisticians the *arithmetic mean* to distinguish it from other kinds of averages. The arithmetic mean of n numbers is defined to be simply the sum of the numbers, divided by n.

Thus, the arithmetic mean of the grades of Section 10.2 is their sum 1444, divided by 20; i.e., 72.2.

The frequency table occasionally affords an appreciable short cut to this result. To find the sum of certain numbers, one may multiply each of the *different* numbers given by its frequency of appearance, and then add the results. (In the case of the data of Section 10.2, this does not help very much. Why not?)

Grouped data supplies even a shorter-cut to the result, although usually at the cost of accuracy. We assume that all of the data falling within an interval fall at the midpoint of the interval. This assumption is, of course, generally false; but with large masses of data, the errors it introduces often come close to cancelling each other out.

The work involved in computing the arithmetic mean of grouped data is illustrated in the following case, which uses the data of Section 10.2.

MIDPOINT OF CLASS INTERVAL	FREQUENCY	
x	f	xf
25	1	25
35	0	0
45	0	0
55	1	55
65	5	325
75	8	600
85	5	425
	20	1430

The arithmetic mean of the grouped data, then, is $\frac{1430}{20}$, or 71.5.

Note that we have used "x" to represent the set of midpoints of the class-intervals chosen in Section 10.2; "f" to represent the frequencies associated with each of these class intervals; and "xf" to represent the products of corresponding elements in (ordered) sets x and f.

We now introduce the notation "Σx" (read "Sigma x" or "summation x") to represent the sum of all the numbers in the column labeled "x."

Thus Σf, in our case, means the sum of all the frequencies, i.e., the total number of grades. In general, if there are n numbers in a set x, and f is defined as above, then:

$$n = \Sigma f$$

and if we define xf as above, then the arithmetic mean (which we denote $\bar{x}$) of the set of numbers x (for either the grouped or ungrouped case) may be given by the formulas:

$$\bar{x} = \frac{\Sigma xf}{\Sigma f} = \frac{\Sigma xf}{n}$$

The arithmetic mean, although the best known of "measures of central tendency," is not always as representative of the original data as we would wish it to be. A student, for example, whose grades in examinations are 90, 81, 0 would have a mean grade of 57. The single grade of 0 has had a catastrophic effect.

There is another type of average, called the *median*, which tends to minimize the effect of extreme values of the data. Assuming that a set of numbers has been written in order, we shall define the median to be either the middle number, if there is one, or the smaller of the two middle numbers, otherwise.

Thus, the median of the numbers 0, 81, 90 is 81; and the median of the numbers 1, 2, 3, 4 is 2.

The cumulative frequency table is useful in determining the median of a distribution, for the median may be equivalently defined as the first item of data which falls at or after a cumulative frequency of $n/2$ (or a cumulative relative frequency of 0.50).

Consulting the ungrouped cumulative frequency table of the preceding section, for example, we discover that the median of the given grades (corresponding to a cumulative frequency of 10, or to a cumulative relative frequency of 0.50) is 73.

In the case of grouped data, we interpolate between the right hand endpoints of the class-intervals to find a number corresponding to a cumulative frequency of $n/2$ (or a cumulative relative frequency of 0.50), and define that number to be the median of the grouped distribution.

In the grouped cumulative frequency table of the preceding section, for example, a cumulative frequency of $n/2$ (i.e., 10) occurs between cumulative frequencies of 7 and 15, corresponding to class-intervals whose right hand endpoints are 70 and 80:

70	7
Median	10
80	15

$$\text{Median} = 70 + \tfrac{3}{8}(10) = 73.8$$

The median may also be determined graphically from the cumulative frequency polygon. The dotted lines in Fig. 10.3 indicate how the median may be found as that number on the horizontal axis which corresponds to a cumulative frequency of $n/2$ (or to a cumulative relative frequency of 0.50) on the vertical axis.

▶ **EXERCISE 51**

1–9. In Problems 1–9, Exercise 50, find the arithmetic mean and median for both the grouped and ungrouped data, and, in the case of the median of the grouped data, illustrate your result on the cumulative frequency polygon.

10.4 OPERATING ON DATA: PERCENTILES

The median of a set of data may be thought of as the first "datum" (i.e., element of data) below which half of the total number of data fall. The idea may be generalized:

Roughly speaking, the pth *percentile* of data is the first datum below which fall $p\%$ of the data.   To phrase the definition more precisely, we consider the ungrouped and grouped cases separately.

In the case of ungrouped data, the pth percentile is the first datum at or after a cumulative relative frequency of $p/100$ [i.e., a cumulative frequency of $(p/100)\cdot n$].

In the case of grouped data, we use interpolation between right-hand endpoints of class-intervals to find a number corresponding to a cumulative relative frequency of $p/100$ [or a cumulative frequency of $(p/100)\cdot n$] and we define that number to be the pth percentile.

For example, in the case of the ungrouped data of Section 10.2, the seventieth percentile is the first grade which occurs at or after a cumulative frequency of $\frac{70}{100}\cdot 20 = 14$.   That grade is 80.

We may interpret this result to mean that about 70% of the given set of grades are less than or equal to the grade of 80; and by the same token, that about 30% of the grades are higher than 80.   (Actually, what is the exact situation here?)

In the case of the grouped data of Section 10.2, the seventieth percentile may be computed by interpolation in the grouped cumulative frequency table; again we seek a grade corresponding to a cumulative frequency of $\frac{70}{100}\cdot 20 = 14$:

70	7
Seventieth percentile	14
80	15

$$\text{Seventieth percentile} = 70 + \tfrac{7}{8}\cdot 10 = 78.8.$$

Of course, the same result may be attained by interpolating in the cumulative *relative* frequency table:

$$\text{Seventieth percentile} = 70 + \left(\frac{0.70 - 0.35}{0.75 - 0.35}\right) 10 = 78.8.$$

In terms of percentiles, the median and certain other related concepts may be defined:

The *median* may be defined to be the 50th percentile.

The *first* (or "*lower*") *quartile* is defined to be the 25th percentile; the *second quartile* the 50th percentile; the *third* (or "*upper*") *quartile* the 75th percentile.

The *first decile* is defined to be the 10th percentile; the *second decile* the 20th *percentile*; etc.

Percentiles, quartiles and deciles for grouped data may be derived graphically from cumulative frequency polygons as in the case of medians.

Note: Students consulting other texts will probably find that definitions of medians, quartiles, etc., occasionally vary slightly from text to text.

▶ **EXERCISE 52**

1–9. In Problems 1–9, Exercise 50, find (for both grouped and un-grouped data) the lower and upper quartiles, the first and ninth deciles, and the 67th percentile. Interpret each result; illustrate by a graphical derivation of each result in the case of grouped data.

10.5 OPERATING ON DATA: MEASURES OF DISPER-SION

In describing data, it is useful to give not only some measure of central tendency, i.e., some " average," but also some measure of the closeness with which the data clusters about this average.

One such measure of " dispersion " or " scatter " or " variability " is the *range*, which we have already defined (for ungrouped data) to be the difference between the smallest and largest data in the set. For grouped data, the range is defined to be the difference between the left-hand endpoint of the first class-interval and the right-hand endpoint of the last class-interval.

For example, the range of the grouped data in Section 10.2 is 70. This information is more meaningful when the actual boundaries of the range are given. It would be better to say: the grouped data in Section 10.2 has a range of 70, from 20 to 90.

The range, however, has several deficiencies as an indicator of scatter about the middle of the data. For one thing, it is affected only by the outermost data. A measure which supplements the range, and helps to repair this deficiency, is the *interquartile range*, defined (for both grouped and ungrouped data) to be the difference between the first and third quartiles.

For example, the interquartile range in the case of the ungrouped data of Section 10.2 is 16, from 64 to 80. This means that about half of all the grades in this distribution fall between 64 and 80.

But we still do not have a measure of dispersion that takes into account *all* values of the data. We proceed to develop such a measure of dispersion about the *mean*. (From now on we shall shorten " arithmetic mean " to " mean.")

If x_1 is an element of a set x whose mean is $\bar{x}$, we define the *deviation* of x_1 from the mean to be $x_1 - \bar{x}$.

For example, the deviation of the grade 80 from the mean 72,2 of the set of grades in Section 10.2 is 7.8; the deviation of the grade 30 in the same case is -42.2.

Now a measure of total dispersion might be attained by adding not the deviations (since then positive and negative deviations would tend to cancel each other out), but the absolute values of the deviations of all the data. For purposes of computation, however, it turns out that a more tractable non-negative quantity than the absolute value of the deviation is the square of the deviation.

Furthermore, to keep our measure from becoming too large a number, we shall seek an *average* rather than a total dispersion.

We therefore define the *variance* v of a set x of n numbers with mean $\bar{x}$ to be 1/nth of the sum of the squares of the deviations from the mean of all the data. We write this symbolically:

$$v = \frac{\sum (x - \bar{x})^2}{n} = \frac{\sum (x - \bar{x})^2}{\sum f}$$

If the data has been arranged into a frequency table in which each element of x is written just once and associated with a frequency taken from a set of frequencies f, then the above formula may be more compactly expressed:

$$v = \frac{\sum (x - \bar{x})^2 f}{n} = \frac{\sum (x - \bar{x})^2 f}{\sum f}$$

If the set x is defined to be the set of midpoints of class intervals, then the above formula applies also to grouped data.

We illustrate by computing the variance first for the ungrouped, and then for the grouped data of Section 10.2.

In the case of the ungrouped data of Section 10.2:

$$(\bar{x} = 72.2)$$

x	f	$x - \bar{x}$	$(x - \bar{x})^2$	$(x - \bar{x})^2 f$
30	1	-42.2	1780.84	1780.84
53	1	-19.2	368.64	368.64
61	1	-11.2	125.44	125.44
64	2	-8.2	67.24	134.48
65	1	-7.2	51.84	51.84
67	1	-5.2	27.04	27.04
71	1	-1.2	1.44	1.44
72	1	$-.2$	.04	.04
73	1	.8	.64	.64
76	1	3.8	14.44	14.44
77	1	4.8	23.04	23.04
80	3	7.8	60.84	182.52
82	1	9.8	96.04	96.04
85	1	12.8	163.84	163.84
86	1	13.8	190.44	190.44
88	1	15.8	249.64	249.64
90	1	17.8	316.84	316.84
	20			3727.20

$$v = \frac{3727.20}{20} = 186.36$$

In the case of the grouped data of Section 10.2:

$$(\bar{x} = 71.5)$$

x	f	$x - \bar{x}$	$(x - \bar{x})^2$	$(x - \bar{x})^2 f$
25	1	-46.5	2162.25	2162.25
35	0			0.00
45	0			0.00
55	1	-16.5	272.25	272.25
65	5	-6.5	42.25	211.25
75	8	3.5	12.25	98.00
85	5	13.5	182.25	911.25
	20			3655.00

$$v = \frac{3655}{20} = 182.75$$

If the original data were, let us say, measurements in *inches*, then if we traced through the steps above we would discover that the variance would be expressed in terms of *square inches*. In order to arrive at a measure whose unit is the same as that of the original data, we define the *standard deviation s* to be the non-negative square root of the variance:

$$s = \sqrt{v}$$

In the case of the ungrouped data of Section 10.2, $s = \sqrt{186.36} = 13.7$. In the case of the grouped data of Section 10.2, $s = \sqrt{182.75} = 13.5$.

The standard deviation s has this important interpretation: Normally (we shall later throw further light on what we mean by "normally") one may expect to find about $\frac{2}{3}$ of all the data within s units of the mean; 95% within $2s$ units of the mean; and nearly all (about 99.7%) within $3s$ units of the mean.

Thus in the case of the ungrouped data of Section 10.2, we would expect to find about $\frac{2}{3} \cdot 20$, or about 13 elements of data between $72.2 - 13.7$ and $72.2 + 13.7$; i.e., between 58.5 and 85.9. (Actually there are 15 such elements.) We would expect to find about 95% of 20, or about 19 or 20 elements of data between $72.2 - 27.4$ and $72.2 + 27.4$, i.e., between 44.8 and 99.6. (Actually there are 19 such elements.) We would expect to find nearly all the data between $72.2 - 41.1$ and $72.2 + 41.1$, i.e., between 31.1 and 113.3. (Actually all but one element of data fall in this range.)

The same interpretation holds in the case of grouped data.

▶ **EXERCISE 53**

1–9. In Problems 1–9, Exercise 50, find and interpret the range, the interquartile range, and the standard deviation for both grouped and ungrouped data.   Compare your interpretation of the standard deviation with the actual situation.

10.6 THE SYMBOL $\sum$

Intuitively it seems plausible that increasing the grade of each student in a class by 5 points will raise the mean of the class by 5 points, and that doubling each grade will double the mean.   In this section we shall develop properties of the symbol $\sum$ which help to prove these and similar facts.

First of all, whenever we use the symbol $\sum$, we shall assume in advance that we know the number of elements in the set to which the symbol applies.

Secondly, having specified that $\sum$ applies to a set of say n elements, when we write $\sum c$, where c is a real number, we shall mean the sum of n numbers, each of which is equal to c.   That is to say:

(1) $$\sum c = nc$$

Now suppose x is the ordered set of numbers: $(x_1, x_2, \cdots, x_n)$.   We have already defined:

$$\sum x = x_1 + x_2 + \cdots + x_n$$

If f is a real-real function and $x = (x_1, x_2, \cdots, x_n)$, we shall now define $f(x)$ to be the ordered set:

$$f(x) = [f(x_1), f(x_2), \cdots, f(x_n)]$$

Thus, if $x = (x_1, x_2, \cdots, x_n)$, then:

$$x^2 = (x_1{}^2, x_2{}^2, \cdots, x_n{}^2)$$
$$2x = (2x_1, 2x_2, \cdots, 2x_n)$$
$$x + 2 = (x_1 + 2, x_2 + 2, \cdots, x_n + 2)$$

Supposing further that y is the ordered set of numbers $(y_1, y_2, \cdots, y_n)$, we define the ordered sets $x + y$ and xy as follows:

$$x + y = (x_1 + y_1, x_2 + y_2, \cdots, x_n + y_n)$$
$$xy = (x_1 y_1, x_2 y_2, \cdots, x_n y_n)$$

To take a particular case, suppose $x = (1, 2, 3, 4)$ and $y = (4, 3, 2, 1)$ then:

$$x^2 = (1, 4, 9, 16)$$
$$2x = (2, 4, 6, 8)$$
$$x + 2 = (3, 4, 5, 6)$$
$$x + y = (5, 5, 5, 5)$$
$$xy = (4, 6, 6, 4)$$

Now the following properties of the symbol Σ are easily proved:

(2) $$\Sigma(x + y) = \Sigma x + \Sigma y$$

(3) $$\Sigma cx = c\Sigma x, \text{ where } c \text{ is a real number}$$

Proof of (2):
$$\begin{aligned}
\Sigma(x + y) &= \Sigma(x_1 + y_1, x_2 + y_2, \cdots, x_n + y_n) \\
&= (x_1 + y_1) + (x_2 + y_2) + \cdots + (x_n + y_n) \\
&= (x_1 + x_2 + \cdots + x_n) + (y_1 + y_2 + \cdots + y_n) \\
&= \Sigma x + \Sigma y
\end{aligned}$$

[The proof of (3) is left as an exercise for the reader.]
Properties (2) and (3) are illustrated in the following table:

x	y	$x + y$	$7x$
1	4	5	7
2	3	5	14
3	2	5	21
4	1	5	28
$\Sigma x = 10$	$\Sigma y = 10$	$\Sigma(x + y) = 20$	$\Sigma 7x = 70$

Here we see that $\Sigma(x + y) = \Sigma x + \Sigma y$ and that $\Sigma 7x = 7\Sigma x$.

Now we apply these properties of the symbol Σ to a proof of the intuitively plausible facts stated in the first paragraph of this section.

Using a bar to indicate the mean of a set of numbers, and notation as above, these facts may be stated more generally:

(4) $$\overline{x + c} = \bar{x} + c$$

(5) $$\overline{cx} = c\bar{x}$$

Proof of (4):

$$\overline{x + c} = \frac{\Sigma(x + c)}{n} \quad \text{(by definition of "mean")}$$

$$= \frac{\Sigma x + \Sigma c}{n} \quad \text{[by (2) above]}$$

$$= \frac{\Sigma x + nc}{n} \quad \text{[by (1) above]}$$

$$= \frac{\Sigma x}{n} + \frac{nc}{n} \quad \text{(why?)}$$

$$= \bar{x} + c \quad \text{(by definition of mean and } \cdots \text{?)}$$

[The proof of (5) is left as an exercise for the reader.]

10.7 SHORT-CUTS

In this section we shall develop several methods which shorten the more tedious computations of Sections 10.3 and 10.5.

First we derive the following formula for the variance in the case of ungrouped data:

(6) $$v = \frac{\Sigma x^2 f}{n} - (\bar{x})^2$$

Proof of (6):

$$v = \frac{\Sigma(x - \bar{x})^2 f}{n}$$

$$= \frac{\Sigma(x^2 f - 2\bar{x}xf + \bar{x}^2 f)}{n}$$

$$= \frac{\Sigma x^2 f}{n} - \frac{\Sigma 2\bar{x}xf}{n} + \frac{\Sigma \bar{x}^2 f}{n} \quad \text{(by (1) above)}$$

$$= \frac{\Sigma x^2 f}{n} - 2\bar{x}\frac{\Sigma xf}{n} + \bar{x}^2 \frac{\Sigma f}{n} \quad \text{(by (3) above)}$$

$$= \frac{\Sigma x^2 f}{n} - 2\bar{x}(\bar{x}) + \bar{x}^2 \left(\frac{n}{n}\right) \quad \text{(by definition of } \bar{x} \text{ and } n)$$

$$= \frac{\Sigma x^2 f}{n} - 2\bar{x}^2 + \bar{x}^2$$

$$= \frac{\Sigma x^2 f}{n} - (\bar{x})^2$$

Now we examine the effect of replacing the set x by the set $y = x + c$, where c is any real number. Supposing v_y represents the variance for the set y we have:

$$v_y = \frac{\Sigma(y - \bar{y})^2 f}{n}$$

But by (4), above, $\bar{y} = \overline{x + c} = \bar{x} + c$. Therefore:

$$v_y = \frac{\Sigma[x + c - (\bar{x} + c)]^2 f}{n} = \frac{\Sigma(x - \bar{x})^2 f}{n} = v$$

so that the variance is unchanged when we replace the set x by the set $x + c$, where c is any real number.

We illustrate by applying the formula (6), and the method of replacing

x by $x + c$, to the computation of the variance in the case of the ungrouped data of Section 10.2.

It helps to choose a value of c which is the opposite of some value at about the middle of the list of data. We choose the value $c = -72$.

Then $y = x - 72$, $\bar{y} = \bar{x} - 72 = 72.2 - 72 = 0.2$.

Proceeding:

x	f	$y = x - 72$	y^2	y^2f
30	1	-42	1764	1764
53	1	-19	361	361
61	1	-11	121	121
64	2	-8	64	128
65	1	-7	49	49
67	1	-5	25	25
71	1	-1	1	1
72	1	0	0	0
73	1	1	1	1
76	1	4	16	16
77	1	5	25	25
80	3	8	64	192
82	1	10	100	100
85	1	13	169	169
86	1	14	196	196
88	1	16	256	256
90	1	18	324	324
	20			3728

$$v = v_y = \frac{\sum y^2 f}{n} - (\bar{y})^2 = \frac{3728}{20} - (0.2)^2 = 186.40 - 0.04 = 186.36, \text{ which}$$

agrees with the result of Section 10.5, and which has been arrived at somewhat more easily.

Now we turn our attention to a simplification of the processes of finding both the mean and the variance in the case of grouped data.

Again we make use of a transformation from a set x to a set y, but this time we examine the effect of the more general transformation: $y = bx + c$, where b and c are real numbers.

In the case of the mean:

$$\bar{y} = \overline{bx + c} = \overline{bx} + c \quad \text{[by (4) above]}$$
$$= b\bar{x} + c \quad \text{[by (5) above]}$$

Solving for $\bar{x}$: $\bar{x} = \dfrac{\bar{y} - c}{b}$.

In the case of the variance:

$$v_y = \frac{\sum(y - \bar{y})^2 f}{n} = \frac{\sum(bx + c - b\bar{x} - c)^2 f}{n}$$

$$= \frac{\sum(bx - b\bar{x})^2 f}{n}$$

$$= \frac{\sum b^2 (x - \bar{x})^2 f}{n}$$

$$= \frac{b^2 \sum(x - \bar{x})^2 f}{n}$$

$$= b^2 v$$

Therefore:
$$v = \frac{v_y}{b^2}$$

Summarizing: If x and y are ordered sets such that $y = bx + c$, then:

$$\bar{x} = \frac{\bar{y} - c}{b}$$

$$v = \frac{v_y}{b^2}$$

(where v is the variance of the set x and v_y is the variance of the set y.)

Now we apply the transformation $y = bx + c$ to the computation of the mean and variance in the case of the grouped data of Section 10.2. When the difference between successive x-values is a constant d, as it is in the case of grouped data, it will be found helpful to let $b = 1/d$.

In the case of the grouped data of Section 10.2, the difference between successive x-values is 10. We therefore let $b = \frac{1}{10} = 0.1$.

Then we let c be the opposite of some value near the middle of the set bx. In our case, we choose $c = -5.5$:

x	f	$y = 0.1x - 5.5$	yf	y^2f
25	1	-3	-3	9
35	0	-2	0	0
45	0	-1	0	0
55	1	0	0	0
65	5	1	5	5
75	8	2	16	32
85	5	3	15	45
	20		33	91

$$\bar{y} = \frac{\sum yf}{n} = \frac{33}{20} = 1.65$$

$$v_y = \frac{\sum y^2 f}{n} - \bar{y}^2 = \frac{91}{20} - (1.65)^2 = 1.8275$$

$$\bar{x} = \frac{\bar{y} - c}{b} = \frac{1.65 + 5.5}{0.1} = 71.5$$

$$v = \frac{v_y}{b^2} = \frac{1.8275}{(0.1)^2} = 182.75$$

agreeing with our results in Sections 10.3 and 10.5.

▶ **EXERCISE 54**

1–9. In Problems 1–9 of Exercise 50, find the variance in the case of the ungrouped data, and the mean and the variance in the case of the grouped data, by the short-cut methods of the preceding section.

10. Prove formula (3) of Section 10.6.

11. Prove formula (5) of Section 10.6.

12. Prove that if x and y are ordered sets of n elements then $\overline{x + y} = \bar{x} + \bar{y}$. Illustrate this result by means of an example.

13.(a) The 9th grade at a certain school is subdivided into three classes of 15, 20, and 25 students each. Suppose that the average (mean) grade of students in these classes are, respectively, 85, 80, and 70. What is the average grade of all 9th grade students at this school?

(b) Prove that $\sum xf = \bar{x}n$, with notation as above. What has this to do with part (a)?

10.8 PROBABILITY

Further progress into the realm of statistics now requires that we develop something of the theory of probability.

Roughly speaking, the science of probability concerns itself with the description, by means of a number, of the "likelihood" of an event. We agree in advance that when an event is impossible we shall say that it has a probability of 0; that when an event is certain, we shall say that it has a probability of 1; and that the probability of *any* event shall be a number between 0 and 1, which by its proximity to 0 or 1 indicates the lesser or greater likelihood of the event.

Thus, if we toss a coin once, the probability that it will fall *both* heads and tails must be 0, since this event is impossible. And again by our agreement, the probability that it will *not* fall both heads and tails must be 1, since this event is certain.

But what probability shall we assign to the likelihood of the coin falling say *heads*?   Assuming, as we shall, that the coin never falls and rests on its edge, and that the coin is uniformly weighted, it seems plausible to say that one of two events is certain to happen, and that they are equally likely.   The two events are, of course, falling heads and falling tails.   We therefore divide the probability 1, representing certainty, equally between these two events, and say that the probability of the coin's falling heads is $\frac{1}{2}$, and the probability of the coin's falling tails is $\frac{1}{2}$.

To put it a little differently, when we toss a coin, we assume that two equally likely events may occur, one which we call "tails" (T) and one which we call "heads" (H).   The set of equally likely events $\{T, H\}$ constitutes what is called the *sample space* for this situation.   Only 1 of the 2 elements of the sample space is H.   Therefore we say that the probability of the coin's falling heads is the ratio of these two numbers: $\frac{1}{2}$.

Consider now the situation in which we roll a single die.   Here any one of six numbers may turn up; we shall assume that the die is not "loaded," so that the numbers are equally likely.   The sample space for this situation is therefore the set of numbers: $\{1, 2, 3, 4, 5, 6\}$.

What is the probability of rolling a "2"?   Since only 1 of the 6 elements of the sample space is "2," the probability of rolling a "2" is $\frac{1}{6}$.

What is the probability of rolling an even number?   Since 3 of the 6 elements of the sample space are even, the probability of rolling an even number is $\frac{3}{6}$, or $\frac{1}{2}$.

Now we shall try to phrase what we have been saying more generally and more precisely.

Every problem in probability involves a so-called *sample-space* of events that may occur.   In this course we shall concern ourselves only with *finite* sample-spaces in which all elements are *equally likely*.

Now suppose we have a condition in mind that is satisfied by s of the n elements in the sample space.   Then we *define* the probability that this condition is satisfied in the given situation to be: s/n.

Illustrative Example 1.   Consider the case above in which we tossed a coin.   Here the "condition" we had in mind was that the result of the toss should be H, which was satisfied by 1 of the 2 elements of the sample space $\{T, H\}$.   Hence $s = 1$, $n = 2$, and the probability that the result of the toss is H is $\dfrac{s}{n} = \dfrac{1}{2}$.

Illustrative Example 2.   In the case of rolling a die, which we considered above, the stipulated condition was that the result be an even number. This condition is satisfied by 3 of the 6 elements of the sample space

$\{1, 2, 3, 4, 5, 6\}$. Hence $s = 3$, $n = 6$, and the probability of throwing an even number in rolling a die is $\dfrac{s}{n} = \dfrac{3}{6} = \dfrac{1}{2}$.

Illustrative Example 3. Suppose two checkers are drawn at random from a box containing two red checkers and one black checker.

Before asking, or answering any questions about this situation we shall construct the sample space involved. We shall find it convenient to denote the two red checkers R_1 and R_2, respectively, and the black checker B. Each drawing of two checkers is a two element subset of the set $\{R_1, R_2, B\}$.

The sample space is then:

$$\Big\{\{R_1, R_2\}, \{R_1, B\}, \{R_2, B\}\Big\}$$

Now we ask (and answer) the questions:

(a) What is the probability that both checkers are red? Answer: $\frac{1}{3}$.

(b) What is the probability that one checker is black? Answer: $\frac{2}{3}$.

(c) What is the probability that both checkers are black? Answer: $\frac{0}{3} = 0$ (i.e., this is impossible).

(d) What is the probability that at least one of the checkers is red? Answer: $\frac{3}{3} = 1$ (i.e., this is certain).

Illustrative Example 4. A box contains two red and one black checker. First one checker is drawn at random from the box (and not replaced), and then another is drawn.

(a) What is the sample space for this situation?

(b) What is the probability that the first checker drawn is red, and the second black?

(c) What is the probability that both checkers which are drawn are red?

(d) What is the probability that the first checker drawn is black and the second red?

SOLUTIONS:

(a) Here the order in which the checkers are drawn is in question, so that the possible draws must be listed as *ordered* pairs (see page 13). The sample space may be derived from that of the preceding example by listing the preceding draws in all possible orders:

$$\{(R_1, R_2), (R_2, R_1), (R_1, B), (B, R_1), (R_2, B), (B, R_2)\}$$

(b) This condition is satisfied by the elements: (R_1, B), (R_2, B). Answer: $\frac{2}{6}$, or $\frac{1}{3}$.

(c) Answer: $\frac{2}{6}$, or $\frac{1}{3}$.

(d) Answer: $\frac{2}{6}$, or $\frac{1}{3}$.

▶ **EXERCISE 55**

1. A letter is drawn at random from the English alphabet. What is the probability that it is
(*a*) "a"?
(*b*) "b"?
(*c*) A vowel?
(*d*) Not a vowel?
(*e*) "π"?

2. In throwing a die, what is the probability of throwing
(*a*) A "six"?
(*b*) A "seven"?
(*c*) An odd number?
(*d*) A number which is a perfect square?
(*e*) An integer?
(*f*) A rational number?
(*g*) An irrational number?
(*h*) A real number?
(*i*) A number greater than $\sqrt{2}$?

3. A playing card is chosen at random from a bridge deck. What is the probability that it is
(*a*) An ace?
(*b*) A spade?
(*c*) The ace of spades?
(*d*) Not an ace?
(*e*) Not a spade?
(*f*) Not the ace of spades?

4. Since there are (excluding the possibility of a leap year) 365 days of the year on which a person may be born, a student reasons that the probability that a person chosen at random has his birthday on July 4 is $\frac{1}{365}$. What can you say about his reasoning?

5. Suppose a *pair* of dice are rolled. To distinguish between them, call one a first die and the other a second die. Denote the result of a roll of the dice by an ordered pair in which the first element indicates the number showing on the first die and the second element indicates the number showing on the second die. For example, we would write the ordered pair (2, 6) to indicate a roll in which the first die falls 2, the second 6. In this case we would say that we had thrown an 8 (= 2 + 6) with the pair of dice.

(*a*) Write the sample space showing all (36) possible rolls of a pair of dice.

(*b*) Find the probability of throwing each of the following numbers in rolling a pair of dice: 1, 2, 3, 4, 5, 6, 7, 8, 9, 10, 11, 12, 13.

(c) "On the next chuck, Charley yells 'money'!—meaning he finally makes his ten, although nobody sees it but him. · · · If Louie has any idea of asking Charley to let him see the dice in the hat · · · he does not speak about the matter · · · ; nobody else says anything either, probably figuring Rusty Charley is not a guy who is apt to let anybody question his word. · · ·

" · · · Nobody as much as opens his face from the time we go in until we start out. · · · It is only just as we get to the door that anybody speaks, · · · 'Charley,' he says, 'do you make it the hard way?'

"Well, everybody laughs, and we go on out, but I never hear myself whether Charley makes his ten with a six and a four or with two fives— which is the hard way to make a ten with the dice— · · ·" (Damon Runyon, *Blood Pressure*).

Why is making a ten with two fives called the "hard" way?

6. Two coins are tossed.

(a) Denoting the result of a toss by an ordered pair in which the first element is T or H according as the first coin falls tails or heads, and similarly for the second element, write the sample space for this situation.

(b) What is the probability that both coins fall heads?

(c) What is the probability that the coins match?

(d) What is the probability that the coins do not match?

7. A coin is tossed three times.

(a) Denoting the possible results of the tosses by ordered triples, write the sample space for this situation.

(b) What is the probability that all three tosses are heads?

(c) What is the probability that the first toss is a head?

(d) Considering only those cases in which the first toss falls heads, what is the probability that the second toss falls heads? (Note that the number of elements in the sample space has been reduced in this part of the question.)

(e) Considering only those cases in which the first and second tosses fell heads, what is the probability that the third coin falls heads?

(f) Explain the statement that "a coin has no memory" in the light of (d) and (e) above. Also, tell what you think of the following strategy: A person betting on the toss of a coin decides to wait until 5 heads have fallen consecutively, and then to bet on tails, since he feels that after a long run of heads, tails are very likely.

8. Answer the questions of Illustrative Example 4 above, assuming that the first checker is put back into the box before the second checker is drawn.

10.9 CARTESIAN PRODUCTS

In many cases, writing out all the elements of a sample space is a tedious task, and in fact unnecessary; for often we are interested only in knowing *how many* elements the sample space contains. There are short cuts to this end which we shall consider in this and subsequent sections.

First of all, we pose this question:

Suppose A is the set of real numbers $\{1, 2, 3\}$, and B the set of real numbers $\{8, 9\}$. How many points in a Cartesian coordinate plane have an x-value chosen from A and a y-value chosen from B?

The answer is clearly: 6, as we may determine by actually writing down the set S of points in question: $S = \{(1, 8), (1, 9), (2, 8), (2, 9), (3, 8), (3, 9)\}$.

Because of this connection with the Cartesian coordinate plane, the set of ordered pairs S above is called the *Cartesian product* of the sets A and B above, and denoted $A \times B$.

In fact, we generalize the concept so that A and B may be any sets whatever:

Definition. If A and B are sets, the *Cartesian product* of A and B, denoted $A \times B$, is defined to be the set of all ordered pairs (a, b), where a is an element of A and b is an element of B.

(We have previously called $A \times B$ simply a " product set." Exercise 2, Problems 13–16 should be read carefully at this point.)

For example, suppose A is the set of first names: $\{$Tom, Dick$\}$ and B the set of second names: $\{$Brown, Smith, Jones, Wilson$\}$. Then $A \times B$ is the following set of names. (We omit the usual parentheses and commas in this listing, since doing so leads to no ambiguity.):

Tom Brown	Dick Brown
Tom Smith	Dick Smith
Tom Jones	Dick Jones
Tom Wilson	Dick Wilson

We note that in each of the two cases above, the number of elements in $A \times B$ is the *product* of the number of elements in A and the number of elements in B. This is plausible. For in the case in which $A = \{1, 2, 3\}$, $B = \{8, 9\}$, each element of A may be combined with each of the 2 elements of B to produce 2 elements of the product set $A \times B$. Since there are 3 elements in A, there exist $3 \cdot 2 = 6$ elements in $A \times B$. Similarly, in the second case above, each first name leads to 4 whole names. Since there are 2 first names, there exist $2 \cdot 4 = 8$ elements in $A \times B$ in this case.

In fact, the following statement which we have induced from several cases, and which we have to some extent justified, may be rigorously proved (by using, for example, the principle of mathematical induction of Section 4.17).

Cardinal Principle of Product Sets. If *A* and *B* are sets of *m* and *n* elements, respectively, then the number of elements in the set $A \times B$ is *mn*.

Illustrative Example 1. A tropical palace has 77 windows and 13 doors which are always open. Every night a bird amuses itself by flying into the palace through a window and out through a door. If the bird never takes the same route twice, for how many nights can it continue to play this game?

SOLUTION. A route may be identified by means of an ordered pair, the first element identifying a window, the second a door; as, for example: (w_1, d_1) may be used to indicate the route in which the bird enters by a window labeled w_1 and leaves by a door labeled d_1.

The total number of such ordered pairs is, by the cardinal principle of product sets: $77 \cdot 13$, or 1001.

Therefore, the bird will be able to play its game for a thousand and one nights.

Illustrative Example 2. In how many different ways may a pair of dice fall?

SOLUTION. We have previously solved this problem by actually enumerating all possible ordered pairs in which each element is one of the six integers between 1 and 6.

By the cardinal principle of product sets, the number of such ordered pairs is $6 \cdot 6$, or 36.

Therefore a pair of dice may fall in 36 different ways.

Illustrative Example 3. In how many different ways may a coin fall if it is tossed:

(*a*) Once.
(*b*) Twice.
(*c*) Three times.
(*d*) *n* times.

SOLUTION.

(*a*) A coin tossed once may fall in 2 different ways: heads (*H*), or tails (*T*).

(*b*) The result of two tosses may be described by an ordered pair in which each of the two elements is one of the two elements: *H*, *T*. Therefore a coin tossed twice may fall in $2 \cdot 2$, or 4 different ways. [Since there are so few possible results in this case, we list them all: (*H*, *H*), (*H*, *T*), (*T*, *H*), (*T*, *T*).]

(*c*) The result of three tosses may be described by an " ordered triple " each of whose three elements is either H or T. For example, (H, H, T) describes a sequence of three tosses in which the first two fall heads and the last tails.

The cardinal principle of product sets may be generalized to apply to cases of three or more sets in this way: *If sets A, B, C contain m, n, r elements, respectively, then the set of ordered triples $A \times B \times C$ contains mnr elements; and similarly for cases involving more than three sets.*

To prove the generalized principle above, note that each ordered triple may be associated with an ordered pair whose first element is itself an ordered pair; for example, the ordered triple (a, b, c) may be made to correspond to the ordered pair whose first element is (a, b) and whose second element is c: $(a, b, c) \leftrightarrow [(a, b), c]$.

In other words, there are as many elements in $A \times B \times C$ as in $(A \times B) \times C$; but by the cardinal principle above, their are mn elements in $A \times B$, hence (again by the same principle) $(mn) \cdot r$ elements, or mnr elements in $(A \times B) \times C$. This proves the generalized principle in the case of three sets; and so on for more than three sets. The " and so on " argument may be rigorized by means of "mathematical induction."

Using the generalized cardinal principle of product sets, the number of ordered triples which may be written using the two letters T, H is $2 \cdot 2 \cdot 2$, or 2^3, or 8.

(d) 2^n.

▶ **EXERCISE 56**

1. In Connecticut, some automobile license plates consist simply of four letters. How many people (theoretically) may have these distinctive markers?

2. How many license plates of four symbols may be printed in which:

(a) The first two symbols are letters and the last two are digits?

(b) Each symbol is a digit?

(c) Each symbol is either a letter or a digit? (Assume that the letters "O" and "I" are indistinguishable from the digits "0" and "1" respectively.)

3.(a) A coin is tossed and a die is rolled. In how many ways may they fall? (i.e., how many elements are there in the sample space for this experiment?)

(b) What is the probability that the coin will falls heads and the die "2"?

(c) What is the probability that the coin will fall heads and the die an even number?

4. A die is rolled three times.

(*a*) How many elements are there in the sample space for this experiment?

(*b*) What is the probability of rolling exactly 3 sixes?

(*c*) What is the probability of rolling no sixes?

(*d*) What is the probability of rolling exactly 1 six?

(*e*) What is the probability of rolling exactly 2 sixes?

5. Ten coins are tossed.

(*a*) How many elements are there in the sample space for this experiment?

(*b*) What is the probability that all the coins fall heads?

6. A card is drawn at random from a bridge deck, replaced, and then a card is drawn again.

(*a*) How many elements are there in the sample space for this experiment?

(*b*) What is the probability that the ace of spades is drawn twice?

(*c*) What is the probability that the ace of spades is drawn at least once?

(*d*) What is the probability that the ace of spades is drawn exactly once?

(*e*) What is the probability that the ace of spades is not drawn?

(*f*) What is the probability that the same card is drawn twice?

(*g*) What is the probability that both cards drawn are of the same suit? (i.e., both clubs, or both diamonds, or both hearts, or both spades.)

7.(*a*) A true-false test has five questions. What is the probability that a student will score 100% purely by guessing?

(*b*) What if the true-false test has 10 questions?

8.(*a*) How many integers less than 1000 can be written with the digits 0, 1, 2, 3?

(*b*) How many of (*a*) are less than 334?

(*c*) How many of (*a*) are even?

9. A monkey pokes twice at the 26 lettered keys of a typewriter. What is the probability that he will write the word "oh"?

10.10 PERMUTATIONS

Some Frenchmen like to eat their dinners not, as we do, by varying a forkful of this with a forkful of that, but by eating all of one item, and then all of another, and so on.

Let us suppose that each evening Pierre's dinner consists of meat (*M*) and potatoes (*P*). To achieve variety, he wishes to consume these items in different orders on different evenings. How many different orders are possible?

Clearly, not a great many; in fact, only 2, which we designate: *MP* and *PM*.

Now suppose that Pierre grows more prosperous, and adds a vegetable (V) to his dinner menu. In how many different orders may he eat these *three* items?

Beginning with the vegetable, he may proceed to eat his meat and potatoes in either of the 2 orders previously determined. We arrive at the two possible orders: VMP, VPM.

But if 2 orders are possible beginning with V, then 2 orders must be possible beginning with M, and 2 orders must be possible beginning with P, making $3 \cdot 2$, or 6 possible orders in all:

VMP	MPV	PVM
VPM	MVP	PMV

Let us now add a salad (S) to Pierre's meal. In how many different ways will he be able to arrange the *four* items?

Beginning with the salad, he may proceed to eat the rest of the meal in any one of the 6 ways determined above. But if 6 orders are possible beginning with S, then 6 orders are possible beginning with *each* of the four items S, M, P, V, making $4 \cdot 6$, or $4 \cdot 3 \cdot 2$ or 24 orders in all:

SVMP	MSVP	PMSV	VMSP
SVPM	MSPV	PMVS	VMPS
SMPV	MVSP	PSMV	VSMP
SMVP	MVPS	PSVM	VSPM
SPVM	MPVS	PVMS	VPMS
SPMV	MPSV	PVSM	VPSM

Proceeding in this way, we conclude that 5 different items may be displayed in $5 \cdot 4 \cdot 3 \cdot 2$, or 120 orders, and so on.

Actually, we have been dealing with ordered sets of elements. Each ordered set of n different elements is called a *permutation* of the n different elements. What we have shown above is that there are 2 permutations possible with 2 elements, $3 \cdot 2$ with 3 elements, $4 \cdot 3 \cdot 2$ with 4 elements, and so on. In fact, the following may be proved to be true:

The number of permutations of a set of n different elements is:

$$(n)(n - 1) \cdots (1).$$

(The last factor of 1 is included to allow for the possibility that we have a set containing only 1 element, in which case only 1 permutation is possible.)

The product $(n)(n - 1) \cdots (1)$, where n is a natural number, is denoted $n!$ (read "n factorial"). The exclamation point calls attention to the surprisingly large values attained by factorial expressions. For example:

$$10! = 10 \cdot 9 \cdot 8 \cdot 7 \cdot 6 \cdot 5 \cdot 4 \cdot 3 \cdot 2 \cdot 1 = 3,628,800$$

Illustrative Example 1.   In how many ways may 3 books be placed next to each other on a shelf?

SOLUTION.   The number of ordered triples which may be formed with 3 different elements is: $3 \cdot 2 \cdot 1$, or 6.

Now we consider a variation on the theme of permutations.   Suppose that we are asked to place 2 books on a shelf, but that we are given 3 books from which to choose the 2.   In how many ways may this be done?

Again we attack the problem first by simple enumeration.   If the given books are denoted a, b, c, then the following ordered pairs of different elements may be formed from these elements:

$$(a, b), (a, c), (b, a), (b, c), (c, a), (c, b)$$

Reasoning similar to that which we used just previously shows why there are 6 ways in which 2 books chosen from 3 may be arranged on a shelf.   For if we place the book a first, then we may place either b or c second, making 2 possible arrangements beginning with a.   If there are 2 arrangements beginning with the book a, then there must be 2 beginning with b and 2 beginning with c, or $3 \cdot 2$ arrangements in all.   Each of these pairs of arrangements appears, of course, in our tabulation above.

Each ordered set of r different elements which constitute a subset of a set of n different elements, is called a *permutation of the n elements taken r at a time*.   We shall denote the *number* of permutations of a set of n elements taken r at a time by the symbol $_nP_r$.

For example, we have determined above that $_3P_2 = 3 \cdot 2 = 6$.

A generalization of the reasoning by which we arrived at this result leads to this conclusion:

$$_nP_r = \overbrace{(n)(n - 1) \cdots}^{r \text{ factors}}$$

Illustrative Example 2.   Candidates for 3 different political offices are to be chosen from a list of 10 people.   In how many ways may this be done?

SOLUTION. $_{10}P_3 = \overbrace{10 \cdot 9 \cdot 8}^{3 \text{ factors}} = 720.$

▶ **EXERCISE 57**

1. Evaluate $n!$ for each integer value of n such that $1 \leqslant n \leqslant 10$.

2. How many different signals may be made with n flags arranged on a vertical staff if $n =$

    (*a*) 1   (*b*) 3   (*c*) 5   (*d*) 10   (*e*) 12

3. Suppose 12 flags are available. How many different signals may be made if each signal consists of the following number of flags arranged on a vertical staff:

(a) 1   (b) 2   (c) 5   (d) 10   (e) 12

4. How many different signals may be made by arranging flags on a vertical staff, if 6 flags are available?

5. A "Scrabble" player has seven different letters before him, from which he wishes to form a word. How many different arrangements of his letters may he consider, if the word is to consist of the following number of letters:

(a) 1   (b) 2   (c) 3   (d) 4   (e) 5   (f) 6   (g) 7

6.(a) A "jotto" player has determined five different letters which he knows will, if properly arranged, form a word that his opponent has written down. If he tries to discover the word by examining all possible arrangements of the five letters, how many arrangements may he have to consider?

(b) If the letters he has determined are a, e, m, s, t, what is the probability that a random arrangement of these letters will form an English word?

7. Three letters are to be mailed and three mail-boxes are available in which to mail them.

(a) In how many ways may the letters be mailed if no box is to receive more than one letter? (*Hint:* Call the letters: 1, 2, 3, and the mail-boxes: a, b, c, and use the ordered triple (c, a, b), for example, to represent a mailing in which letter 1 is dropped into box c, letter 2 into box a, and letter 3 into box b.)

(b) In how many ways may the letters be mailed if the restriction of (a) above is removed?

8. Two secretaries leave an office for lunch. One has 2 letters to mail and passes 3 mail-boxes on her way; the other has 3 letters and passes 2 mail-boxes. Who may mail her letters in a greater variety of ways? (See Problem 7 above.)

9. In how many ways may 10 policemen be assigned to 2 beats? 2 policemen among 10 beats? 2 policemen among 10 beats, assuming that both cannot be assigned to the same beat? (See Problem 7 above.)

10.(a) In how many ways may the letters v, w, x, y, z be arranged to form a nonsense word of five letters?

(b) In how many ways, if the first letter must be v?

(c) In how many ways, if the middle letter must be v?

(d) In how many ways, if the first letter must be v and the last z?

(e) How many five-letter nonsense words may be made with these letters if repetition of letters is allowed?

(*f*) How many nonsense words may be made with these letters if repetition is not allowed, but the word may have any number of letters?

11.(*a*) Five teams compete in a contest. How many different rankings of the teams (assuming no ties) are possible at the end of the contest?

(*b*) In how many different ways may a first and second prize be awarded in this contest?

(*c*) Assuming the teams to be evenly matched, what is the probability that a given team will win first prize? second prize? one prize?

12. The same as Problem 11 above, but with six, rather than five, teams competing.

13. If two cards are dealt from a bridge deck, what is the probability that they will both be aces?

14.(*a*) $_nP_n = ?$

(*b*) Replace the circled numbers in parentheses by correct expressions, in the order indicated by the circled numbers:

$$n! = \underbrace{\overbrace{(n)\,(n-1)\,\cdots\,(④)}^{(r)\text{ factors}}\,\overbrace{(③)\,\cdots\,(1)}^{(②)\text{ factors}}}_{(①)\text{ factors}}$$

(*c*) Express $n!$ in terms of $_nP_r$ and $(n-r)!$

(*d*) What is the "last" (i.e., the smallest) factor in the formula:

$$_nP_r = (n)\,(n-1)\,\cdots\,(\quad)$$

10.11 PERMUTATIONS WITH REPEATED ELEMENTS

There is a well-known story about a Texan returning home by train one day, who fell in with a boastful Easterner. "All right," said the Texan, "this is my ranch we happen to be passing, and that is my herd of cattle. If you're as smart as you say you are, perhaps you can estimate the number of cattle in that herd?" The Easterner glanced out the window and said: "1,684." "Why that's *exactly* right," blurted the amazed Texan. "How in the world did you do it?" "It was easy," replied the Easterner. "I just counted their feet and divided by 4."

In this section we shall find that a method like the Easterner's may actually be useful.

We know that the letters of the word "toe" may be arranged in 6 different ways, but what about the letters in the word "too"?

If the two "o's" were to be considered as different letters, say o_1 and o_2, then 6 arrangements would be possible:

(1)
$$\begin{cases} to_1o_2,\ o_1to_2,\ o_1o_2t \\ to_2o_1,\ o_2to_1,\ o_2o_1t \end{cases}$$

But since we are interested at the moment only in arrangements in which the two "o's" are not considered to be different, the 6 arrangements above yield only three in which we are interested:

(2)   too, oto, oot

In fact, the second line of (1) above was derived from the first simply by interchanging o_1 and o_2 in each case.

The number of different ways in which the letters of the word "too" may be arranged may be derived, then, by dividing the 6 ways of (1) above by the number 2, which is the number of ways in which the letters o_1 and o_2 may be arranged.

Before generalizing, we consider two other cases.

In how many ways may the letters of the word "loll" be arranged?

If the three "l's" were different, we know that the answer to this problem would be $4 \cdot 3 \cdot 2 \cdot 1$, or 24. We group these 24 arrangements strategically:

$$(3) \quad \begin{cases} ol_1l_2l_3, & l_1ol_2l_3, & l_1l_2ol_3, & l_1l_2l_3o \\ ol_1l_3l_2, & l_1ol_3l_2, & l_1l_3l_2o, & l_1l_3l_2o \\ ol_2l_1l_3, & l_2ol_1l_3, & l_2l_1ol_3, & l_2l_1l_3o \\ ol_2l_3l_1, & l_2ol_3l_1, & l_2l_3ol_1, & l_2l_3l_1o \\ ol_3l_1l_2, & l_3ol_1l_2, & l_3l_1ol_2, & l_3l_1l_2o \\ ol_3l_2l_1, & l_3ol_2l_1, & l_3l_2ol_1, & l_3l_2l_1o \end{cases}$$

In fact, the last 5 lines of (3) above were derived by writing l_1, l_2, l_3 in all possible orders other than that of the first line, and leaving o in fixed position. There are, of course, 6 arrangements of l_1, l_2, l_3 that are possible, which accounts for the 6 lines of (3) above.

The 24 arrangements of (3) above may therefore be separated into $\frac{24}{6}$, or 4 groups [the columns of (3) above], such that each group leads (by dropping subscripts) to only one arrangement of the letters l, o, l, l, and such that all arrangements are thereby derived:

olll,   loll,   llol,   lllo

The number of different ways in which the letters of the word "loll" may be arranged may be derived then, by dividing the 24 ways of (3) above by the number 6, which is the number of ways in which the letters l_1, l_2, l_3 may be arranged.

Finally, we consider the number of ways in which the letters of the word "hubbub" may be arranged.

Here each arrangement of the letters h, u, b, b, u, b, leads to 6 arrangements when the letters b, b, b are considered to be different, and *each* of these 6 yields 2 arrangements when the letters u, u are considered to be different. Thus, each arrangement of the letters h, u, b, b, u, b leads to $6 \cdot 2$ or 12 arrangements when these letters are considered to be 6 different letters. There are 6! or, 720 permutations of 6 different letters. Therefore they are $\frac{720}{12}$, or 60 possible ways of arranging the letters of the word " hubbub."

In general:

Suppose that in an ordered n-tuple, the elements which occur more often than once occur with multiplicity r, s, $\cdots$.

Then the number of permutations of the given n-tuple is given by the formula:

$$\frac{n!}{(r!)\,(s!)\cdots}$$

NOTE: Actually, we have so far defined only a permutation of a set of *n different* elements. More generally, a permutation may be defined as follows:

Given an ordered *n*-tuple, a permutation of the given ordered *n*-tuple is an ordered *n*-tuple whose elements are the same, and occur with the same multiplicity, as those of the given ordered *n*-tuple.

Illustrative Example. In how many ways may the letters of the word " Mississippi " be arranged?

SOLUTION. $\dfrac{11!}{4!\,4!\,2!} = \dfrac{11 \cdot 10 \cdot 9 \cdot 8 \cdot 7 \cdot 6 \cdot 5 \cdot 4 \cdot 3 \cdot 2}{4 \cdot 3 \cdot 2 \cdot 4 \cdot 3 \cdot 2 \cdot 2} = 34,650$

▶ EXERCISE 58

1. In how many ways may the letters of the following words be arranged?

(*a*) yoyo   (*b*) polo   (*c*) sissy

(*d*) scissors   (*e*) banana   (*f*) Massachusetts

2. How many linear patterns may be formed with

(*a*) 3 red checkers and 3 black checkers?

(*b*) 3 red checkers and 2 black checkers?

(*c*) 3 pennies, 2 dimes, and 1 nickel?

3. If 3 red checkers and 3 black checkers are arranged at random on a line, what is the probability that red and black will alternate?

4. How many baseball teams could be made using 9 players if:

(*a*) Any man can play any position?

(*b*) Jones can only pitch, but the others can play any position?

(*c*) Smith and Brown can only pitch or catch, but the others can play any position?

5. How many three letter arrangements of the letters of the word "troops" may be made? (*Hint:* consider three cases, according as to whether the three-letter word contains 0, 1 or 2 o's.)

6. How many arrangements of 5 letters or less may be made with the letters of the word "speed"? (See Problem 5.)

7. How many arrangements of 5 letters or less may be made with the letters of the word "seeds"? (See Problem 5.)

8. If the letters of the word "loop" are arranged at random, what is the probability that they will spell an English word?

9. In how many ways may 4 people be seated around a table? (*Hint:* Suppose we write the ordered set (a, b, c, d) to mean that b sits to the right of a, c to the right of b, etc. Then the ordered sets (a, b, c, d), (b, c, d, a), (c, d, a, b), (d, a, b, c) all represent the same arrangement around a table. Every arrangement around the table leads to 4 arrangements in a line, and the number of arrangements around a table may be found by dividing the number of linear arrangements by 4.)

10. In how many ways may 7 people be seated around a table? (See Problem 9.)

11. In how many ways may King Arthur and six of his knights be seated around the Round Table, if one of the seats is a throne upon which King Arthur must sit?

12. How many different patterns of wins and losses can a winning team post in a World Series contest between two baseball teams? (*Hint:* The Series is won as soon as one team wins 4 games. The Series may therefore be won in 4 or 5 or 6 or 7 games. The only pattern possible in a 4 game Series is (W, W, W, W), where W represents a win; etc.)

10.12 CHOICE (ORDERED)

The reasoning process that led to our formula for $_nP_r$ leads also to the following very general and very useful rule:

Suppose that a certain element of an ordered n-tuple may be chosen from a set of r elements, and that after that element has been chosen, another element of the ordered n-tuple may be chosen from a set of s elements; and so on.

Then the ordered n-tuple may be chosen in $(r)(s)\cdots$ways.

In fact, the principles we have set down concerning the number of elements in a set of permutations or in a Cartesian product may be considered to be special cases of this rule; and the examples we have worked by these principles, and other examples of a more complicated nature, may be solved by means of this rule.

The student may find the following more intuitive phrasing of the rule helpful in applying it to particular situations:

Suppose that a first act may be performed in r ways; and that after the first has been performed, a second act may be performed in s ways; and so on.

Then the number of ways in which the first act, followed by the second, and so on, may be performed is given by the product:

$$(r)(s)\cdots$$

Illustrative Example 1. How many four-letter license plates are possible if the first and last letters are to be the same?

SOLUTION. The first letter may be chosen in 26 ways.

After the first letter has been chosen, the last letter, since it must be the same as the first, must be chosen from a set containing only 1 element.

After these two choices have been made, the second letter may be chosen is 26 ways, and then the third letter may be chosen in 26 ways.

Therefore there are $26 \cdot 1 \cdot 26 \cdot 26$ four-letter license plates possible in which the first and last letters are the same.

In problems like the preceding, we find it convenient to write down a number of boxes to represent the places of the n-tuple in question, and then to fill in the appropriate boxes successively with the numbers $r, s, \cdots$ of the rule above. For example, the following pattern may be constructed for the problem above:

and the product of the numbers entered is the solution to this problem.

Illustrative Example 2. How many four-letter "words" (in the sequel we shall use "word" to mean any sequence of letters) which begin and end with a vowel may be formed from the letters a, e, i, p, q.

(a) if no repetitions are allowed?

(b) if repetitions are allowed?

SOLUTION. (a) We construct a pattern of four boxes to represent the four letters of the word to be formed:

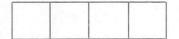

Since the word is to begin with a vowel, the first letter may be chosen in 3 ways:

Since the word must end with a vowel, and repetition of letters is not allowed, after the first place has been chosen only 2 letters remain from which to choose the letter in last place:

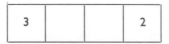

Having chosen first and last letters, thus using up two letters of the original five, 3 letters are left from which to choose the letter in second position:

Finally, 3 letters having been used, there remain 2 from which to choose the letter in third position:

The answer to (*a*) above, then, is: $3 \cdot 3 \cdot 2 \cdot 2$, or 36 words.

(*b*) If repetitions are allowed, we arrive at the following array:

so that 225 words may be formed in this case.

Illustrative Example 3. In how many ways may 3 girls and 3 boys stand in line, if boys and girls are to alternate?

SOLUTION 1. Clearly, there are 6 choices for first place. But after a choice for first place has been made, second place must be given to one of the 3 persons of sex opposite to that of the first choice.

Now a boy and a girl have been assigned, and 2 boys and 2 girls remain to be assigned. Third place must go to someone of sex opposite to that of the second choice; there are, therefore, 2 choices for third place; etc.:

The solution: 72 ways.

SOLUTION 2.   If the line begins with a boy, the number of possible ways of forming a line in which boys and girls alternate is given by the product of the numbers in the following array:

3	3	2	2	1	1

Hence we see that there are 36 ways to form the line with a boy in first place.   There must be an equal number with a girl in first place.   There are, therefore, 36 + 36 or 72 different ways to form the line as required.

Illustrative Example 4.   In how many ways may four bridge hands be dealt?

SOLUTION.   The first hand may be dealt in $_{52}P_{13}$ ways.   After that 39 cards are left, and the second hand may be dealt in $_{39}P_{13}$ ways, and so on. The four hands may be dealt in the following number of ways:

$$(1) \qquad (_{52}P_{13})(_{39}P_{13})(_{26}P_{13})(_{13}P_{13})$$

(Note that not all these hands are different.   Some are the same hands dealt in different orders.)

We leave the computation of the number expressed in (1) above to the student with a great deal of time, or an adequate computing machine, at his disposal.

▶ **EXERCISE 59**

1. How many four-letter license plates may be issued in which:
(*a*) All the letters are the same?
(*b*) All the letters are different?
2. Using the English alphabet, how many "words" are there:
(*a*) Of 3 letters?
(*b*) Of 3 different letters?
(*c*) Of 3 letters, of which exactly two are the same?
(*Hint:* First find how many there are in which the *first* two are the same. How many other cases, in which there are as many possibilities as in this case, must be considered?)
3. A man who plans to drive from New York to Los Angeles and back, both by way of Chicago, finds 3 routes which he likes between New York and Chicago and 4 between Chicago and Los Angeles.   He has a choice of how many routes going from New York to Los Angeles?   How many for the round trip?   How many for the round trip if the trip returning is to be

totally different from the trip going? How many for the round trip if the trip returning is to be at least partially different from the trip going? How many for the round trip if the trip returning is to be partially but not totally different from the trip going?

4. How many linear patterns may be made with 3 red and 3 black checkers if the first and last checkers must be red?

5. A man has 3 jackets, 2 vests, and 4 pairs of trousers, all of which match. How many different costumes consisting of jacket, vest, and trousers does he have at his disposal?

6. In how many ways may:

(a) 3 billiard balls be dropped into 4 pockets?

(b) 4 billiard balls be dropped into 3 pockets?

(c) 3 billiard balls be dropped into 4 pockets, but not more than one in the same pocket?

7. How many five-letter nonsense words may be made with the letters p, q, a, e, r if the middle letter is to be a vowel?

8. How many even three-digit positive integers are there? How many of them are less than 399? How many of them are greater than 599?

9. In how many ways may five people be seated on a straight bench, if two of them refuse to sit together? In how many ways if two of them insist on sitting together?

10. The same as Problem 9, but suppose that the bench is circular.

11. Five couples for a square dance are to be chosen from a group consisting of 5 women and 5 men. How many different sets of five couples may be chosen, if each couple is to consist of one man and one woman?

12. Assuming that each seat has a window position and an aisle position, in how many ways may 5 men and 5 women be seated in 5 double seats on a train? In how many ways if each double seat is to be occupied by one man and one woman? In how many ways if the window seats are to be occupied by women?

13. A test consists of three "sometimes-always-never" questions and three "true-false" questions. What is the probability that a student will score 100% simply by guessing? What is the probability that he will do equally well in a test consisting of ten "true-false" questions?

14. The same as Problem 13, except that the student knows that no two consecutive answers are ever the same.

15. How many different necklaces may be made with:

(a) 3 different beads?

(b) 5 different beads?

(c) 7 different beads?

16. "Once upon a time a statistician made rapid calculations with graphs, slide rules, and simple arithmetic. Then he announced that the

chance of anyone picking the exact order of finish in either league was one in 40,400. The chance of making the correct predictions in both leagues is one in 1,625,702,400. Figures like that shake a fellow's confidence, and this soothsayer is beginning to doubt that he can do it." (Arthur Daley, "Sports of the Times," *New York Times*, April 14, 1957.)

Show that one of Mr. Daley's figures is approximately, the other exactly, correct. (The leagues to which he refers each contain eight teams.)

10.13 CHOICE (UNORDERED)

How many different committees of two people may be chosen from a group of three people?

This problem can easily be solved simply by setting down all of the possibilities in this case. If the set of three people is denoted $\{a, b, c\}$, the following committees of two may be formed:

(1) $$\{a, b\}, \{a, c\}, \{b, c\}$$

The answer to our problem, then, is: three committees.

Each of these 2-element subsets of the set of 3 elements $\{a, b, c\}$ is called a *combination of* 3 *things taken* 2 *at a time*. In general, an r-element subset of a set of n elements is called a *combination of n things taken r at a time*. The total possible number of combinations of n things taken r at a time, i.e., the number of r-element subsets of a set with n elements, is denoted $\binom{n}{r}$; what we have determined above may be expressed, then, in the following way:

$$\binom{3}{2} = 3$$

Note that combinations of r things differ from permutations of r things in that *order* is not at issue in the case of combinations. In fact, when order is taken into account, the combination $\{a, b\}$ leads to the permutations (a, b) and (b, a).

There is involved in the preceding statement a connection between combinations and permutations that will enable us to derive a formula for combinations from a known formula for permutations.

We know that the number of permutations taken 2 at a time of the 3 letters a, b, c is $3 \cdot 2$, or 6. In fact, these 6 permutations are:

(2) $$(a, b) \quad (a, c) \quad (b, c)$$
$$(b, a) \quad (c, a) \quad (c, b)$$

The 6 permutations of (2) above may be derived by writing each of the three sets of (1) above in all possible (namely 2) orders. In this case, there are *half* as many combinations as permutations.

Before generalizing, let us examine another case.

How many different committees of 3 people may be chosen from a group of 4 people?

If the set of 4 people is denoted $\{a, b, c, d\}$, the committees possible in this case may again easily be listed. (In fact, in both of the above cases, all we need do is omit one of the original set to form a committee as required):

(3) $\{a, b, c\}$ $\{a, b, d\}$ $\{a, c, d\}$ $\{b, c, d\}$

In this case, each combination of 3 elements gives rise to $3 \cdot 2 \cdot 1$, or 6 permutations of 3 elements. For example, the combination $\{a, b, c\}$ gives rise to the permutations:

$$(a, b, c) \quad (a, c, b) \quad (b, a, c) \quad (b, c, a) \quad (c, a, b) \quad (c, b, a)$$

Each combination in (3) above gives rise to 6 permutations. In this case, the number of combinations is *one-sixth* the number of permutations.

In general, each combination of r things gives rise to $r!$ permutations of the same elements; and the number of *combinations* of n things taken r at a time is $\frac{1}{r!}$ times the number of *permutations* of n things taken r at a time.

Or, in symbols:

$$\binom{n}{r} = \frac{{}_nP_r}{r!} = \frac{\overbrace{(n)(n-1)\cdots(\quad)}^{r \text{ factors}}}{(1)(2)\cdots(r)}$$

Illustrative Example 1. How many different three-card hands may be dealt from a bridge deck?

SOLUTION. $\binom{52}{3} = \frac{52 \cdot 51 \cdot 50}{1 \cdot 2 \cdot 3} = 22,100$

Note the difference between this example, and one like Illustrative Example 4 of the preceding section. Since the order in which the cards are dealt is immaterial so far as the final hand is concerned, we are dealing here with *combinations* rather than *permutations*.

Illustrative Example 2. Using the English alphabet, how many " words " of five letters may be formed, if exactly two of the letters are to be the same?

SOLUTION. First of all which two shall be the same? 2 places may be chosen out of 5 in $\binom{5}{2}$, or 10 ways.

After the choice has been made as to which two places shall be the same, the single letter that is to fill each of these places may be chosen in 26 ways.

There are left three places which may now be filled successively in 25, 24, and 23 ways.

The answer to the problem is therefore: $10 \cdot 26 \cdot 25 \cdot 24 \cdot 23$ ways.

[Compare this example with Problem 2(c) and the accompanying hint of the preceding exercise.]

Illustrative Example 3. What is the probability that a hand of 2 cards dealt from a bridge deck:

(a) will contain 2 red cards?
(b) will contain exactly one red card?
(c) will contain no red cards?

SOLUTION. (a) There are $\binom{52}{2} = \dfrac{52 \cdot 51}{1 \cdot 2}$ different hands of 2 cards which may be dealt from a deck of 52 cards.

Hands containing only red cards must be chosen from the 26 red cards of the deck. Therefore there are $\binom{26}{2} = \dfrac{26 \cdot 25}{1 \cdot 2}$ of the above hands of 2 cards which contain only red cards.

The probability, then, that a hand of 2 cards will contain only red cards is:

$$\frac{\binom{26}{2}}{\binom{52}{2}} = \frac{26 \cdot 25}{52 \cdot 51} = \frac{25}{102}$$

(b) A single red card may be chosen from the deck in $\binom{26}{1}$, or 26 ways.

A single black card may then also be selected in 26 ways. One red and one black card may therefore be chosen in $26 \cdot 26$ ways. The required probability is therefore:

$$\frac{26 \cdot 26}{\binom{52}{2}} = \frac{26 \cdot 26}{26 \cdot 51} = \frac{26}{51}$$

(c) This hand must contain 2 black cards. The symmetry of the situation implies that the answer is the same as for part (a): $\frac{25}{102}$.

[Note that the probabilities in cases (a), (b), (c) add up to 1; this is to be expected, since it is *certain*, when two cards are dealt as described, that exactly one of the events (a), (b), (c) will occur.]

▶ **EXERCISE 60**

1. Evaluate:

(a) $\binom{5}{4}$ (b) $\binom{5}{1}$ (c) $\binom{7}{3}$ (d) $\binom{7}{4}$

(e) $\binom{8}{6}$ (f) $\binom{8}{2}$ (g) $\binom{n}{n}$ (h) $\binom{n}{0}$

(*Hint:* $\binom{n}{0}$ represents, given an n-element set, the number of subsets of that set which contain 0 elements. A set with 0 elements is called? How many such sets are there?)

2. From the results of Problem 1, one may induce that $\binom{n}{r} = \binom{n}{?}$.

3.(a) In how many ways may two apples be chosen from a box of eight apples?

(b) In how many ways may eight apples be divided equally among four people? (*Hint:* In how many ways may the first two apples be chosen? then the second two? etc.)

4. In how many ways may six people be separated into three equal groups? Into two equal groups? [See Problem 3(b) above.]

5. In how many ways may seven people be separated into a group of three people and a group of four people?

6.(a) In how many ways may five people be separated into a group of three people and a group of two people?

(b) In how many ways may a set of three people be chosen from a group of five people?

(c) In how many ways may a set of two people be chosen from a group of five people?

(d) How do you explain the interesting relationship among the answers to (a), (b), (c) above?

7. How many 3-element subsets does a set with 6 elements contain? How many 4-element subsets? How many 6-element subsets? How many null subsets?

8. How many subsets in all does a set with the following number of elements contain?

(a) 0   (b) 1   (c) 2   (d) 3   (e) 4   (f) n

9. Three musketeers arrive at an airport at the same time as three other people. All six want to board a plane which has only three available seats. They agree to decide who makes the trip by drawing straws.

(a) What is the probability that the three musketeers make the trip?

(b) What is the probability that Athos and Porthos go, but not Aramis?

(c) What is the probability that exactly two of the musketeers make the trip?

(d) What is the probability that exactly one of the musketeers makes the trip?

(e) What is the probability that none of the musketeers makes the trip?

10. The same as Problem 9, except that this time the three musketeers find themselves competing only with Cardinal Richelieu.

11. The same as Problem 10, except that Cardinal Richelieu says that even if he wins a seat he will give it up rather than ride with Athos.

12. In how many ways may 2 jackets, a vest, and 3 pairs of trousers be chosen from 3 jackets, 3 vests, and 6 pairs of trousers?

13. A committee consisting of two Russians, two Englishmen and two Irishmen is to be chosen from a group consisting of ten Russians, ten Englishmen and ten Irishmen. How many such committees are possible?

14. How many different two-card hands may be dealt from a bridge deck? How many different four-card hands?

15. What is the probability that a hand of two cards dealt from a bridge deck:

(a) will contain 2 spades?

(b) will contain exactly 1 spade?

(c) will contain no spades?

(d) will contain the ace of spades?

16. What is the probability that a hand of four cards dealt from a bridge deck will contain one card from each suit?

17 (a). Which is more likely, that all cards in a hand of four cards dealt from a bridge deck will be from different suits, or that they will all be from the same suit?

(b) What if only two cards are dealt?

18. Using the English alphabet, how many "words" of 4 letters may be formed if:

(a) all the letters are to be different?

(b) exactly 2 of the letters are to be the same?

(c) exactly 3 of the letters are to be the same?

(d) all the letters are to be the same?

(e) the first and last letters are to be the same?

19. (Compare this problem with Problem 8 above.) How many different amounts of money may be made with:

(a) a penny and a nickel?

(b) a penny, a nickel, and a dime?

(c) a penny, a nickel, a dime, and a quarter?

(*d*) a penny, a nickel, a dime, a quarter, and a half-dollar?

(*e*) a penny, a nickel, a dime, a quarter, a half-dollar, and a dollar?

20. In how many ways may a committee of 3 people be chosen from a group of 10 people? In how many ways if 2 of the 10 will only serve together? In how many ways if 2 of the 10 refuse to serve together?

21.(*a*) How many straight lines are determined by the vertices of a regular decagon?

(*b*) How many diagonals does a regular decagon have?

(*c*) How many diagonals does a regular *n*-sided polygon have? Verify for the cases $n = 3, 4, 5, 6$.

*22. Show that:

(*a*) $\binom{n}{k} (n - k)! = \dfrac{n!}{k!}$ hence that $\binom{n}{k} = \dfrac{n!}{k!\,(n - k)!}$

(*b*) Suppose $n = r + s$. Show, using (*a*) above that:

$$\binom{n}{r} = \frac{n!}{r!\,s!}$$

$$\binom{n}{s} = \frac{n!}{s!\,r!}$$

hence that $\quad\quad\quad\quad \binom{n}{r} = \binom{n}{s}$

hence that $\quad\quad\quad\quad \binom{n}{r} = \binom{n}{n - r}$

(Compare with Problems 1, 2, and 6 above.)

23. Using the last formula proved in Problem 22 above, evaluate:

(*a*) $\binom{10}{9}$ $\quad\quad\quad$ (*b*) $\binom{20}{18}$ $\quad\quad\quad$ (*c*) $\binom{25}{21}$

(*d*) $\binom{50}{48}$ $\quad\quad\quad$ (*e*) $\binom{50}{49}$ $\quad\quad\quad$ (*f*) $\binom{50}{50}$

*10.14 COMBINATIONS AND THE BINOMIAL THEOREM

(This section requires a prior consideration of the material of Section 7.5.)

An examination of the coefficient of $x^{n-r}y^r$ in the binomial expansion of $(x + y)^n$ on page 202 shows that this coefficient is nothing but our new friend $\binom{n}{r}$.

The elements of the "Pascal triangle" on page 201 are, then, the values of $\binom{n}{r}$. In fact, $\binom{n}{r}$ is the $(r + 1)$st entry in the $(n + 1)$st row of the Pascal triangle, as we have written it.

The fact that $\binom{n}{r} = \binom{n}{n-r}$ (see Problem 22, Exercise 60) now supplies a proof of our statement (see page 201) that the coefficients of a standard binomial expansion form a symmetric array about the middle of the expansion; for $\binom{n}{r}$ is the coefficient of $x^{n-r}y^r$, and $\binom{n}{n-r}$ is the coefficient of $x^r y^{n-r}$.

There is an intuitive explanation for the fact that the coefficient of $x^r y^{n-r}$ in the binomial expansion of $(x + y)^n$ is $\binom{n}{r}$: Consider, for example, the coefficient of $x^2 y^3$ in the expansion of $(x + y)^5 = (x +)(x + y)(x + y)(x + y)(x + y)$. All the terms of this product may be arrived at by choosing either an x or a y (but not both) from each of the five factors $(x + y)$; for example, choosing an x from the first, a y from the second, and an x from each of the three remaining factors, one arrives at the term $xyxxx$, or $x^4 y$. A term $x^2 y^3$ arises in this multiplication by choosing x's from two of the five factors, and allowing the remaining factors to be y. But the two factors $(x + y)$ which are to supply x's may be chosen from among the five factors $(x + y)$ in $\binom{5}{2}$ ways; hence $x^2 y^0$ occurs as a summand in the expansion of $(x + y)^5$, $\binom{5}{2}$ times, and when we add $x^2 y^3$, $\binom{5}{2}$ times, the result is $\binom{5}{2} x^2 y^3$. A general, and rigorous proof may be constructed along the lines of this intuitive argument.

If we let $x = 1$ and $y = 1$ in the binomial expansion of $(x + y)^n$, we arrive at the interesting result:

$$(1 + 1)^n = \binom{n}{0}(1)^n(1)^0 + \binom{n}{1}(1)^{n-1}(1)^1 + \binom{n}{2}(1)^{n-2}(1)^2 + \cdots$$

$$+ \binom{n}{n-1}(1)^1(1)^{n-1} + \binom{n}{n}(1)^0(1)^n$$

or:
$$2^n = \binom{n}{0} + \binom{n}{1} + \cdots + \binom{n}{n}$$

We have therefore proved that the number of subsets of a set with n elements (including the nullset as one subset), is 2^n (cf. Problem 10 of Exercise 2). If we exclude the nullset, then a set with n elements has $2^n - 1$ subsets. Another way of stating this result is: The number of combinations of n things taken any positive number at a time is $2^n - 1$.

This result has a direct application to problems such as Problem 19, Exercise 60.

*▶ EXERCISE 61

1. In the binomial expansion of each of the following expressions, find the term in which the highest power of x or y is the given one:

(a) $(x - y)^7$; x^2 (b) $(x + y)^7$; x^5

(c) $(x + y)^{10}$; y^3 (d) $(x + y)^{10}$; y^7

(e) $(x - y)^{10}$; y^7 (f) $(x - 2y)^{10}$; x^8

(g) $(x - 2y)^{10}$; x^2 (h) $\left(x + \dfrac{1}{x}\right)^6$; x^0

(i) $\left(x - \dfrac{1}{x}\right)^5$; x (j) $\left(x - \dfrac{1}{x}\right)^{10}$; x^6

2. The construction of Pascal's triangle uses the following fact:

$$\binom{n}{r-1} + \binom{n}{r} = \binom{n+1}{r}$$

Prove that this equation is true. [*Hint:* Use the formula for $\binom{n}{k}$ in Problem 22(a) of Exercise 60, and the fact that $(m + 1)! = (m!)(m + 1)$.]

3. Prove:

$$\binom{100}{0} + \binom{100}{2} + \cdots + \binom{100}{100} = \binom{100}{1} + \binom{100}{3} + \cdots + \binom{100}{99}.$$

10.15 RELATED PROBABILITIES

We turn to an examination of the sample space for the experiment in which a coin is tossed 3 times, in order to induce a number of facts concerning the probabilities of certain related events:

$$\begin{Bmatrix} TTT, & TTH & THT, & THH \\ HTT, & HTH, & HHT, & HHH \end{Bmatrix}$$

First of all we ask: What are the respective probabilities that 0, 1, 2, 3 heads appear in 3 tosses of a coin?

The subsets of the sample space and the probabilities associated with these four possibilities are:

      0 heads: $\{TTT\}$;   (probability $\frac{1}{8}$)

      1 head: $\{TTH, THT, HTT\}$;   (probability $\frac{3}{8}$)

      2 heads: $\{THH, HTH, HHT\}$;   (probability $\frac{3}{8}$)

      3 heads: $\{HHH\}$;   (probability $\frac{1}{8}$)

Note that these subsets are disjoint and exhaustive. (See Exercise 2, Problem 17.)

Note also that the probabilities associated with these four possibilities have a sum of 1.

We shall call events *disjoint* if they are associated with disjoint subsets, and *exhaustive* if they are associated with exhaustive subsets of the sample space for these events. Intuitively, events are disjoint if no two of them can happen simultaneously. In three tosses of a coin, for example, one cannot achieve both exactly one head and exactly two heads. These events are disjoint. On the other hand, three tosses of a coin may simultaneously produce *at least one head* and *at least one tail*. (How?) These events are not disjoint.

Again intuitively, events are exhaustive if at least one of them must happen in the experiment with which they are associated. Thus, in three tosses of a coin, at least one of the possibilities 0, 1, 2, 3, heads must occur; therefore these events form an exhaustive set.

Now the above discussion of the coin experiment suggests the following general rule:

The sum of the probabilities of a set of disjoint, exhaustive events is 1.

PROOF. Let the set of disjoint, exhaustive events be associated with the set of disjoint, exhaustive subsets A, B, C, $\cdots$ of the sample space S. Suppose that the subsets A, B, C, $\cdots$ contain a, b, c, $\cdots$ elements, respectively, and that S contains s elements. Then since the sets A, B, C are disjoint, and their union is S (cf. Exercise 2, Problem 18):

$$a + b + c + \cdots \quad = s$$

Dividing through by s:

$$\frac{a}{s} + \frac{b}{s} + \frac{c}{s} + \cdots \quad = 1$$

but the left-hand side of the above equation is the sum of the probabilities of the given set of events, so that our rule has now been proved to be true.

Now suppose we know the probability that an event E will occur. What is the probability that it will *not* occur? Suppose we call the event that it does not occur $\not\!E$. Then since an event cannot both occur and not occur, E and $\not\!E$ are disjoint. Also, since at least one of the two possibilities E, $\not\!E$ must occur, the events E, $\not\!E$ are exhaustive. Therefore the sum of their probabilities is 1. We therefore have, as a corollary to the above rule:

If p is the probability that an event will occur, then $1 - p$ *is the probability that it will not occur.*

Illustrative Example I. If a coin is tossed three times, what is the probability that it will not happen that all three tosses fall tails?

SOLUTION. Since the probability that all three fall tails is $\frac{1}{8}$, the probability that this event does not happen is $1 - \frac{1}{8}$, or $\frac{7}{8}$.

Referring once more to the experiment of tossing a coin three times, we ask the question: What is the probability that either exactly 1 head or exactly 2 heads appear? The answer is clearly $\frac{6}{8}$, since exactly 1 or 2 heads appear in 6 of the 8 elements of the sample space. But note that $\frac{6}{8}$ is the sum of the probabilities of the events that exactly 1 head appears and that exactly 2 heads appear.

In fact in general:

If disjoint events have probability $p, q, \cdots$ of occurring, then the probability that at least one of the events will occur is: $p + q + \cdots$.

(The proof of this rule is omitted, since it is very much like the preceding proof.)

Illustrative Example 2. If a coin is tossed three times, what is the probability that at least 1 coin will fall heads?

SOLUTION. We shall use both of the two preceding rules in solving this problem.

First of all, by the preceding rule, the answer to the problem is $\frac{3}{8} + \frac{3}{8} + \frac{1}{8}$, or $\frac{7}{8}$.

Problems like this are often done more easily, however, by first finding the probability that the event in question will *not* happen. In our problem, if it does *not* happen that at least 1 coin falls heads, then all three must fall tails. The probability that all three fall tails is $\frac{1}{8}$. Therefore the probability that at least one coin falls heads is $1 - \frac{1}{8}$, or $\frac{7}{8}$.

10.16 INDEPENDENT AND DEPENDENT EVENTS

Suppose we toss an unbiased coin once; then the probability that it falls heads is $\frac{1}{2}$. Suppose, however, that the coin falls tails, and we toss it again. What is the probability that the second throw falls heads? Does the event that the first throw falls tails increase the probability that the second throw falls heads?

Let us examine the sample space for two throws of a coin: It is: $\{TT, TH, HT, HH\}$. If we are willing to admit that all of these possibilities are equally likely, then even after the first toss falls tails, the probability that the second falls heads is still only $\frac{1}{2}$. For there are two cases in which the first falls tails: TT and TH; and of these, there is exactly one case in which the second falls heads, namely TH. Even after the first toss falls tails, then, the probability that the second toss falls heads remains $\frac{1}{2}$; "the coin has no memory" (cf. Problem 7, Exercise 55).

When the probability that an event E occurs is unaffected by the occurrence or nonoccurrence of another event F, we say that the event E is *independent* of the event F. We have just observed that the event that a coin falls heads is independent of the event that it falls tails on a preceding throw.

We shall use the notation $P(E)$ to represent the probability of an event E, and $P(E\mid D)$ to represent the probability of an event E, given that an event D has occurred. Thus if E is the event "the second coin falls heads" and D the event "the first coin falls tails," we may write:

$$P(E) = \tfrac{1}{2}; \quad P(D) = \tfrac{1}{2}; \quad P(E\mid D) = \tfrac{1}{2}$$

Our definition of independence may now be more precisely phrased: *Event E is independent of event D if $P(E\mid D) = P(E)$.*

We are often interested in the probability that events E and D *both* occur. We denote this probability: $P(E \text{ and } D)$. With E and D as in the preceding example, $P(E \text{ and } D) = \tfrac{1}{4}$, for the events E and D both occur in exactly one of the four elements of the sample space for two throws of a coin.

We now derive a formula for $P(E \text{ and } D)$.

Suppose that event D contains d elements of a sample space of x elements (as for example, with D as above, $d = 1$ and $x = 2$), and that after D has occurred, E contains e elements of a sample space of y elements (as for example with E as above $e = 1$, $y = 2$). Then the sample space in which E and D may both occur is the Cartesian product of the sample spaces for E and D and contains xy elements; E and D both occur in de of these elements. Therefore:

$$P(E \text{ and } D) = \frac{de}{xy} = \frac{d}{x} \cdot \frac{e}{y}$$

But $\dfrac{d}{x} = P(D)$, and $\dfrac{e}{y} = P(E\mid D)$. Therefore:

$$P(E \text{ and } D) = P(D) \cdot P(E\mid D)$$

Illustrative Example. A card is drawn from a deck, and then another. What is the probability that:

(a) They are both spades, assuming that the first card is not replaced before the second is drawn?

(b) They are both spades, assuming that the first card is replaced and the deck shuffled before the second is drawn?

(c) They are of the same suit, assuming that the first card is not replaced before the second is drawn?

SOLUTION. (*a*) Let E be the event "the second card is a spade," D the event "the first card is a spade." $P(D) = \frac{13}{52} = \frac{1}{4}$; $P(E \mid D) = \frac{12}{51} = \frac{4}{17}$ (since after a spade has been drawn, there are 51 cards containing 12 spades from which to make the second choice). Therefore: $P(E \text{ and } D) = \frac{1}{4} \cdot \frac{4}{17} = \frac{1}{17}$.

(*b*) With E and D as above in (*a*), $P(D) = \frac{13}{52} = \frac{1}{4}$ as before, but in this case $P(E \mid D) = \frac{1}{4}$. Therefore $P(E \text{ and } D) = \frac{1}{16}$.

(*c*) Two cards will be of the same suit if they are both spades, or both diamonds, or both clubs, or both hearts. These are four disjoint events, so that the probability that at least one will occur is the sum of their respective probabilities of occurrence; but the four events are equally likely, so that the sum of the four probabilities is just four times the probability that any one of them will occur. We have found in (*a*) above that the probability that both cards are spades is $\frac{1}{17}$. Therefore the desired probability is $4 \cdot \frac{1}{17}$, or $\frac{4}{17}$.

▶ **EXERCISE 62**

1. A coin is tossed and a single die is rolled. What is the probability that:
   (*a*) The coin falls heads?
   (*b*) The coin does not fall heads?
   (*c*) The die falls "6?"
   (*d*) The die does not fall "6?"
   (*e*) The coin falls heads and the die falls "6?"
   (*f*) The coin falls heads and the die does not fall "6?"

2. A die is rolled twice. What is the probability that:
   (*a*) The first roll falls "1?"
   (*b*) The first roll does not fall "1?"
   (*c*) The second roll falls an even number?
   (*d*) The second roll does not fall an even number?
   (*e*) The first roll falls "1" and the second roll falls an even number?
   (*f*) The first roll falls "1" and the second roll falls an odd number?

3. A coin is tossed 10 times. What is the probability that there appear exactly:

(*a*) 0 tails?	(*b*) 1 tail?
(*c*) 0 tails or 1 tail?	(*d*) 2 or more tails?
(*e*) 8 or fewer heads?	

4. A coin is tossed 8 times. What is the probability that there appear

(*a*) 0 heads?	(*b*) 1 head?
(*c*) 2 heads?	(*d*) 2 heads or fewer?
(*e*) 3 heads or more?	(*f*) at most 5 tails?

5. A card is drawn from a bridge deck, and then another. Compute the probabilities of the following events, first assuming that the first card is not replaced, then that it is replaced before the second is drawn:

(*a*) Two aces.　　(*b*) An ace and a king.　　(*c*) No aces.

6. A baby has two sets of alphabet blocks to play with, each set containing each of the letters from A to Z just once. The baby chooses four blocks at random. What is the probability that he choses in succession the letters B, A, B, Y?

7. A box contains 3 red checkers and 4 black checkers. Three checkers are drawn in succession from the box. Compute the probabilities of the following events, first assuming that no checker is replaced after it is drawn, and then assuming that each checker is replaced before the next one is drawn:

(*a*) 3 red checkers.

(*b*) 3 black checkers.

(*c*) No red checkers.

(*d*) The first checker is red, the second black, and the third red.

(*e*) Only one of the checkers is red.

8.(*a*) Prove that if event E is independent of event D, then $P(E$ and $D)$ $= P(E) \cdot P(D)$.

(b) Prove that independence of events is a symmetric relationship.

10.17 EMPIRICAL PROBABILITY

Sometimes a sample space or a probability is arrived at purely by mathematical computation (in which case we say that we are dealing with *a priori* probability), and sometimes by a physical experiment (in which case we say we are dealing with *empirical* probability). Empirical probability, as we shall soon see, forms a link between abstract probability theory and concrete statistical applications.

First of all, we offer some examples of both a priori and empirical probability. We have computed the a priori probability that a coin tossed twice falls heads both times to be $\frac{1}{4}$. Now if we conducted 100 experiments in which we tossed a coin twice and found that in 23 of these the coin fell heads twice, the empirical probability in this experiment, for the event that the coin fall heads twice, would be $\frac{23}{100}$.

When we determine the probability that a student chosen at random from a class will be a blonde, by actually counting the number of blondes and the number of students in the class and taking the ratio of the two; and when we assume that a baseball player's batting average represents the probability that he will get a hit in his next time at bat—we are once more dealing with empirical probability.

Illustrative Example 1. Suppose that it has been determined by actual experiment that the probability that a certain coin fall heads is 0.8.

(a) If the coin is tossed twice, what is the probability that two heads appear?

(b) If the coin is tossed three times, what is the probability that at least one head appears?

(c) If the coin is tossed four times, what is the probability that the first two fall heads and the second two do not?

(d) If the coin is tossed four times, what is the probability that exactly two heads appear?

(e) If the coin is tossed four times, what is the probability that at least two heads appear?

SOLUTION. (a) The probability that a head appears the first time and a head appears the second time is $(0.8)(0.8)$, or 0.64.

(b) Here it is easier to compute the probability that the event in question does not happen, and then to subtract that probability from 1.

If it does not happen that at least one head appears, then 0 heads appear, i.e., no toss falls heads. The probability that a toss does not fall heads is $1 - 0.8$, or 0.2. The probability that three successive tosses do not fall heads is $(0.2)(0.2)(0.2)$, or 0.008. Therefore the required probability is $1 - 0.008$, or 0.992.

(c) The probability that these events occur in succession is $(0.8)(0.8)(0.2)(0.2) = 0.0256$.

(d) First we find the number of ways in which the two tosses which are to fall heads may be chosen. This is $\binom{4}{2}$. In each of these cases, the probability that the chosen two will fall heads and the other two will not is $(0.8)^2(0.2)^2$. Therefore the probability that exactly two will fall heads is $\binom{4}{2}(0.8)^2(0.2)^2$, or $(6)(0.0256)$, or 0.1536.

(e) At least two heads includes the cases exactly two heads, or exactly three heads, or exactly four heads.

We have already computed the probability of exactly two heads to be $\binom{4}{2}(0.8)^2(0.2)^2$.

The probability that a particular triple will fall heads, and the fourth not, is $(0.8)^3(0.2)$. A particular triple to fall heads may be chosen in $\binom{4}{3}$ ways. Therefore the probability that exactly three heads fall is $\binom{4}{3}(0.8)^3(0.2)$.

The probability that all four tosses fall heads may be computed directly as $(0.8)(0.8)(0.8)(0.8)$, or following the reasoning of the preceding cases as $\binom{4}{4}(0.8)^4(0.2)^0$, which comes to the same thing.

The probability that at least two heads appear is therefore:

$$\binom{4}{2}(0.8)^2(0.2)^2 + \binom{4}{3}(0.8)^3(0.2) + (0.8)^4$$
$$= 0.1536 + 0.4096 + 0.4096$$
$$= 0.9728$$

Illustrative Example 2. A baseball player has a batting average of .333 (which we approximate by the fraction $\frac{1}{3}$). Assuming that this represents the probability that he hits safely when he bats, what is the probability that he will garner at least one hit in three times at bat?

SOLUTION. (The answer " 1 " which suggests itself turns out to be wrong. It is *not* certain that this player will get a hit in 3 times at bat. The player, for example, might maintain his 0.333 average by hitting only in the last two of each set of six trips to the plate.)

We compute the probability of the negative of the required event, namely that he does not hit in each of three times at bat. This is $(\frac{2}{3})(\frac{2}{3})(\frac{2}{3}) = \frac{8}{27}$. Therefore the probability that he does hit at least once in 3 times at bat is $1 - \frac{8}{27}$, or $\frac{19}{27}$.

Illustrative Example 3. The following is a "mortality table" similar to those used by insurance companies in establishing their rates:

Age	1	20	40	60	80
No. living	100,000	95,000	88,000	68,000	18,000

What is the probability that a man of age 40 will live to age 60? SOLUTION. The required probability is $\frac{68}{88}$, or approximately 0.77.

▶ **EXERCISE 63**

1. A coin is thrown 10,000 times and falls heads 6,000 times.

(*a*) In this case, what is the empirical probability that the coin falls heads? (Use this probability in the following examples.)

(*b*) If the coin is thrown twice, what is the probability of the result *HT*? of the result *TH*? of throwing two heads? of throwing two tails? What is the sum of these probabilities? Why?

(*c*) If the coin is thrown three times, what is the probability of the result *HTT*? of throwing exactly one head? of throwing exactly two heads? of throwing three heads? of throwing no heads?

2. The same as Problem 1, except that the coin falls heads 4,000 times.

3. The probability that a certain coin falls heads is 0.1; the coin is tossed five times. What is the probability that:

(*a*) No heads appear   (*b*) Exactly 1 head appears
(*c*) Exactly 2 heads appear   (*d*) Exactly 3 heads appear
(*e*) Exactly 4 heads appear   (*f*) Five heads appear
(*g*) At least 1 head appears   (*h*) Three or more heads appear

4. A baseball player has a batting average of 0.333. What is the probability that he does not go hitless in four trips to the plate? in six trips?

5. A baseball player has a batting average of 0.250. What is the probability that he gets at least one hit in four times at bat? in five times?

6. In a survey made in a certain freshman class, it was found that 90% of all students who passed mathematics passed physical education, 80% of all students who passed physical education passed mathematics, and 60% of the class passed both mathematics and physical education.

Interpreting these percentages as probabilities, and using the formula $P(E \text{ and } D) = P(D) \cdot P(E \mid D)$, what percentage of the class passed mathematics? what percentage passed physical education?

7. It is reported that in a certain town, twice as many people own dogs as own cats, but 15% of all people who own dogs also own cats, and 10% of all people who own cats also own dogs. Can this report be accurate? (See Problem 6.)

8. An anti-aircraft battery has been found to be 50% effective; i.e., the probability that it will shoot down a plane passing over it is 0.5. Suppose a plane must pass two such batteries in succession to reach a target. How effective will the two batteries be? (*Hint:* First find the probability that the plane is *not* shot down by the successive batteries.)

9.(*a*) If an anti-aircraft battery is 80% effective, what will be the effectiveness of three such batteries over which a plane must fly in succession? (See Problem 8.)

(*b*) What must the effectiveness of anti-aircraft battery be if two such batteries over which a plane must fly in succession are to have an effectiveness of 99%.

10. A certain finished product is assembled from three components. When components are inspected separately, it is found that about 1% of each are defective. Suppose only the finished product is inspected. What proportion may be expected to be defective? (*Hint:* First find the proportion *not* defective.)

11. Using the table of Illustrative Example 3 above:

(*a*) What is the probability that a 20-year old man will live for at least 20 years more?

(*b*) What is the probability that an infant 1 year old will attain the age of 80? 60? 40? 20?

(*c*) What is the probability that a 20-year old man will live until he is 40? 60? 80?

(*d*) What is the probability that a 40-year old man will die before he is 60? 80?

10.18 ODDS AND EXPECTATION

"Odds" are simply a popular way of expressing probability. They compare the probability that an event will occur with the probability that it will not. More precisely: If p is the probability of an event, then we say that the odds in favor of this event is the ratio $p: (1 - p)$, read: "p to $1 - p$."

$\left(\text{The ratio } p: (1 - p) \text{ is, of course, equal to the fraction } \dfrac{p}{1 - p}.\right)$

For example, if the probability of an event is $p = \frac{2}{3}$, then $1 - p = \frac{1}{3}$, and the odds in favor of this event are $\frac{2}{3} : \frac{1}{3}$, or 2 : 1.

Conversely, if we are given the odds $r : s$ in favor of an event, we may determine the probability p of the event. For:

(1) $$\frac{p}{1 - p} = \frac{r}{s}$$

Solving this equation for p we find:

(2) $$p = \frac{r}{r + s}$$

For example, if the odds in favor of an event are 2:3, then the probability of the event is $\frac{2}{5}$.

Odds are used to determine the amount of a "fair" wager. If the odds in favor of a certain event are 2:1, for example, then a fair bet would be one in which a man betting $2 on the event would win $1 if the event occurs, and lose $2 if the event fails to occur.

To see why this is a fair bet, note that the odds of 2:1 reflect the expectation that in a large number of trials of this event, the event will occur twice as often as it fails to occur. In 300 trials, for example, the event might be expected to occur 200 times, and to fail to occur 100 times. A man betting $2 at the above odds 300 times might be expected to win a total of (200)($1), or $200, and lose a total of (100)($2), or $200, and finally, therefore, to "break even." Neither "odds" nor "probability," however, *guarantee* that these expectations will be fulfilled. They only express likelihoods in which we can place more and more confidence with a larger and larger number of trials.

Allied to the concept of a fair wager is that of *mathematical expectation*: Suppose E_1, E_2, $\cdots$ are disjoint, exhaustive events with probabilities p_1, p_2, $\cdots$, respectively. Suppose that the events E_1, E_2, $\cdots$ are associated respectively with amounts of money m_1, m_2, $\cdots$ (which may be rewards or losses when the associated event occurs, depending on whether the "m" involved is $+$ or $-$). Then the *mathematical expectation* for this situation is defined to be:

$$m_1 p_1 + m_2 p_2 + \cdots$$

Thus, in the case of the bet we have just considered, the set of disjoint, exhaustive events is: E (the event in question occurs), and E (the event in question does not occur). The probabilities of E, E are $\frac{2}{3}$, $\frac{1}{3}$ respectively. The associated monetary rewards are \$1, \$ $-$ 2, respectively. The mathematical expectation in this case is \$[(\frac{2}{3})(1) + (\frac{1}{3})(-2)], or \$0.

In fact, we may *define* a bet to be fair if it results in a mathematical expectation of 0.

The mathematical expectation of a game may be thought of as the average amount which one may expect to win in the game. In a game with mathematical expectation \$5, for example, one may expect to win \$500 in 100 games. Virtually all commercial gambling enterprises, of course, involve games with negative expectations (for the customer).

Illustrative Example. 1. In rolling a pair of dice, what are the odds in favor of a "2?"

SOLUTION. We have already (see Problem 5 of Exercise 55) computed the probability of this event to be $\frac{1}{36}$. The odds in favor of this event are therefore $\frac{1}{36} : (1 - \frac{1}{36})$, or 1:35.

Illustrative Example 2. A person bets \$5 at odds of 1:30 that a roll of a pair of dice will show "2." What is his mathematical expectation?

SOLUTION. If he wins, he wins \$150. If he loses, he loses \$5. The probabilities of these two events are $\frac{1}{36}$, $\frac{35}{36}$, respectively. His mathematical expectation is therefore:

$$\$[(150)(\tfrac{1}{36}) + (-5)(\tfrac{35}{36})]$$

or about $-69\cancel{c}$. He may expect to lose an average of 69$\cancel{c}$ per bet in a large number of these bets.

Illustrative Example 3.   An insurance company finds from a mortality table that the probability that a certain man will live until the expiration of a short-term policy of $1000 is 0.99.   Suppose the company feels that it needs a profit of $3 to cover expenses on this policy.   What should the charge for the policy be?

SOLUTION.   Let x dollars be the required charge.   The expectation of the insurance company in this "game" is to be $3.   If the insured lives, the insurance company "wins" x dollars.   If the insured dies, the insurance company keeps x dollars and pays out $1000, a net gain of $(x - 1000)$ dollars.   The probabilities of these two events are 0.99, 0.01, respectively.   Therefore the expectation is:

(3) $$0.99x + 0.01(x - 1000) = 3$$

The solution of this equation is $x = 13$, so that the required charge is $13.

▶ **EXERCISE 64**

1. Using the results of Problem 5(b) of Exercise 55, find the odds in favor of rolling each of the numbers from 1 to 12 with a pair of dice.

2. "· · · the odds in any country in the world that a guy does not make a ten with a pair of dice before he rolls seven, is two to one."   (Damon Runyon, *Blood Pressure*.)

Show that these odds are correct, using the following fact (which may be proved): The odds that one of two events occurs before another in successive trials of an experiment is the ratio of the probability of the first event to the probability of the second event.

3. The odds that a certain horse will win a race are 9:1.   What is the probability that the horse will win?

4.(a) Solve equation (2) above for p, to arrive at equation (1).

(b) Solve equation (3) above, to show that $x = 13$.

5. In a certain "numbers game," a person bets at odds of 600:1 on three digits of his own choice.   If the digits he chooses are the last three digits (in the correct order) of the daily U.S. Treasury balance, as reported in the next day's newspapers, he wins.

(a) What is the probability that he guesses the three digits, in their correct order?

(b) If he bets $10, what is his expectation?

(c) If he bets 10¢ a day, every day for a year, how much may he expect to win or lose?

6. If the probability that a man dies before the expiration of a certain short-term policy is 0.05, and an insurance company charges $60 for a

$1000 policy insuring the life of the man for that period, what part of the $60 may be considered to be for the purpose of paying expenses of running the company? What may be considered to be the purpose of the remaining part of the $ 60 charge?

7. If the probability that a man dies before the expiration of a certain short-term policy is 0.02, what should an insurance company charge for a policy insuring the life of that person for $1000 for that period, if expenses of $ 10 must be covered?

8. Show that if the odds (to win) on two horses in a two-horse race are 5:3 and 1:2, then it is possible to place bets on the two horses in such a way as to be sure that the amount won will be greater than the amount lost.

9.(*a*) Suppose that the odds (to win) on two horses in a two-horse race are $a:b$ and $c:d$. Prove that it is possible to place bets on the two horses in such a way as to be sure that the amount won will be greater than the amount lost, if and only if $ac < bd$.

(*b*) Show that if the preceding odds are translated into probabilities, then the condition $bd > ac$ is equivalent to the condition that the sum of the probabilities is less than 1.

10.19 DECISION AND DESIGN

Statistics is more and more coming to be regarded as the science of making "wise decisions in the face of uncertainty." In this section we shall examine statistical problems which illustrate this point of view.

Our principal tool in the solution of the problems of decision which we shall propose, will be the following theorem (whose proof we shall omit):

Suppose that in one trial of an experiment, an event has an a priori probability p of occurrence. Then in n trials of the event, the mean number of occurrences of the event is given by the formula m = np, and the standard deviation for n trials is given by the formula s = $\sqrt{np\,(1-p)}$.

For example, suppose we consider the experiment of tossing a coin $n = 3$ times, and the event of showing heads, whose a priori probability in one toss is $p = \frac{1}{2}$. The sample space for this experiment is:

$$\{HHH,\ HHT,\ HTH,\ HTT,\ THH,\ THT,\ TTH,\ TTT\}$$

A frequency table for the number of heads appearing in elements of this sample space, and columns necessary to compute the mean $m = \bar{x}$ and the standard deviation s for this distribution follow:

NUMBER OF HEADS x	FREQUENCY f	xf	$x - \bar{x}$	$(x - \bar{x})^2 f$
0	1	0	-1.5	2.25
1	3	3	-0.5	0.75
2	3	6	0.5	0.75
3	1	3	1.5	2.25
	8	12		6.00

$$m = \bar{x} = \frac{12}{8} = 1.5$$

$$s - \sqrt{\frac{6}{8}} = \sqrt{0.75}$$

According to the formulas given above, $m = np = (3)(\frac{1}{2}) = 1.5$, and $s = \sqrt{np\,(1 - p)} = \sqrt{(3)(\frac{1}{2})(\frac{1}{2})} = \sqrt{0.75}$. We see, then, that these formulas are correct, at least in the case we have just considered.

Now we attack a problem of decision:

Illustrative Example 1. A coin is tossed 100 times, and comes up heads 75 times. Decide whether or not the coin is "true," i.e., unweighted.

SOLUTION. We must understand first of all that it is quite possible for a perfectly true coin to fall heads 75 out of 100 tosses; in fact, if we had the patience and time to continue the experiment for a *very* long time, it is *almost certain* that we would even be able to make 100 tosses in which *all* the tosses fell heads.

In order to make a decision in cases like that of our problem, then, we are forced arbitrarily to choose some measure of likelihood beyond which we will not accept a result as being due simply to chance variation.

We recall (see page 301) that with a sufficiently numerous set of "normal" data one may expect that only about 5% of the data will fall further than two standard deviations from the mean, and only about 0.3% will fall further than three standard deviations from the mean.

Our method, in this introductory treatment, will be crude, since, for one thing, we shall not look too carefully at what constitutes a "sufficiently numerous" n. It turns out, however, that for the values of n to which we shall apply the preceding principles, the results are fairly accurate.

Suppose we agree, as a practical matter, to consider a coin untrue if it produces an event which falls further than three standard deviations from the mean.

In the case of the coin of our illustrative example, $n = 100$, $p = \frac{1}{2}$,

$m = np = 50$, $s = \sqrt{np(1 - p)} = \sqrt{(100)(\frac{1}{2})(\frac{1}{2})} = 5$. To be within 3 standard deviations of the mean, the number of heads would have to lie between $50 - 15$ and $50 + 15$, i.e., between 35 and 65; the given number of heads, 75, lies outside this interval. According to our arbitrary criterion of decision, this coin is untrue.

It is high time that we offered our promised explanation of what we mean by the term "normal," as applied to a set of data. Furthermore, it would be appropriate now to re-examine once more the nature of mathematics, its connection with the material world, and how this chapter on statistics and probability fits into the general picture. For the two are related: the question of "normality" in statistics touches upon the place which statistics holds in mathematics as a whole.

We have indicated earlier that although a great deal of mathematics has been suggested by material phenomena, there is also a considerable body of mathematics that has stemmed directly from the mathematician's imagination; in any case, whatever the source, pure mathematics is independent of the physical world. Pure mathematics consists of a set of axioms, from which the mathematician, using the rules of deductive logic, wrings consequences.

When a set of axioms "fits" a concrete situation, then we say that the set of axioms (and the consequences of these axioms) form a "mathematical model" for the concrete situation. (For example, the axioms of geometry form a mathematical model for the concrete world of strings and boxes and bridges, and so on.)

But this "fitting" is always more or less approximate; for it depends on the senses of man, and the senses of man are notoriously inexact. What, for example, is the width of this page? The mathematical model called "Euclidean geometry" assumes that there is one and only one real number that expresses that width. To determine that unique real number is, however, as a practical matter quite impossible. The most accurate of measurements vary upon repetition.

The physicist and engineer, therefore, tend now to deal with *average* measurements, characterized by a *probability*, rather than a *certainty* of exactness. And just because of the inexactness with which mathematical models mirror the physical world, statistics and probability, which measure and deal with uncertainty, have within recent years begun to assume a tremendously important role in the applications of mathematics. The chemist or physicist, for example, is now likely to say not that if one does so and so, then such and such will happen, but if one does so and so, then *there is a probability of so much* that such and such will happen.

Now, to get back to the question of "normality."

We have built up an abstract, "a priori" theory of probability which, as a matter of fact, is a part of our theory of sets. When we analyze the events that may happen when a coin falls twice, let us say, we built up a set of ordered pairs $\{HH, HT, TH, TT\}$, and actually this has nothing to do with a coin. Even a penniless beggar could work out the probabilities in this situation. We assume, however, that a "true" coin would, in some fashion, fit this analysis. What justification is there for our faith in the application of abstract probability theory to concrete problems? The answer is the same as that for geometry: it works, at least accurately enough for practical needs. It passes the "pragmatic" test.

In certain collections of data, there is a distribution of frequencies which resembles that of a coin tossing experiment. That is to say, there is a "middle" value which occurs with maximum frequency, and frequencies diminish as we move left or right of the middle value. (See the frequency polygons of Section 10.2). Very roughly speaking, this is what we mean by a "normal" distribution. More precisely, it is a distribution to which the abstract probability theory we have developed and stated above applies (approximately, of course). We assume that a large number of tosses of a coin or rolls of a die or cards drawn from a pack will conform to this theory, and experience shows that our assumption works fairly well in practice. We assume that certain random collections of data, like the heights of all male students at X college, are "normal" also, and again experience has confirmed that our mathematical model is adequately faithful. But it is important to note that not *all* collections of data form normal distributions; for example, suppose we tabulated the *ages* of all male students at X college. Because of the drop-out in successive semesters, freshmen students predominate; the frequency polygon does not assume the symmetric bell-shape of the normal distribution.

We continue with further examples of statistical approaches to problems of decision.

Illustrative Example 2. A true-false test consists of 100 questions. Will a student be able to get as many as 60 right simply by guessing? How about 70?

SOLUTION. The probability that a student will guess the answer to a question correctly is $p = \frac{1}{2}$. The number of questions is $n = 100$; $m = np = 50$; $s = \sqrt{np(1 - p)} = 5$.

If we accept only results further than two standard deviations from the mean as being unlikely to be attained by chance (we shall call this the "$2s$" criterion), then getting as many as 60 right would be just barely possible by guessing, but getting as many as 70 right would not.

If we use a $3s$ criterion, then as many as 60 right would have to be regarded as being possible by pure chance, but as many as 70 would not; using the $3s$ criterion, $50 + 3s = 65$ is the "borderline" case.

In the case of small n, our statements about the percentage of data to be expected within 1, 2, and 3 standard deviations from the mean no longer hold. An alternative analysis is applied in the next example.

Illustrative Example 3. In a true-false test of 10 questions, can one get at least 6 right by guessing? 7? 8? 9? 10?

SOLUTION. The probability of getting exactly the following number right by guessing [see Illustrative Example 1(d), Section 10.17], is:

6 right: $\dbinom{10}{6}\left(\dfrac{1}{2}\right)^6\left(\dfrac{1}{2}\right)^4 = \dbinom{10}{6}\left(\dfrac{1}{2}\right)^{10} = \dbinom{10}{4}\left(\dfrac{1}{2}\right)^{10} = \dfrac{210}{1024}$

7 right: $\dbinom{10}{7}\left(\dfrac{1}{2}\right)^7\left(\dfrac{1}{2}\right)^3 = \dbinom{10}{7}\left(\dfrac{1}{2}\right)^{10} = \dbinom{10}{3}\left(\dfrac{1}{2}\right)^{10} = \dfrac{120}{1024}$

8 right: $\dbinom{10}{8}\left(\dfrac{1}{2}\right)^8\left(\dfrac{1}{2}\right)^2 = \dbinom{10}{8}\left(\dfrac{1}{2}\right)^{10} = \dbinom{10}{2}\left(\dfrac{1}{2}\right)^{10} = \dfrac{45}{1024}$

9 right: $\dbinom{10}{9}\left(\dfrac{1}{2}\right)^9\left(\dfrac{1}{2}\right)^1 = \dbinom{10}{9}\left(\dfrac{1}{2}\right)^{10} = \dbinom{10}{1}\left(\dfrac{1}{2}\right)^{10} = \dfrac{10}{1024}$

10 right: $\dbinom{10}{10}\left(\dfrac{1}{2}\right)^{10}\left(\dfrac{1}{2}\right)^0 = \dbinom{10}{10}\left(\dfrac{1}{2}\right)^{10} = (1)\left(\dfrac{1}{2}\right)^{10} = \dfrac{1}{1024}$

Summing the appropriate probabilities, the probability of getting at least the following number right is:

$$\text{At least 6 right:} \quad \frac{386}{1024} \doteq 0.377$$

$$\text{At least 7 right:} \quad \frac{176}{1024} \doteq 0.172$$

$$\text{At least 8 right:} \quad \frac{56}{1024} \doteq 0.055$$

$$\text{At least 9 right:} \quad \frac{11}{1024} \doteq 0.011$$

$$\text{All 10 right:} \quad \frac{1}{1024} \doteq 0.001$$

Assuming that an event with a probability of less than 0.06 (let us say) is unlikely to occur by chance, we decide that one may get as many as 7 right by guessing, but not 8 or more. (A 0.05 criterion here would correspond to the $2s$ criterion we used previously; see page 347.)

In fact the method of this example is sharper than our previous approach, and is applicable to the same problems. However, for large n the computations involved may be tedious. Fortunately, tables are available that greatly reduce the labor of computation by giving values of $\binom{n}{r}(p)^r(1 - p)^{1-r}$, and sums of these values, for a large number of values of n, r, and p.

Note that the expression $\binom{n}{r}p^r(1 - p)^{1-r}$ is one of the terms of the binomial expansion of $[p + (1 - p)]^n$. It is for this reason that what we have (loosely) called a "normal" distribution is often called a "binomial" distribution. We make this distinction however: although we have reserved the term "normal" to apply only to large n, binomial distributions exist for all positive integer values of n.

Illustrative Example 4. Tom claims that he has mysterious powers of extra-sensory perception (ESP). He does not claim to be infallible, but he says, for example, that he can tell significantly often in advance whether a coin will fall heads or tails. When pressed as to what he means by significantly often, he expresses the conviction that it is about 8 times out of 10. Design a fair test of his powers of ESP.

SOLUTION. Suppose we make the test involve 36 tosses of a coin. We would not be surprised at anyone's getting 18 right; that could easily happen by chance. We would demand that a person get more than 18 right before we would put any stock in his claim to ESP. The question is: how much more?

Tom, on the other hand, although he has laid claim to being able to guess right 0.8 of the time, would not abandon his claim if he guessed somewhat fewer than $(0.8)(36) \doteq 29$ on this particular test. Eight out of ten is his average feat, he says, and that figure may vary somewhat from test to test. Here the question is: How many fewer than 29 right will convince Tom that he is not particularly psychic?

Somewhere between 18 and 29 we must choose a number which will suit both the tester and Tom.

In this situation, $n = 36$. If the guessing were purely random, $p = \frac{1}{2}$. Under this hypothesis, $m = np = 18$, $s = \sqrt{np(1 - p)} = 3$. Using the $2s$ criterion, any number greater than $18 + 6 = 24$ right would be unusual, so that the tester feels that Tom must get at least 24 right to demonstrate that he has any ESP at all.

Under Tom's hypothesis, $n = 36$, $p = 0.8$, $m = 28.8$, $s = 2.4$. Using the $2s$ criterion, any number fewer than $28.8 - 4.8 = 24$ right would be unlikely. Tom agrees that if he gets fewer than 24 right, he will modify his claim.

The test we design, then, is this: A coin is tossed 36 times. If Tom gets 24 or more right, we admit that Tom does have significant powers of ESP. If Tom gets fewer than 24 right we deny his claims.

It is purely fortuitous that in this example both hypotheses as to the value of p led to the same critical number: 24. In fact with a smaller number of tosses, the two parties to the experiment might find themselves in conflict with regard to a fair critical number; with a larger number of tosses, as might be expected, agreement would be easier, and one might even expect to be able to use the more stringent $3s$ criterion.

It should be stressed that the result of any experiment of this sort cannot ever be considered to be quite conclusive. There is always *some* possibility that real ability may not evidence itself, or that we may be led by chance to discover ability that does not actually exist. Furthermore, it should be noted that we have here considered only a mathematical aspect of the problem of designing an experiment, and that very briefly. There are, among others, mechanical and psychological aspects to be considered also. There is a great deal more that can be said about such problems. In fact the field is one which, like all of mathematics, both pure and applied, is still very far from being a closed book.

▶ EXERCISE 65

1. Verify the correctness of the formulas $m = np$ and $s = \sqrt{np(1 - p)}$ for the case of four tosses of a coin.

2. In each of the following cases, the number of heads which a coin shows in a certain number of tosses is given. Discuss the question of whether the coin is a properly balanced one.

(*a*) 60 heads in 100 tosses.

(*b*) 240 heads in 400 tosses.

3. The same as Problem 2 above for the cases:

(*a*) 31 heads in 49 tosses.

(*b*) 62 heads in 100 tosses.

(*c*) 4 heads in 5 tosses. (*Hint:* Use the technique of Illustrative Example 3.)

4. Discuss the "normality" of the following sets of data:

(*a*) The grades in an examination of 1000 students.

(*b*) The grades in an examination of 30 students.

(*c*) The grades in an examination of 10 students.

(*d*) The heights of all voters in Boston.

(*e*) The heights of all basketball players in the U.S.

(*f*) The incomes in a given year of all people in the U.S. who earned money in that year.

(g) The incomes in a given year of all people in the U.S. whose earnings exceeded $10,000 in that year.

5. A pair of dice comes up 7 the following number of times in the following number of rolls. Are the dice loaded?

(a) 25 times out of 80 rolls.

(b) 20 times out of 80 rolls.

(c) 15 times out of 80 rolls.

(d) 11 times out of 45 rolls.

(e) 14 times out of 45 rolls.

(f) 16 times out of 45 rolls.

(g) 4 times out of 4 rolls. (*Hint:* Use the technique of Illustrative Example 3.)

6. What would you say about a pair of dice which rolled "2" twice in succession?

7. If a passing grade is 70%, will a student be likely to pass a true-false test of the following number of questions simply by guessing?

(a) 81   (b) 64   (c) 49   (d) 36   (e) 25

(f) 5 (Use the technique of Illustrative Example 3.)

8. If a passing grade is 60%, will a student be likely to pass an "always-sometimes-never" test of the following number of questions simply by guessing?

(a) 100   (b) 50   (c) 25   (d) 5

9. Suppose that p_1 represents the probability which Tom claims describes his ability to predict the fall of a coin. Discuss the feasibility of designing a test of his claim which involves the following number of tosses, n, and if a test is feasible with this number, specify the test.

(a) $n = 25$, $p_1 = 0.7$ (b) $n = 36$, $p_1 = 0.7$

(c) $n = 64$, $p_1 = 0.7$ (d) $n = 100$, $p_1 = 0.7$

(e) $n = 144$, $p_1 = 0.7$ (f) $n = 25$, $p_1 = 0.8$

(g) $n = 100$, $p_1 = 0.8$

10. In a certain large city 100 randomly chosen people are polled as to their preference between candidates A and B for a certain office. How many of these, in favor of candidate A, would convince you that he will probably win the election? (*Hint:* Suppose A's probability of winning were $\frac{1}{2}$. Then with $p = \frac{1}{2}$, $n = 100$, find numbers at 2 (or 3) standard deviations from the mean. More votes than these in favor of A in this sample would be very unlikely if A's actual probability of winning were only $\frac{1}{2}$, and even less likely if his probability of winning were $< \frac{1}{2}$.)

Note: The student should not be deluded by the ease with which this example can be worked out. Almost everyone, for example, has encountered at least one public opinion poll of notorious inaccuracy. A major difficulty, and one which we have not considered at all, is the selection of a truly random sample.

11. The same as Problem 10 above, but 900 people are polled.

12. Nine hundred randomly chosen people are telephoned at a certain hour and asked whether they are tuned in on " Uncle Jackie." How many answers in the affirmative would convince you that at least 10% of our population viewed " Uncle Jackie's " program that hour?

13. Five per cent of a certain population has been succumbing to a certain virus. A new vaccine is tested on a random sample of 171 people, and it is found that only 4 of these (i.e., less than $2\frac{1}{2}\%$) succumb to the virus. Is the vaccine effective?

14. It is found that of a randomly chosen sample of 100 " Glowell " light bulbs, 90% have a burning life of at least 1000 hours.

Show that it is likely that of a very large number of " Glowell " light bulbs, at least 80% will have burning lives of 1000 hours or more.

11 MATRICES AND DETERMINANTS

11.1 INTRODUCTION

Matrices were first invented and investigated about 100 years ago by the English mathematician Arthur Cayley (1821–1895). We have mentioned before that significantly many portions of pure mathematics, produced without any thought of possible use, have nevertheless turned out to be of great practical importance. There is no better example of this phenomenon than Cayley's theory of matrices. Cayley himself would undoubtedly be astonished to learn of the countless ways in which his matrices are applied today in the physical and social sciences, and in commerce and industry.

In this introductory treatment, although we shall make only one application of matrix theory, it will be one of the most important of all the applications that are made of matrices: namely, to the solution of linear simultaneous equations, which themselves arise in so many practical problems.

11.2 LINEAR SIMULTANEOUS EQUATIONS AND MATRICES

Consider the set of linear equations:

$$(1) \qquad \begin{aligned} 2x + 3y &= 8 \\ 5x - 2y &= 1 \end{aligned}$$

355

We observe that on the left and right sides of (1), there are exhibited the rectangular arrays of numbers:

(2)
$$\begin{pmatrix} 2 & 3 \\ 5 & -2 \end{pmatrix}$$

(3)
$$\begin{pmatrix} 8 \\ 1 \end{pmatrix}$$

A rectangular array of (complex) numbers is called a *matrix* (plural: matrices). As above, we shall generally enclose the elements of a matrix in parentheses. In the set of equations (1), the matrix (2) is called the *matrix of coefficients*, and the matrix (3) is called the *matrix of constants*. (In writing the matrices of a set of linear equations, it is assumed that the equations are written with each variable appearing in only one column, and with the constant terms on the right of the equations.)

The *rows* of matrix (2) are the matrices $(2 \quad 3)$, $(5 \quad -2)$. The columns of matrix (2) are the matrices $\begin{pmatrix} 2 \\ 5 \end{pmatrix}$, $\begin{pmatrix} 3 \\ -2 \end{pmatrix}$. If a matrix has r rows and c columns, we say that it is an $r \times c$ (read "r by c") matrix, or that its *order* is $r \times c$. Thus matrix (2) is a 2×2 matrix.

The rows of matrix (3) are the 1×1 matrices (8), (1). Matrix (3) has only one column: $\begin{pmatrix} 8 \\ 1 \end{pmatrix}$. A matrix with only one column is called a *column matrix*. Thus, matrix (3) is a 2×1 column matrix. Similarly, of course, a matrix with only one row is called a *row matrix*. The only matrix that is both a row matrix and a column matrix is a 1×1 matrix, i.e., a complex number. A 1×1 matrix may be written with or without parentheses; for example: $(7) = 7$.

Now we return to our original equations (1). In solving (1), we seek a value of x and a value of y, which when they are substituted in the array $\begin{pmatrix} 2x + 3y \\ 5x - 2y \end{pmatrix}$, will yield the array $\begin{pmatrix} 8 \\ 1 \end{pmatrix}$. It is easy to see for example, that $x = 5$, $y = 6$ will not do the trick. For if $x = 5$, and $y = 6$, then $\begin{pmatrix} 2x + 3y \\ 5x - 2y \end{pmatrix} = \begin{pmatrix} 28 \\ 13 \end{pmatrix}$.

Since the result of our substitution into (1) is a column matrix, we shall find it convenient to write the numbers substituted as a column matrix also. That is to say, we shall speak of substituting into $\begin{pmatrix} 2x + 3y \\ 5x - 2y \end{pmatrix}$, the column matrix $\begin{pmatrix} 5 \\ 6 \end{pmatrix}$ when we mean that we are going to substitute into $\begin{pmatrix} 2x + 3y \\ 5x - 2y \end{pmatrix}$ the values $x = 5$, $y = 6$.

By way of further example, the result of substituting $\begin{pmatrix}1\\2\end{pmatrix}$ into $\begin{pmatrix}2x+3y\\5x-2y\end{pmatrix}$

is: $\begin{pmatrix}2\cdot1+3\cdot2\\5\cdot1-2\cdot2\end{pmatrix}=\begin{pmatrix}8\\1\end{pmatrix}$. Thus $\begin{pmatrix}1\\2\end{pmatrix}$, i.e., $x=1$, $y=2$, is a solution of the

set of simultaneous linear equations (1).

In our substitution, it is clear that the coefficients involved are important, and in fact determine the outcome.   Roughly speaking, we may say

that in our preceding computations the matrix of coefficients $\begin{pmatrix}2&3\\5&-2\end{pmatrix}$

operated on the matrix $\begin{pmatrix}5\\6\end{pmatrix}$ in a certain way to yield the matrix $\begin{pmatrix}28\\13\end{pmatrix}$, and

on the matrix $\begin{pmatrix}1\\2\end{pmatrix}$ in the same way to yield the matrix $\begin{pmatrix}8\\1\end{pmatrix}$.   We shall call

this operation multiplication of matrices, so that our immediately preceding remarks may be written:

(4)
$$\begin{pmatrix}2&3\\5&-2\end{pmatrix}\begin{pmatrix}5\\6\end{pmatrix}-\begin{pmatrix}28\\13\end{pmatrix}$$

(5)
$$\begin{pmatrix}2&3\\5&-2\end{pmatrix}\begin{pmatrix}1\\2\end{pmatrix}=\begin{pmatrix}8\\1\end{pmatrix}$$

The formula that defines the "certain way" in which the matrix of coefficients operates on a given pair of values of x and y is:

(6)
$$\begin{pmatrix}2&3\\5&-2\end{pmatrix}\begin{pmatrix}x\\y\end{pmatrix}=\begin{pmatrix}2x+3y\\5x-2y\end{pmatrix}$$

Ilustrative Example I.   Given the set of equations:

$$x+2y-z=5$$
$$2x-y+3z=10$$

(a) Write the matrix of coefficients.

(b) Write a formula to show how the coefficients operate on values of x, y, z.

(c) Use the formula of (b) to find the result of substituting $x=7$, $y=8$, $z=9$ into the left side of the given equations.

(d) In the product of matrices you have written in answering part (c), state the orders of the first matrix, the second matrix, and the product matrix.

SOLUTION:

(a) $\begin{pmatrix}1&2&-1\\2&-1&3\end{pmatrix}$

(b) $\begin{pmatrix} 1 & 2 & -1 \\ 2 & -1 & 3 \end{pmatrix} \begin{pmatrix} x \\ y \\ z \end{pmatrix} = \begin{pmatrix} x + 2y - z \\ 2x - y + 3z \end{pmatrix}$

(c) $\begin{pmatrix} 1 & 2 & -1 \\ 2 & -1 & 3 \end{pmatrix} \begin{pmatrix} 7 \\ 8 \\ 9 \end{pmatrix} = \begin{pmatrix} 7 + 2 \cdot 8 - 9 \\ 2 \cdot 7 - 8 + 3 \cdot 9 \end{pmatrix} = \begin{pmatrix} 14 \\ 33 \end{pmatrix}$

(d) Orders of first, second, and product matrices in part (c) are respectively: $2 \times 3, 3 \times 1, 2 \times 1$.

Illustrative Example 2. Given the equation:

$$2x + 3y - 4z = 5$$

answer the questions posed in Illustrative Example 1.

SOLUTION:

(a) $(2 \quad 3 \quad -4)$

(b) $(2 \quad 3 \quad -4) \begin{pmatrix} x \\ y \\ z \end{pmatrix} = (2x + 3y - 4z)$

(c) $(2 \quad 3 \quad -4) \begin{pmatrix} 7 \\ 8 \\ 9 \end{pmatrix} = (2 \cdot 7 + 3 \cdot 8 - 4 \cdot 9) = 2$

(d) Orders of first, second, and product matrices in part (c) are respectively: $1 \times 3, 3 \times 1, 1 \times 1$.

▶ **EXERCISE 66**

In each of the following cases, there is given the left side of a set of linear simultaneous equations (the right being a column of constants). In each case, answer the questions of Illustrative Example 1 in the preceding section.

1. $2x + 3y$
   $4x + 5y$

2. $2x - 4y$
   $3x + y$

3. $2x + 3y + z$
   $3x - y - z$

4. $x - y - z$
   $x + y - z$

5. $3x - 2y + z$

6. $x - y + z$

7. $x + y$

8. $x - y$

9. x

10. $5y$

11. $2x$
    $3x$

12. $x + y - z$
    $x - y + z$
    $x - y - z$

13. $x + y$
    $y + z$
    $x + z$

14. x
    y
    z

11.3 THE PRODUCT OF MATRICES

In this section we shall examine the information we have already compiled on the product of matrices, and from that information we shall frame a general definition for the product of matrices.

First of all we note that, in every instance in which we multiplied matrices, the number of columns in the first matrix has been equal to the number of rows in the second. That is to say, whenever we multiplied an $r_1 \times c_1$ matrix by an $r_2 \times c_2$ matrix, it was always the case that $c_1 = r_2$. [See, for example, part (d) in Illustrative Examples 1, 2 of the preceding section, and also in Problems 1–14 of the preceding exercise.]

Furthermore, in all of the cases noted, the product matrix turned out to have as many rows as the first matrix and as many columns as the second. That is to say, in multiplying an $r_1 \times c_1$ matrix by an $r_2 \times c_2$ matrix, not only have we had $c_1 = r_2$ in each case but also the product in each case has been an $r_1 \times c_2$ matrix.

For these reasons, we begin our definition of the product of matrices as follows:

1. *If A is an $r \times n$ matrix and B is an $n \times c$ matrix, then the matrix product AB is defined, and is an $r \times c$ matrix.*

Statement 1 tells us that certain pairs of matrices may be multiplied, and how many rows and columns such a product of matrices will have. The question still remains, however, as to how we shall determine the element that belongs in each position of the product matrix.

We will answer that question first in the case where the first matrix is a row matrix, the second a column matrix; that is to say, the first a $1 \times n$, the second an $n \times 1$ matrix. According to statement 1, the product must be a 1×1 matrix, i.e., a number. Illustrative Example 2 of the preceding section as well as Problems 5–10 of the preceding exercise suggest that this number should be defined as follows:

2. *If A is the row matrix $(a_1 \ a_2 \ \cdots \ a_n)$ and B is the column matrix*
$$\begin{pmatrix} b_1 \\ b_2 \\ \vdots \\ b_n \end{pmatrix}, \text{ then we define:}$$

$$AB = (a_1 \quad a_2 \quad \cdots \quad a_n) \begin{pmatrix} b_1 \\ b_2 \\ \vdots \\ b_n \end{pmatrix} = a_1 b_1 + a_2 b_2 + \cdots + a_n b_n$$

Now, in order to complete our definition, we introduce the following notation:

$^i A$: the ith row of matrix A (if A has one);

$_iA$: the ith column of matrix A (if A has one);

A_{ij}: the element in the ith row and the jth column of A (if A has an ith row and a jth column). Also called: "the ijth element of A."

For example, suppose $A = \begin{pmatrix} 2 & 3 \\ 5 & -2 \end{pmatrix}$. Then:

$$^1A = (2 \quad 3) \quad ^2A = (5 \quad -2) \quad _1A = \begin{pmatrix} 2 \\ 5 \end{pmatrix} \quad _2A = \begin{pmatrix} 3 \\ -2 \end{pmatrix}$$

$$A_{11} = 2 \quad A_{12} = 3 \quad A_{21} = 5 \quad A_{22} = -2$$

Now let us examine the product (6) of the preceding section. Letting $A = \begin{pmatrix} 2 & 3 \\ 5 & -2 \end{pmatrix}$, and $B = \begin{pmatrix} x \\ y \end{pmatrix}$, we see that the element in the 1st row and 1st column of AB, i.e., $2x + 3y$, is the product (see statement 2 of this section) of the 1st row of A by the 1st column of B: $(2 \quad 3) \begin{pmatrix} x \\ y \end{pmatrix}$. That is to say: $(AB)_{11} = (^1A)(_1B)$.

And the element in the 2nd row and 1st column of AB, i.e., $5x - 2y$, is the product of the 2nd row of A by the 1st column of B: $(5 \quad -2) \begin{pmatrix} x \\ y \end{pmatrix}$. That is to say: $(AB)_{21} = (^2A)(_1B)$. The following definition is suggested by these and our other previous results on the products of matrices:

3. *If A, B are matrices, and $(AB)_{ij}$ is an element of their product AB, then:* $(AB)_{ij} = (^iA)(_jB)$.

Illustrative Example 1. Find the product AB, if

$$A = \begin{pmatrix} 1 & 2 \\ 3 & -1 \end{pmatrix}, \quad B = \begin{pmatrix} 4 & -5 & 6 \\ 7 & 8 & -9 \end{pmatrix}.$$

SOLUTION. Since A, B are of orders 2×2, 2×3, AB exists and is of order 2×3.

$$(AB)_{11} = (^1A)(_1B) = (1 \quad 2) \begin{pmatrix} 4 \\ 7 \end{pmatrix} = 18$$

$$(AB)_{12} = (^1A)(_2B) = (1 \quad 2) \begin{pmatrix} -5 \\ 8 \end{pmatrix} = 11$$

$$(AB)_{13} = (^1A)(_3B) = (1 \quad 2) \begin{pmatrix} 6 \\ -9 \end{pmatrix} = -12$$

$$(AB)_{21} = (^2A)(_1B) = (3 \quad -1) \begin{pmatrix} 4 \\ 7 \end{pmatrix} = 5$$

$$(AB)_{22} = (^2A)(_2B) = (3 \quad -1) \begin{pmatrix} -5 \\ 8 \end{pmatrix} = -23$$

$$(AB)_{23} = (^2A)(_3B) = (3 \quad -1) \begin{pmatrix} 6 \\ -9 \end{pmatrix} = 27$$

Therefore:

$$AB = \begin{pmatrix} 1 & 2 \\ 3 & -1 \end{pmatrix} \begin{pmatrix} 4 & -5 & 6 \\ 7 & 8 & -9 \end{pmatrix} = \begin{pmatrix} 18 & 11 & -12 \\ 5 & -23 & 27 \end{pmatrix}$$

(With a little practice, much of what we have written out in detail in the above example can be done mentally, perhaps with the help of one finger scanning a row of A as another scans a column of B.)

Illustrative Example 2. Find the product AB if:

(a) $A = 7, B = (1 \quad 2 \quad 5)$

(b) $A = \begin{pmatrix} 0 \\ 1 \end{pmatrix}, B = 7$

SOLUTION. (a) Since A is 1×1, and B is 1×3, the product AB exists and is 1×3; i.e., AB has one row and three columns.

The element in the first row and first column of AB is the first row of A times the first column of B: $7 \cdot 1 = 7$.

The element in the first row and second column of AB is the first row of A times the second column of B: $7 \cdot 2 = 14$.

The element in the first row and third column of AB is the first row of A times the third column of B: $7 \cdot 5 = 35$.

Thus: $7 \cdot (1 \quad 2 \quad 5) = (7 \quad 14 \quad 35)$.

(b) Since in this case A is 2×1, and B is 1×1, the product AB exists and is 2×1; i.e., AB has two rows and one column.

The element in the first row and first column of AB is the first row of A times the first column of B: $0 \cdot 7 = 0$.

The element in the second row and first column of AB is the second row of A times the first column of B: $1 \cdot 7 = 7$.

Thus:

$$\begin{pmatrix} 0 \\ 1 \end{pmatrix} \cdot 7 = \begin{pmatrix} 0 \\ 7 \end{pmatrix}$$

We note, in Illustrative Example 2, that the effect of multiplying a matrix M by a 1×1 matrix k, when that multiplication is possible, is always simply to multiply each element of M by k, whether the product is kM or Mk. Such a product is often called a *scalar* product, and the 1×1 matrix k is called a *scalar*.

We shall find it convenient to extend the definition of a scalar product, guided by the property just noted:

4. *If k is a number and B an $r \times c$ matrix, we define $kB = Bk$ to be an $r \times c$ matrix such that $(kB)_{ij} = (Bk)_{ij} = k \cdot (B_{ij})$.*

For example: $2 \cdot \begin{pmatrix} 1 & 3 \\ 5 & 7 \end{pmatrix} = \begin{pmatrix} 2 & 6 \\ 10 & 14 \end{pmatrix} = \begin{pmatrix} 1 & 3 \\ 5 & 7 \end{pmatrix} \cdot 2$

Now statements 1, 2, 3, and 4 together constitute our complete definition for the product of matrices. Note that our definition will carry us further than the examples which suggested the definition; for one thing, in all of our examples, the second matrix of a product of two matrices was always a column matrix. Our next illustrative example will consider a case in which this is not so.

Note further, however, that our definition does not go so far as to define a product for *any* two matrices. It does not, for example, define a product (1 2 3)·(4 5); for these matrices have orders 1×3 and 1×2; since $3 \neq 1$, and since neither matrix is a scalar, the requirement of neither statement 1 nor 4 is satisfied, so that the given product is not defined.

▶ **EXERCISE 67**

1. Compute the product, if it exists, and identify those that are scalar products:

(a) $(1 \quad 2)\begin{pmatrix} 1 \\ 2 \end{pmatrix}$

(b) $(1 \quad 2 \quad 3)\begin{pmatrix} 4 \\ 5 \\ 6 \end{pmatrix}$

(c) $\begin{pmatrix} 1 \\ 2 \end{pmatrix}(1 \quad 2)$

(d) $\begin{pmatrix} 4 \\ 5 \\ 6 \end{pmatrix}(1 \quad 2 \quad 3)$

(e) $\begin{pmatrix} 1 \\ 2 \end{pmatrix}(1 \quad 2 \quad 3)$

(f) $(1 \quad 2 \quad 3)\begin{pmatrix} 1 \\ 2 \end{pmatrix}$

(g) $(7)(1 \quad -4 \quad 5)$

(h) $(10)\begin{pmatrix} 1 & 2 \cdot 3 & 4 \\ 5 & 6 & 7 & 8 \end{pmatrix}$

(i) $\begin{pmatrix} 1 & 2 \\ 2 & 1 \end{pmatrix}\cdot 4$

(j) $\begin{pmatrix} 1 \\ -4 \end{pmatrix}(7)$

(k) $(1 \quad -2)\begin{pmatrix} 1 & 2 \\ 3 & -1 \end{pmatrix}$

(l) $\begin{pmatrix} 1 & 2 \\ 3 & -1 \end{pmatrix}(1 \quad -2)$

(m) $\begin{pmatrix} 2 & 7 \\ 4 & -5 \end{pmatrix}\begin{pmatrix} 3 & 1 \\ -2 & 1 \end{pmatrix}$

(n) $\begin{pmatrix} 3 & 1 \\ -2 & 1 \end{pmatrix}\begin{pmatrix} 2 & 7 \\ 4 & -5 \end{pmatrix}$

(o) $\begin{pmatrix} 2 & 7 \\ 4 & -5 \end{pmatrix}\begin{pmatrix} 1 & -1 \\ 2 & 3 \\ 1 & -2 \end{pmatrix}$

(p) $\begin{pmatrix} 1 & -1 \\ 2 & 3 \\ 1 & -2 \end{pmatrix}\begin{pmatrix} 2 & 7 \\ 4 & -5 \end{pmatrix}$

(q) $\begin{pmatrix} 1 & 2 & -1 \\ 2 & 1 & -1 \\ -1 & 2 & 1 \end{pmatrix}\begin{pmatrix} 1 & 2 & 1 \\ 2 & 1 & 1 \\ 1 & 2 & 1 \end{pmatrix}$

(r) $\begin{pmatrix} 1 & 2 & 1 \\ 2 & 1 & 1 \\ 1 & 2 & 1 \end{pmatrix}\begin{pmatrix} 1 & 2 & -1 \\ 2 & 1 & -1 \\ -1 & 2 & 1 \end{pmatrix}$

(s) $\begin{pmatrix} 1 & 0 \\ 0 & 1 \end{pmatrix}\begin{pmatrix} a & b \\ c & d \end{pmatrix}$

(t) $\begin{pmatrix} a & b \\ c & d \end{pmatrix}\begin{pmatrix} 1 & 0 \\ 0 & 1 \end{pmatrix}$

(u) $\begin{pmatrix} 1 & 0 \\ 0 & 1 \end{pmatrix} \begin{pmatrix} x \\ y \end{pmatrix}$ $\qquad\qquad$ (v) $(x \quad y) \begin{pmatrix} 1 & 0 \\ 0 & 1 \end{pmatrix}$

(w) $\begin{pmatrix} 1 & 0 & 0 \\ 0 & 1 & 0 \\ 0 & 0 & 1 \end{pmatrix} \begin{pmatrix} a & b & c \\ d & e & f \\ g & h & i \end{pmatrix}$ $\qquad$ (x) $\begin{pmatrix} a & b & c \\ d & e & f \\ g & h & i \end{pmatrix} \begin{pmatrix} 1 & 0 & 0 \\ 0 & 1 & 0 \\ 0 & 0 & 1 \end{pmatrix}$

(y) $\begin{pmatrix} 1 & 0 & 0 \\ 0 & 1 & 0 \\ 0 & 0 & 1 \end{pmatrix} \begin{pmatrix} x \\ y \\ z \end{pmatrix}$ $\qquad$ (z) $\begin{pmatrix} x \\ y \\ z \end{pmatrix} \begin{pmatrix} 1 & 0 & 0 \\ 0 & 1 & 0 \\ 0 & 0 & 1 \end{pmatrix}$

2. Suppose $ad - bc = D \neq 0$, $A = \begin{pmatrix} a & b \\ c & d \end{pmatrix}$, $B = \begin{pmatrix} d/D & -b/D \\ -c/D & a/D \end{pmatrix}$.

Compute AB and BA.

3. Is multiplication of matrices commutative? Justify your answer.

4. In each of the following cases, compute AB, BC, $(AB)C$ and $A(BC)$:

(a) $A = (1 \quad 2)$, $B = \begin{pmatrix} 2 \\ 4 \end{pmatrix}$, $C - (5 \quad 6 \quad 7)$

(b) $A = \begin{pmatrix} 1 \\ 2 \end{pmatrix}$, $B = (2 \quad 1)$, $C = \begin{pmatrix} 5 & 6 \\ 7 & 8 \end{pmatrix}$

(c) $A = 5$, $B = \begin{pmatrix} 1 & 2 \\ 4 & 3 \end{pmatrix}$, $C = \begin{pmatrix} -1 \\ 2 \end{pmatrix}$

(d) $A = 1/D$, $B = \begin{pmatrix} d & -b \\ -c & a \end{pmatrix}$, $C = \begin{pmatrix} a & b \\ c & d \end{pmatrix}$, where $ad - bc = D \neq 0$.

5. If A, B are each $n \times n$ matrices, show that

$$(AB)_{ij} = A_{i1}B_{1j} + A_{i2}B_{2j} + \cdots + A_{in}B_{nj},$$

where i, j are positive integers $\leqslant n$.

11.4 PROPERTIES OF MATRIX MULTIPLICATION

In this section we shall examine the operation of matrix multiplication that we have defined to see which of the general properties of operations that we have discussed earlier are exhibited by matrix multiplication, and which are not.

Closure. Since matrix multiplication is not even defined for all pairs of matrices, matrix multiplication in the set of all matrices is not closed. But matrix multiplication may be closed in certain subsets of the set of all matrices. For example, since the product of any 3×3 matrix A by any 3×3 matrix B is always defined, and is always a 3×3 matrix, matrix multiplication in the set of all 3×3 matrices is closed. In fact, for any positive integer n, multiplication in the set of all $n \times n$ matrices is closed.

Commutativity. We have already encountered many examples of matrices A, B in which $AB \neq BA$. Matrix multiplication is, therefore, not commutative in the set of all matrices. However, commutativity holds in certain restricted situations, although the restrictions in the case of this property are rather severe. For example, matrix multiplication in the set of all 1×1 matrices is commutative. This is not at all surprising, of course, since matrix multiplication in the set of all 1×1 matrices is nothing other than multiplication in the set of all complex numbers. Also, a scalar always "commutes" with any matrix; i.e., if k is a number and M any matrix: $kM = Mk$. We shall soon encounter other examples in which commutativity in some form holds.

Associativity. The fact that products of matrices are not even defined for all pairs of matrices, immediately precludes the possibility that multiplication of matrices may be associative (as we have defined the term) in the set of all matrices. However, as Problem 4 of the preceding exercise suggests, the following modified associative property holds true: If A, B, C are matrices of orders $r \times m$, $m \times n$, $n \times c$ respectively, then $(AB)C = A(BC)$. Also, for example, if k is a scalar and B, C as above, $(kB)C = k(BC)$. [We leave proofs of these statements to a more complete course in matrix theory; in general it can be shown that, if the product of matrices $(AB)C$ exists, then so does $A(BC)$, and the two products are equal.]

Unity Element. In the set of complex numbers, there is a number, namely 1, which, when it multiplies any complex number c on either side, leaves the complex number unchanged; i.e.: $1 \cdot c = c$, $c \cdot 1 = c$. Is there a matrix I with an analogous property, that is to say, a matrix I which, when it multiplies any matrix, leaves the matrix unchanged? If there were, the matrix I would be called a unity element in the set of all matrices. The answer to our question is "no," there is obviously not a unity element in the set of all matrices; for given any $r \times c$ matrix I, there are many matrices it cannot multiply at all. However, once more a restriction will rescue the concept.

Consider, for example the matrix $R = \begin{pmatrix} 1 & 0 \\ 0 & 1 \end{pmatrix}$, called the 2×2 identity matrix. If M is any 2×2 matrix, (see Problems 1s and 1t of the preceding exercise), then $RM = MR = M$. That is to say, $\begin{pmatrix} 1 & 0 \\ 0 & 1 \end{pmatrix}$ is a unity element in the set of all 2×2 matrices.

*One may go even further. It may be proved that $\begin{pmatrix} 1 & 0 \\ 0 & 1 \end{pmatrix}$ is a *left unity* in the set of all $2 \times c$ matrices; i.e., if M is any two-row matrix,

$\begin{pmatrix} 1 & 0 \\ 0 & 1 \end{pmatrix} \cdot M = M$; and $\begin{pmatrix} 1 & 0 \\ 0 & 1 \end{pmatrix}$ is a *right unity* in the set of all $r \times 2$ matrices;

i.e., if M is any two-column matrix, $M \cdot \begin{pmatrix} 1 & 0 \\ 0 & 1 \end{pmatrix} = M$.

Similarly (see Problems 1w and 1x of the preceding exercise), it is easy to prove that $S = \begin{pmatrix} 1 & 0 & 0 \\ 0 & 1 & 0 \\ 0 & 0 & 1 \end{pmatrix}$, the 3×3 identity matrix, is a unity element in the set of all 3×3 matrices.

Note that in the matrix R, $R_{11} = R_{22} = 1$, and all other elements of R are equal to zero. In the matrix S, $S_{11} = S_{22} = S_{33} = 1$, and all other elements of S are equal to zero. In any matrix M, the elements M_{ij} in which $i = j$ are called the elements in the "main diagonal" of M. R and S may, therefore, be respectively described as 2×2 and 3×3 matrices, in which each element in the main diagonal is equal to 1 and all other elements are equal to 0.

More generally, an identity matrix I_n is an $n \times n$ matrix (or "square matrix of order n") in which each element in the main diagonal is equal to 1, i.e., $(I_n)_{ij} = 1$ for $i = j$, and all other elements are equal to zero, i.e., $(I_n)_{ij} = 0$ for $i \neq j$. Statements analogous to those we made for $R = I_2$ and $S = I_3$ may be made for an identity matrix of any order.

It follows that, although multiplication of matrices is not commutative in the set of all matrices, at least the $n \times n$ identity element I_n does commute with each $n \times n$ matrix A, i.e., $I_n A = A I_n$, for $I_n A = A$ and $A I_n = A$.

Inverses. Suppose A, B are $n \times n$ matrices such that $AB = BA = I_n$. Then A is said to be the *inverse* of B, and B is said to be the *inverse* of A. For example, it may easily be verified that:

$$\begin{pmatrix} 5 & 2 \\ 2 & 1 \end{pmatrix} \begin{pmatrix} 1 & -2 \\ -2 & 5 \end{pmatrix} = \begin{pmatrix} 1 & 0 \\ 0 & 1 \end{pmatrix} \quad \text{and} \quad \begin{pmatrix} 1 & -2 \\ -2 & 5 \end{pmatrix} \begin{pmatrix} 5 & 2 \\ 2 & 1 \end{pmatrix} = \begin{pmatrix} 1 & 0 \\ 0 & 1 \end{pmatrix}$$

Therefore, $\begin{pmatrix} 5 & 2 \\ 2 & 1 \end{pmatrix}$ and $\begin{pmatrix} 1 & -2 \\ -2 & 5 \end{pmatrix}$ are each other's inverses.

Not all square matrices have inverses. For example, it is easy to show that $\begin{pmatrix} 1 & 1 \\ 1 & 1 \end{pmatrix}$ does not have an inverse. For suppose this matrix does have an inverse: $\begin{pmatrix} a & b \\ c & d \end{pmatrix}$. Then:

$$\begin{pmatrix} 1 & 1 \\ 1 & 1 \end{pmatrix} \begin{pmatrix} a & b \\ c & d \end{pmatrix} = \begin{pmatrix} 1 & 0 \\ 0 & 1 \end{pmatrix}$$

i.e.:

$$\begin{pmatrix} a + c & b + d \\ a + c & b + d \end{pmatrix} = \begin{pmatrix} 1 & 0 \\ 0 & 1 \end{pmatrix}$$

There follows: $a + c = 1$, $a + c = 0$, hence $1 = 0$, which is, of course, impossible.

11.5 INVERSES AND DETERMINANTS OF 2 × 2 MATRICES

We have noted that not all square matrices have inverses. The question then arises: Exactly which do and which do not? We proceed to answer that question in the case of 2×2 matrices.

First of all, we consider what must be true when a matrix $A = \begin{pmatrix} a & b \\ c & d \end{pmatrix}$ does have an inverse $B = \begin{pmatrix} r & s \\ t & u \end{pmatrix}$. In that case:

$$\begin{pmatrix} a & b \\ c & d \end{pmatrix} \begin{pmatrix} r & s \\ t & u \end{pmatrix} = \begin{pmatrix} 1 & 0 \\ 0 & 1 \end{pmatrix}$$

i.e.:

(1) $$\begin{pmatrix} ar + bt & as + bu \\ cr + dt & cs + du \end{pmatrix} = \begin{pmatrix} 1 & 0 \\ 0 & 1 \end{pmatrix}$$

There follows:

(2) $$ar + bt = 1$$

(3) $$cr + dt = 0$$

We eliminate t by multiplying (2) by d, (3) by b, and subtracting:

(4) $$(ad - bc)r = d$$

And similarly we eliminate r from (2), (3):

$$(ad - bc)t = -c$$

i.e.:

(5) $$-(ad - bc)t = c$$

Now, also from (1), we have:

(6) $$cs + du = 1$$

Substituting (4) and (5) into (6):

(7) $$-(ad - bc)st + (ad - bc)ru = 1$$

i.e.:

(8) $$(ad - bc)(ru - st) = 1$$

At this point we note that the numbers $ad - bc$ and $ru - st$ are related to the matrices A, B respectively in the same way: Each is the product of the elements in the main diagonal minus the product of the elements in the other diagonal. Each is called the *determinant* of its respective matrix:

Definition. If A is a 2×2 matrix, the *determinant* of A, denoted $|A|$, is the number $A_{11}A_{22} - A_{12}A_{21}$.

From (8), we see that $ad - bc$, i.e., $|A|$, cannot be 0, for, if it were, then $0 = 1$. We have proved the following theorem.

Theorem. If a 2×2 matrix A has an inverse, then $|A| \neq 0$.

We note that there is one more consequence of (1) that we have not yet used:

(9) $$as + bu = 0$$

From (6) and (9), it is left to the student to derive:

(10) $$(ad - bc)s = -b$$

(11) $$(ad - bc)u = a$$

From (4), (10), (5) and (11) we have: $r = d/|A|$, $s = -b/|A|$, $t = -c/|A|$, $u = a/|A|$. Hence, assuming that $\begin{pmatrix} a & b \\ c & d \end{pmatrix}$ has an inverse, we have shown that that inverse must be:

(12) $$\begin{pmatrix} d/|A| & -b/|A| \\ -c/|A| & a/|A| \end{pmatrix} = (1/|A|) \begin{pmatrix} d & -b \\ -c & a \end{pmatrix}$$

(Hence, if a 2×2 matrix has an inverse, that inverse is unique. This justifies our use of the phrase " *the* inverse of a matrix.")

Now we are in a position to prove the converse of the preceding theorem.

Theorem. If A is a 2×2 matrix such that $|A| \neq 0$, then A has an inverse.

PROOF: Suppose $A = \begin{pmatrix} a & b \\ c & d \end{pmatrix}$. We know that, if A has an inverse, it must be given by (12) above. Since $|A| \neq 0$, (12) is actually defined. It is left to the student to prove that (12) is the inverse of A.

Illustrative Example I. Find the inverse of the matrix $\begin{pmatrix} 1 & 2 \\ 3 & 4 \end{pmatrix}$.

SOLUTION. The formula (12) may be worded in the following way: To find the inverse (when it exists) of a 2×2 matrix M, interchange the terms in the main diagonal, change the signs of the terms in the other diagonal, and multiply the resulting matrix by $1/|M|$.

Thus, the inverse of $\begin{pmatrix} 1 & 2 \\ 3 & 4 \end{pmatrix}$ is $(-\frac{1}{2}) \begin{pmatrix} 4 & -2 \\ -3 & 1 \end{pmatrix} = \begin{pmatrix} -2 & 1 \\ \frac{3}{2} & -\frac{1}{2} \end{pmatrix}$. The student should verify that both products of this matrix and the given matrix are equal to the 2 × 2 identity matrix.

Before terminating this section, we point out an interesting result to which (8) leads. Since $ad - bc$ and $ru - st$ are the determinants of the matrices we have denoted A, B respectively, (8) may be written:

$$(13) \qquad\qquad |A| \cdot |B| = 1$$

That is to say: If a pair of 2 × 2 matrices are each other's inverses, then their determinants are each other's reciprocals.

But note further: AB is the 2 × 2 identity matrix, and the determinant of the 2 × 2 identity matrix is 1. Hence (13) may be written:

$$(14) \qquad\qquad |A| \cdot |B| = |AB|$$

Now the interesting fact is that (14) is true not only for matrices A, B that are each other's inverses but also for all $n \times n$ matrices A, B. The proof of this statement in the case $n = 2$ is left as an exercise for the student. [We shall not prove (14) in the more general case, but leave the proof to a more comprehensive course in matrix theory.]

▶ **EXERCISE 68**

1. In each of the following sets, state whether matrix multiplication is closed, commutative, or associative; also tell whether a unity element exists in the set, and which, if any, elements in the set have inverses in the set.

(a) The set of all 1 × 1 matrices.

(b) The set of all 2 × 2 matrices.

(c) The set of all 2 × 2 matrices in which each element in the second row is equal to zero.

(d) The set of all 2 × 2 matrices in which each element in the first row is equal to zero.

(e) The set of all 1 × 2 matrices.

(f) The set of all "diagonal" 2 × 2 matrices. (A *diagonal* matrix is one in which each element not in the main diagonal is equal to zero.)

(g) The set of all "scalar" 2 × 2 matrices. [A *scalar* matrix is a square diagonal matrix in which the elements in the main diagonal are all equal; note that a scalar $n \times n$ matrix is *not* a scalar unless $n = 1$. However, the name derives from the fact that scalar matrices behave very much like scalars. For example, compare the effect of multiplying a 2 × 2 matrix by the scalar k, and by the scalar matrix $\begin{pmatrix} k & 0 \\ 0 & k \end{pmatrix}$.]

(h) The set of all 2×2 "triangular" matrices. (A triangular matrix is a matrix in which all the elements below the main diagonal are equal to 0.)

2. Prove that if A is any $m \times n$ matrix, then $AI_n = A$; and that if A is any $n \times m$ matrix, then $I_nA = A$. [*Hint:* Prove that $(AI_n)_{ij} = A_{ij}$, for each element A_{ij} of A, using Exercise 67, Problem 5.]

3. Find the determinant and inverse (if it exists) of each of the following matrices, and verify that the matrices you claim to be inverses actually are.

(a) $\begin{pmatrix} 1 & 2 \\ 2 & 6 \end{pmatrix}$

(b) $\begin{pmatrix} 1 & 1 \\ 5 & 6 \end{pmatrix}$

(c) $\begin{pmatrix} 1 & -1 \\ 2 & -3 \end{pmatrix}$

(d) $\begin{pmatrix} 1 & 1 \\ 2 & 2 \end{pmatrix}$

(e) $\begin{pmatrix} 1 & 0 \\ 0 & 0 \end{pmatrix}$

(f) $\begin{pmatrix} 2 & 0 \\ 0 & 2 \end{pmatrix}$

(g) $\begin{pmatrix} 1 & 0 \\ 0 & 1 \end{pmatrix}$

(h) $\begin{pmatrix} 4 & -1 \\ 2 & -3 \end{pmatrix}$

(i) $\begin{pmatrix} 6 & 12 \\ 2 & 4 \end{pmatrix}$

(j) $\begin{pmatrix} -1 & -2 \\ -3 & -4 \end{pmatrix}$

4. In each of the following cases, find $|A|$, $|B|$, AB, and $|AB|$.

(a) $A = \begin{pmatrix} 4 & 2 \\ 1 & 3 \end{pmatrix}$, $B = \begin{pmatrix} 1 & 1 \\ 1 & 3 \end{pmatrix}$

(b) $A = \begin{pmatrix} 3 & 2 \\ 6 & 4 \end{pmatrix}$, $B = \begin{pmatrix} -1 & 2 \\ -1 & 3 \end{pmatrix}$

(c) $A = \begin{pmatrix} 1 & -2 \\ 2 & 3 \end{pmatrix}$, $B = \begin{pmatrix} 2 & 3 \\ -1 & 4 \end{pmatrix}$

5. Induce (and prove) a general statement from the results of Problem 4.

6. Arthur Cayley was actually led to his invention of matrices by a "linear transformation" problem of the following sort: Suppose

$$x = 2u - 3v \quad \text{and} \quad u = 3r + 2s$$
$$y = u + v \qquad \qquad v = 4r - 2s,$$

express x in terms of r and s, and y in terms of r and s.

(a) Solve this problem by direct substitution.

(b) We may express the first equation in the matric form: $\begin{pmatrix} x \\ y \end{pmatrix} = \begin{pmatrix} 2 & -3 \\ 1 & 1 \end{pmatrix} \begin{pmatrix} u \\ v \end{pmatrix}$. Similarly express the second equation.

(c) Show how one may derive from (b) the result (a). (Note that it is necessary to use the associativity of matrix multiplication in the derivation.)

(d) More generally, suppose the equations are:

$$x = au + bv \quad \text{and} \quad u = er + fs$$
$$y = cu + dv \qquad \qquad v = gr + hs$$

Answer the questions (*a*) through (*c*) with respect to these equations, and thus exhibit another motivation for the definition of the product of matrices.

7. In the preceding section:

(*a*) Write out the details of the derivation of equations (4), (5) from (2), (3).

(*b*) Derive equations (10), (11) from (6), (9).

8. In the preceding section, prove that the matrix (12) is the inverse of the matrix A (assuming $|A| \neq 0$).

*9. Given a pair of 2×2 matrices A, B, we showed in the preceding section that, if A and B are each other's inverses, then $|A| \cdot |B| = 1$. Prove that the converse of this statement is not true.

*10. Suppose A is a 2×2 matrix. Prove that $|A| = 0$ if and only if one of the rows of A is a scalar multiple of the other. What about the columns of A?

11.6 MATRIC SOLUTION OF TWO LINEAR SIMULTANE-OUS EQUATIONS IN TWO UNKNOWNS

We have developed enough theory now to enable us to solve a pair of linear simultaneous equations in two unknowns by means of matrices, when a unique solution exists.

For example, consider the set of equations:

(1)
$$x + 2y = 7$$
$$2x - y = 11$$

Using matrices, these equations may be written as the single equation:

(2)
$$\begin{pmatrix} x + 2y \\ 2x - y \end{pmatrix} = \begin{pmatrix} 7 \\ 11 \end{pmatrix}$$

for (1) is true if and only if (2) is true. (We assume here the following definition of equality of matrices: Matrices A, B are equal if and only if they have the same order, and $A_{ij} = B_{ij}$ for every pair of elements A_{ij}, B_{ij}.)

Now letting $A = \begin{pmatrix} 1 & 2 \\ 2 & -1 \end{pmatrix}$, $X = \begin{pmatrix} x \\ y \end{pmatrix}$, $C = \begin{pmatrix} 7 \\ 11 \end{pmatrix}$, equation (2) may be written:

(3)
$$AX = C$$

We wish to solve equation (3) for X. How do we solve the equation $2x = 6$? We multiply both sides by the (multiplicative) "inverse" of 2, namely $\frac{1}{2}$, to arrive at an equivalent equation. How do we solve equation (3)? In exactly the same way: We multiply both sides by the inverse of the coefficient of the unknown (if such an inverse exists).

[In what follows we shall use the fact that $(I_2)X = X$. (See Exercise 67, Problem 1u, and Exercise 68, Problem 2.)]

Suppose, for the moment, that A has an inverse B. Then there follows from (3):

(4) $$B(AX) = BC$$

Equations (3) and (4) are equivalent, since not only does (4) follow from (3) but also (3) follows from (4). (How?)

Now $B(AX) = (BA)X = (I_2)X = X$. Therefore (4) is equivalent to:

(5) $$X = BC$$

In the particular case that we are considering, the inverse of the matrix of coefficients A is $(-\frac{1}{5}) \begin{pmatrix} -1 & -2 \\ -2 & 1 \end{pmatrix}$. Hence the solution we seek is:

$$\begin{pmatrix} x \\ y \end{pmatrix} - (-\tfrac{1}{5}) \begin{pmatrix} -1 & -2 \\ -2 & 1 \end{pmatrix} \begin{pmatrix} 7 \\ 11 \end{pmatrix} - (-\tfrac{1}{5}) \begin{pmatrix} -29 \\ -3 \end{pmatrix} = \begin{pmatrix} 29/5 \\ 3/5 \end{pmatrix}$$

i.e., $x = 29/5$, $y = 3/5$.

Illustrative Example I. Solve:

$$2x + y = 9$$
$$4x + 3y = 15$$

SOLUTION. The matrix of coefficients is $\begin{pmatrix} 2 & 1 \\ 4 & 3 \end{pmatrix}$.

The inverse of the matrix of coefficients is $(\tfrac{1}{2}) \begin{pmatrix} 3 & -1 \\ -4 & 2 \end{pmatrix}$.

Therefore: $\begin{pmatrix} x \\ y \end{pmatrix} = (\tfrac{1}{2}) \begin{pmatrix} 3 & -1 \\ -4 & 2 \end{pmatrix} \begin{pmatrix} 9 \\ 15 \end{pmatrix} = (\tfrac{1}{2}) \begin{pmatrix} 12 \\ -6 \end{pmatrix} = \begin{pmatrix} 6 \\ -3 \end{pmatrix}$.

▶ **EXERCISE 69**

1. Use the results of Exercise 68, Problem 3, to solve each of the following sets of simultaneous equations by the matric method of the preceding section.

(a) $x + 2y = 29$
    $2x + 6y = 80$
(c) $x + y = 7$
    $5x + 6y = -11$

(b) $x + 2y = 0$
    $2x + 6y = 0$
(d) $x - y = 4$
    $2x - 3y = 1$

2.(*a*)–(*e*) Where possible, solve each of the sets of simultaneous equations in Exercise 40, Problem 1*a* through 1*e* by the matric method of the preceding section.

3. Suppose we are given the set of simultaneous equations:

$$ax + by = r$$
$$cx + dy = s$$

and suppose $|A| \neq 0$, where A is the matrix of coefficients $\begin{pmatrix} a & b \\ c & d \end{pmatrix}$.

(*a*) Use the matric method of the preceding section to solve the given set of simultaneous equations for x and y.

(*b*) Let $A * 1$ denote the matrix that results when column 1 of A is replaced by the column of constants, and $A * 2$ the matrix that results when column 2 of A is replaced by the column of constants; i.e.:

$$A * 1 = \begin{pmatrix} r & b \\ s & d \end{pmatrix}, \quad A * 2 = \begin{pmatrix} a & r \\ c & s \end{pmatrix}$$

Show that the solution for x and y of the given set of simultaneous equations is

$$x = \frac{|A * 1|}{|A|}, \quad y = \frac{|A * 2|}{|A|}$$

(This formula is the special case of "Cramer's rule" that applies to two linear simultaneous equations in two unknowns when, of course, $|A| \neq 0$; cf. Section 11.16.)

4.(*a*)–(*d*) Use the special case of Cramer's rule, derived in the preceding problem, to solve each of the sets of simultaneous equations in Problem 1*a* through 1*d* above.

11.7 PERMUTATION FUNCTIONS AND DETERMINANTS

If "inverses" and "determinants" and the method of solving simultaneous linear equations by means of inverse matrices all applied only to 2×2 matrices, then the importance of these concepts and this method would certainly be small. We now seek to generalize the concepts and the method to apply to $n \times n$ matrices, where n is any natural number.

Toward this end, we first introduce a special kind of function, suggested by the determinant of a 2×2 matrix A, whose value is given by:

(1) $$|A| = A_{11}A_{22} - A_{12}A_{21}$$

Note that the subscripts in each term exhibit a function with domain $\{1, 2\}$ and range $\{1, 2\}$, if we think of each first subscript ("prescript") as an element of our domain and each second subscript ("postscript") as the image of its prescript. The first function p_1 is an identity function, since $p_1(1) = 1$, $p_1(2) = 2$. The second function, p_2, has the following mapping: $p_2(1) = 2$, $p_2(2) = 1$. Clearly both p_1 and p_2 are one–one functions whose domain and range are the same set $\{1, 2\}$.

Definition. A one–one function whose domain and range are the same set is called a *permutation function*.

For example, there are six permutation functions, $p_1, \cdots, p_6$, with domain $\{1, 2, 3\}$:

x	$p_1(x)$	$p_2(x)$	$p_3(x)$	$p_4(x)$	$p_5(x)$	$p_6(x)$
1	1	1	2	2	3	3
2	2	3	1	3	1	2
3	3	2	3	1	2	1

The student will recognize the six possible ordered sets of images as the six permutations of the integers 1, 2, 3. (Hence, of course, the name "permutation" function.) Given a set S with n elements, there will exist $n!$ permutation functions with domain S (see Section 10.10). Thus, a domain of two elements admits of exactly $2! = 2$ permutation functions, and, in fact, the two terms of a 2×2 matrix [see (1) above] exhibit both of the permutation functions with domain $\{1, 2\}$.

This would suggest that the determinant of a 3×3 matrix should contain $3! = 6$ terms, each exhibiting one of the six permutation functions with domain $\{1, 2, 3\}$. In fact, we shall define the determinant of a 3×3 matrix, indeed of any $n \times n$ matrix, in this fashion. But one point remains to be settled: One term of $|A|$ in (1) above is preceded by a "$-$" sign, i.e., a factor of -1. Which terms in the determinant of a 3×3 matrix and which in the determinant of any $n \times n$ matrix should be so treated?

The answer is to be found in a classification of permutation functions as "even" or "odd," which we now examine.

Consider the function p_2 with domain $\{1, 2\}$ just defined. Note that although $1 < 2$, $p_2(1) > p_2(2)$. Whenever p is a permutation function and $i < j$ a pair of elements in its domain such that $p(i) > p(j)$, we say that p effects (or "has") an inversion. Thus the function p_1 with domain

$\{1, 2\}$ has 0 inversions, and the function p_2 with domain $\{1, 2\}$ has 1 inversion. A permutation function is classified as "even" or "odd" according as to whether it effects an even or an odd number of inversions in its domain; the function p_1 with domain $\{1, 2\}$ then, is even, and the function p_2 with domain $\{1, 2\}$ is odd.

Now (1) above suggests that we settle the question of sign as follows: terms that exhibit odd permutation functions are to be preceded by "−" signs. (We shall presently state this more precisely.) To produce an explicit formula for the determinant of a 3×3 matrix requires, then, that we determine the parity (see Exercise 5, Problem 4) of each of the functions $p_1, \cdots, p_6$ with domain $\{1, 2, 3\}$, defined in the preceding table.

First of all, it is clear that p_1 inverts the order of no elements; p_1 has 0 inversions; p_1 is even.

In the case of p_2, we see that although $2 < 3$, $p_2(2) = 3 > p_2(3) = 2$. This is the only inversion effected by p_2; p_2 has 1 inversion; p_2 is odd.

But let us see whether we can streamline this tedious process. The images that p_2 assigns to 1, 2, 3 are respectively 1, 3, 2. An inversion occurs whenever an element in this sequence is followed by a smaller element (for as we go from left to right, an element in the domain, as we have written it, must be less than any element that follows it). In the sequence 1, 3, 2, we first examine 1; it is followed by no smaller element; we count no inversions; then we examine the next element, 3; it is followed by one smaller element, 2; we count 1 inversion. Total: 1 inversion.

Let us use this method in the case of the function p_6: ordered image set 3, 2, 1; the first element 3 is followed by 2 smaller elements, 2, 1; we count 2 inversions; the second element 2 is followed by 1 smaller element, 1; we count 1 inversion. Total: 3 inversions; p_6 is odd.

We leave it to the student to verify that p_3 is odd, p_4 is even, and p_5 is even.

Now we write the definition of $|A|$ (when A is a 3×3 matrix), to which we are led by the preceding remarks:

$$
\begin{aligned}
|A| = {} & A_{11}A_{22}A_{33} && \text{(term exhibiting even permutation } p_1) \\
& + A_{12}A_{23}A_{31} && \text{(term exhibiting even permutation } p_4) \\
& + A_{13}A_{21}A_{32} && \text{(term exhibiting even permutation } p_5) \\
& - A_{11}A_{23}A_{32} && \text{(term exhibiting odd permutation } p_2) \\
& - A_{12}A_{21}A_{33} && \text{(term exhibiting odd permutation } p_3) \\
& - A_{13}A_{22}A_{31} && \text{(term exhibiting odd permutation } p_6)
\end{aligned}
$$

Fortunately, there are at least two simple ways of remembering this definition (of the determinant of a 3×3 matrix), and they are given by the following patterns (in the first, the first two columns of the determinant are repeated after the given determinant):

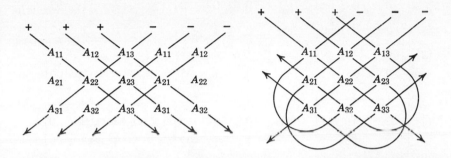

We note here that in writing the determinant of a matrix whose elements are displayed, the parentheses enclosing the elements are generally deleted. Thus, for example, $\left|\begin{pmatrix} a & b \\ c & d \end{pmatrix}\right|$ is generally written: $\begin{vmatrix} a & b \\ c & d \end{vmatrix}$.

(*Warning!:* The above patterns for evaluating the determinant of a 3 × 3 matrix do *not* generalize to matrices of higher order. Indeed, we shall devote the next section to laying the foundation for a general definition and method of evaluation of the determinant of *any* square matrix.)

Illustrative Example I.

$$\text{Evaluate:} \quad \begin{vmatrix} 2 & 1 & -1 \\ 3 & 0 & 4 \\ 1 & -1 & -2 \end{vmatrix}.$$

SOLUTION. By the definition of the determinant of a 3 × 3 matrix (as given by the second pattern above), the given determinant is equal to:

$$[(2 \cdot 0 \cdot -2) + (1 \cdot 4 \cdot 1) + (-1 \cdot -1 \cdot 3)]$$
$$- [(-1 \cdot 0 \cdot 1) + (1 \cdot 3 \cdot -2) + (2 \cdot -1 \cdot 4)] = 21.$$

▶ **EXERCISE 70**

1. Evaluate the following determinants:

(a) $\begin{vmatrix} 3 & -2 & 1 \\ 5 & 1 & 3 \\ -1 & -1 & 2 \end{vmatrix}$ (b) $\begin{vmatrix} 3 & 5 & -1 \\ -2 & 1 & -1 \\ 1 & 3 & 2 \end{vmatrix}$ (c) $\begin{vmatrix} 0 & 0 & 0 \\ 0 & 0 & 0 \\ 0 & 0 & 0 \end{vmatrix}$

$$(d)\begin{vmatrix} 1 & 0 & 0 \\ 0 & 1 & 0 \\ 0 & 0 & 1 \end{vmatrix} \quad (e)\begin{vmatrix} 2 & 0 & 0 \\ 0 & 2 & 0 \\ 0 & 0 & 2 \end{vmatrix} \quad (f)\begin{vmatrix} 0 & 0 & 0 \\ 1 & 2 & 3 \\ 7 & 11 & 97 \end{vmatrix}$$

$$(g)\begin{vmatrix} 2 & 0 & 0 \\ 0 & 3 & 0 \\ 0 & 0 & 5 \end{vmatrix} \quad (h)\begin{vmatrix} 2 & 4 & -7 \\ 1 & 2 & 2 \\ 3 & -1 & 5 \end{vmatrix} \quad (i)\begin{vmatrix} 1 & 2 & 2 \\ 2 & 4 & -7 \\ 3 & -1 & 5 \end{vmatrix}$$

$$(j)\begin{vmatrix} 1 & 0 & 0 \\ 2 & 4 & -3 \\ 3 & 5 & 7 \end{vmatrix} \quad (k)\begin{vmatrix} 1 & 2 & 3 \\ 2 & 4 & 6 \\ 7 & 11 & 97 \end{vmatrix} \quad (l)\begin{vmatrix} 1 & 13 & 3 \\ 2 & 69 & 6 \\ 3 & 17 & 9 \end{vmatrix}$$

2. Find the number of inversions effected by each of the functions p_3, p_4, p_5 defined in the preceding section, and thus verify the statements made there about their parities.

3. Find the number of inversions of each of the following permutation functions with domain {1, 2, 3, 4} and tell whether each function is even or odd.

(a)

x	$p_1(x)$	$p_2(x)$	$p_3(x)$	$p_4(x)$	$p_5(x)$	$p_6(x)$
1	1	1	1	1	1	1
2	2	2	3	3	4	4
3	3	4	2	4	2	3
4	4	3	4	2	3	2

(b)

x	$p_7(x)$	$p_8(x)$	$p_9(x)$	$p_{10}(x)$	$p_{11}(x)$	$p_{12}(x)$
1	2	2	2	2	2	2
2	1	1	3	3	4	4
3	3	4	1	4	1	3
4	4	3	4	1	3	1

(c)

x	$p_{13}(x)$	$p_{14}(x)$	$p_{15}(x)$	$p_{16}(x)$	$p_{17}(x)$	$p_{18}(x)$
1	3	3	3	3	3	3
2	1	1	2	2	4	4
3	2	4	1	4	1	2
4	4	2	4	1	2	1

(d)

x	$p_{19}(x)$	$p_{20}(x)$	$p_{21}(x)$	$p_{22}(x)$	$p_{23}(x)$	$p_{24}(x)$
1	4	4	4	4	4	4
2	1	1	2	2	3	3
3	2	3	1	3	1	2
4	3	2	3	1	2	1

4. Suppose A is a 4×4 matrix. Tell whether each of the following terms of $|A|$ should be preceded by a "$+$" or a "$-$" sign.

(a) $A_{11}A_{22}A_{33}A_{44}$ (b) $A_{14}A_{23}A_{31}A_{42}$

(c) $A_{11}A_{24}A_{32}A_{43}$ (d) $A_{11}A_{23}A_{34}A_{42}$

(e) $A_{13}A_{21}A_{34}A_{42}$ (f) $A_{13}A_{22}A_{31}A_{44}$

5. Write a formula for the determinant of a 4×4 matrix.

6.(a) Prove that, if any row of a 3×3 matrix consists entirely of zeros, then the determinant of the matrix is equal to zero.

(b) Prove that, if any column of a 3×3 matrix consists entirely of zeros, then the determinant of the matrix is equal to zero.

7.(a) Prove that, if the second row of a 3×3 matrix is a scalar multiple of the first row, then the determinant of the matrix is equal to zero.

(b) Prove an analogous statement about the columns of a 3×3 matrix.

(c) Generalize these results.

11.8 PROPERTIES OF PERMUTATION FUNCTIONS

Consider the even permutation function p_1 and the odd permutation function p_2, each with domain $\{1, 2\}$, defined in the preceding section.

One may form from these functions both composites and inverses (see Section 6.7), which turn out to be themselves permutation functions with domain $\{1, 2\}$. What can be said about the parity of these composites and inverses?

First let us examine the composite $p_1 p_2$:

$$p_1 p_2(1) = p_1[p_2(1)] = p_1(2) = 2$$
$$p_1 p_2(2) = p_1[p_2(2)] = p_1(1) = 1$$

Indeed, we see that the function $p_1 p_2$ is identical with the function p_2: $p_1 p_2 = p_2$. Hence, in this case in which p_1 and p_2 have opposite parity, the composite $p_1 p_2$ is odd.

It will be left to the student to show similarly that $p_2 p_1 = p_2$, $p_1 p_1 = p_1$, $p_2 p_2 = p_1$. One may induce from all this the following statements, which may be proved, in fact, to be true:

Theorem PI. The composite of permutation functions with domain D is a permutation function with domain D.

★PROOF: Suppose p, q are permutation functions with domain D. Then by the theorem preceding Exercise 26, the domain of pq is D; and by Exercise 26, Problem 6f, pq is one–one. There remains to prove only that the range of pq, $R(pq)$, is D also. We accomplish this by showing that $R(pq) \subset D$ and $D \subset R(pq)$.

Suppose $d \in D$. Then since q has domain D and range D, $q(d) \in D$; and since p has domain D and range D, $p[q(d)] \in D$. But $pq(d) = p[q(d)]$. Therefore $pq(d) \in D$ for each $d \in D$. That is to say, $R(pq) \subset D$.

Suppose again that $d \in D$. Then since p has domain D and range D, there exists $c \in D$ such that $p(c) = d$; and since q has domain D and range D, there exists $b \in D$ such that $q(b) = c$. Now $pq(b) = p[q(b)] = p(c) = d$. Thus $d \in R(pq)$. Therefore, since we have shown that each element $d \in D$ must be an element of $R(pq)$, $D \subset R(pq)$, and our proof is complete.

Theorem P2. In the domain $D = \{1, \cdots, n\}$, a composite of permutation functions of the same parity is even, of opposite parity odd.

★PROOF: Suppose p, q are the given permutation functions. We note that, since q is a permutation function, its domain must be the same as its range; that is to say, the set of integers $\{1, \cdots, n\}$ is the same as the set of integers $\{q(1), \cdots, q(n)\}$. Therefore we can find the number of inversions of p by finding the number of cases in which $q(i) < q(j)$, but $p[q(i)] > p[q(j)]$, where i, j are integers in D.

But this situation may occur sometimes when $i < j$ and sometimes when $i > j$, and in no other case (Why not?). We therefore tabulate the following two cases. We suppose that for all integers i, j in D:

I. $i < j, q(i) < q(j), p[q(i)] > p[q(j)]$ occurs r times.
II. $i > j, q(i) < q(j), p[q(i)] > p[q(j)]$ occurs s times.

Now, letting a represent the total number of inversions of p, there follows:

(1) $$a = r + s$$

To find the number of inversions of q, we may as usual find the number of cases in which $i < j$, but $q(i) > q(j)$, where i, j are integers in D. But this situation occurs either when $p[q(i)] < p[q(j)]$ or when $p[q(i)] > p[q(j)]$, and in no other case (Why not?). We therefore tabulate two more cases. We suppose that for all integers i, j in D:

III. $i < j, q(i) > q(j), p[q(i)] < p[q(j)]$ occurs t times.
IV. $i < j, q(i) > q(j), p[q(i)] > p[q(j)]$ occurs u times.

Now, letting b represent the total number of inversions of q, there follows:

(2) $$b = t + u$$

Similarly (how?), letting c represent the total number of inversions of pq:

(3) $$c = r + u$$

Note that the letters i, j used in framing statements I through IV are "dummy" letters. They may be replaced by any other pair, hence even interchanged without altering the truth of these statements. But if we interchange i and j in statement II, we arrive at the assertion that situation III occurs s times. Therefore:

(4) $$s = t$$

From (1) through (4) there follows:

(5) $$a + b + c = 2r + 2t + 2u$$

Hence:

(6) $$c = 2r + 2t + 2u - (a + b)$$

Now suppose p, q are of the same parity, i.e., a, b are both even or both odd. Then $a + b$ is even, hence from (6) c must be even, i.e., pq is an even function, Q.E.D.

On the other hand, if p, q are of opposite parity, then $a + b$ is odd, hence from (6) c must be odd, i.e., pq is an odd function, completing our proof.

It is easy to show that the inverse of a permutation function with domain D is again a permutation function with domain D (see Exercise 26, Problem 4), but what about the parity of a permutation function and its inverse? In the case of the functions p_1 and p_2 with domain $\{1, 2\}$ for example, since $p_1(1) = 1$ and $p_1(2) = 2$, it follows that $p_1^{-1}(1) = 1$, $p_1^{-1}(2) = 2$, i.e., $p_1^{-1} = p_1$; and since $p_2(1) = 2$, $p_2(2) = 1$, we have $p_2^{-1}(1) = 2$, $p_2^{-1}(2) = 1$, so that $p_2^{-1} = p_2$. Of course, it does not happen that every permutation function is identical with its inverse, but it is true that the two are always of the same parity, and indeed, this follows from the preceding theorem:

Theorem P3. Permutation functions p^{-1}, p have the same parity.

*PROOF: Suppose D is the domain of p, and let I_D be the "identity" permutation function with domain D [i.e., $I_D(x) = x$ for each $x \in D$]. Then I_D has 0 inversions, i.e., I_D is an even permutation function. Furthermore, (see Exercise 26, Problem 6b), $p^{-1}p = I_D$. Now by the preceding theorem, if p^{-1} and p were of opposite parity, then their composite would be odd, contradicting the fact that I_D is even. Therefore p^{-1} and p must be of the same parity.

We shall find the following theorems and notation useful in developing the general theory of determinants:

Theorem P4. Let $P = \{p_1, \cdots, p_r\}$ be the set of all permutation functions with a given domain D, and let $Q = \{p_1^{-1}, \cdots, p_r^{-1}\}$ be the set of all inverses of elements of P. Then $P = Q$.

*PROOF. Since the inverse of a permutation function with domain D is a permutation function with domain D, we know that each element of Q belongs to P. To prove that $P = Q$, there remains to show only that, if p is any element of P, then $p \in Q$.

Toward this end, let $q = p^{-1}$. Then $q \in Q$, by the definition of Q; hence $q \in P$, since each element of Q belongs to P. Therefore $q^{-1} \in Q$, again by the definition of Q. But $q^{-1} = p$ (see Exercise 26, Problem 6c). Therefore $p \in Q$, Q.E.D.

Theorem P5. Let $P = \{p_1, \cdots, p_r\}$ be the set of all permutation functions with a given domain D, let q be any element of P, and let $T = \{p_1q, \cdots, p_rq\}$. Then $P = T$.

*PROOF. By Theorem P1, $T \subset P$. There remains to prove, then, only that $P \subset T$, i.e., that, if $x \in P$, then $x \in T$. But we know that $q^{-1} \in P$, hence, again by Theorem P1, $xq^{-1} \in P$. Therefore, by our definition of T, $(xq^{-1})q \in T$. But (see Exercise 26, Problem 6) $(xq^{-1})q = x(q^{-1}q) = xI_D = x$. Therefore $x \in T$, Q.E.D.

Definition P1. Suppose $S = \{s_1, \cdots, s_r\}$, and f is a function with domain S and range consisting of complex numbers. Then we define the symbols $\sum_S f$ (read: "sigma over S of f") and $\prod_S f$ (read: "pi over S of f") as follows:

$$\sum_S f = f(s_1) + \cdots + f(s_r)$$
$$\prod_S f = f(s_1)f(s_2) \cdots f(s_r)$$

Theorem P6. Suppose f is a function with domain $D = \{1, \cdots, n\}$ and range consisting of complex numbers, and p is a permutation function with domain D.

Then:

$$(a) \quad \sum_D fp = \sum_D f$$
$$(b) \quad \prod_D fp = \prod_D f$$

PROOF OF (a): We note first that, since p is a permutation function, its range R must be the same as its domain D. Now:

$$\sum_D fp = fp(1) + \cdots + fp(n)$$
$$= f[p(1)] + \cdots + f[p(n)]$$
$$= \sum_R f$$
$$= \sum_D f, \text{ Q.E.D.}$$

The proof of (b) is similar, and is left as an exercise for the student.

Definition P2. We define the "sign function" s as follows: If p is any permutation function, $s(p) = 1$ if p is even, and $s(p) = -1$ if p is odd.

For example, in the case of the functions p_1, p_2 with domain $\{1, 2\}$, $s(p_1) = 1$, $s(p_2) = -1$.

We can now easily prove:

Theorem P7. If p, p^{-1} are permutation functions, then $s(p) = s(p^{-1})$.

Theorem P8. If p, q are permutation functions with the same domain, and q is odd, then $s(p) = -s(pq)$.

The proofs of Theorems P7 and P8 are left as exercises for the student.

Definition P3. A permutation function is called a *transposition* if it interchanges two elements in its domain and leaves all other elements in its domain fixed. Thus, a permutation function t with domain $D = \{1, \cdots, n\}$ is a transposition if there are two elements $u < v$ in D such that $t(u) = v$ and $t(v) = u$, and $t(d) = d$ for all other elements $d \in D$.

Theorem P9. A transposition is an odd function.

PROOF. Let D, t, be as in Definition P3. We examine the sequence

$$[t(1), \cdots, t(n)] = (1, \cdots, u - 1, v, u + 1, \cdots, v - 1, u, v + 1, \cdots, n)$$

to see how many cases we can count in which a number in the sequence is followed by a smaller number. Suppose there are k integers between (but excluding) u and v. Then in the above sequence, the first number to be followed by smaller numbers is v, and it is followed by the $k + 1$ smaller numbers $u + 1, \cdots, v - 1, u$. Then each of the k numbers between (but excluding) u and v is followed by one smaller number, namely u; and that is all: t has $k + 1 + k = 2k + 1$ inversions. Therefore t is odd, Q.E.D.

Theorem P10. If p is any permutation function and t is a transposition, both with domain D, then $s(p) = -s(pt)$.

The proof of Theorem P10 is left as an exercise for the student.

▶ **EXERCISE 71**

1. Suppose p_1, p_2 are the permutation functions with domain $\{1, 2\}$ defined in Section 11.7; show that $p_2 p_1 = p_2$, $p_1 p_1 = p_1$, and $p_2 p_2 = p_1$.

2. Suppose $p_1, \cdots, p_6$ are all the permutation functions with domain $D = \{1, 2, 3\}$, as defined by the table in Section 11.7. We compute from this table, by way of example, the composite (or "product") $p_2 p_3$:

$$p_2 p_3(1) = p_2[p_3(1)] = p_2(2) = 3$$
$$p_2 p_3(2) = p_2[p_3(2)] = p_2(1) = 1$$
$$p_2 p_3(3) = p_2[p_3(3)] = p_2(3) = 2$$

Examining the table once more, we see that $p_2 p_3$ has the same effect on each element of D as the function p_5; thus, $p_2 p_3 = p_5$.

Similarly, compute the following products:

(a) $p_3 p_2$ (b) $p_1 p_2$ (c) $p_2 p_1$ (d) $p_2 p_4$
(e) $p_4 p_2$ (f) $p_1 p_3$ (g) $p_3 p_1$ (h) $p_2 p_2$
(i) $p_3 p_3$ (j) $p_4 p_4$ (k) $p_1 p_1$ (l) $p_5 p_5$

3. With $p_1, \cdots, p_6$ as in Problem 2, complete the following table of products:

	p_1	p_2	p_3	p_4	p_5	p_6
p_1						
p_2			p_5			
p_3						
p_4						
p_5						
p_6						

4.(*a*)–(*l*) Verify in each of the cases of Problem 2 that Theorem P2 holds true.

5.(*a*) Suppose that $p_1, \cdots, p_6$ are as in Problem 2. By way of example, we compute p_4^{-1}: Since $p_4(1) = 2$, $p_4(2) = 3$, $p_4(3) = 1$, it follows that $p_4^{-1}(1) = 3$, $p_4^{-1}(2) = 1$, $p_4^{-1}(3) = 2$, so that $p_4^{-1} = p_5$. Similarly compute $p_1^{-1}, p_2^{-1}, p_3^{-1}, p_5^{-1}, p_6^{-1}$.

(*b*) Using the results of (*a*), verify for each of the functions $p_1, \cdots, p_6$ of (*a*) that Theorem P3 holds true.

(*c*) Using the results of (*a*), verify that Theorem P4 holds true for the set P of all permutation functions with domain $D = \{1, 2, 3\}$.

6. With $p_1, \cdots, p_6$ as in Problem 2, compute $p_1q, \cdots, p_6q$, with $q = p_3$, and thus verify that Theorem P5 holds true in this special case.

7. Suppose that $P = \{p_1, \cdots, p_6\}$, with $p_1, \cdots, p_6$ as in Problem 2, and f is a function with domain P.

(*a*) Find $s(p)$ for each $p \in P$.

(*b*) Find $\sum_P s$.

(*c*) What sum does $\sum_P f$ represent?

(*d*) If Q is the set of all inverses of elements of P: $\{p_1^{-1}, \cdots, p_6^{-1}\}$, what sum does $\sum_Q f$ represent? Show that $\sum_P f = \sum_Q f$, and show also that $\prod_P f = \prod_Q f$.

(*e*) Find $\sum_D fp_3$ and $\prod_D fp_3$ and thus verify that Theorem P6 holds true in this special case. (Remember that as in Problem 2, $D = \{1, 2, 3\}$ in this case.)

8. Prove part (*b*) of Theorem P6.

9. Prove Theorem P7.

10. Prove Theorem P8. (*Hint:* Consider two cases, p odd, and p even.)

11. Prove that the inverse of a permutation function with domain D is a permutation function with domain D. (*Hint:* Use Exercise 26, Problem 4.)

12.(*a*) Of the functions p_1, p_2 with domain $\{1, 2\}$ defined in Section 11.7, which are transpositions?

(*b*) Of the functions $p_1, \cdots, p_6$, with domain $\{1, 2, 3\}$ defined by the table in Section 11.7, which are transpositions?

(*c*) Verify for each of the transpositions you have listed that Theorem P9 is true.

13. Prove Theorem P10.

*14. It can be proved (by means of the Principle of Mathematical Induction) that for a given f, $\sum_s f$ is *well- efined*. What does this mean, and from what field properties does this follow?

11.9 THE $n \times n$ DETERMINANT DEFINED

We are now ready to make a precise definition of the determinant of an

$n \times n$ matrix A. In framing the general definition, we shall be guided by our definition in the 3×3 case (see Section 11.7).

We see in the case that A is a 3×3 matrix, that $|A|$ is a sum of six terms, each determined by one of the permutation functions with domain $\{1, 2, 3\}$. For example, the permutation function p_3, which is defined by $p_3(1) = 2$, $p_3(2) = 1$, $p_3(3) = 3$ determines the term: $-A_{12}A_{21}A_{33}$. But note that, since p_3 is an odd function, $s(p_3) = -1$. Therefore the term determined by p_3 can be written: $s(p_3) \cdot A_{1\,p_3(1)}\,A_{2\,p_3(2)}\,A_{3\,p_3(3)}$.

Now suppose we let $P = \{p_1, \cdots, p_6\}$, where $p_1, \cdots, p_6$ are as in the table of Section 11.7, and we define the function f with domain P as follows: For each $p \in P$, $f(p) = s(p) \cdot A_{1\,p(1)}\,A_{2\,p(2)}\,A_{3\,p(3)}$. Then $f(p_3)$, for example would be equal to $s(p_3) \cdot A_{1\,p_3(1)}\,A_{2\,p_3(2)}\,A_{3\,p_3(3)}$; thus $|A|$, in this case, is simply: $f(p_1) + f(p_2) + \cdots + f(p_6)$, i.e., $\sum_P f$. This suggests the following general definition:

Definition D1. Let A be an $n \times n$ matrix, $D = \{1, \cdots, n\}$, $P = \{p_1, \cdots, p_r\}$, the set of all permutation functions with domain D, f the function with domain P whose mapping is given by: $f(p) = s(p) \cdot A_{1\,p(1)} \cdots A_{n\,p(n)}$.

Then the determinant of A is defined as follows:

$$|A| = \sum_P f$$

11.10 THE DETERMINANT OF THE TRANSPOSE OF A MATRIX

The student may have noticed that the matrices (which we now denote A, A' respectively) of the determinants (a), (b) of Exercise 70, Problem 1, are related in an interesting way: Each row of A' is identical with the corresponding column of A; for example, the first row of A' is identical with the first column of A. That is to say, the jth element in the first row of A' is the same as the jth element in the first column of A. More generally, the jth element in the ith row of A', i.e., A'_{ij}, is the same as the jth element in the ith column of A, i.e., A_{ji}.

A' is called the *transpose* of A. We are led to the following definition:

Definition D2. Let A be an $m \times n$ matrix. Then A', the *transpose* of A, is defined to be an $n \times m$ matrix satisfying the following condition: If A'_{ij} is any element of A', then $A'_{ij} = A_{ji}$.

The student may also have noticed another interesting fact about the aforesaid determinants (a) and (b): They are equal; in fact each is equal to 37. One might wonder whether it is always true that the determinant of a square matrix is equal to the determinant of its transpose. The answer is "yes."

Theorem D1.   Let A be an $n \times n$ matrix.   Then $|A| = |A'|$.

[Proofs of Theorem D1 in the cases $n = 1, 2, 3$ are easily given by direct calculation, and are left as exercises for the student. A general proof for all natural numbers n follows. (Throughout the rest of this section, A, D, P and f will be assumed to be as in Definition D1.)]

*PROOF: In the course of this proof we shall find it useful, given $p \in P$, to define function g with domain D as follows: For each $d \in D$, $g(d) = A_{d\,p^{-1}(d)}$.

Note that by Definition D1, $|A'| = \sum_P f'$, where for each $p \in P$:

$$
\begin{aligned}
f'(p) &= s(p) \cdot A'_{1\,p(1)} \cdots A'_{n\,p(n)} \\
&= s(p) \cdot A_{p(1)\,1} \cdots A_{p(n)\,n} \quad \text{(why?)} \\
&= s(p) \cdot A_{p(1)\,p^{-1}[p(1)]} \cdots A_{p(n),\,p^{-1}[p(n)]} \quad \text{(why?)} \\
&= s(p) \cdot g[p(1)] \cdots g[p(n)] \quad \text{(why?)} \\
&= s(p) \cdot gp(1) \cdots gp(n) \quad \text{(why?)} \\
&= s(p) \cdot g(1) \cdots g(n) \quad \text{(by Theorem P6}b) \\
&= s(p^{-1}) \cdot A_{1\,p^{-1}(1)} \cdots A_{n\,p^{-1}(n)} \quad \text{(why?)} \\
&= f(p^{-1}) \quad \text{(why?)}
\end{aligned}
$$

Therefore, for each $p \in P$:

(1) $$f'(p) = f(p^{-1})$$

Now:

$$
\begin{aligned}
|A'| &= \sum_P f' \quad \text{(by Definition D1)} \\
&= f'(p_1) + \cdots + f'(p_r) \quad \text{(by Definition P1)} \\
&= f(p_1^{-1}) + \cdots + f(p_r^{-1}) \quad \text{[by (1)]} \\
&= \sum_Q f \quad \text{(by Definition P1, with } Q \text{ as in Theorem P4)} \\
&= \sum_P f \quad \text{(by Theorem P4)} \\
&= |A| \quad \text{(by Definition D1); Q.E.D.}
\end{aligned}
$$

11.11 FACTORS OF A DETERMINANT

It is easy to verify that:

$$\begin{vmatrix} ka & kb \\ c & d \end{vmatrix} = k \cdot \begin{vmatrix} a & b \\ c & d \end{vmatrix}$$

and

$$\begin{vmatrix} a & b \\ kc & kd \end{vmatrix} = k \cdot \begin{vmatrix} a & b \\ c & d \end{vmatrix}$$

From this we may induce the following statement, which we shall prove to be true:

Theorem D2.   If A and B are $n \times n$ matrices such that one row of A is

k times the corresponding row of B, and the other corresponding rows of A and B are identical, then $|A| = k \cdot |B|$.

*PROOF: Suppose that u is a positive integer $\leqslant n$, $^uA = k \cdot {}^uB$, and $^iA = {}^iB$ for $i \neq u$. Then by Definition D1, $|A| = \sum_P f$, and $|B| = \sum_P g$, where for each $p \in P$,

$$
\begin{aligned}
g(p) &= s(p)[B_{1\ p(1)} \cdots ?][B_{u\ p(u)}][? \cdots B_{n\ p(n)}] \\
f(p) &= s(p)[A_{1\ p(1)} \cdots ?][A_{u\ p(u)}][? \cdots A_{n\ p(n)}] \\
&= s(p)[B_{1\ p(1)} \cdots ?][k \cdot B_{u\ p(u)}][? \cdots B_{n\ p(n)}] \quad \text{(why?)} \\
&= k \cdot s(p)[B_{1\ p(1)} \cdots ?][B_{u\ p(u)}][? \cdots B_{n\ p(n)}] \quad \text{(why?)} \\
&= k \cdot g(p) \quad \text{(why?)}
\end{aligned}
$$

Now

$$
\begin{aligned}
|A| = \sum_P f &= f(p_1) + \cdots + f(p_r) \\
&= k \cdot g(p_1) + \cdots + k \cdot g(p_r) \\
&= k \cdot \sum_P g \\
&= k \cdot |B|, \quad \text{Q.E.D.}
\end{aligned}
$$

It may be suspected that an analogous statement holds true for columns, as indeed it does:

Theorem D2′. If A and B are $n \times n$ matrices such that one column of A is k times the corresponding column of B, and the other corresponding columns of A and B are identical, then $|A| = k \cdot |B|$.

PROOF: A' and B' are $n \times n$ matrices such that one row of A' is k times the corresponding row of B', and the other corresponding rows of A' and B' are identical. Therefore $|A'| = k \cdot |B'|$ (why?). Therefore $|A| = k \cdot |B|$ (why?), Q.E.D.

A very useful consequence of Theorems D2 and D2′ is:

Theorem D3. If the elements in any row (or column) of an $n \times n$ matrix A are all zero, then $|A| = 0$.

PROOF: Let $B = A$. Then one row (or column) of A, namely the row (or column) consisting entirely of zeros, is 0 times the corresponding row (or column) of B, and the other corresponding rows (or columns) of A and B are identical. Therefore (why?) $|A| = 0 \cdot |B| = 0$, Q.E.D.

Illustrative Example.

$$
\begin{vmatrix} 2 & 4 & 6 \\ 3 & 6 & 3 \\ 7 & 8 & 9 \end{vmatrix} = 2 \cdot \begin{vmatrix} 1 & 2 & 3 \\ 3 & 6 & 3 \\ 7 & 8 & 9 \end{vmatrix} \quad \text{(by Theorem D2, applied to row 1)}
$$

$$= 2 \cdot 3 \cdot \begin{vmatrix} 1 & 2 & 3 \\ 1 & 2 & 1 \\ 7 & 8 & 9 \end{vmatrix} \quad \text{(by Theorem D2, applied to row 2)}$$

$$= 2 \cdot 3 \cdot 2 \cdot \begin{vmatrix} 1 & 1 & 3 \\ 1 & 1 & 1 \\ 7 & 4 & 9 \end{vmatrix} \quad \text{(by Theorem D2', applied to column 2)}$$

Taking another path:

$$\begin{vmatrix} 2 & 4 & 6 \\ 3 & 6 & 3 \\ 7 & 8 & 9 \end{vmatrix} = 2 \cdot \begin{vmatrix} 2 & 2 & 6 \\ 3 & 3 & 3 \\ 7 & 4 & 9 \end{vmatrix} \quad \text{(by Theorem D2', applied to column 2)}$$

$$= 2 \cdot 3 \cdot \begin{vmatrix} 2 & 2 & 2 \\ 3 & 3 & 1 \\ 7 & 4 & 3 \end{vmatrix} \quad \text{(by Theorem D2', applied to column 3)}$$

$$= 2 \cdot 3 \cdot 2 \cdot \begin{vmatrix} 1 & 1 & 1 \\ 3 & 3 & 1 \\ 7 & 4 & 3 \end{vmatrix} \quad \text{(by Theorem D2, applied to row 1)}$$

It is left to the student to verify that the two simplifications of the given determinant are equal.

▶ **EXERCISE 72**

1.(c)–(l) Write the transpose of each matrix in Exercise 70, Problem 1, and verify Theorem D1 in each case.

2. In the illustrative example of Section 11.11, verify that the two simplifications of the given determinant are equal.

3.(a) Suppose $A = \begin{pmatrix} a & b \\ c & d \end{pmatrix}$. Then what is A'? Compute $|A|$ and $|A'|$ and thus prove Theorem D1 in the case $n = 2$.

(b) Prove Theorem D1 by direct calculation in the case $n = 3$.

4. Using Theorems D2 and D2', express each of the following determinants as a multiple k of $\begin{vmatrix} 1 & 2 & 1 \\ 2 & 1 & 1 \\ 1 & 2 & 3 \end{vmatrix}$.

(a) $\begin{vmatrix} 2 & 4 & 2 \\ 2 & 1 & 1 \\ 1 & 2 & 3 \end{vmatrix}$
(b) $\begin{vmatrix} 3 & 2 & 1 \\ 6 & 1 & 1 \\ 3 & 2 & 3 \end{vmatrix}$

(c) $\begin{vmatrix} 6 & 4 & 2 \\ 6 & 1 & 1 \\ 3 & 2 & 3 \end{vmatrix}$ (d) $\begin{vmatrix} -3 & 2 & -1 \\ 6 & -1 & 1 \\ 3 & -2 & 3 \end{vmatrix}$

(e) $\begin{vmatrix} 1 & 2 & -1 \\ -2 & -1 & 1 \\ . 1 & 2 & -3 \end{vmatrix}$ (f) $\begin{vmatrix} 10 & 12 & 4 \\ 30 & 9 & 6 \\ 25 & 30 & 30 \end{vmatrix}$

5. Verify that Theorem D3 is true in the following cases.

(a) $\begin{vmatrix} 0 & 0 \\ 7 & 11 \end{vmatrix}$ (b) $\begin{vmatrix} 0 & 7 \\ 0 & 11 \end{vmatrix}$

(c) $\begin{vmatrix} 1 & 2 & 3 \\ 0 & 0 & 0 \\ 3 & 2 & 1 \end{vmatrix}$ (d) $\begin{vmatrix} a & b & 0 \\ c & d & 0 \\ e & f & 0 \end{vmatrix}$

6.(a) By actual computation show that the determinant of the $n \times n$ identity matrix I_n (see Section 11.4) is equal to 1, in the cases $n = 1$ and $n = 2$.

(b) By actual computation show that the determinant of an $n \times n$ diagonal matrix (see Exercise 68, Problem 1f) is equal to the product of the elements in the main diagonal, in the cases $n = 1$ and $n = 2$.

*(c) Prove that the determinant of any $n \times n$ diagonal matrix A is equal to the product of the elements in the main diagonal of A. [*Hint:* Use Definition D1, and show that $f(p)$ has a zero factor, hence $f(p) = 0$, unless p is the identity permutation function, in which case $f(p) = ?$] Derive as a corollary that the determinant of any $n \times n$ identity matrix I_n is equal to 1.

*(d) Prove that, if A is an $n \times n$ matrix in which all the elements above the main diagonal are equal to zero, then $|A|$ is equal to the product of the elements in the main diagonal of A. [*Hint:* Elements $A_{i\,p(i)}$ above the main diagonal are those in which $p(i) > i$. We are given, then, that $A_{i\,p(i)} = 0$ if $p(i) > i$. Therefore, in order for $f(p)$ to be different from zero, we must have $p(i) \leqslant i$ for each $i \in \{1, \cdots, n\}$. Hence, in order for $f(p)$ to be different from zero, what must be true about $p(1)$? and then about $p(2)$? and then about $p(3)$? Proceeding thus, what function, in fact, must p be?]

*(e) Prove that, if A is an $n \times n$ triangular matrix (see Exercise 68, Problem 1h), then $|A|$ is equal to the product of the elements in the main diagonal of A.

*7. Care must be exercised to distinguish between the product of a number by a matrix (i.e., a scalar product), and the product of a number by the determinant of a matrix.

(a) Show that although $\begin{vmatrix} ka & kb \\ c & d \end{vmatrix} = k \cdot \begin{vmatrix} a & b \\ c & d \end{vmatrix}$, it is not in general true that $\begin{pmatrix} ka & kb \\ c & d \end{pmatrix} = k \cdot \begin{pmatrix} a & b \\ c & d \end{pmatrix}$.

(b) Prove that, if k is a number and A is an $n \times n$ matrix, then $|kA| = k^n \cdot |A|$. (*Hint:* Use Definition D1.)

*8. Using Definition D1, derive a formula for the determinant of a 1×1 matrix (k). What is the transpose of the 1×1 matrix (k)? Verify that Theorems D1, D2, D2′, and D3 are true in the case $n = 1$.

*9. Prove that, if A is an $m \times n$ matrix and B is an $n \times p$ matrix, then $(AB)' = B'A'$.

11.12 FURTHER THEOREMS ON DETERMINANTS

The theorems of this section, all of which may be induced fairly easily from special cases, will soon be found to be useful in the evaluation of determinants.

Theorem D4. Interchanging two rows of an $n \times n$ matrix changes the sign of the determinant of the matrix.

More precisely, suppose A, B are $n \times n$ matrices, and $u < v$ are positive integers $\leqslant n$ such that $^uB = {}^vA$, $^vB = {}^uA$, and $^iB = {}^iA$ for $i \neq u, v$. Then $|B| = -|A|$.

*PROOF. Let D, P, f be as in Definition D1, and define the transposition t with domain D such that $t(u) = v, t(v) = u$, and $t(i) = i$ for $i \neq u, v$. Note first that by Theorem P10, $s(p) = -s(pt)$ for each $p \in P$. Note also that $|B| = \sum_P g$, where

$$
\begin{aligned}
g(p) &= s(p) \cdot B_{1\,p(1)} \cdots B_{u\,p(u)} \cdots B_{v\,p(v)} \cdots B_{n\,p(n)} \\
&= s(p) \cdot A_{1\,p(1)} \cdots A_{v\,p(u)} \cdots A_{u\,p(v)} \cdots A_{n\,p(n)} \\
&= -s(pt) \cdot A_{1\,pt(1)} \cdots A_{v\,pt(v)} \cdots A_{u\,pt(u)} \cdots A_{n\,pt(n)} \\
&= -f(pt)
\end{aligned}
$$

for each $p \in P$. Therefore:

$$
\begin{aligned}
|B| = \sum_P g &= g(p_1) + \cdots + g(p_r) \\
&= -f(p_1 t) - \cdots - f(p_r t) \\
&= -\sum_T f \quad (\text{where } T = \{p_1 t, \cdots, p_r t\}) \\
&= -\sum_P f \quad (\text{by Theorem P5}) \\
&= -|A| \quad (\text{by Definition D1}); \quad \text{Q.E.D.}
\end{aligned}
$$

Illustrative Example I. By an earlier computation, (Section 11.7, Illustrative Example 1), we know that:

$$\begin{vmatrix} 2 & 1 & -1 \\ 3 & 0 & 4 \\ 1 & -1 & -2 \end{vmatrix} = 21. \quad \text{Therefore, by Theorem D4:} \begin{vmatrix} 1 & -1 & -2 \\ 3 & 0 & 4 \\ 2 & 1 & -1 \end{vmatrix} = -21,$$

since the second matrix is derived from the first by interchanging rows 1 and 3 of the first matrix.

Theorem D4'. Interchanging two columns of an $n \times n$ matrix changes the sign of the determinant of the matrix.

PROOF: Suppose matrix B is derived from $n \times n$ matrix A by interchanging two columns of A. Then matrix B' may be derived from $n \times n$ matrix A' by interchanging two rows of A'. Therefore (why?) $|B'| = -|A'|$; hence $|B| = -|A|$ (why?), Q.E.D.

Theorem D5. If two rows (or two columns) of an $n \times n$ matrix A are identical, then $|A| = 0$.

PROOF: Let matrix B be derived from the given matrix A by interchanging a pair of identical rows (or columns) of A. Then, of course, $A = B$, so that $|A| = |B|$. But by Theorem D4 (or D4'), $|A| = -|B|$. Therefore $2|A| = 0$, from which $|A| = 0$, Q.E.D.

Illustrative Example 2. By Theorem D5, we know immediately that:

$$\begin{vmatrix} 1 & 2 & 7 \\ 1 & 2 & 7 \\ 4 & 8 & 5 \end{vmatrix} = 0 \quad \text{and} \quad \begin{vmatrix} 2 & 7 & 2 \\ 3 & 7 & 3 \\ 5 & 6 & 5 \end{vmatrix} = 0$$

Theorem D6. If one row of an $n \times n$ matrix A is a scalar multiple of another, then $|A| = 0$.

PROOF:

$$\begin{vmatrix} a_1 & a_2 & \cdots & a_n \\ ka_1 & ka_2 & \cdots & ka_n \end{vmatrix} = k \cdot \begin{vmatrix} a_1 & a_2 & \cdots & a_n \\ a_1 & a_2 & \cdots & a_n \end{vmatrix} \quad \text{(why?)}$$

$$= k \cdot 0 \quad \text{(why?)}$$
$$= 0, \text{ Q.E.D.}$$

Theorem D6'. If one column of an $n \times n$ matrix A is a scalar multiple of another, then $|A| = 0$.

The proof of Theorem D6′ is left as an exercise for the student.

Illustrative Example 3. Theorem D6 tells us immediately that the determinant of Exercise 70, Problem 1*k* is equal to 0, since the second row of its matrix is two times the first; and Theorem D6′ tells us that the determinant of Problem 1*l* of that exercise is also equal to 0, since the third column of its matrix is three times the first.

So far we have defined only one operation, namely multiplication, in the set of all matrices. At this point, because it will be helpful in our further study of the determinant of a matrix, we introduce a second operation—addition—in the set of all matrices. In the case of this operation, the most obvious definition that suggests itself turns out to be the most useful, and we therefore adopt it. If A, B are both $r \times c$ matrices, we define $A + B$ to be an $r \times c$ matrix satisfying the following condition: If $(A + B)_{ij}$ is any element of $A + B$, then $(A + B)_{ij} = A_{ij} + B_{ij}$. For example:

$$\begin{pmatrix} 1 & 2 \\ 3 & 4 \end{pmatrix} + \begin{pmatrix} 2 & 3 \\ 5 & 7 \end{pmatrix} = \begin{pmatrix} 3 & 5 \\ 8 & 11 \end{pmatrix}$$

$$(1 \quad 4) + (5 \quad 3) = (6 \quad 7)$$

$$\begin{pmatrix} 7 \\ 2 \end{pmatrix} + \begin{pmatrix} 2 \\ 6 \end{pmatrix} = \begin{pmatrix} 9 \\ 8 \end{pmatrix}$$

In particular, we shall now be able to speak of adding rows to rows and columns to columns of a matrix. For example, the sum of the rows of the matrix $\begin{pmatrix} 1 & 2 \\ 3 & 4 \end{pmatrix}$ is the 1×2 matrix $(4 \quad 6)$, and the sum of the columns of the matrix $\begin{pmatrix} 1 & 2 \\ 3 & 4 \end{pmatrix}$ is the 2×1 matrix $\begin{pmatrix} 3 \\ 7 \end{pmatrix}$.

Although addition of matrices may be carried out very easily, there is, unfortunately, in general, no way of finding the sum of the determinants of two matrices except by direct computation of each determinant. Sometimes, however, a simplification may be effected: When two $n \times n$ matrices are identical in at least $n - 1$ of their n rows (or columns), then the sum of their determinants is the determinant of a matrix which agrees with the original matrices in the aforesaid $n - 1$ rows (or columns), and whose other row (or column) is the sum of the corresponding rows (or columns) of the original matrices. For example, the student may verify that:

$$(1) \quad \begin{vmatrix} 2 & 3 \\ 1 & 4 \end{vmatrix} + \begin{vmatrix} 2 & 3 \\ 1 & 5 \end{vmatrix} = \begin{vmatrix} 2 & 3 \\ 2 & 9 \end{vmatrix} \quad \text{(first row held fixed; second rows added)}$$

(2) $\begin{vmatrix} 5 & 1 \\ 3 & 2 \end{vmatrix} + \begin{vmatrix} 4 & 1 \\ 6 & 2 \end{vmatrix} = \begin{vmatrix} 9 & 1 \\ 9 & 2 \end{vmatrix}$ (second column held fixed; first columns added)

(3) $\begin{vmatrix} 2 & 1 & -1 \\ 3 & 0 & 4 \\ 1 & -1 & -2 \end{vmatrix} + \begin{vmatrix} 2 & 1 & -1 \\ 3 & 0 & 4 \\ 1 & -1 & -2 \end{vmatrix} = \begin{vmatrix} 2 & 1 & -1 \\ 6 & 0 & 8 \\ 1 & -1 & -2 \end{vmatrix}$ (first and third rows held fixed; second rows added)

The following two theorems present this method of addition in a form amenable to proof.

Theorem D7. (Addition of determinants.) Suppose A, B, C are $n \times n$ matrices identical at least in all rows other than row u, and suppose $^uA + {}^uB = {}^uC$. Then $|A| + |B| = |C|$.

[*Note:* In this proof we shall use the fact that, if a, k, l, c are complex numbers, then $akc + alc = a(k + l)c$. Why is this true?]

*PROOF: Let P be as in Definition D1. Then $|A| = \sum_P f$, $|B| = \sum_P g$, $|C| = \sum_P h$, where for each $p \in P$:

(4) $\qquad f(p) = s(p) \cdot [A_{1\,p(1)} \cdots ?] [A_{u\,p(u)}] [? \cdots A_{n\,p(n)}]$

(5) $\qquad g(p) = s(p) \cdot [B_{1\,p(1)} \cdots ?] [B_{u\,p(u)}] [? \cdots B_{n\,p(n)}]$

(6) $\qquad h(p) = s(p) \cdot [C_{1\,p(1)} \cdots ?] [C_{u\,p(u)}] [? \cdots C_{n\,p(n)}]$

But since we know matrices A, B, C to be identical in rows other than row u, and since $^uC = {}^uA + {}^uB$, there follows from (5) and (6):

(7) $\qquad g(p) = s(p) \cdot [A_{1\,p(1)} \cdots ?] [\quad B_{u\,p(u)} \quad] [? \cdots A_{n\,p(n)}]$

(8) $\qquad h(p) = s(p) \cdot [A_{1\,p(1)} \cdots ?] [A_{u\,p(u)} + B_{u\,p(u)}] [? \cdots A_{n\,p(n)}]$

Therefore, from (4), (7) and (8), for each $p \in P$:

(9) $\qquad\qquad\qquad f(p) + g(p) = h(p)$ (why?)

Therefore:

$$\begin{aligned} |A| + |B| &= \sum_P f + \sum_P g \\ &= [f(p_1) + \cdots f(p_r)] + [g(p_1) + \cdots + g(p_r)] \quad \text{(why?)} \\ &= [f(p_1) + g(p_1)] + \cdots + [f(p_r) + g(p_r)] \quad \text{(why?)} \\ &= h(p_1) + \cdots + h(p_r) \quad \text{(why?)} \\ &= \sum_P h \quad \text{(why?)} \\ &= |C|, \text{ Q.E.D.} \end{aligned}$$

Theorem D7$'$. (It is left to the student to state and prove this theorem on the addition of determinants, which concerns columns rather than rows.)

Now suppose that from the matrix of the determinant $\begin{vmatrix} 2 & 3 \\ 1 & 4 \end{vmatrix}$, we form a new matrix by leaving the first row fixed, and adding to the second row twice the first: Then the determinant of the new matrix is $\begin{vmatrix} 2 & 3 \\ 5 & 10 \end{vmatrix}$. The interesting fact to note is that the new determinant is equal to the old, both being, in fact, equal to 5. Let us try this sort of thing again. If we leave our original first column fixed and add to the second column -4 times the first, we arrive at the new determinant: $\begin{vmatrix} 2 & -5 \\ 1 & 0 \end{vmatrix}$, which again has the value 5. We arc led to induce the following two theorems.

Theorem D8. If A is an $n \times n$ matrix, $|A|$ is not changed by adding to any row of A a scalar multiple of another row of A.

PROOF: Suppose $A = \begin{pmatrix} a_1 & \cdots & a_n \\ \vdots & & \vdots \\ b_1 & \cdots & b_n \end{pmatrix}$. Then:

$$\begin{vmatrix} a_1 + kb_1 & \cdots & a_n + kb_n \\ b_1 & \cdots & b_n \end{vmatrix} = \begin{vmatrix} a_1 & \cdots & a_n \\ b_1 & \cdots & b_n \end{vmatrix} + \begin{vmatrix} kb_1 & \cdots & kb_n \\ b_1 & \cdots & b_n \end{vmatrix} \quad \text{(why?)}$$

$$= |A| + k \cdot \begin{vmatrix} b_1 & \cdots & b_n \\ b_1 & \cdots & b_n \end{vmatrix} \quad \text{(why?)}$$

$$= |A| + k \cdot 0 \quad \text{(why?)}$$

$$= |A|, \text{ Q.E.D.}$$

Theorem D8′. (It is left to the student to state and prove this theorem, which concerns the addition of a scalar multiple of a column to another column of a matrix.)

Illustrative Example 4. Evaluate the determinant $\begin{vmatrix} 1 & 2 & 3 \\ 4 & 5 & 1 \\ 6 & 9 & 7 \end{vmatrix}$

SOLUTION. By Theorem D8, leaving the first and third rows fixed, and adding twice the first to the second, the given determinant is equal to:

$$\begin{vmatrix} 1 & 2 & 3 \\ 6 & 9 & 7 \\ 6 & 9 & 7 \end{vmatrix} = 0 \quad \text{(by Theorem D5)}$$

▶ **EXERCISE 73**

1. State and prove Theorem D8′.

2. Using the fact (when it is applicable) that $\begin{vmatrix} 2 & 1 & -1 \\ 3 & 0 & 4 \\ 1 & -1 & -2 \end{vmatrix} = 21$, evaluate each of the following determinants as expeditiously as possible, and justify your answers.

(a) $\begin{vmatrix} 3 & 0 & 4 \\ 2 & 1 & -1 \\ 1 & -1 & -2 \end{vmatrix}$ (b) $\begin{vmatrix} 2 & -1 & 1 \\ 3 & 4 & 0 \\ 1 & -2 & -1 \end{vmatrix}$ (c) $\begin{vmatrix} 2 & 1 & -1 \\ 3 & 0 & 4 \\ 3 & -3 & -6 \end{vmatrix}$

(d) $\begin{vmatrix} 2 & 1 & -1 \\ 0 & 0 & 0 \\ 1 & -1 & -2 \end{vmatrix}$ (e) $\begin{vmatrix} -2 & 1 & -1 \\ -3 & 0 & 4 \\ -1 & -1 & -2 \end{vmatrix}$ (f) $\begin{vmatrix} 2 & 1 & -1 \\ 3 & 0 & 4 \\ -2 & 2 & 4 \end{vmatrix}$

(g) $\begin{vmatrix} 2 & 1 & -1 \\ 3 & 0 & 4 \\ -3 & 0 & -4 \end{vmatrix}$ (h) $\begin{vmatrix} 2 & -4 & -1 \\ 3 & -6 & 4 \\ 1 & -2 & -2 \end{vmatrix}$ (i) $\begin{vmatrix} 2 & 1 & -1 \\ 3 & 0 & 4 \\ 2 & 1 & -1 \end{vmatrix}$

(j) $\begin{vmatrix} 2 & 1 & -1 \\ 3 & 0 & 4 \\ 4 & -1 & 2 \end{vmatrix}$ (k) $\begin{vmatrix} 2 & 1 & 1 \\ 3 & 0 & 4 \\ 1 & -1 & -4 \end{vmatrix}$ (l) $\begin{vmatrix} 2 & 0 & -1 \\ 3 & 0 & 4 \\ 1 & 0 & -2 \end{vmatrix}$

(m) $\begin{vmatrix} 8 & 2 & -2 \\ 6 & 0 & 4 \\ 2 & -1 & -2 \end{vmatrix}$ (n) $\begin{vmatrix} 2 & 2 & -1 \\ 3 & -4 & 4 \\ 1 & 1 & -2 \end{vmatrix}$ (o) $\begin{vmatrix} 4 & 2 & -2 \\ 6 & 0 & 8 \\ 2 & -2 & -4 \end{vmatrix}$

(p) $\begin{vmatrix} 2 & 0 & 0 \\ 0 & 3 & 0 \\ 0 & 0 & 4 \end{vmatrix}$ (q) $\begin{vmatrix} 0 & 0 & a \\ 0 & b & 0 \\ c & 0 & 0 \end{vmatrix}$ (r) $\begin{vmatrix} 0 & 0 & 2 \\ 0 & 3 & 0 \\ 4 & 0 & 0 \end{vmatrix}$

3. Prove Theorem D6′.
4. State and prove Theorem D7′.

11.13 MINORS

We have developed practicable methods for computing the determinant of an $n \times n$ matrix when $n = 2$ or 3 (see Section 11.7), but not when $n > 3$. In this section we shall consider the method of "expansion by minors" which reduces the problem of evaluating the determinant of a square matrix of any order (greater than 1) to that of evaluating determinants of matrices of lower order.

We begin by examining a 3×3 matrix. Suppose we have given such a matrix:

$$(1) \qquad A = \begin{pmatrix} a & b & c \\ d & e & f \\ g & h & i \end{pmatrix}$$

Then:

$$(2) \qquad |A| = aei + bfg + cdh - ceg - bdi - afh$$

The number on the right side of (2) may be written as a sum of products of the elements in the first row of A:

$$(3) \qquad |A| = a(ei - fh) - b(di - fg) + c(dh - eg)$$

or as a sum of products of the elements in the second column of A:

$$(4) \qquad |A| = -b(di - fg) + e(ai - cg) - h(af - cd)$$

or in several other similar ways.

The student may wonder why we chose factors $-b$, $-h$ rather than b, h. The reason is that, with this choice, a rather neat result follows: (3) may be written,

$$(5) \qquad |A| = a \begin{vmatrix} e & f \\ h & i \end{vmatrix} - b \begin{vmatrix} d & f \\ g & i \end{vmatrix} + c \begin{vmatrix} d & e \\ g & h \end{vmatrix}$$

and (4) may be written,

$$(6) \qquad |A| = -b \begin{vmatrix} d & f \\ g & i \end{vmatrix} + e \begin{vmatrix} a & c \\ g & i \end{vmatrix} - h \begin{vmatrix} a & c \\ d & f \end{vmatrix}$$

and we note that each of the 2×2 matrices in (5) and (6) may be derived from A by deleting a row and a column of A. In fact, the matrix whose determinant multiplies a in (5) is the "submatrix" of A that results when the row and column in which a appears is deleted from A; and the matrix whose determinant multiplies b in (5) and (6) is the submatrix of A that results when the row and column in which b appears is deleted from A; and so on.

We are led to the following definition:

Definition D3. Suppose A_{ij} is an element of an $n \times n$ matrix A $(n > 1)$. Then the *minor* of A_{ij}, which we shall denote M_{ij}, is the determinant of the $(n - 1) \times (n - 1)$ matrix that results when the ith row and jth column of A are deleted.

Now what about the minus signs that obtruded into some of the terms in (5) and (6)? We note first of all that the signs alternate on the right-hand sides of equations (5) and (6). Secondly we see that, in case (5), where we "expanded" $|A|$ by means of minors of row 1 of A, the initial sign was $+$; and in case (6), where we expanded $|A|$ by means of minors of column 2 of A, the initial sign was $-$. We are led to induce the following Theorem D9 (which we shall prove later, after stating it in slightly different form in Theorems D10 and D10′).

Theorem D9. Let $(a_1, \cdots, a_n)$ be the kth row or $\begin{pmatrix} a_1 \\ \vdots \\ a_n \end{pmatrix}$ the kth column of an $n \times n$ matrix A $(n > 1)$, and let $m_1, \cdots, m_n$ be the minors of $a_1, \cdots, a_n$ respectively. Then:

If k is odd, $|A| = a_1m_1 - a_2m_2 + \cdots \pm a_nm_n$.
If k is even, $|A| = -a_1m_1 + a_2m_2 - \cdots \pm a_nm_n$.

Illustrative Example I. Evaluate:

$$|A| = \begin{vmatrix} 2 & 7 & 1 & -1 \\ 3 & 9 & 0 & 4 \\ 0 & 1 & 0 & 0 \\ 1 & 8 & -1 & -2 \end{vmatrix}$$

SOLUTION. The third row, since it has a maximum number of zeros, seems to be the best row to use in expanding $|A|$ by minors in this example. Since 3 is odd, the initial sign in this expansion is $+$:

$$|A| = 0 \cdot m_1 - 1 \cdot \begin{vmatrix} 2 & 1 & -1 \\ 3 & 0 & 4 \\ 1 & -1 & -2 \end{vmatrix} + 0 \cdot m_3 - 0 \cdot m_4 = -21$$

(see Problem 2 of the preceding exercise).

Note that, in this process, we need not compute the minors of zero elements; indeed, in actual practice, we may omit terms in the expansion of $|A|$ that involve 0 factors entirely, although the existence of these terms must be kept in mind in determining the proper sign to be affixed to each term of the expansion.

The proper sign to be affixed to each term may be conveniently found by counting from the upper left-hand corner of the matrix to the element whose minor is being determined, in the following "checkerboard" pattern of alternating signs:

$$
\begin{array}{cccccccc}
+ & - & + & - & \cdot & & \cdot & \\
- & + & - & + & \cdot & \cdot & \cdot & \\
+ & - & + & - & \cdot & & \cdot & \\
- & + & - & + & \cdot & & \cdot & \\
\cdot & \cdot & \cdot & \cdot & & & & \\
\cdot & \cdot & \cdot & \cdot & & & &
\end{array}
$$

In the preceding example, we would actually have been interested only

in the proper sign to be affixed to the term: $1 \cdot \begin{vmatrix} 2 & 1 & -1 \\ 3 & 0 & 4 \\ 1 & -1 & -2 \end{vmatrix}$. Counting,

in the original matrix A, to the term $A_{32} = 1: \begin{array}{c} + \\ - \\ + \ - \end{array}$, we see that the proper

sign is "$-$".

Illustrative Example 2. Evaluate:

$$
|A| = \begin{vmatrix}
-6 & 1 & -5 & 4 \\
9 & 6 & 5 & 4 \\
6 & 4 & -2 & 8 \\
3 & 1 & 2 & -1
\end{vmatrix}
$$

SOLUTION. Rather than expand immediately by minors, we first seek to remove common factors and to produce a row or column with three zeros.

$$
|A| = 3 \begin{vmatrix}
-2 & 1 & -5 & 4 \\
3 & 6 & 5 & 4 \\
2 & 4 & -2 & 8 \\
1 & 1 & 2 & -1
\end{vmatrix}
$$
(factoring 3 out of column 1, by Theorem D2')

$$
= 3 \cdot 2 \begin{vmatrix}
-2 & 1 & -5 & 4 \\
3 & 6 & 5 & 4 \\
1 & 2 & -1 & 4 \\
1 & 1 & 2 & -1
\end{vmatrix}
$$
(factoring 2 out of row 3, by Theorem D2)

$$
= 6 \begin{vmatrix}
0 & 3 & -1 & 2 \\
0 & 3 & -1 & 7 \\
0 & 1 & -3 & 5 \\
1 & 1 & 2 & -1
\end{vmatrix}
$$
(multiplying row 4 by 2, -3, -1 and adding to rows 1, 2, 3 respectively; we have telescoped three applications of Theorem D8 into one step)

$$= (6)(-1) \begin{vmatrix} 3 & -1 & 2 \\ 3 & -1 & 7 \\ 1 & -3 & 5 \end{vmatrix} \quad \text{(expanding by minors of column 1, by Theorem D9)}$$

$$= -6 \begin{vmatrix} 3 & -1 & 2 \\ 0 & 0 & 5 \\ 1 & -3 & 5 \end{vmatrix} \quad \text{(multiplying row 1 by } -1 \text{ and adding to row 2, by Theorem D8)}$$

$$= (-6)(-5) \begin{vmatrix} 3 & -1 \\ 1 & -3 \end{vmatrix} = (30)\,[(-9) - (-1)] = (30)(-8) = -240$$

Of course, minor determinants do not always turn out to be as tractable as in the preceding example. Suppose, for example, that beginning with the second step we had elected to work with the last column rather than with the last row. Then our solution might have continued:

$$3 \cdot 2 \begin{vmatrix} -2 & 1 & -5 & 4 \\ 3 & 6 & 5 & 4 \\ 1 & 2 & -1 & 4 \\ 1 & 1 & 2 & -1 \end{vmatrix} = 6 \begin{vmatrix} 2 & 5 & 3 & 4 \\ 7 & 10 & 13 & 4 \\ 5 & 6 & 7 & 4 \\ 0 & 0 & 0 & -1 \end{vmatrix} \quad \begin{array}{l}\text{(adding column 4 to columns 1, 2; and multiplying column 4 by 2 and adding to column 3; all by Theorem D8')}\end{array}$$

$$= (6)(-1) \begin{vmatrix} 2 & 5 & 3 \\ 7 & 10 & 13 \\ 5 & 6 & 7 \end{vmatrix} \quad \begin{array}{l}\text{(expanding by minors of row 4, by Theorem D9)}\end{array}$$

$$= -6 \begin{vmatrix} 2 & 5 & 1 \\ 7 & 10 & 6 \\ 5 & 6 & 2 \end{vmatrix} \quad \begin{array}{l}\text{(subtracting column 1 from column 3; i.e., multiplying column 1 by } -1 \text{ and adding to column 3, by Theorem D8')}\end{array}$$

$$= -6 \begin{vmatrix} 2 & 5 & 1 \\ -5 & -20 & 0 \\ 1 & -4 & 0 \end{vmatrix} \quad \begin{array}{l}\text{(multiplying row 1 by } -6, -2, \text{ and adding to rows 2, 3, respectively, both by Theorem D8)}\end{array}$$

$$= (-6)(1) \begin{vmatrix} -5 & -20 \\ 1 & -4 \end{vmatrix} = (-6)(40) = -240$$

Now we investigate further the question of why minus signs appear in some of the terms of (5) and (6). We note that $a = A_{11}$, $c = A_{13}$, $e = A_{22}$, while $b = A_{12}$, $h = A_{32}$. Apparently a factor of -1 makes its appearance only when the sum of the subscripts of A_{ij} is odd. The expression $(-1)^{i+j}$ takes care of this nicely, for it is equal to -1 when

$i + j$ is odd, and it is equal to 1 when $i + j$ is even. We are led to make the following definition:

Definition D4. Suppose A_{ij} is an element of an $n \times n$ matrix A ($n > 1$). Then the *cofactor* of A_{ij}, which we shall denote K_{ij}, is defined as follows: $K_{ij} = (-1)^{i+j} \cdot M_{ij}$ (where M_{ij} is the minor of A_{ij}).

Now, using the notation of Definition D4, Theorem D9 may be separated into two theorems which may be stated as follows:

Theorem D10. Let $(A_{i1}, \cdots, A_{in})$ be a row of an $n \times n$ matrix A ($n > 1$). Then $|A| = A_{i1}K_{i1} + \cdots + A_{in}K_{in}$.

Theorem D10'. Let $\begin{pmatrix} A_{1j} \\ \vdots \\ A_{nj} \end{pmatrix}$ be a column of an $n \times n$ matrix A ($n > 1$).

Then $|A| = A_{1j}K_{1j} + \cdots + A_{nj}K_{nj}$.

We shall prove Theorem D10 (and leave the proof of Theorem D10' as an exercise for the student). In proving Theorem D10, we shall make use of several lemmas; the first involves an interesting method for evaluating determinants that follows from Exercise 72, Problem 6d (which see). In applying the method, we transform a given square matrix into a square matrix in which all the elements above the main diagonal are equal to zero, and such that its determinant is the same as that of the given matrix. The following example shows how this may be carried out in one special case. (The proof of Lemma 1 then exhibits the general method underlying the steps taken in the example.)

$$\begin{vmatrix} 1 & -2 & 3 & 1 \\ 2 & -4 & 1 & 7 \\ 2 & 1 & 3 & 3 \\ -1 & 1 & -2 & 1 \end{vmatrix} = \begin{vmatrix} 1 & 0 & 0 & 0 \\ 2 & 0 & -5 & 5 \\ 2 & 5 & -3 & 1 \\ -1 & -1 & 1 & 2 \end{vmatrix}$$

(multiplying column 1 by 2, -3, -1, and adding to columns 2, 3, 4 respectively)

$$= \begin{vmatrix} 1 & 0 & 0 & 0 \\ 2 & -5 & -5 & 5 \\ 2 & 2 & -3 & 1 \\ -1 & 0 & 1 & 2 \end{vmatrix}$$

(adding column 3 to column 2)

$$= \begin{vmatrix} 1 & 0 & 0 & 0 \\ 2 & -5 & 0 & 0 \\ 2 & 2 & -5 & 3 \\ -1 & 0 & 1 & 2 \end{vmatrix}$$

(multiplying column 2 by -1, 1, and adding to columns 3, 4, respectively)

$$= \begin{vmatrix} 1 & 0 & 0 & 0 \\ 2 & -5 & 0 & 0 \\ 2 & 2 & -5 & 0 \\ -1 & 0 & 1 & \frac{13}{5} \end{vmatrix} \quad \begin{array}{l} \text{(multiplying column 3 by} \\ \frac{3}{5} \text{ and adding to column 4)} \end{array}$$

$$= 65 \quad \text{(by Exercise 72, Problem 6}d\text{).}$$

Lemma 1. Any $n \times n$ matrix A may be transforme'd into an $n \times n$ matrix F in which all elements above the main diagonal are equal to zero, and in which the determinant of A is preserved (i.e. $|F| = |A|$).

*PROOF: Suppose the first row of A in which not all elements above the main diagonal are equal to zero is the kth.

If $A_{kk} \neq 0$, and an element A_{kr} above the main diagonal is unequal to zero, add $-A_{kr}/A_{kk}$ times the kth column of A to the rth column of A. This operation (repeated as often as necessary) will transform A into an $n \times n$ matrix in which all elements above the main diagonal in all rows up to and including the kth are equal to zero, and in which the determinant of A is preserved (why?).

If, however, $A_{kk} = 0$, then some later element in the kth row, say A_{kl}, must be unequal to zero (why?). In that case, add the lth column of A to the kth column of A. The result will be an $n \times n$ matrix B in which all the elements above the main diagonal in the rows before the kth are still equal to zero, and in which the determinant of A is preserved (i.e., $|B| = |A|$), but such that $B_{kk} \neq 0$; and now we may proceed as in the preceding paragraph.

Repetition of this process (if necessary) in later rows will result eventually in a final matrix F in which all elements above the main diagonal are equal to zero, and such that $|F| = |A|$, Q.E.D.

Lemma 2. If A is an $n \times n$ matrix $(n > 1)$, in which all elements above the main diagonal are equal to zero, then $|A| = A_{11}M_{11}$ (where M_{11} is the minor of A_{11}).

PROOF: $|A| = A_{11}A_{22} \cdots A_{nn}$, and $M_{11} = A_{22} \cdots A_{nn}$, (both by Exercise 72, Problem 6d). Therefore $|A| = A_{11}M_{11}$, Q.E.D.

Lemma 3. If A is an $n \times n$ matrix $(n > 1)$ in which each element in the first row above the main diagonal is equal to zero, then $|A| = A_{11}M_{11}$. That is to say:

$$\begin{vmatrix} A_{11} & 0 & \cdots & 0 \\ A_{21} & A_{22} & \cdots & A_{2n} \\ & & \vdots & \\ A_{n1} & A_{n2} & \cdots & A_{nn} \end{vmatrix} = A_{11} \cdot \begin{vmatrix} A_{22} & \cdots & A_{2n} \\ & \vdots & \\ A_{n2} & \cdots & A_{nn} \end{vmatrix}$$

PROOF: We may apply Lemma 1, arriving at an $n \times n$ matrix F in which it will be true not only that all elements above the main diagonal are equal to zero, and that $|F| = |A|$, but also that $A_{11} = F_{11}$ (why?), and $M_{11} = N_{11}$, where N_{11} is the minor of F_{11}. (Why does $M_{11} = N_{11}$?)

Therefore

$$|A| = |F| = F_{11}N_{11} \quad \text{(why?)}$$
$$= A_{11}M_{11}, \text{ Q.E.D.}$$

Lemma 4. Suppose A_{ij} is an element of an $n \times n$ matrix A $(n > 1)$, such that all other elements of the ith row of A are equal to zero. Then $|A| = A_{ij}K_{ij}$ (where K_{ij} is as in Definition D4). That is to say:

$$\begin{vmatrix} A_{11} & \cdots\cdots\cdots\cdots\cdots\cdots & A_{1n} \\ \vdots & & \\ 0 & \cdots \quad 0 \quad A_{ij} \quad 0 \quad \cdots \quad 0 \\ \vdots & & \\ A_{n1} & \cdots\cdots\cdots\cdots\cdots\cdots & A_{nn} \end{vmatrix} = (A_{ij})(-1)^{i+j}M_{ij}$$

Before we prove Lemma 4, we illustrate by means of an example in which $A_{ij} = A_{02}$. Suppose $A = \begin{pmatrix} 1 & 3 & 5 & 7 \\ 2 & 4 & 6 & 8 \\ 0 & 9 & 0 & 0 \\ 1 & 1 & 1 & 1 \end{pmatrix}$. Then:

$$|A| = (-1) \begin{vmatrix} 1 & 3 & 5 & 7 \\ 0 & 9 & 0 & 0 \\ 2 & 4 & 6 & 8 \\ 1 & 1 & 1 & 1 \end{vmatrix} \quad \text{(why?)}$$

$$= (-1)^2 \begin{vmatrix} 0 & 9 & 0 & 0 \\ 1 & 3 & 5 & 7 \\ 2 & 4 & 6 & 8 \\ 1 & 1 & 1 & 1 \end{vmatrix} \quad \text{(why?)}$$

$$= (-1)^3 \begin{vmatrix} 9 & 0 & 0 & 0 \\ 3 & 1 & 5 & 7 \\ 4 & 2 & 6 & 8 \\ 1 & 1 & 1 & 1 \end{vmatrix} \quad \text{(why?)}$$

$$= 9(-1)^3 \begin{vmatrix} 1 & 5 & 7 \\ 2 & 6 & 8 \\ 1 & 1 & 1 \end{vmatrix} \quad \text{(why?)}$$

On the other hand, $A_{ij}K_{ij} = (A_{ij})(-1)^{i+j}M_{ij} = (A_{32})(-1)^5 M_{32} =$

$9(-1)^5 \begin{vmatrix} 1 & 5 & 7 \\ 2 & 6 & 8 \\ 1 & 1 & 1 \end{vmatrix}$, so that Lemma 4 is verified in this special case (why?).

Now we prove Lemma 4, following the lines laid down in this example.

PROOF OF LEMMA 4.   By $i - 1$ successive interchanges of a row with its predecessor, and then by $j - 1$ interchanges of a column with its predecessor, we arrive at a matrix B such that $|A| = (-1)^{i+j-2}|B|$, $B_{11} = A_{ij}$, the minor N_{11} of B_{11} is equal to the minor M_{ij} of A_{ij}, and each element in the first row of B above the main diagonal is equal to zero.   Therefore

$$\begin{aligned} |A| &= (-1)^{i+j}|B| \quad \text{(why?)} \\ &= (-1)^{i+j}B_{11}N_{11} \quad \text{(by Lemma 3)} \\ &= (-1)^{i+j}A_{ij}M_{ij} \quad \text{(why?)} \\ &= A_{ij}K_{ij} \quad \text{(why?), Q.E.D.} \end{aligned}$$

Now we are ready to prove Theorem D10.

PROOF OF THEOREM D10:

$$|A| = \begin{vmatrix} A_{11} & \cdots\cdots & A_{1n} \\ & \vdots & \\ A_{i1} & \cdots\cdots & A_{in} \\ & \vdots & \\ A_{n1} & \cdots\cdots & A_{nn} \end{vmatrix}$$

$$= \begin{vmatrix} A_{11} & \cdots\cdots & A_{1n} \\ & \vdots & \\ A_{i1} & 0 \cdots & 0 \\ & \vdots & \\ A_{n1} & \cdots\cdots & A_{nn} \end{vmatrix} + \begin{vmatrix} A_{11} & \cdots\cdots\cdots & A_{1n} \\ & \vdots & \\ 0 & A_{i2} \; 0 \;\cdots & 0 \\ & \vdots & \\ A_{n1} & \cdots\cdots\cdots & A_{nn} \end{vmatrix}$$

$$+ \cdots + \begin{vmatrix} A_{11} & \cdots\cdots & A_{1n} \\ & \vdots & \\ 0 & \cdots 0 & A_{in} \\ & \vdots & \\ A_{n1} & \cdots\cdots & A_{nn} \end{vmatrix} \quad \text{(why?)}$$

$$= A_{i1}K_{i1} + A_{i2}K_{i2} + \cdots + A_{in}K_{in} \quad \text{(Why?), Q.E.D.}$$

▶ **EXERCISE 74**

1.(a)–(l) Evaluate the determinants in Exercise 70, Problem 1a through 1l, making use of some or all of Theorems D1 through D9.

2. Evaluate:

(a) $\begin{vmatrix} 1 & 2 & 3 & 7 \\ 2 & -1 & 4 & 6 \\ 2 & -2 & -1 & 7 \\ 1 & 2 & 3 & 7 \end{vmatrix}$

(b) $\begin{vmatrix} 1 & 2 & -2 & 4 \\ 3 & 1 & 1 & 2 \\ 4 & -1 & -1 & -2 \\ -1 & 2 & -2 & 4 \end{vmatrix}$

(c) $\begin{vmatrix} 1 & 2 & 3 & 7 \\ 2 & -1 & 4 & 1 \\ 3 & 1 & 7 & 8 \\ 1 & 2 & 3 & 7 \end{vmatrix}$

(d) $\begin{vmatrix} -4 & 2 & -4 & 1 \\ 6 & 7 & 6 & 2 \\ 2 & 1 & 3 & 3 \\ 4 & 2 & 4 & -2 \end{vmatrix}$

(e) $\begin{vmatrix} 3 & -1 & -2 & 4 \\ 1 & 2 & -4 & 3 \\ 1 & -1 & 3 & 5 \\ 2 & 4 & 1 & -1 \end{vmatrix}$

(f) $\begin{vmatrix} 3 & 1 & 1 & 2 \\ -1 & 2 & -1 & 4 \\ -2 & -4 & 3 & 1 \\ 4 & 3 & 5 & -1 \end{vmatrix}$

(g) $\begin{vmatrix} 1 & 1 & 1 \\ x & y & z \\ x^2 & y^2 & z^2 \end{vmatrix}$

(h) $\begin{vmatrix} 1 & 1 & 1 & 1 \\ x & y & z & u \\ x^2 & y^2 & z^2 & u^2 \\ x^3 & y^3 & z^3 & u^3 \end{vmatrix}$

*3. Prove Theorem D10'. [*Hint:* If K'_{ij} is the cofactor of the element A'_{ij} of the matrix A' (where A' is, of course, the transpose of matrix A), what cofactor of what element of matrix A is K'_{ij} equal to?]

11.14 INVERSES OF $n \times n$ MATRICES

We recall (see Section 11.4) that the identity matrix I_n is defined to be an $n \times n$ matrix such that $(I_n)_{ij} = 1$ for $i = j$ and $(I_n)_{ij} = 0$ for $i \neq j$; and that an $n \times n$ matrix B is said to be the inverse of an $n \times n$ matrix A if $AB = BA = I_n$.

Furthermore (see Section 11.5) we recall that in the special case in which A is a 2×2 matrix:

(1) $$A = \begin{pmatrix} a & b \\ c & d \end{pmatrix},$$

the inverse of A (which we now denote A^{-1}) is:

(2) $$A^{-1} = \frac{1}{|A|} \begin{pmatrix} d & -b \\ -c & a \end{pmatrix},$$

assuming $|A| \neq 0$.

How can we generalize this formula so that it applies to square matrices of order higher than 2? The answer lies in expressing each element in the matrix $\begin{pmatrix} d & -b \\ -c & a \end{pmatrix}$ above as a *cofactor* of an element in A. The cofactor of an element of a matrix (see Definition D4) is plus or minus the minor of the element, and the proper sign may be determined either by the formula $(-1)^{i+j}$ of Definition D4 or, equivalently, by the checkerboard pattern noted in Illustrative Example 1 of the preceding section.

Thus, in the matrix A, the cofactor of a, which we denote here by K_a, is d; and also, $K_b = -c$, $K_c = -b$, $K_d = a$. Thus we may write (2) as:

$$(3) \qquad\qquad A^{-1} = \frac{1}{|A|} \begin{pmatrix} K_a & K_c \\ K_b & K_d \end{pmatrix}$$

The matrix $\begin{pmatrix} K_a & K_c \\ K_b & K_d \end{pmatrix}$ may be derived from A by replacing each term of A by its cofactor and then taking the transpose of the resulting matrix. We are led to induce the following theorem:

Theorem. Let A be an $n \times n$ matrix such that $|A| \neq 0$. Define the matrix K to be an $n \times n$ matrix derived from A by replacing each term in A by its cofactor. Then: $A^{-1} = (1/|A|)K'$.

Before we prove this theorem, we give an example of its use.

Illustrative Example. Find the inverse of the matrix:

$$A = \begin{pmatrix} 2 & 1 & -1 \\ 3 & 0 & 4 \\ 1 & -1 & -2 \end{pmatrix}$$

SOLUTION: $|A| = 21 \neq 0$ (see Section 11.7, Illustrative Example 1). Therefore the preceding theorem applies. We proceed to compute the cofactors of the elements of A in order to determine the matrix K. The *minor* of the element in row 1, column 1, of A is $\begin{vmatrix} 0 & 4 \\ -1 & -2 \end{vmatrix} = 4$. Therefore the *cofactor* of this element, by the checkerboard rule, is also 4. The minor of the element in row 1, column 2, is $\begin{vmatrix} 3 & 4 \\ 1 & -2 \end{vmatrix} = -10$. Therefore the cofactor of this element, by the checkerboard rule, is $-(-10) = 10$; and so on, until we have K entirely determined:

$$K = \begin{pmatrix} 4 & 10 & -3 \\ 3 & -3 & 3 \\ 4 & -11 & -3 \end{pmatrix}$$

Therefore:

$$A^{-1} = \frac{1}{|A|} K' = \frac{1}{21} \begin{pmatrix} 4 & 3 & 4 \\ 10 & -3 & -11 \\ -3 & 3 & -3 \end{pmatrix}$$

The student may now verify that both AA^{-1} and $A^{-1}A$ are equal to the 3×3 identity matrix.

Caution: The number 3 may not be factored out of the second column above, since we are dealing with a *matrix*, not a determinant (see Exercise 72, Problem 7). Conversely, to multiply the preceding matrix by the scalar $\frac{1}{21}$, each element of the matrix must be multiplied by $\frac{1}{21}$, by the definition of a scalar product of a *matrix*. Thus, if we wish, we may write the preceding A^{-1}:

$$A^{-1} = \begin{pmatrix} 4/21 & 3/21 & 4/21 \\ 10/21 & -3/21 & -11/21 \\ -3/21 & 3/21 & -3/21 \end{pmatrix}$$

Now, to prove the theorem of this section, we shall make use of two lemmas.

We know that the determinant of a square matrix is equal to the sum of the products of the elements of any row of the matrix by the respective cofactors of these elements. But what if we take the sum of the products of the elements of one row of the matrix by the respective cofactors of the corresponding elements of *another* row of the matrix? The following lemmas state that the resulting expression, as well as the analogous expression for a column expansion, must always be equal to zero. (The notation of Definition D4 is used in the following lemmas and proofs.)

*Lemma I. If A is an $n \times n$ matrix and $u \neq v$ are positive integers $\leqslant n$, then $A_{u1}K_{v1} + \cdots + A_{un}K_{vn} = 0$.

PROOF: Define the matrix B so that it is identical with A, except that its vth row is the uth row of A. Then ${}^uB = {}^uA$ and ${}^vB = {}^uA$, and $u \neq v$ by hypothesis, so that by Theorem D5, $|B| = 0$.

Now we expand $|B|$ by minors of its vth row. But since B is identical with A in all rows except the vth, the minors of the vth row of B are identical with the corresponding minors of the vth row of A. Hence:

$$0 = |B| = B_{v1}K_{v1} + \cdots + B_{vn}K_{vn}$$
$$= A_{u1}K_{v1} + \cdots + A_{un}K_{vn} \quad (\text{since } {}^vB = {}^uA), \text{ Q.E.D.}$$

*Lemma 2. If A is an $n \times n$ matrix and $u \neq v$ are positive integers $\leqslant n$, then $A_{1u}K_{1v} + \cdots + A_{nu}K_{nv} = 0$.

The proof of Lemma 2 is left as an exercise for the student.

*PROOF OF THEOREM: Let $B = (1/|A|)K'$. We wish to show:

$$\text{(i)} \quad AB = I_n$$
$$\text{(ii)} \quad BA = I_n$$

To prove (i), it is sufficient to show that $(AB)_{ij} = 1$ if $i = j$, and $(AB)_{ij} = 0$ if $i \neq j$.

We first note that $B_{ij} = (1/|A|)K'_{ij} = (1/|A|)K_{ji}$. Then:

$$
\begin{aligned}
(AB)_{ij} &= A_{i1}B_{1j} + \cdots + A_{in}B_{nj} \quad \text{[by Section 11.3, (3)]} \\
&= A_{i1}(1/|A|)K_{j1} + \cdots + A_{in}(1/|A|)K_{jn} \\
&= (1/|A|)(A_{i1}K_{j1} + \cdots + A_{in}K_{jn})
\end{aligned}
$$

$\therefore \quad (AB)_{ij} = (1/|A|)(|A|) = 1 \quad$ if $i = j$ (by Theorem D10,

and

$\qquad (AB)_{ij} = (1/|A|)(0) = 0 \quad$ if $i \neq j$ (by Lemma 1)

Q.E.D.

The proof of (ii) is left as an exercise for the student.

We have shown that if A is a square matrix such that $|A| \neq 0$, then A has an inverse. But what if $|A| = 0$? It may be proved (we leave the proof to the student, in an optional exercise) that, if $|A| = 0$, then A has no inverse.

▶ **EXERCISE 75**

1.(a)–(l) Find the inverse (if it exists) of each of the matrices displayed in Exercise 70, Problem 1a through 1l, and when an inverse exists, verify by multiplication of matrices that your answer is correct.

*2. Prove Lemma 2.

*3. Prove part (ii) of the theorem of the preceding section.

*4. Prove that, if A is a square matrix such that $|A| = 0$, then A has no inverse. [*Hint:* Although we have not proved it in this text (see the remarks following Section 11.5 (14)), use the fact that if A, B are $n \times n$ matrices, $|A| \cdot |B| = |AB|$; also use the fact (see Exercise 72, Problem 6c) that $|I_n| = 1$.]

11.15 MATRIC SOLUTION OF n LINEAR SIMULTANEOUS EQUATIONS IN n UNKNOWNS

If we are given n linear simultaneous equations in n unknowns, they may be expressed in the following form (see Section 11.6):

$$\text{(1)} \qquad\qquad AX = C$$

where A is the matrix of coefficients, X is the matrix of unknowns, and C is the matrix of constants. Now if $|A| \neq 0$, we know that A^{-1} exists. Multiplying both sides of (1) by A^{-1}, we have: $A^{-1}(AX) = A^{-1}C$. But:

$$A^{-1}(AX) = (A^{-1}A)X \quad (\text{why?})$$
$$= I_n X \quad (\text{why?})$$
$$= X \quad (\text{why?})$$

Therefore, if $|A| \neq 0$, there follows from (1):

(2) $$X = A^{-1}C$$

Conversely, it is easy to show that (1) follows from (2); thus, if $|A| \neq 0$, (1) and (2) are equivalent. Therefore, when $|A| \neq 0$, (2) represents the unique solution of (1).

Illustrative Example. Solve the simultaneous set of linear equations:

$$2x + y - z = 1$$
$$3x + 4z = -1$$
$$x - y - 2z = 3$$

SOLUTION: The matrix of coefficients is $A = \begin{pmatrix} 2 & 1 & -1 \\ 3 & 0 & 4 \\ 1 & -1 & -2 \end{pmatrix}$. We have

already determined (Section 11.7, Illustrative Example 1) that $|A| \neq 0$, and (Section 11.14, Illustrative Example 1) that

$$A^{-1} = \frac{1}{21} \begin{pmatrix} 4 & 3 & 4 \\ 10 & -3 & -11 \\ -3 & 3 & -3 \end{pmatrix}.$$

Therefore, by (2) above:

$$\begin{pmatrix} x \\ y \\ z \end{pmatrix} = X = A^{-1}C = \frac{1}{21} \begin{pmatrix} 4 & 3 & 4 \\ 10 & -3 & -11 \\ -3 & 3 & -3 \end{pmatrix} \begin{pmatrix} 1 \\ -1 \\ 3 \end{pmatrix}$$

$$= \frac{1}{21} \begin{pmatrix} 13 \\ -20 \\ -15 \end{pmatrix} = \begin{pmatrix} 13/21 \\ -20/21 \\ -15/21 \end{pmatrix}$$

i.e., $x = 13/21$, $y = -20/21$, $z = -15/21$.

Now what if the determinant of the matrix of coefficients is equal to zero? It turns out that, in that case, either there exists no solution or there exist an infinite number of solutions of a set of n linear simultaneous equations in n unknowns (i.e., the equations are then inconsistent or dependent). However, the proof of this statement and an analysis of this case lie beyond the scope of this introduction treatment, and we shall therefore leave them to a more complete course in matrix theory. (See, however, Section 8.15.)

▶ **EXERCISE 76**

1. Using information available in the illustrative example of the preceding section, solve each of the following sets of simultaneous equations:

(a)
$$2x + y - z = 2$$
$$3x + 4z = 7$$
$$x - y - 2z = -2$$

(b)
$$2x + y - z = 1$$
$$3x + 4z = 15$$
$$x - y - 2z = -7$$

(c)
$$2x + y - z = 0$$
$$3x + 4z = 0$$
$$x - y - 2z = 0$$

(d)
$$2x + y - z = 1$$
$$3x + 4z = 0$$
$$x - y - 2z = -1$$

2. Where they apply, use the results of Exercise 75, Problem 1 and the method of the preceding section to solve each of the following sets of simultaneous equations. Where the method of the preceding section does not apply, use the method of Section 8.15, and identify the set of equations as dependent or inconsistent.

(a)
$$3x - 2y + z = 4$$
$$5x + y + 3z = 8$$
$$-x - y + 2z = 1$$

(b)
$$3x + 5y - z = 4$$
$$-2x + y - z = 0$$
$$x + 3y + 2z = 5$$

(c)
$$2x + 4y - 7z = 1$$
$$x + 2y + 2z = 2$$
$$3x - y + 5z = 3$$

(d)
$$x + 2y + 2z = 1$$
$$2x + 4y - 7z = -2$$
$$3x - y + 5z = 3$$

(e)
$$x + 2y + 3z = 0$$
$$2x + 4y + 6z = 0$$
$$7x + 11y + 97z = 0$$

(f)
$$x + 13y + 3z = 1$$
$$2x + 69y + 6z = 3$$
$$3x + 17y + 9z = 2$$

3.(a)–(h) Solve each of the sets of simultaneous equations of Exercise 40, Problem 2, by the method of the preceding section, whenever that method applies.

4. Show that (1) of the preceding section follows from (2); i.e., show that if A, C, X are $n \times n$, $n \times 1$, $n \times 1$ matrices respectively, such that $|A| \neq 0$ and the relation (2) holds true, then (1) holds true also.

11.16 CRAMER'S RULE

Closely related to the matric solution of n linear simultaneous equations in n unknowns given in the preceding section is "Cramer's rule," which also applies only when the determinant of the matrix of coefficients is unequal to zero.

Cramer's Rule. Suppose we are given a set of n linear simultaneous equations in the n unknowns $x_1, \cdots, x_n$, written in the form:

(1) $$AX = C$$

and suppose $|A| \neq 0$.

If j is any positive integer $\leqslant n$, denote by $A * j$ the matrix that is identical with A, except that its jth column has been replaced by the column of constants C.

Then the unique solution of (1) is:

$$x_j = \frac{|A * j|}{|A|}$$

for each positive integer $j \leqslant n$.

Before we prove Cramer's rule to be correct, we give an example of its use.

Illustrative Example. Solve the set of simultaneous equations of the illustrative example in the preceding section, by Cramer's rule.

SOLUTION: Here the unknowns x_1, x_2, x_3 are x, y, z respectively. We compute:

$$|A| = \begin{vmatrix} 2 & 1 & -1 \\ 3 & 0 & 4 \\ 1 & -1 & -2 \end{vmatrix} = 21$$

$$|A * 1| = \begin{vmatrix} 1 & 1 & -1 \\ -1 & 0 & 4 \\ 3 & -1 & -2 \end{vmatrix} = 13$$

$$|A * 2| = \begin{vmatrix} 2 & 1 & -1 \\ 3 & -1 & 4 \\ 1 & 3 & -2 \end{vmatrix} = -20$$

$$|A * 3| = \begin{vmatrix} 2 & 1 & 1 \\ 3 & 0 & -1 \\ 1 & -1 & 3 \end{vmatrix} = -15$$

Therefore, by Cramer's rule:

$$x = \frac{|A * 1|}{|A|} = \tfrac{13}{21} \qquad y = \frac{|A * 2|}{|A|} = -\tfrac{20}{21} \qquad z = \frac{|A * 3|}{|A|} = -\tfrac{15}{21}$$

*PROOF OF CRAMER'S RULE: First of all we expand $|A * j|$ by minors of its jth column. Since $A * j$ is identical with A except in its jth column, the cofactors of the elements in its jth column are the same as the cofactors of the corresponding elements in the jth column of A itself. Remembering, that the jth column of $A * j$ is the matrix of constant terms:

$$C = \begin{pmatrix} C_{11} \\ \vdots \\ C_{n1} \end{pmatrix}$$

We have:

(1) $$|A*j| = C_{11}K_{1j} + \cdots + C_{n1}K_{nj}$$

(where the notation agrees with that of Definition D4).

Next we recall that $A^{-1} = (1/|A|)K'$ (see the theorem of Section 11.14), so that for all integers $i, j \leqslant n$:

(2) $$(A^{-1})_{ij} = (1/|A|)(K'_{ij}) = (1/|A|)(K_{ji})$$

Now we have, from the solution of the preceding section:

$$\begin{aligned} x_j = X_{j1} = (A^{-1}C)_{j1} &= (A^{-1})_{j1}C_{11} + \cdots + (A^{-1})_{jn}C_{n1} \quad \text{(why?)} \\ &= (1/|A|)K_{1j}C_{11} + \cdots + (1/|A|)K_{nj}C_{n1} \quad \text{(why?)} \\ &= (1/|A|)(C_{11}K_{1j} + \cdots + C_{n1}K_{nj}) \quad \text{(why?)} \\ &= (1/|A|)\,|A * j| \quad \text{(why?)} \\ &= \frac{|A * j|}{|A|}, \quad \text{Q.E.D.} \end{aligned}$$

▶ **EXERCISE 77**

1.(*a*)–(*d*) Solve, by means of Cramer's rule, each of the sets of simultaneous equations in Exercise 76, Problem 1.

2.(*a*)–(*f*) Solve, by means of Cramer's rule, each of the sets of simultaneous equations in Exercise 76, Problem 2, that can be solved by this rule.

3.(*a*)–(*h*) Solve, by means of Cramer's rule, each of the sets of simultaneous equations in Exercise 40, Problem 2, that can be solved by this rule.

12 LOGIC

12.1 INTRODUCTION

Aristotle (384–322 B.C.) was the first great logician. And "logic," or more precisely "deductive logic," (called by him "analytic") is still best described in his own words, as a study of the circumstances under which "certain things being stated, something other than what is stated follows of necessity····." We shall be concerned with precisely this question. First we shall investigate a few very simple ways of modifying and combining statements which, nevertheless, are widely inclusive in the range of statements they enable us to form, then we shall consider methods of determining whether or not a new statement is a logical consequence of an original set of assertions.

Our treatment will go beyond that of Aristotle. Although little was added to the field of logic for over 2000 years, about 100 years ago Aristotle's work was enormously enriched by the contributions of the Englishman George Boole (1815–1864). Much of what we shall have to say in this section stems from this very great mathematician, who brought into clear focus the interdependency of logic and mathematics and who stimulated a period of remarkable advances in logic that has not yet run its course.

12.2 NEW STATEMENTS FROM OLD

Negation. The very first method that we shall consider for deriving a statement from a given statement shows quite clearly that a new statement formed from a given statement need *not* be a logical consequence of the given statement. It is the method of *negation*.

411

By way of example, the negation of the statement:

1. "All brides are beautiful" is:
2. "Not all brides are beautiful."

If p represents a statement we shall let *not p*, or even more concisely p' represent the negation of p.

We shall have to beware, however, of certain pitfalls in language. What, for example, is the negation of "I do"? It is "I do not"; and what is the negation of "I am warm"? It is "I am not warm." Apparently, sometimes one forms the negation of a statement by placing the word "not" in front of the statement, sometimes after, and sometimes somewhere in the middle. But not without care; if for example, we made the negation of statement 1:

3. "All brides are not beautiful,"

we would be forming a statement subject to an interpretation quite different from statement 2 that which would be apt to cause considerably more resentment among grooms.

There is a simple way out of this difficulty of language. Note that we have not yet actually defined the negation of a statement. The difficulty is cleared up when we do so. We define the negation of a statement p to be the statement: "It is not the case that p." Thus, the negation of statement 1 is: "It is not the case that all brides are beautiful." Of course, any sentence that unambiguously has the same meaning is equally acceptable; statement 2, for example, is the negation of statement 1, but the slanderous statement 3 is not.

Conjunction. If p, q are statements, the statement "p and q" is called the *conjunction* of the statements p, q. For example, the conjunction of the statements "I do," "I don't" is "I do and I don't." Although a natural symbol for the conjunction of p and q would seem to be "$p + q$," we shall find before very long that things work out better if we use "pq," or "$p \cdot q$" to represent "p and q," and reserve the symbol "$+$" for our next connective. Therefore, in this text, if p, q are statements, then "pq," "$p \cdot q$," although they may be read as usual "p times q," will have the alternative reading: "p and q."

We note that "either $\cdots$ or $\cdots$" is synonymous with "or"; the phrases may be used interchangeably, but considerations of English style sometimes make one preferable to the other.

Disjunction. If p, q are statements, the statement "p or q" is called the disjunction of the statements p, q. For example, the disjunction of the statements "I do," "I don't" is "I do or I don't." If p, q are statements, we shall use the symbol "$p + q$" to mean "p or q." Therefore, in this text, if p, q are statements, then "$p + q$," although it may be read as usual "p plus q," will have the alternative reading "p or q." As we have remarked, this apparently unnatural use of the symbol turns out to be, on the contrary, most useful and therefore reasonable.

Implication. If p, q are statements, the statement "If p then q" is called an *implication*. We have already used the symbol "$p \Rightarrow q$" to mean "If p then q." We recall that "$p \Rightarrow q$" is also read "p implies q." (As a matter of fact all of Section 4.9 applies and should be reviewed at this point.)

Note that $+$, and $\cdot$, as we have just defined them, are operations in the set of all statements; for if p, q are statements, $p + q$ and $p \cdot q$ are statements also. But then so is $\Rightarrow$ an operation in the set of all statements; for if p, q are statements, $p \Rightarrow q$ is a statement also. To emphasize this common property of $+$, $\cdot$, and $\Rightarrow$, we shall use the symbol "$*$" as synonymous with "$\Rightarrow$"; thus: "$p * q$" may be read "p star q" or "p implies q" or "If p, then q," etc.

Equivalence. If p, q are statements, we may form the statement "p is equivalent to q," the symbol for which is "$p \Leftrightarrow q$." This new type of statement may be defined in terms of earlier types as follows: $p \Leftrightarrow q$ means $p \Rightarrow q$ and $q \Rightarrow p$ (again, see Section 4.9).

But $\Leftrightarrow$ is, of course, an operation also. From now on, to emphasize this fact, we shall use the symbol "$**$" as synonymous with "$\Leftrightarrow$." Thus "$p ** q$" may be read as "p double star q" or "p is equivalent to q" or "p if and only if q," etc.

12.3 OPEN STATEMENTS AND QUANTIFIERS

The methods, notation, and terminology of the last section apply even to *open* statements, that is to say, to statements like "x is a dog," that take on meaning only when the *variable* (in our example the symbol "x") is replaced by an appropriate word (in our example a proper noun, like "Lassie" or "Black Beauty"). Open statements are also called *propositional functions*, because they assign statements to particular values of x.

The concept of an open statement is invaluable in mathematics. (What, for example, is an equation that we are asked to solve? cf. Section 8.1.) Open statements are equally indispensable in logic. Consider, for example, the statement "All dogs are animals." That there is an implication hidden within this assertion becomes clear when we phrase the assertion, using the language of open statements: "If x is a dog, then x is an animal." Implications are, of course, the business of logic, and one of the reasons for the importance of open statements in logic is that they enable us to widen the class of statements expressible as implications.

Two principal methods of modifying open statements are important.

The Existential Quantifier. "x is a dog" and "x is a unicorn" are open statements from which new statements may be formed by preceding each with the phrase, "There exists x such that." The result is a statement on which opinions may be held. Most people, for example, would agree that "There exists x such that x is a dog," but few that "There exists x such that x is a unicorn."

Actually, however, every open statement is made with a "universal set" (or sets) in mind, from which replacements for the variable (or variables) are to be chosen. The universal set must be known before one can agree or disagree with the statement. Thus, if the universal set is the set of all horses, one would hesitate to agree that "There exists x such that x is a dog." If the universal set is the set of all real numbers, we would agree that "There exists x such that $x^2 = 2$;" but if the universal set is the set of all rational numbers, we would not (in the light of Section 3.3) agree with this statement.

The phrase "There exists x such that" is called an *existential quantifier*. The reason for the first part of this rather imposing name is fairly obvious; the reason for the second part also becomes evident when we note that the phrase does have something to do with quantity: it is, in fact, synonymous with the phrase "For some x." Here "some" is understood to mean "at least one." Thus the statement "For some x, x is a dog" has exactly the same meaning as "For at least one x, x is a dog," which in turn is equivalent to "There exists x such that x is a dog."

The symbol for the existential quantifier is $(\exists x)$, which may be read "There exists x such that," or "For some x," or "For at least one x." Thus the statement "Some cats are black" may be written

$$(\exists x) \ [(x \text{ is a cat}) \cdot (x \text{ is black})], \quad \text{(universal set: set of all living beings)}$$

or,

$$(\exists x) \ (x \text{ is black}), \quad \text{(universal set?)}$$

And the statement $(\exists x) \ (x \text{ likes coffee})$, which may be read literally as "There exists x such that x likes coffee," may also be translated into "Some people like coffee." (Universal set?)

Universal Quantifier. The *universal quantifier* is the name given to the phrase "For all x," a symbol for which is (x). Thus, "$(x) \ (x \text{ likes coffee})$"

may be read " For all x, x likes coffee," and may be translated " All people like coffee," or " Everybody likes coffee," etc. (Universal set?) Alternatively, (x) may be read " For each x" and " For every x."

▶ **EXERCISE 78**

1. Suppose p represents the statement: " Rain falls," q: " I wear rubbers," r: " I catch cold." Translate each of the following into a verbal statement:

(a) pq
(b) $q + r$
(c) $p * q$
(d) $q' * p'$
(e) $q + p'$
(f) $q * p$
(g) $p' ** q$
(h) pq'
(i) $pq' * r$
(j) $pq * r'$
(k) $q' * pr$
(l) $r' * (p' + q)$
(m) $(pr)' * q$
(n) $(p' + q)'$
(o) $(p'q')'$

2. Assign letters to the component statements of each of the following assertions and write in symbolic form.

(a) They come and they go.

(b) If I play, then I win.

(c) I win, or I don't play.

(d) If I go, then she goes; she goes or I don't go.

(e) Sticks and stones will break my bones.

(f) Neither sticks nor stones will break my bones.

(g) Sticks will break my bones, and stones will not.

(h) If you see the whites of their eyes, then you fire.

(i) Either you see the whites of their eyes or you don't fire.

(j) I like him and he likes me, or else I don't like him or he doesn't like me.

(k) I like him or he likes me, or else I don't like him and he doesn't like me.

(l) It never rains except when I forget my umbrella.

3. Given the following pairs of statements, form from them the negation of each, their conjunction, their disjunction, two implications, and an equivalence. Also, assign a symbol to each of the given statements and give the symbolic form of each of the statements you have formed.

(a) I work; I eat.

(b) I like her; she likes me.

(c) All brides are beautiful; everything is for the best.

(d) You will love logic; I will know the reason why.

4. Write out each of the following statements as it would be read, and also give a verbal translation. In each case, name an appropriate universal set.

(a) $(x)[(x \text{ is a bride}) * (x \text{ is beautiful})]$

(b) $(\exists x)[(x \text{ is a bride})(x \text{ is beautiful})]$

(c) $(x)'[(x \text{ is a bride}) * (x \text{ is beautiful})]$
(d) $(\exists x)'[(x \text{ is a bride})(x \text{ is beautiful})]$
(e) $(x)(x \text{ dreams})$ (f) $(\exists x)(x \text{ dreams})$
(g) $(x)'(x \text{ dreams})$ (h) $(\exists x)(x \text{ dreams})'$
(i) $(\exists x)'(x \text{ dreams})$ (j) $(x)(x \text{ dreams})'$
(k) $(x)[(x \text{ knows her}) * (x \text{ loves her})]$
(l) $(x)'[(x \text{ glitters}) * (x \text{ is gold})]$
(m) $(\exists x)[(x \text{ is a man})(x \text{ lives in our town})]$
(n) $(x)[(x = \text{Caesar}) * (x \text{ was ambitious})]$
(o) $(\exists x)(x^2 = -1)$
(p) $(x)[(x - 1)(x + 1) = x^2 - 1]$
(q) $(x)'(x/x = 1)$

5. Note the ambiguity in the statement, "All emus do not fly." It might mean that all emus are incapable of flight or that not all emus but only some emus fly. Express each of the interpretations symbolically.

6. Express symbolically:

(a) All men are mortal.

(b) Some people like olives, and some don't.

(c) Every little breeze seems to whisper "Louise."

(d) No gentleman would do that.

(e) If someone doesn't volunteer, I'll do it myself.

(f) Some or all of you are guilty.

(g) Nobody moves, or everyone dies.

7. Suppose the universal set is the set of all complex numbers. What quantifier should precede each of the following open statements?

(a) $x = x$ (b) $(x/x) = 1$
(c) $x = x + 1$ (d) $(\sqrt{x})^2 = x$
(e) $\sqrt{x^2} = x$ (f) $x^2 = -1$

12.4 TRUTH AND CONSEQUENCES

We have remarked earlier in this book on the fact that mathematicians are not concerned with "truth." The same is true of logicians. These statements are, in fact, not as startling as they sound: Few people, for example, would call upon a mathematician or a logician to decide, let us say, as to the truth or falsity of the statement "All brides are beautiful." However, a question not of truth but of *consequences*, would fall legitimately within the domain of logic. The logician *could* assure us, for example, that a consequence of the statements, "All brides have sparkling eyes" and "No one with sparkling eyes can fail to be beautiful," is: "All brides are beautiful."

Nevertheless, books on mathematics and logic are full of assertions that this or that statement is "true" and that this or that statement is "false." The resolution of this apparent contradiction lies in the fact that the word "true," as used in mathematics and logic, does not connote "absolute" truth, but is used only to apply to statements set down at the beginning of a discourse ("axioms," "postulates," "first principles," etc.), and their logical consequences.

If a statement p, then, is one of our axioms or "assumed" statements, we shall say that p is true. If a statement p is true, we shall find it convenient to assign to it the "truth value" 1, and to write "$p = 1$." Thus, if p is a statement, then "$p = 1$," besides being read "p equals one," may be read "p is true."

We complete our definition of the word "true" by stipulating that, if p is true and q is a logical consequence of p, then we shall say that q is true also. That is to say:

1. If p, q are statements such that $p = 1$ and $(p * q) = 1$, then $q = 1$.

(Statement 1 is known as the "rule of detachment" and also as the "rule of modus ponens.")

We shall assume, until further notice, that we are dealing only with statements that are either true or not true, i.e., *false*. (Thus, we are excluding open statements, for example.) If a statement p is false, we shall assign to it a truth value of 0, and write "$p = 0$." Thus, if p is a statement, then "$p = 0$," besides being read "p equals zero," may be read "p is false."

We now consider the circumstances under which new statements formed from old may be considered true or false.

First, the statement p', i.e., "not p." Clearly, if a statement is true, then to deny it is false, and if we deny a false statement, we are speaking truth. We therefore define the "truth value" of p' as follows: If p is true then p' is false, and if p is false, then p' is true; or otherwise expressed: If $p = 1$, then $p' = 0$, and if $p = 0$, then $p' = 1$. Even more compactly: $1' = 0$ and $0' = 1$.

Next, the statement pq, i.e., "p and q." Following common usage, we

p	p	pq
1	1	1
1	0	0
0	1	0
0	0	0

consider "p and q" to be true if and only if p is true and q is true. Expressed otherwise: $pq = 1$ if $p = 1$ and $q = 1$; and $pq = 0$ if $p = 1$, $q = 0$, or if $p = 0$, $q = 1$, or if $p = 0$, $q = 0$. This definition is more neatly given in the "truth table" on the previous page.

Truth tables are often written with "T" in place of our "1" and "F" in place of our "0." However, there is a considerable advantage in our use of numerals, and of the notation "pq" for "p and q." The student will note that, with our notation, the truth value of pq is always just the ordinary arithmetic product of the truth values of p and q. (With this observation, the need for memorizing the truth table for pq is obviated.)

We go on to the statement $p + q$, i.e., "p or q." Since we have in mind the inclusive "or" (see Section 1.6, Note 2), we define "p or q" to be true if and only if at least one of the statements p, q is true. Expressed otherwise: $p + q = 1$ if $p = 1$, $q = 1$, or if $p = 1$, $q = 0$, or if $p = 0$, $q = 1$; and $p + q = 0$ if $p = 0$, $q = 0$. In truth table form, this definition may be given as follows:

p	q	$p + q$
1	1	1
1	0	1
0	1	1
0	0	0

Now we see the advantage of the notation "$p + q$" for "p or q." With only one exception, the truth value of $p + q$ is always just the ordinary arithmetic sum of the truth value of p and the truth values of q. The exception is that when $p = 1$ and $q = 1$, $p + q = 1$. That is to say, in "Boolean arithmetic," $1 + 1 = 1$.

At this point we pause to summarize:

2. "*Boolean arithmetic*" *operates in the set* $\{0, 1\}$. *So far as* $+$ *and* $\cdot$ *are concerned, Boolean arithmetic is just like ordinary arithmetic, except that in Boolean arithmetic,* $1 + 1 = 1$. *A special unary operation in Boolean arithmetic is* ′, *which operates as follows:* $1' = 0, 0' = 1$.

Now for the statement $p * q$, i.e., "p implies q." Here we subdivide our discussion into cases.

Case 1. $p = 1, q = 1$; i.e., p is true and q is true. What shall we say of $p * q$? We have two choices: Either $p * q = 0$, or $p * q = 1$. Suppose we define $p * q = 0$ in this case, i.e., suppose we say that "p implies q" is false. Then what we are saying is that q does not follow from p. In that case, q must be false, i.e., $q = 0$. But this contradicts our assumption that $q = 1$. Hence it would be unreasonable to define $p * q = 0$ in this case. Therefore, if $p = 1$ and $q = 1$, we define $p * q = 1$.

Case 2. $p = 1$, $q = 0$. Suppose $p * q = 1$. Then by statement 1, $q = 1$. But this contradicts our assumption that $q = 0$. Hence, if $p = 1$ and $q = 0$, we define $p * q = 0$.

Case 3. $p = 0$, $q = 1$. In this case we begin with a false hypothesis, namely p. To reason from a false hypothesis would seem to be something to be avoided, but, unfortunately, we cannot always do so. Indeed, it is sometimes necessary to draw conclusions from a hypothesis, even when we do not know whether it is true or whether it is false. One hopes, for example, that the hypothesis that a nuclear bomb will ever fall in a populated area is false, but it would be foolhardy not to examine the consequences of the hypothesis in any case.

Suppose then that we defined $p * q = 0$ in this case. That would mean that $p * q$ is false if $p = 0$ and $q = 1$, that is to say, q cannot follow from p if p is false and q is true; in other words, a true statement can never follow from a false statement.

But actually, it is commonplace for a true statement to follow from a false statement. (For example, suppose we begin with the false assumption that there are exactly 100 words in the English language. It is a consequence of this assumption that there are more than 50 words in the English language, which is, of course, true.)

Since assuming that $p * q = 0$ if $p = 0$ and $q = 1$ has led to this contradictory situation, we therefore define $p * q = 1$ if $p = 0$ and $q = 1$.

Case 4. $p = 0$, $q = 0$. Suppose that $p * q = 0$ in this case. Then that would mean that a false statement could never follow from a false statement. We leave it to the student's ingenuity to produce an example in which a false statement follows from a false statement; it is because such examples exist that we define $p * q = 1$ if $p = 0$ and $q = 0$.

Summarizing:

3. *In Boolean arithmetic, $p * q = 1$ always, with the one exception: $1 * 0 = 0$.*

Finally we consider the statement $p ** q$, i.e., "p is equivalent to q." We recall that $p ** q$ has been defined to mean: $p * q$ and $q * p$, i.e., $(p * q) \cdot (q * p)$. We can therefore compute the truth values of $p ** q$ by computing the corresponding truth values of $(p * q) \cdot (q * p)$. For example, suppose $p = 1$, $q = 1$. Then,

$$(p * q) \cdot (q * p) = (1 * 1) \cdot (1 * 1)$$
$$= 1 \cdot 1 \quad \text{(by statement 3)}$$
$$= 1 \quad \text{(by statement 2)}$$

Therefore, for $p = 1$, $q = 1$, $p ** q = 1$.

It is left to the student to compute the truth values of $p ** q$ in the three other possible cases and so to prove our last rule of Boolean arithmetic:

4. $\cdot p ** q = 1$ when $p = q$, and $p ** q = 0$ when $p \neq q$ (i.e., two statements are equivalent when and only when they are both true, or both false).

Because of statement 4, we may, if we wish, attach still another meaning to the symbol "$=$": If p and q are statements, "$p = q$" may also be read "p is equivalent to q."

The consequences of our definition of the truth values of $p * q$ are both amusing and a little incredible. For example, consider the statements: "If all fish play the violin, then some grass is green" and "If all fish play the violin, then no grass is green." Despite the fact that in each case the hypothesis and the conclusion seem to have no connection whatever with each other, *both are true*! (We make the rather reasonable assumptions that "All fish play the violin" and "No grass is green" are false statements, hence that "Some grass is green" is true.) For the first statement is in the form $p * q$ with $p = 0$, $q = 1$, and the second in the form $p * q$ with $p = 0$, $q = 0$, and by our definitions, in each case $p * q = 1$, i.e., q does follow from p.

But despite wry consequences like the above, the implication we have defined ("material implication") is that which mathematicians find most useful. Attempts to define other types of implication that would avoid these consequences have not yet led to satisfactory replacements for material implication.

▶ **EXERCISE 79**

1. Produce an example in which a false statement plausibly follows from a false statement.

2. Complete the computation of the truth values of $p ** q$ in the three cases not computed in the preceding section.

3. Write out truth tables defining the truth values of p', $p * q$, $p ** q$.

4. The "exclusive or," which we shall denote "$\oplus$" is defined as follows: $p \oplus q$ means that exactly one of the statements p, q is true. Write out a truth table defining the truth values of $p \oplus q$. Describe the Boolean arithmetic of the operation $\oplus$.

5. Compute:

(a) $(0 + 1)'$ (b) $(1 + 1)'$ (c) $(0 * 1) * 1$

(d) $(1 * 0) + 1$ (e) $(1 * 0) + (0 * 1)$ (f) $[(1 * 1)(0 * 0)]'$

(g) $(1 * 1)'(0 * 0)'$ (h) $(1' ** 0)*0$ (i) $1(0 + 0)$

(j) $p ** (q * q')$, if $p = 0, q = 0$

(k) $(p * q) + q'$, if $p = 0, q = 1$

(l) $(p * q)' q$, if $p = 1, q = 0$

(m) $(p' * q) * q'$, if $p = 1, q = 1$

6.(a) Which operations of Boolean arithmetic are commutative and which are not? Justify your answers and interpret them in terms of statements. (For example, "·" can be shown to be commutative. Hence, if p, q are statements, "p and q" has the same meaning as "q and p.")

*(b) Prove that the operation $*$ of Boolean arithmetic is not associative.

*(c) Prove that the operations $+$, $\cdot$, and $**$ of Boolean arithmetic are associative.

*(d) Prove that in Boolean arithmetic, $+$ is distributive over $\cdot$, and $\cdot$ is distributive over $+$.

7. Explain why the following statements are correct:

(a) A false statement implies any statement.

(b) A true statement is implied by any statement.

8. Discuss the truth of the assertion, "If baby eats all his cereal, Mommy will give him a toy," if the following statements are true.

(a) Baby eats all his cereal; Mommy gives him no toy.

(b) Baby does not eat all his cereal; Mommy gives him a toy.

(c) Baby does not eat all his cereal; Mommy gives him no toy.

(d) Baby eats all his cereal; Mommy gives him a toy.

12.5 TAUTOLOGIES

The statement: $(p')' ** p$, i.e., "Not not p is equivalent to p," is an example of a statement of logic that is extremely useful in mathematics and, indeed, wherever exact reasoning is applied. Its usefulness stems first of all from the fact that it is true of all statements p of the type we are discussing (i.e., those that must be either true or false). Statements that are true regardless of the truth value of their component statements are called *tautologies*.

We now prove that $(p')' ** p$ actually is true, no matter what the truth value of p.

Theorem LI. $(p')' ** p$ is a tautology.

PROOF: We need merely show that for $p = 0$ and for $p = 1$, $(p')' ** p = 1$.

But for $p = 0$, $(p')' ** p = (0')' ** 0 = 1' ** 0 = 0 ** 0 = 1$.

And for $p = 1$, $(p')' ** p = (1')' ** 1 = 0' ** 1 = 1 ** 1 = 1$, Q.E.D.

From the definition of the truth values of "$**$", Theorem L1 may be interpreted as follows:

Law of Double Negation. $(p')'$ is true if and only if p is true.

We now consider another important tautology.

Theorem L2. $(p * q) ** (q' * p')$ is a tautology.

PROOF: Here there are four possible cases, and we shall find it convenient to use tabular form:

p	q	$(p * q) ** (q' * p')$
1	1	$(1 * 1) ** (0 * 0) = 1 ** 1 = 1$
1	0	
0	1	
0	0	

It is left to the student to show that in each of the three remaining cases the truth value of the given statement is 1 also, so that the given statement is a tautology, Q.E.D.

A little thought will show that this theorem is intuitively plausible. It says, for example, that the following statements are equivalent:

1. If Johnny is good, Johnny gets dessert.

2. If Johnny does not get dessert, Johnny is not good. It is clear that if we accept statement 1, and if Johnny does not get his dessert, then Johnny cannot be good. That is to say, statement 2 follows from statement 1. Similarly, statement 1 follows from statement 2, so that statements 1 and 2 are equivalent, as Theorem L2 says they should be.

The statement $q' * p'$ is called the *contrapositive* of the statement $p * q$. That is to say, the contrapositive of the statement "p implies q" or "If p, then q" is the statement "Not q implies not p" or "If not q, then not p." The preceding theorem may now be stated:

Theorem L2. The contrapositive of a given implication is equivalent to the given implication

From the definition of the truth values of equivalence, Theorem L2 may be interpreted as follows:

Law of Contrapositive. The contrapositive of a given implication is true if and only if the given implication is true.

In mathematics, for example, one uses Theorem L2 in situations like the following. Suppose we know that in a triangle, if $\angle A = \angle B$, then side $a =$ side b. Then we know immediately from Theorem L2, without further proof, that if side $a \neq$ side b, then $\angle A \neq \angle B$; or if we knew the second statement about the triangle to be true, Theorem L2 would justify the assertion that the first is true also; or if we wanted to prove that either is true, Theorem L2 says that it would suffice to prove that the other is true, so that we may work with whichever seems the more convenient of the two statements.

Two other classical variations on implications are the following.

The *converse* of the statement $p * q$ is the statement $q * p$. [This is the definition usually given for " converse " in logic, and the one that we shall use in this chapter; but note that the sense in which mathematicians use the term (cf. Section 4.8) is broader in its coverage.]

It is definitely *not* true that the converse of a statement is always equivalent to the original statement. (Example?) That is to say, $(p * q) ** (q * p)$ is not a tautology. Let us prove this formally:

Theorem L3. $(p * q) ** (q * p)$ is not a tautology.

PROOF: Suppose $p = 1$, $q = 0$. Then $(p * q) ** (q * p) = (1 * 0) ** (0 * 1) = 0 ** 1 = 0$. Therefore the given statement is not true for all statements, i.e., it is not a tautology, Q.E.D.

The *inverse* of the statement $p * q$ is the statement $p' * q'$. The inverse of a statement is not always equivalent to the original statement either. For example, the inverse of " If you tickle me, I'll laugh " is " If you don't tickle me, I won't laugh." It is quite possible for the first to be true and the second false, so that this statement and its inverse are clearly not equivalent.

In other words, $(p * q) ** (p' * q')$ is not a tautology. It is left to the student to supply a formal proof that it is not.

Finally, we consider a tautology that involves three variables.

Theorem L4. $[(p * q)(q * r)] * (p * r)$ is a tautology.

PROOF: Since there are two possibilities for each of p, q, r, there are eight cases that we must consider. Again we resort to tabular form to list all the possible cases as on the next page.

It is left to the student to show that in each of the seven remaining cases, the truth value of the given statement is 1 also, so that the given statement is a tautology, Q.E.D.

p	q	r	$[(p * q)(q * r)] * (p * r)$
1	1	1	$[(1 * 1)(1 * 1)] * (1 * 1) = [(1)(1)] * (1) = 1 * 1 = 1$
1	1	0	
1	0	1	
1	0	0	
0	1	1	
0	1	0	
0	0	1	
0	0	0	

Actually the labor involved in the preceding proof may be shortened. For we know (see Section 12.4, statement 3) that if $r = 1$, then $p * r = 1$; and if $p * r = 1$, then by the same argument, $[(p * q)(q * r)] * (p * r) = 1$. Hence, if $r = 1$, the truth value of the given statement is 1.

There remain to consider, therefore, only the cases in which $r = 0$. But in these cases, if $p = 0$, then $p * r = 1$, and as before, the truth value of the given statement is 1.

Thus we have reduced the set of cases that we must consider to those in which $r = 0$ and $p = 1$, that is to say, only to the two cases $r = 0, p = 1$, $q = 0; r = 0, p = 1, q = 1$.

From the rule of detachment (Section 12.4, statement 1) and Theorem L4 there follows:

Law of Syllogism. If $p * q$ and $q * r$ are true, then $p * r$ is true.

▶ **EXERCISE 80**

1. Complete the proof of Theorem L2.

2.(*a*) Prove: $(p * q) ** (p' * q')$ is not a tautology (i.e., a statement is not always equivalent to its inverse).

(*b*) Give an example of an implication and its inverse that are not equivalent.

(c) Give an example of an implication and its inverse that are equivalent.

3.(*a*) Give an example of an implication and its converse that are not equivalent.

(b) Give an example of an implication and its converse that are equivalent.

4. Complete the proof of Theorem L4.

5. Write the inverse, converse, and contrapositive of each of the

following implications; also, assign a reasonable truth value to the given and to the derived implications.

(*a*) If it is a fish, then it swims.

(*b*) All birds fly.

(*c*) If it is a whale, then it does not fly.

(*d*) No fish plays the violin.

(*e*) If an integer is odd, then it is not divisible by 2.

(*f*) If an integer is not divisible by 2, then it is not even.

(*g*) If a triangle is scalene, it is not isosceles.

(*h*) An equilateral triangle is always isosceles.

(*i*) If it rains, and I do not wear rubbers, then I catch cold.

(*j*) A necessary condition for flowers in May is showers in April.

(*k*) A sufficient condition for residing in New York State is residing in New York City.

(*l*) Virtue implies a long life.

(*m*) The good die young.

6.(*a*) Suppose *r* is the implication: "If he stays, then I go." Find the converse of the inverse of *r*, and the inverse of the converse of *r*, and compare your final statements with the contrapositive of *r*.

(*b*) Given the implication $p * q$, find the converse of its inverse and the inverse of its converse (thus proving that the contrapositive of an implication is the converse of its inverse and also the inverse of its converse).

7.(*a*) Suppose *r* is as in Problem 6*a*. Find the contrapositive of the converse of *r* and compare your resulting statement with the inverse of *r*.

(*b*) Given the implication $p * q$, show that its inverse is the contrapositive of its converse, and use this fact to justify the assertion that the inverse of an implication is always equivalent to the converse of the implication.

8. Prove that the following statements are tautologies, and in parts (*c*) through (*n*), supply verbal interpretations like those given in parts (*a*) and (*b*).

(*a*) $(pp')'$ [*Note:* To say that for all statements p, $(pp')' = 1$ is equivalent to saying that for all statements p, $pp' = 0$, i.e., *p and not p cannot both be true* (the law of contradiction).]

(*b*) $p + p'$ [*Either p or not p must be true* (the law of the excluded middle).]

(*c*) $(p + q)' ** p'q'$ ⎫
(*d*) $(pq)' ** (p' + q')$ ⎬(DeMorgan's laws)

(*e*) $p * p$

(*f*) $(pq) * p$

(*g*) $(p + p) ** p$

(*h*) $p * (p + q)$

(*i*) $(p * q) ** (p' + q)$

(*j*) $(p ** q) ** (p' ** q')$

(*k*) $(p * q)' ** (pq')$

(*l*) $(p ** q) ** (pq + p'q')$

(*m*) $(p ** q)' ** (pq' + p'q)$

(*n*) $[(p ** q)(q ** r)] * (p ** r)$

9. Prove the commutative laws of Boolean algebra, namely, that the following are tautologies:

(a) $(p + q) ** (q + p)$ (b) $(pq) ** (qp)$

10. Prove the distributive laws of Boolean algebra, namely, that the following are tautologies:

(a) $[p(q + r)] ** (pq + pr)$ (b) $(p + qr) ** (p + q)(p + r)$

11. Prove the associative laws of Boolean algebra, namely, that the following are tautologies:

(a) $[p + (q + r)] ** [(p + q) + r]$ (b) $[p(qr)] ** [(pq)r]$

12.6 NEGATION

In developing logic logically, it is not necessary to introduce the existential and universal quantifiers as independent concepts, for, as a matter of fact, either may be expressed in terms of the other and negation. The statement "Some chairs are comfortable," for example, is identical in meaning with "Not all chairs are uncomfortable," and the statement "All fish swim" is identical in meaning with "There does not exist a fish that does not swim." It appears that the following are reasonable statements:

Q1. $(\exists x)(p) ** [(x)(p')]'$ (*The statement* "*For some x, p*" *is equivalent to the statement* "*Not for all x, not p.*")

Q2. $(x)(p) ** [(\exists x)(p')]'$ (*The statement* "*For all x, p*" *is equivalent to the statement* "*There does not exist x such that not p.*")

Actually, Q1 and Q2 may be proved to be equivalent statements, but since we do not wish to go too deeply into the matter here, we shall accept them both as assumptions, i.e., as true statements.

We now turn our attention to the question of obtaining the negations of some statements in a form less awkward and more useful than that which results from placing before them the phrase "It is not the case that $\cdots$"

First we consider the negation of a quantification. To deny, for example, that "Some chairs are comfortable" is equivalent to saying "All chairs are uncomfortable," and to deny that "All fish swim" is equivalent to saying that "Some fish do not swim." We are led to assume (although the following may actually be proved from Q1 and Q2):

Q1'. $[(\exists x)(p)]' ** [(x)(p')]$ (*The negation of* "*For some x, p,*" *is* "*For all x, not p.*")

Q2'. $[(x)(p)]' ** [(\exists x)(p')]$ (*The negation of* "*For all x, p, is* "*For some x, not p.*")

Note: In Q1' and Q2', "is" means (as it often does) "is equivalent to."

Illustrative Example 1. Write the negation of the statement "The square of any real number is positive."

SOLUTION. Letting the universal set be the set of all real numbers, the given statement may be written: $(x)(x^2 > 0)$. By Q2', the negation of this statement is: $(\exists x)(x^2 > 0)'$, i.e., "There exists a real number whose square is not positive."

DeMorgan's laws (see Problems 8c and 8d of the preceding exercise) enable us to write the negations of disjunctions and conjunctions in simple and useful form. They say that the negation of "p or q" is "not p and not q," and the negation of "p and q" is "not p or not q."

Illustrative Example 2. Write the negation of the statements:

1. The owl and the pussycat went to sea.
2. These are sides of an equilateral triangle and they are unequal in length.
3. $x \geqslant 0$.

SOLUTION. The negation of statement 1 (which is in the form "p and q") is "Either the owl did not go to sea or the pussycat did not go to sea"; the negation of statement 2 (which is also in the form "p and q") is "Either these are not sides of an equilateral triangle, or they are equal in length"; the negation of statement 3 is: "$x \not> 0$ and $x \neq 0$."

Negations of implications and equivalences are given by Problems 8k and 8m of the preceding exercise. They say that the negation of "p implies q" is "p and not q," and the negation of "p is equivalent to q" is "either p and not q, or q and not p."

Illustrative Example 3. Write the negatives of the statements:
1. If I win this bet, then I stop gambling.
2. A triangle is equilateral if and only if it is isosceles.

SOLUTION. By Problem 8k of the preceding section, the negation of statement 1 is: "I win this bet and I do not stop gambling."

Statement 2 is best handled by letting the universal set be the set of all triangles and writing statement 2 in the form: $(x)[(x$ is equilateral$) ** (x$ is isosceles$)]$. The negation of statement 2 is then: $(\exists x)[(x$ is equilateral$) ** (x$ is isosceles$)]'$, which, by Problem 8m of the preceding exercise, is equivalent to:

$$(\exists x)[(x \text{ is equilateral})(x \text{ is isosceles})' + (x \text{ is isosceles})(x \text{ is equilateral})'].$$

Verbally, the negation of statement 2 is "There exists a triangle that is either equilateral and not isosceles or isosceles and not equilateral."

▶ **EXERCISE 81**

1. Write the negation of each of the following statements:

(*a*) All brides are beautiful.

(*b*) All brides are unbeautiful.

(*c*) Some brides are beautiful.

(*d*) Some brides are unbeautiful.

(*e*) Roses are red.

(*f*) If winter comes, then spring is not far behind.

(*g*) He says " bananna " and she says " banahna."

(*h*) He laughed and sang the livelong day.

(*i*) All college men are either handsome or rich.

(*j*) I will pass this course, or I'll be a monkey's uncle.

(*k*) $5 \geqslant 7$.

(*l*) Some triangles have four sides.

(*m*) Some rectangles are squares.

(*n*) All squares are rectangles.

(*o*) If a real number is not negative, it is positive.

(*p*) If a number is rational, it is real.

(*q*) A number is real if and only if it is rational.

(*r*) $0 < 5 < 3$.

(*s*) The cube of a negative number is negative.

(*t*) An even power of a negative number is negative.

(*u*) All prime numbers are odd.

2. In each of the following cases, tell whether the given statement or its negation is true, and justify your answer.

(*a*) Illustrative Example 1 of Section 12.6.

(*b*) Illustrative Example 3, statement 2, of Section 12.6.

(*c*) Problem 1*l*	(*d*) Problem 1*m*
(*e*) Problem 1*n*	(*f*) Problem 1*o*
(*g*) Problem 1*p*	(*h*) Problem 1*q*
(*i*) Problem 1*r*	(*j*) Problem 1*s*
(*k*) Problem 1*t*	(*l*) Problem 1*u*

12.7 PROOF

The student will recall that in mathematics, in proving an implication $p * q$ to be true, one often sets down p (the "antecedent") as "given," and then one proceeds to derive therefrom the "consequent" q. The logical justification for the process is this: We know (from our definition of the truth values of $p * q$) that, if p is false, then $p * q$ will be true, no matter what the truth value of q. Therefore, in proving $p * q$ to be true, we need be concerned only with the case in which p is true (and in that case we must show that q is true also); and when we set down p as "given," we are simply labeling p as true.

(The following possible source of confusion should be noted: In mathematics, and in other situations also, one speaks of "proving that p implies q," and "the theorem: p implies q," when what is meant is "proving that 'p implies q' *is true*," and "the theorem: 'p implies q' *is true*.")

The popular method called the "indirect method" is that in which we prove that p implies q, by assuming that, with the hypothesis p, not q is true, and showing that this assumption leads to a "contradiction" (a contradiction being a statement of the form r and not r.)

For example, suppose we wish to prove the following statement by the indirect method: "If two sides of a triangle are unequal, then their opposite angles are unequal." We assume, then, that two sides of a triangle are unequal, and that their opposite angles are *not* unequal, i.e., that their opposite angles are equal. We can now derive the two statements: "The opposite sides are equal" and "The opposite sides are unequal," a contradiction. Hence, we say, our original statement is proved.

Logically, the method rests on the following tautology (whose proof is left to the student):

(1) $[(pq') * (rr')] * (p * q)$ (If p *and not* q implies a contradiction r *and not* r, then p implies q.)

Sometimes (as in the preceding example) we can show that p *and not* q implies *not* p, so that p *and not* p serves as the sought for contradiction. The following tautology directly justifies the indirect method in this special case (proof again left to student):

(2) $(pq' * p') * (p * q)$ (If p *and not* q implies *not* p, then p implies q.)

Here is how tautology (1) is used in an indirect proof that a statement $p * q$ is true: Since (1) is a tautology, (1) is true no matter what the statements p, q, and r are. Therefore, by the rule of detachment (Section 12.4, statement 1, $p * q$ would be true if $(pq') * (rr')$ were true. Our job, then is to prove that $(pq') * (rr')$ is true. As explained above, in proving that $(pq') * (rr')$ is true, we need only consider the case in which $pq' = 1$ (i.e., in which p and not q is true), and in that case we must show that $rr' = 1$. But $pq' = 1$ when and only when $p = 1$ and $q' = 1$, and $rr' = 1$ when and only when $r = 1$ and $r' = 1$. That is why, in order to prove that $p * q$ is true, it suffices to assume that $p = 1$ and $q' = 1$, and to show that for some statement r, $r = 1$ and $r' = 1$.

It is left to the student to explain how tautology (2) is used in an indirect proof.

Illustrative Example 1 *Given:*
1. If you stay, then he goes.
2. If I stay, then she stays.
3: If he goes, then she goes.
Prove:
4. If you stay, then I go.

PROOF: Assign the following notation: p—You stay, q—I go, r—She stays, s—He goes.

Then the problem may be rephrased:

Given: (a) $p * s$,   (b) $q' * r$,   (c) $s * r'$.
Prove: (d) $p * q$.

PROOF: We shall use the indirect method. That is to say, we shall assume that $p = 1$ and $q' = 1$. In that case, using the rule of detachment, with (a) and (b), we have $s = 1$ and $r = 1$. Now, using the rule of detachment with (c), we have $r' = 1$. Having shown that from our assumption $p = 1$ and $q' = 1$, there follows $r = 1$ and $r' = 1$, our proof by the indirect method that $p * q$ is true is complete.

[Other proofs are possible. For example, from (a) and (c), by the law of syllogism (Section 12.5) $p * r'$ is true. From (b), by the laws of contrapositive and double negation, we have that $r' * q$ is true. Hence again by the law of syllogism, $p * q$ is true, Q.E.D.]

Our methods enable us not only to prove that certain statements are logical consequences of others but also to determine when this is not the case; that is to say, we can now distinguish between *valid* and *invalid* reasoning.

Illustrative Example 2. Is the following reasoning valid?

Given: If I don't gamble, I don't lose money.
               If I don't lose money, I am happy.
Conclusion: If I gamble, I am unhappy.

SOLUTION. Assigning the following notation, p: I gamble, q: I lose money, r: I am happy, the reasoning in question may be stated:

Given: $p' * q'$, $q' * r$.
Conclusion: $p * r'$.

We note that the hypothesis is satisfied when $p = 1$, $q = 0$, $r = 1$, and also when $p = 0$, $q = 0$, $r = 1$. But in the first case $p * r' = 1 * 0 = 0$, i.e., $p * r'$ is false, and in the second case $p * r' = 0 * 0 = 1$, i.e., $p * r'$ is truc. Thus, with the given hypothesis, the given conclusion need not necessarily be true: it may be true or false. The given reasoning is not valid.

► **EXERCISE 82**

1. *Given:* If Fred is not dead, then Field hasn't squealed.
      If the thread is red, then Field has squealed.
   Prove: If the thread is red, then Fred is dead.
2. *Given:* If you don't date, you don't rate.
      You rate.
   Prove: You date.
3. *Given:* If wishes were horses, then beggars would ride in style.
      It would be a sad state of affairs, if wishes were not horses.
      A sad state of affairs is sufficient to make all men weep.
   Prove: If beggars don't ride in style, then all men weep.
4. (Lewis Carroll).
   Given: Babies are illogical.
      Nobody is despised who can manage a crocodile.
      Illogical persons are despised.
   Prove: Babies cannot manage crocodiles.
   (*Hint:* Assign the notation p: It is a baby, q: It is illogical, etc.; then the first given statement becomes $p * q$, etc.)
5. (Lewis Carroll)   What conclusions may be derived from the following set of hypotheses: No ducks waltz.   No officers ever decline to waltz. All my poultry are ducks.
   In the problems that follow, prove either that the conclusion is true, or that the reasoning is not valid.
6. *Given:* If my calculations are correct, we are not far from land.   If, you are not telling the truth, we are far from land.
   Conclusion: If my calculations are correct, you are telling the truth.
7. *Given:* A necessary condition for this year to be 1962 is that last year was 1961.   This year is 1962.
   Conclusion: Last year was 1961.
8. *Given:* A sufficient condition for this year to be 1962 is that last year was 1961.   This year is 1962.
   Conclusion: Last year was 1961.
9. *Given:* I'll eat my hat if Zilch wins.   I will not eat my hat.
   Conclusion: Zilch will not win.
10. *Given:* Great heat implies discomfort.   High humidity implies discomfort.   It is very hot and uncomfortable.
   Conclusion: It is very humid.

11. *Given:* If I drink coffee, I don't sleep nights. I am grumpy if my dinner is incomplete. In order for my dinner to be complete, it is necessary that I drink coffee.

Conclusion: If I sleep nights, I am grumpy.

12. *Given:* A man is happy if and only if he is healthy. If a man is unhappy, he needs help.

Conclusion: If a man is healthy, he does not need help.

13. *Given:* If I fly, I won't take my violin. If I don't go by train, I'll fly.

Conclusion: If I go by train, I'll take my violin.

14. Explain how tautology (2) of the preceding section is used in an indirect proof.

12.8 BOOLEAN ALGEBRAS AND SOME OF THEIR DIVERSE APPLICATIONS

We summarize here some of the important information we have gleaned about the algebra of statements:

If p, q are statements, then $p + q$ is defined to be the statement "p or q" and $p \cdot q$ is defined to be the statement "p and q." If p is a true statement we write: $p = 1$, and if p is a false statement we write: $p = 0$. We assume that each of the statements with which we deal is either true or false, and if p, q are statements, we write $p = q$ if and only if p, q are both true or both false.

With these definitions of the relation $=$ and the operations $+$, $\cdot$ in the set of all statements, we derive an arithmetic of statements (see Section 12.4, statement 2), and it turns out that:

1. S is a set and $+$, $\cdot$ are operations such that:

(i) $+$, $\cdot$ are well-defined, closed, commutative, and associative operations in S.

(ii) $+$, $\cdot$ are distributive over each other; i.e., if p, q, $r \in S$, then $p(q + r) = pq + pr$, and $p + qr = (p + q)(p + r)$.

(iii) There exist elements 0, 1 such that for each $p \in S$:

$$p + 0 = p, \qquad p \cdot 1 = p$$

(iv) For each $p \in S$, there exists $p' \in S$ such that:

$$p + p' = 1, \qquad pp' = 0$$

We have considered most of these properties either in the preceding sections or in preceding exercises. Actually, since each element of S is equal to either 0 or 1, the statements (i) through (iv) may be proved to be true simply by considering all possible cases. For example, statement (iii) requires only two cases:

PROOF OF (iii): *Case* 1. $p = 0$. Then $p + 0 = 0 + 0 = 0 = p$, and $p \cdot 1 = 0 \cdot 1 = 0 = p$, Q.E.D.

Case 2. $p = 1$. Then $p + 0 = 1 + 0 = 1 = p$, and $p \cdot 1 = 1 \cdot 1 = 1 = p$, Q.E.D.

Now we point out that the conditions of statement 1 are satisfied not only by the algebra of statements; for example, they are also satisfied by algebras of *subsets of a set*. That is to say:

Suppose A is any set, and S is the set of all subsets of A. Let the symbol "0" denote the null subset of A, the symbol "1" the set A itself, and let the symbols "+" and "·" denote "∪" and "∩" respectively. Finally, if B is a subset of A, let B' denote the complement of B in A (see Exercise 2, Problem 20). Then it may be verified that, with this symbolism, all the conditions of statement 1 are satisfied.

Any set S, with operations +, · satisfying statement 1 is called a Boolean algebra. We have so far encountered two examples of Boolean algebras: the algebra of statements and the algebra of subsets of a set. We show now how the algebra of subsets of a set may be used to solve logical problems.

Illustrative Example. Solve Problem 4 of the preceding exercise by means of the algebra of subsets of a set.

SOLUTION. Let S be the set of all people, and define the following subsets of S: B, the set of all babies; I, the set of all illogical people; D, the set of all despised people; M, the set of all people who can manage crocodiles.

Then the statement "Babies are illogical" may be expressed: $B \subset I$, which is equivalent to saying that the intersection of the sets B, I is B:

$$(1) \qquad\qquad BI = B$$

The statement "Nobody is despised who can manage a crocodile" means that the sets D, M have no common element, i.e., their intersection is the nullset:

$$(2) \qquad\qquad DM = 0$$

The statement "Illogical persons are despised" may be expressed: $I \subset D$, i.e.:

$$(3) \qquad\qquad ID = I$$

Therefore: $BD = (BI)D$ [by (1)]
$\qquad\qquad = B(ID)$ (since · is associative)
$\qquad\qquad = BI$ [by (3)]
$\qquad\qquad = B$ [by (1)]

So that:

(4) $$BD = B$$

But $BD = B$ is equivalent to: $B \subset D$. Thus, one of the logical consequences of the given information is: "Babies are despised."

Also: $BM = (BD)M$ [by (4)]
   $= B(DM)$ (since $\cdot$ is associative)
   $= B \cdot 0$ [by (2)]
   $= 0$ (why?)

Therefore, $BM = 0$; i.e., the set of babies and the set of people who can manage crocodiles have no elements in common: "Babies cannot manage crocodiles."

Now, to illustrate the power of the abstract approach to mathematics, we present an application of Boolean algebra to a practical problem apparently remote from either logic or set theory, namely, to a problem in electric circuitry.

The problem is this: A light in the center of a long hallway is to be actuated by two switches, one at each end of the hallway. It is desired that the light may be controlled by either switch, i.e., if the light is on, flipping either switch will turn it off, and if the light is off, flipping either switch will turn it on. How can this be arranged?

To solve the problem, we first develop a little switching theory:

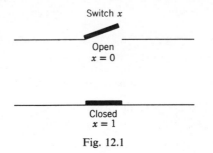

Switch x

Open
$x = 0$

Closed
$x = 1$

Fig. 12.1

In Fig. 12.1, we see a diagram of a switch, in open and closed positions. If we denote a given switch by "x," we shall write "$x = 0$" if the switch does not permit current to flow through it (i.e., if the switch is open), and we shall write "$x = 1$" if the switch permits current to flow through it (i.e., if the switch is closed).

A pair of switches x, y may be connected either in "series" or in "parallel" (see Fig. 12.2).

We note that in series connection, when both switches are open, i.e., when $x = 0$ and $y = 0$, then no current can flow; we denote this result by

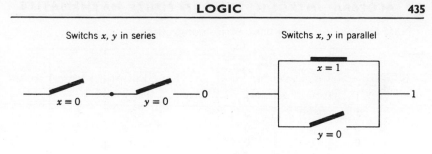

Fig. 12.2

"0"; on the other hand, for example, in parallel connection, when x is closed and y is open, i.e., when $x = 1$ and $y = 0$, then current can flow; we denote this result by "1". With this notation, all possibilities in both series and parallel connections of two switches x, y are tabulated below:

x	y	SERIES	PARALLEL
1	1	1	1
1	0	0	1
0	1	0	1
0	0	0	0

Now we see that Boolean arithmetic is involved: With the operations of Boolean arithmetic, xy represents the switches x, y in series connection, and $x + y$ represents the switches x, y in parallel connection.

We may even assign an interpretation to x': In Boolean arithmetic, $x' = 0$ if $x = 1$ and $x' = 1$ if $x = 0$. Thus, if x is a switch, x' should be a switch that is constrained to be open when x is closed, and closed when x is open. In Fig. 12.3 we see one way in which such an arrangement may be effected.

Finally, to carry the analogy with Boolean arithmetic further, if two switches are so connected that when one is closed the other is closed, and when one is open the other is open, we assign the same symbol to both (see Fig. 12.4).

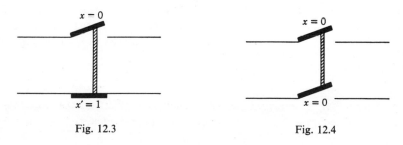

Fig. 12.3   Fig. 12.4

Note then the following basic series connections:

x	y	xy	xy'	$x'y$	$x'y'$
1	1	1	0	0	0
1	0	0	1	0	0
0	1	0	0	1	0
0	0	0	0	0	1

Now we return to the switching problem proposed above. Let x, y represent the two switches, and suppose that when x, y are both closed, the light is on (i.e., current flows); then with $x = 1$, $y = 1$, the result is 1. Flipping either switch must turn the light off; i.e., with $x = 1$, $y = 0$ or with $x = 0$, $y = 1$, the result must be 0. But now, if either switch is flipped, the light must go on again; i.e., with $x = 0$, $y = 0$, the result must be 1. We tabulate these statements below:

x	y	DESIRED RESULT
1	1	1
1	0	0
0	1	0
0	0	1

But consulting the table of basic series connections above, we see that $xy + x'y'$ yields the desired results; $xy + x'y'$ is to be interpreted as a

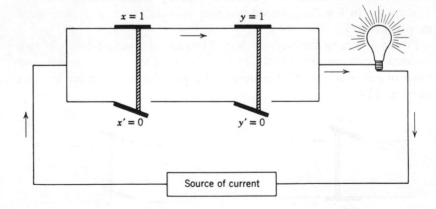

Fig. 12.5

pair of switches x, y connected in series, and a pair of switches x', y' connected in series, and the two pairs then connected in parallel (see Fig. 12.5).

It is clear that the switching circuit of Fig. 12.5 will do the required job. For when x, y are both closed, current flows through the upper branch and the light goes on. If either x or y is now flipped to the opposite position, the circuit is broken and no path remains for the current—the light goes out. And now if either switch is flipped, the circuit is once more closed and the light goes on again.

▶ **EXERCISE 83**

1. In each of the following cases, find logical consequences of the given set of statements by means of the algebra of subsets of a set, as in the illustrative example of the preceding section.

(*a*) Problem 5 of the preceding exercise.

(*b*) (Aristotle via Boole)
Passions are not things which are accompanied by deliberate preference.
Virtues are things which are accompanied by deliberate preference.

(*c*) (Lewis Carroll)
Everyone who is sane can do logic;
No lunatics are fit to serve on a jury;
None of your sons can do logic.

(*d*) (Lewis Carroll)
All puddings are nice;
This dish is a pudding;
No nice things are wholesome.

(*e*) (Lewis Carroll)
Nobody, who really appreciates Beethoven, fails to keep silence while the Moonlight Sonata is being played.
Guinea pigs are hopelessly ignorant of music.
No one, who is hopelessly ignorant of music, ever keeps silence while the Moonlight Sonata is being played.

(*f*) (Lewis Carroll)
Promise breakers are untrustworthy.
Wine drinkers are very communicative.
A man who keeps his promises is honest.
No teetotalers are pawnbrokers.
One can always trust a very communicative person.

2. Suppose that in the switching problem of the preceding section, it was required that the light should be on if either switch is closed, and off only if both are open. Design a circuit to accomplish this, and draw a diagram of the circuit.

3. Construct a table of basic series connections for three switches x, y, z.   (*Hint:* The table will have eight rows, and there are eight basic series connections: xyz, xyz', etc.)

4. Design a circuit of three switches so that a light may be controlled by any one of the three switches, and draw a diagram of the circuit.

5. The same as Problem 4, with four switches.

13 GROUPS

13.1 INTRODUCTION

In Chapter 4 we studied the abstract structure called a "field"; that is to say, we derived a number of consequences of a set of axioms called the "field" axioms. Many examples of fields exist: the complex number field, the real number field, and the rational number field are among the most important. Since all of these structures satisfy the field axioms, all of the statements that we have proved to be a consequence of the field axioms apply, of course, to each of these fields.

There are many important mathematical structures, however, that satisfy some rather than all of the field axioms. Of these, undoubtedly the most famous and the most important are the structures known as *groups*.

A characteristic of modern mathematics is its concern with form and pattern, both physical and conceptual. Nowhere in mathematics does this aspect lie closer to the surface than in the study of groups; indeed, group theory has been described as the mathematical analysis of symmetry. We shall begin our brief introduction to group theory with an example that brings out the close connection between groups and geometric designs.

13.2 THE GROUP OF A GEOMETRIC FIGURE

Suppose we have given a nonsquare rectangle $ABCD$ (Fig. 13.1).

In how many ways may the rectangle be picked up and put down again, or in any other fashion moved, so that it occupies or "fits" into its original

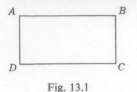

Fig. 13.1

position? That is to say, what are the functions that (without breaking or distortion) map the rectangle $ABCD$ onto itself?

First of all, of course, there is the identity function e such that, for each point P of the rectangle, $e(P) = P$. In other words, one may pick up the rectangle and put it down so that each point of the rectangle falls exactly where it fell before. Thus: $e(A) = A$, $e(B) = B$, $e(C) = C$, $e(D) = D$. We shall abbreviate the preceding four equations:

$$(1) \qquad e(ABCD) = (ABCD)$$

In fact, the function e is completely determined by (1); for obviously the position of each point on our rectangle is determined by the position of the vertices of the rectangle.

Secondly, one may rotate the rectangle about an axis bisecting the sides AD, BC. Thus, we have a function f mapping the rectangle $ABCD$ onto itself such that:

$$(2) \qquad f(ABCD) = (DCBA)$$

Thirdly, a similar rotation, about an axis bisecting sides AB, CD:

$$(3) \qquad g(ABCD) = (BADC)$$

Fourthly, one may rotate the rectangle through an angle of 180°, about an axis through its center, perpendicular to the plane of the rectangle:

$$(4) \qquad h(ABCD) = (CDAB)$$

The student may now convince himself that there are no other ways in which the rectangle may (without breaking or distortion) be fitted upon itself.

It is interesting to note that our last fitting h could have been attained by two successive rotations about our axes in the plane of the rectangle rather than by one rotation about an axis perpendicular to the plane. For if we followed function f by function g:

$$gf(ABCD) = g(DCBA) = (CDAB)$$

(since, by (3), $g(D) = C$, etc.).

That is to say, $gf = h$.

It should not surprise us that the composite of two of the functions mapping rectangle $ABCD$ onto itself is equal to a third such function, for clearly, if we twice pick up a rectangle and put it down upon its original position, it rests finally in its original position, with certain possible changes in the position of its vertices.

In other words, our set of functions $\{e, f, g, h\}$ under the operation of composition of functions (see Section 6.7) is *closed*.

The fact that this operation is closed becomes evident also when we compute its "operation table":

	e	f	g	h
e	e	f	g	h
f	f	e	h	g
g	g	h	e	f
h	h	g	f	e

Besides being closed, we note secondly that the operation of composition in the set $\{e, f, g, h\}$ is *associative* [see Exercise 26, Problem 6e]. For example (from the table above), $f(gh) = ff = e$ and $(fg)h = hh = e$, so that $f(gh) = (fg)h$.

Thirdly, we note that there is an *identity* element in the set $\{e, f, g, h\}$ for the operation of composition; that is to say, there is an element e in the set $\{e, f, g, h\}$ such that, for any x in that set: $ex = x$, $xe = x$. (Since e is the function which places each point of our rectangle in its original position, we are not surprised that fitting e followed by fitting x, as well as fitting x followed by fitting e, should amount simply to fitting x.)

Fourthly, we note that, if the rectangle is moved so that it fits some way into its original position, one may always by a second motion bring *each point* of the rectangle back into its original position. Indeed, since any motion fitting our rectangle onto its original position may be reversed to give us again such a motion, the *inverse* (see Section 6.7) of any function of the set $\{e, f, g, h\}$ must also be a member of the set.

For example, the motions represented by g, g^{-1} effect the following mappings of vertices:

$$
\begin{array}{cc}
g & g^{-1} \\
A \longrightarrow B & B \longrightarrow A \\
B \longrightarrow A & A \longrightarrow B \\
C \longrightarrow D & D \longrightarrow C \\
D \longrightarrow C & C \longrightarrow D
\end{array}
$$

Clearly, both g followed by g^{-1} and g^{-1} followed by g place each vertex, hence each point of the rectangle, in its original position; i.e., $gg^{-1} = e$, and $g^{-1}g = e$.

Now we have said that g^{-1} must be a member of the set $\{e, f, g, h\}$. But which? It is easy to see, in fact, that $g^{-1} = g$; that is to say, g is its own inverse. For $g^{-1}(A) = B = g(A)$, etc. Indeed, from the geometrical point of view, it is clear that $gg = e$; for g is a rotation of $180°$ about a line; and two successive rotations of $180°$ about the same line must, of course, restore each point of a figure to its original position. (Similarly, we may see that each one of the elements of the particular set $\{e, f, g, h\}$ is its own inverse under the operation of composition.)

The four properties noted above are known as the *group* properties, and any set, together with an operation in the set that satisfies these properties, is called a *group*. We recapitulate:

Definition. A set S, together with a closed, associative operation $\circ$ in S, is called a *group* if:

1. There exists an element $e \in S$ such that for each $a \in S$:

$$e \circ a = a \circ e = a$$

(*e* is called the *identity* element of the group.)

2. For each element $a \in S$, there exists an element $a^{-1} \in S$ such that:

$$a \circ a^{-1} = e, \qquad a^{-1} \circ a = e$$

(a^{-1}, read: "*a* inverse," is called the *inverse* of a.)

NOTE ON "$=$": We assume here that the relation $=$ is (as it is everywhere in mathematics) reflexive, symmetric, and transitive, and that all operations with which we deal are *well-defined* (see Section 4.3); thus, if a, b, x, y are elements of a group with operation $\circ$, and $a = x$ and $b = y$, then all of the following statements are consequences of our assumption that $\circ$ is well-defined:

$$a \circ b = a \circ y, \qquad a \circ b = x \circ b, \qquad a \circ b = x \circ y$$

We have seen, then, that the above set of functions $\{e, f, g, h\}$ that map a nonsquare rectangle onto itself is a group under the operation of composition of functions. This group is called "the group of nonsquare rectangle." [It is also called "the Klein fourgroup," after the German mathematician, Felix Klein (1849–1925)].

Many, many groups exist, of course; in fact, group theory is one of the richest areas of exploration in contemporary mathematics. (It is interesting to note that foremost among the discoverers of the concept of a group was the young French genius Evariste Galois, of whom we spoke in Chapter 8.)

For example, the set of all real numbers under the operation $+$ is a group; indeed, any set which is a field under $+$, $\cdot$ is easily seen to be a group under $+$. (But not under $\cdot$. Why not?)

▶ **EXERCISE 84**

1. Complete the following table of notation, where $+$, $\cdot$ are addition and multiplication in the set of complex numbers:

Operation	$\circ$	$+$	
Identity element	e		
Inverse of a	a^{-1}		

2. Using the operation table of the preceding section, verify the following cases of the associativity of the operation:

(a) $(fh)g = f(hg)$ (b) $(fg)f = f(gf)$
(c) $(hh)g = h(hg)$ (d) $(ff)f = f(ff)$

3. Find the group of each of the following geometric figures (i.e., name the elements of the group and write out its operation table).

(a) A triangle that is isosceles, but not equilateral.
(b) A scalene triangle (i.e., one that is not isosceles).
(c) An equilateral triangle.
(d) A square.

4. In each of the following cases, tell whether or not the given set and operation constitute a group. If not, tell why not.

(a) The set of all real numbers; $\cdot$
(b) The set of all rational numbers; $+$
(c) The set of all rational numbers; $\cdot$
(d) The set of all nonzero rational numbers; $+$
(e) The set of all nonzero rational numbers; $\cdot$
(f) The set of all nonzero real numbers; $+$
(g) The set of all nonzero real numbers; $\cdot$
(h) The set of all positive real numbers; $+$
(i) The set of all positive real numbers; $\cdot$
(j) The set of all positive rational numbers; $+$
(k) The set of all positive rational numbers; $\cdot$
(l) The set of all integers; $+$
(m) The set of all integers; $\cdot$
(n) The set of all nn; $+$

(*o*) The set of all nn; ·

(*p*) {0, 1, 2}; + mod 3 (see Exercise 23, Problem 16)

(*q*) {0, 1, 2}; · mod 3

(*r*) {1, 2}; · mod 3

(*s*) {0, 1, 2, 3}; + mod 4

(*t*) {0, 1, 2, 3}; · mod 4

(*u*) {1, 2, 3}; · mod 4

5. A group is called *commutative* or *abelian* [after the Norwegian mathematician Niels Abel (1802–1829)] if its operation ∘ is commutative. For each of the groups of Problems 3 and 4, tell whether or not the group is abelian and, if it is not, justify your answer.

6. Two-dimensional vectors (see Section 5.3) may be represented as ordered pairs of real numbers (a, b), and addition is defined for vectors (a, b), (c, d) as follows: $(a, b) + (c, d) = (a + c, b + d)$. Show that the set of all two-dimensional vectors, under this operation $+$, is an abelian group.

7. Prove that, if S is a given set, the set of all permutation functions with domain S is a group under the operation of composition of functions (see Section 11.7).

8. Write out an operation table for the group of all permutation functions (operation: composition) with the following domain:

(*a*) {1}   (*b*) {1, 2}   (*c*) {1, 2, 3}

9. Which of the groups of Problem 8 are abelian, and which not? Justify your answer.

10. How can one tell by examining an operation table whether or not:

(*a*) The operation is closed?

(*b*) The operation is commutative?

(*c*) An identity element exists in the set of the operation?

(*d*) A given element in the set of the operation has an inverse in that set?

11. Show that the elements of the group of Problem 3*c* that are *rotations* of the triangle about an axis perpendicular to its plane form a group (called a subgroup of the group of Problem 3*c*). *Note:* The identity mapping may be regarded as a rotation of 0°.

12. Find a geometric figure whose group contains exactly three elements.

13. In each of the following cases, tell whether or not the given set and operation constitute a group, and justify your answer. (In each case, $m \neq n$ are positive integers.)

(*a*) The set of all $m \times n$ matrices; $+$

(*b*) The set of all $m \times m$ matrices; $+$

(*c*) The set of all $m \times m$ matrices; ·

(d) The set of all $m \times m$ matrices whose determinants are unequal to 0; · (A matrix whose determinant is unequal to 0 is called *nonsingular*.)

(e) The set of all nonsingular $m \times m$ matrices; +

13.3 GROUP THEOREMS

We shall now derive a number of consequences of our axioms for a group (as stated in our definition of a group). Throughout this chapter, *a group G* will mean a set S together with an operation ∘ as described in our definition of a group. We shall follow the custom of speaking of an element a belonging to G when we actually mean that it belongs to S; and, unless otherwise noted, lower-case letters will represent members of a group G.

Theorem G1. (Uniqueness of identity element) If e, f are identity elements of a group G, then $e = f$.

PROOF

1. e is an identity element of G,   1.
   and $f \in G$
2. ∴ $e \circ f = f$ 2. Def. of identity elt.
3. f is an identity element of G,   3.
   and $e \in G$
4. ∴ $e \circ f = e$ 4.
5. ∴ $e = f$ 5.

It is Theorem G1 that justifies our use of the phrase "*the* identity element of a group."

Theorem G2. (Uniqueness of inverse.) If b, c are inverses of a, then $b = c$.

PROOF

1. $b = b \circ e$ 1. Def. of identity elt. and hyp.
2. $= b \circ (a \circ c)$ 2. Def. of inverse elt. and well-definedness of ∘ and hyp.
3. $= (b \circ a) \circ c$ 3.
4. $= e \circ c$ 4.
5. $= c$ 5.
6. ∴ $b = c$ 6.

(The use of what phrase is justified by Theorem G2?)

Theorem G3. (Well-definedness of inverse.) If $a = b$, then $a^{-1} = b^{-1}$.

PROOF

1. $a \circ b^{-1} = b \circ b^{-1}$ 1. Hyp., and well-definedness of $\circ$
2. $= e$ 2.
3. $\therefore a \circ b^{-1} = e$ 3.
4. $b^{-1} \circ a = b^{-1} \circ b$ 4.
5. $= e$ 5.
6. $\therefore b^{-1} \circ a = e$ 6.
7. $\therefore b^{-1}$ is an inverse of a 7. Def. of inverse elt. and steps 3, 6
8. $\therefore a^{-1} = b^{-1}$ 8. Theorem G2

Theorem G4. (Left cancellation law.) If $a \circ b = c \circ d$, and $a = c$, then $b = d$.

PROOF

1. $b = e \circ b$ 1.
2. $= (a^{-1} \circ a) \circ b$ 2.
3. $= a^{-1} \circ (a \circ b)$ 3.
4. $= a^{-1} \circ (c \circ d)$ 4.
5. $= a^{-1} \circ (a \circ d)$ 5.
6. $= (a^{-1} \circ a) \circ d$ 6.
7. $= e \circ d$ 7.
8. $= d$ 8.
9. $\therefore b = d$ 9.

Theorem G5. (Right cancellation law; statement and proof to be supplied by student.)

13.4 THE CONCEPT OF AN INTERPRETATION

An interpreter is someone who translates from one language into another; in doing so, he gives meaning to the matter being translated. The very important mathematical concept of an *interpretation* conforms closely to this idea.

A particular group is defined when we are given a particular set S and a particular operation $\circ$ satisfying the conditions in our definition of a group. For example, the set S of all real numbers together with the operation + constitutes a group (called the additive group of all real numbers). That is to say, if we translate S as "set of all real numbers" and ∘ as "+", all the conditions in our definition of a group become true statements. Since the theorems in the preceding section have been derived from these conditions, each of these theorems will remain true if we translate S by "all real numbers" and "∘" by +. The translated theorem is called an *interpretation* of the original theorem of abstract group theory.

Thus, for the additive group of all real numbers, the interpretation of Theorem G4 is: If a, b, c, d are real numbers, and $a + b = c + d$, and $a = c$, then $b = d$.

It happens also that the set S of all nonzero real numbers, under the operation ·, forms a group (called the multiplicative group of all nonzero real numbers). For this group, the interpretation of Theorem G4 is: If a, b, c, d are nonzero real numbers, and $ab = cd$, and $a = c$, then $b = d$.

The primary importance of group theory lies in the fact that, whenever we have several particular groups at hand, all of the theorems that we have proved in our abstract group theory, when interpreted in the languages of our particular groups, become valid theorems for our particular groups. Thus, we kill many birds with one stone: A single proof serves to justify a number of results. Of further interest is the fact that different interpretations of the same theorem may sometimes seem to be not at all related. (An example will be given in the next section.) Thus group theory often serves the very basic mathematical purpose of revealing common elements in theories that at first glance may seem quite unrelated. In this way group theory helps to unify, simplify, and organize coherently the constantly growing body of mathematical knowledge. (Similar remarks may be made, of course, about fields and other abstract mathematical structures.)

▶ **EXERCISE 85**

1. Fill in the blanks in the proof of Theorem:

(*a*) G1   (*b*) G2   (*c*) G3   (*d*) G4

2. Answer the question following the proof of Theorem G2.
3. State and prove a right cancellation law for groups (Theorem G5).
4. In Chapter 4, identify theorems and problems that are interpretations of Theorems G1 through G5 (their proofs, therefore, may be given simply by showing that they *are* interpretations of Theorems G1 through G5).
5. State a number of interpretations of Theorems G1 through G5 not to be found in Chapter 4.

13.5 FURTHER GROUP THEOREMS

Theorem G6. If $a \circ b = e$, then $b^{-1} = a$.

PROOF

1. $b^{-1} = e \circ b^{-1}$ 1.
2. $= (a \circ b) \circ b^{-1}$ 2.
3. $= a \circ (b \circ b^{-1})$ 3.
4. $= a \circ e$ 4.
5. $= a$ 5.
6. $\therefore b^{-1} = a$ 6.

Theorem G7. If $a \circ b = e$, then $a^{-1} = b$.   (To be proved by student.)

In the light of Theorems G6 and G7, then, one way of proving that two elements of a group are each other's inverses is to prove that the "product" of the two elements is the identity element of the group. For example:

Theorem G8. $(a \circ b)^{-1} = b^{-1} \circ a^{-1}$.

PROOF

1. $(a \circ b) \circ (b^{-1} \circ a^{-1}) = [(a \circ b) \circ b^{-1}] \circ a^{-1}$ 1.
2. $= [a \circ (b \circ b^{-1})] \circ a^{-1}$ 2.
3. $= [a \circ e] \circ a^{-1}$ 3.
4. $= a \circ a^{-1}$ 4.
5. $= e$ 5.
6. $\therefore (a \circ b) \circ (b^{-1} \circ a^{-1}) = e$ 6.
7. $\therefore$ $(a \circ b)^{-1} = b^{-1} \circ a^{-1}$ 7. Theorem G7

Theorem G9. $(a^{-1})^{-1} = a$.

PROOF

1. $a \circ a^{-1} = e$ 1.
2. $\therefore (a^{-1})^{-1} = a$ 2. Theorem G6

Now we define a new operation: $*$. Although this operation is suggested to us by particular well-known operations, we shall for the moment not reveal to the student the motivation for its definition. Our reason is two-fold: For one thing, knowing too much is sometimes actually a handicap in careful reasoning, for then it often becomes difficult to distinguish between that which we have proved and that which we think must be true. For another, progress in mathematics requires that occasionally we follow an argument or strike out in a direction not related to previous concrete experience, and the student should sometimes experience this sort of mathematical activity.

Definition.   The operation $*$ is defined in group G as follows: $a * b = a \circ b^{-1}$.

Theorem G10. $(a * b)^{-1} = b * a$.

PROOF

1. $(a * b)^{-1} = (a \circ b^{-1})^{-1}$ 1. Def. of $*$ and well-definedness of inverse

2. $= (b^{-1})^{-1} \circ a^{-1}$ 2. Theorem G?

3. $= b \circ a^{-1}$ 3.

4. $= b * a$ 4.

5. $\therefore$ $(a * b)^{-1} = b * a$ 5.

Now let us examine several interpretations of the preceding definition and theorem.

In the additive group of real numbers, $a * b = a \circ b^{-1} = a + (-b) = a - b$. Thus, in the additive group of real numbers, the interpretation of "$a * b$" is "$a - b$" and the interpretation of Theorem G10 is: If a, b are real numbers, $-(a - b) = b - a$.

It will be left to the student to interpret "$a * b$" and the preceding theorem in the multiplicative group of nonzero real numbers, and thus to discover that two familiar, but apparently quite different, statements of elementary algebra are essentially the same, both being interpretations of the same theorem of group theory.

▶ **EXERCISE 86**

1. Fill in the blanks in the proof of Theorem:
   (a) G6   (b) G8   (c) G9   (d) G10
2. Prove Theorem G7.
3. Interpret "$a * b$" and Theorem G10 in the multiplicative group of nonzero real numbers.
4. In Chapter 4, identify theorems and problems that are interpretations of Theorems G6 through G10.
5. State a number of interpretations of Theorems G6 through G10 not to be found in Chapter 4.

APPENDIX

TABLES

TABLE I. COMMON LOGARITHMS

N	0	1	2	3	4	5	6	7	8	9
10	0000	0043	0086	0128	0170	0212	0253	0294	0334	0374
11	0414	0453	0492	0531	0569	0607	0645	0682	0719	0755
12	0792	0828	0864	0899	0934	0969	1004	1038	1072	1106
13	1139	1173	1206	1239	1271	1303	1335	1367	1399	1430
14	1461	1492	1523	1553	1584	1614	1644	1673	1703	1732
15	1761	1790	1818	1847	1875	1903	1931	1959	1987	2014
16	2041	2068	2095	2122	2148	2175	2201	2227	2253	2279
17	2304	2330	2355	2380	2405	2430	2455	2480	2504	2529
18	2553	2577	2601	2625	2648	2672	2695	2718	2742	2765
19	2788	2810	2833	2856	2878	2900	2923	2945	2967	2989
20	3010	3032	3054	3075	3096	3118	3139	3160	3181	3201
21	3222	3243	3263	3284	3304	3324	3345	3365	3385	3404
22	3424	3444	3464	3483	3502	3522	3541	3560	3579	3598
23	3617	3636	3655	3674	3692	3711	3729	3747	3766	3784
24	3802	3820	3838	3856	3874	3892	3909	3927	3945	3962
25	3979	3997	4014	4031	4048	4065	4082	4099	4116	4133
26	4150	4166	4183	4200	4216	4232	4249	4265	4281	4298
27	4314	4330	4346	4362	4378	4393	4409	4425	4440	4456
28	4472	4487	4502	4518	4533	4548	4564	4579	4594	4609
29	4624	4639	4654	4669	4683	4698	4713	4728	4742	4757
30	4771	4786	4800	4814	4829	4843	4857	4871	4886	4900
31	4914	4928	4942	4955	4969	4983	4997	5011	5024	5038
32	5051	5065	5079	5092	5105	5119	5132	5145	5159	5172
33	5185	5198	5211	5224	5237	5250	5263	5276	5289	5302
34	5315	5328	5340	5353	5366	5378	5391	5403	5416	5428
35	5441	5453	5465	5478	5490	5502	5514	5527	5539	5551
36	5563	5575	5587	5599	5611	5623	5635	5647	5658	5670
37	5682	5694	5705	5717	5729	5740	5752	5763	5775	5786
38	5798	5809	5821	5832	5843	5855	5866	5877	5888	5899
39	5911	5922	5933	5944	5955	5966	5977	5988	5999	6010
40	6021	6031	6042	6053	6064	6075	6085	6096	6107	6117
41	6128	6138	6149	6160	6170	6180	6191	6201	6212	6222
42	6232	6243	6253	6263	6274	6284	6294	6304	6314	6325
43	6335	6345	6355	6365	6375	6385	6395	6405	6415	6425
44	6435	6444	6454	6464	6474	6484	6493	6503	6513	6522
45	6532	6542	6551	6561	6571	6580	6590	6599	6609	6618
46	6628	6637	6646	6656	6665	6675	6684	6693	6702	6712
47	6721	6730	6739	6749	6758	6767	6776	6785	6794	6803
48	6812	6821	6830	6839	6848	6857	6866	6875	6884	6893
49	6902	6911	6920	6928	6937	6946	6955	6964	6972	6981
50	6990	6998	7007	7016	7024	7033	7042	7050	7059	7067
51	7076	7084	7093	7101	7110	7118	7126	7135	7143	7152
52	7160	7168	7177	7185	7193	7202	7210	7218	7226	7235
53	7243	7251	7259	7267	7275	7284	7292	7300	7308	7316
54	7324	7332	7340	7348	7356	7364	7372	7380	7388	7396

From "College Algebra and Trigonometry," by F. H. Miller. Publisher: John Wiley and Sons (1945).

N	0	1	2	3	4	5	6	7	8	9
55	7404	7412	7419	7427	7435	7443	7451	7459	7466	7474
56	7482	7490	7497	7505	7513	7520	7528	7536	7543	7551
57	7559	7566	7574	7582	7589	7597	7604	7612	7619	7627
58	7634	7642	7649	7657	7664	7672	7679	7686	7694	7701
59	7709	7716	7723	7731	7738	7745	7752	7760	7767	7774
60	7782	7789	7796	7803	7810	7818	7825	7832	7839	7846
61	7853	7860	7868	7875	7882	7889	7896	7903	7910	7917
62	7924	7931	7938	7945	7952	7959	7966	7973	7980	7987
63	7993	8000	8007	8014	8021	8028	8035	8041	8048	8055
64	8062	8069	8075	8082	8089	8096	8102	8109	8116	8122
65	8129	8136	8142	8149	8156	8162	8169	8176	8182	8189
66	8195	8202	8209	8215	8222	8228	8235	8241	8248	8254
67	8261	8267	8274	8280	8287	8293	8299	8306	8312	8319
68	8325	8331	8338	8344	8351	8357	8363	8370	8376	8382
69	8388	8395	8401	8407	8414	8420	8426	8432	8439	8445
70	8451	8457	8463	8470	8476	8482	8488	8494	8500	8506
71	8513	8519	8525	8531	8537	8543	8549	8555	8561	8567
72	8573	8579	8585	8591	8597	8603	8609	8615	8621	8627
73	8633	8639	8645	8651	8657	8663	8669	8675	8681	8686
74	8692	8698	8704	8710	8716	8722	8727	8733	8739	8745
75	8751	8756	8762	8768	8774	8779	8785	8791	8797	8802
76	8808	8814	8820	8825	8831	8837	8842	8848	8854	8859
77	8865	8871	8876	8882	8887	8893	8899	8904	8910	8915
78	8921	8927	8932	8938	8943	8949	8954	8960	8965	8971
79	8976	8982	8987	8993	8998	9004	9009	9015	9020	9025
80	9031	9036	9042	9047	9053	9058	9063	9069	9074	9079
81	9085	9090	9096	9101	9106	9112	9117	9122	9128	9133
82	9138	9143	9149	9154	9159	9165	9170	9175	9180	9186
83	9191	9196	9201	9206	9212	9217	9222	9227	9232	9238
84	9243	9248	9253	9258	9263	9269	9274	9279	9284	9289
85	9294	9299	9304	9309	9315	9320	9325	9330	9335	9340
86	9345	9350	9355	9360	9365	9370	9375	9380	9385	9390
87	9395	9400	9405	9410	9415	9420	9425	9430	9435	9440
88	9445	9450	9455	9460	9465	9469	9474	9479	9484	9489
89	9494	9499	9504	9509	9513	9518	9523	9528	9533	9538
90	9542	9547	9552	9557	9562	9566	9571	9576	9581	9586
91	9590	9595	9600	9605	9609	9614	9619	9624	9628	9633
92	9638	9643	9647	9652	9657	9661	9666	9671	9675	9680
93	9685	9689	9694	9699	9703	9708	9713	9717	9722	9727
94	9731	9736	9741	9745	9750	9754	9759	9763	9768	9773
95	9777	9782	9786	9791	9795	9800	9805	9809	9814	9818
96	9823	9827	9832	9836	9841	9845	9850	9854	9859	9863
97	9868	9872	9877	9881	9886	9890	9894	9899	9903	9908
98	9912	9917	9921	9926	9930	9934	9939	9943	9948	9952
99	9956	9961	9965	9969	9974	9978	9983	9987	9991	9996

TABLE II. COMPOUND INTEREST (AMOUNT OF I)
$$(1 + i)^n$$

n	$\frac{1}{4}\%$	$\frac{1}{2}\%$	1%	$1\frac{1}{2}\%$	2%	$2\frac{1}{2}\%$	3%	$3\frac{1}{2}\%$	4%	5%
1	1.00250	1.00500	1.01000	1.01500	1.02000	1.02500	1.03000	1.03500	1.04000	1.05000
2	1.00501	1.01003	1.02010	1.03023	1.04040	1.05063	1.06090	1.07123	1.08160	1.10250
3	1.00752	1.01508	1.03030	1.04568	1.06121	1.07689	1.09273	1.10872	1.12486	1.15763
4	1.01004	1.02015	1.04060	1.06136	1.08243	1.10381	1.12551	1.14752	1.16986	1.21551
5	1.01256	1.02525	1.05101	1.07728	1.10408	1.13141	1.15927	1.18769	1.21665	1.27628
6	1.01509	1.03038	1.06152	1.09344	1.12616	1.15969	1.19405	1.22926	1.26532	1.34010
7	1.01763	1.03553	1.07214	1.10984	1.14869	1.18869	1.22987	1.27228	1.31593	1.40710
8	1.02018	1.04071	1.08286	1.12649	1.17166	1.21840	1.26677	1.31681	1.36857	1.47746
9	1.02273	1.04591	1.09369	1.14339	1.19509	1.24886	1.30477	1.36290	1.42331	1.55133
10	1.02528	1.05114	1.10462	1.16054	1.21899	1.28008	1.34392	1.41060	1.48024	1.62889
11	1.02785	1.05640	1.11567	1.17795	1.24337	1.31209	1.38423	1.45997	1.53945	1.71034
12	1.03042	1.06168	1.12683	1.19562	1.26824	1.34489	1.42576	1.51107	1.60103	1.79586
13	1.03299	1.06699	1.13809	1.21355	1.29361	1.37851	1.46853	1.56396	1.66507	1.88565
14	1.03557	1.07232	1.14947	1.23176	1.31948	1.41297	1.51259	1.61869	1.73168	1.97993
15	1.03816	1.07768	1.16097	1.25023	1.34587	1.44830	1.55797	1.67535	1.80094	2.07893
16	1.04076	1.08307	1.17258	1.26899	1.37279	1.48451	1.60471	1.73399	1.87298	2.18287
17	1.04336	1.08849	1.18430	1.28802	1.40024	1.52162	1.65285	1.79468	1.94790	2.29202
18	1.04597	1.09393	1.19615	1.30734	1.42825	1.55966	1.70243	1.85749	2.02582	2.40662
19	1.04858	1.09940	1.20811	1.32695	1.45681	1.59865	1.75351	1.92250	2.10685	2.52695
20	1.05121	1.10490	1.22019	1.34686	1.48595	1.63862	1.80611	1.98979	2.19112	2.65330
21	1.05383	1.11042	1.23239	1.36706	1.51567	1.67958	1.86029	2.05943	2.27877	2.78596
22	1.05647	1.11597	1.24472	1.38756	1.54598	1.72157	1.91610	2.13151	2.36992	2.92526
23	1.05911	1.12155	1.25716	1.40838	1.57690	1.76461	1.97359	2.20611	2.46472	3.07152
24	1.06176	1.12716	1.26973	1.42950	1.60844	1.80873	2.03279	2.28333	2.56330	3.22510
25	1.06441	1.13280	1.28243	1.45095	1.64061	1.85394	2.09378	2.36324	2.66584	3.38635
26	1.06707	1.13846	1.29526	1.47271	1.67342	1.90029	2.15659	2.44596	2.77247	3.55567
27	1.06974	1.14415	1.30821	1.49480	1.70689	1.94780	2.22129	2.53157	2.88337	3.73346
28	1.07241	1.14987	1.32129	1.51722	1.74102	1.99650	2.28793	2.62017	2.99870	3.92013
29	1.07510	1.15562	1.33450	1.53998	1.77584	2.04641	2.35657	2.71188	3.11865	4.11614
30	1.07778	1.16140	1.34785	1.56308	1.81136	2.09757	2.42726	2.80679	3.24340	4.32194
31	1.08048	1.16721	1.36133	1.58653	1.84759	2.15001	2.50008	2.90503	3.37313	4.53804
32	1.08318	1.17304	1.37494	1.61032	1.88454	2.20376	2.57508	3.00671	3.50806	4.76494
33	1.08589	1.17891	1.38869	1.63448	1.92223	2.25885	2.65234	3.11194	3.64838	5.00319
34	1.08860	1.18480	1.40258	1.65900	1.96068	2.31532	2.73191	3.22086	3.79432	5.25335
35	1.09132	1.19073	1.41660	1.68388	1.99989	2.37321	2.81386	3.33359	3.94609	5.51602
36	1.09405	1.19668	1.43077	1.70914	2.03989	2.43254	2.89828	3.45027	4.10393	5.79182
37	1.09679	1.20266	1.44508	1.73478	2.08069	2.49335	2.98523	3.57103	4.26809	6.08141
38	1.09953	1.20868	1.45953	1.76080	2.12230	2.55568	3.07478	3.69601	4.43881	6.38548
39	1.10228	1.21472	1.47412	1.78721	2.16474	2.61957	3.16703	3.82537	4.61637	6.70475
40	1.10503	1.22079	1.48886	1.81402	2.20804	2.68506	3.26204	3.95926	4.80102	7.03999
41	1.10780	1.22690	1.50375	1.84123	2.25220	2.75219	3.35990	4.09783	4.99306	7.39199
42	1.11057	1.23303	1.51879	1.86885	2.29724	2.82100	3.46070	4.24126	5.19278	7.76159
43	1.11334	1.23920	1.53398	1.89688	2.34319	2.89152	3.56452	4.38970	5.40050	8.14967
44	1.11612	1.24539	1.54932	1.92533	2.39005	2.96381	3.67145	4.54334	5.61652	8.55715
45	1.11892	1.25162	1.56481	1.95421	2.43785	3.03790	3.78160	4.70236	5.84118	8.98501
46	1.12171	1.25788	1.58046	1.98353	2.48661	3.11385	3.89504	4.86694	6.07482	9.43426
47	1.12452	1.26417	1.59626	2.01328	2.53634	3.19170	4.01190	5.03728	6.31782	9.90597
48	1.12733	1.27049	1.61223	2.04348	2.58707	3.27149	4.13225	5.21359	6.57053	10.40127
49	1.13015	1.27684	1.62835	2.07413	2.63881	3.35328	4.25622	5.39606	6.83335	10.92133
50	1.13297	1.28323	1.64463	2.10524	2.69159	3.43711	4.38391	5.58493	7.10668	11.46740

This table is reproduced by permission of the Society of Actuaries.

TABLE III. PRESENT VALUE OF I

n	$\frac{1}{4}\%$	$\frac{1}{2}\%$	1%	$1\frac{1}{2}\%$	2%	$2\frac{1}{2}\%$	3%	$3\frac{1}{2}\%$	4%	5%
1	.99751	.99502	.99010	.98522	.98039	.97561	.97087	.96618	.96154	.95238
2	.99502	.99007	.98030	.97066	.96117	.95181	.94260	.93351	.92456	.90703
3	.99254	.98515	.97059	.95632	.94232	.92860	.91514	.90194	.88900	.86384
4	.99006	.98025	.96098	.94218	.92385	.90595	.88849	.87144	.85480	.82270
5	.98759	.97537	.95147	.92826	.90573	.88385	.86261	.84197	.82193	.78353
6	.98513	.97052	.94205	.91454	.88797	.86230	.83748	.81350	.79031	.74622
7	.98267	.96569	.93272	.90103	.87056	.84127	.81309	.78599	.75992	.71068
8	.98022	.96089	.92348	.88771	.85349	.82075	.78941	.75941	.73069	.67684
9	.97778	.95610	.91434	.87459	.83676	.80073	.76642	.73373	.70259	.64461
10	.97534	.95135	.90529	.86167	.82035	.78120	.74409	.70892	.67556	.61391
11	.97291	.94661	.89632	.84893	.80426	.76214	.72242	.68495	.64958	.58468
12	.97048	.94191	.88745	.83639	.78849	.74356	.70138	.66178	.62460	.55684
13	.96806	.93722	.87866	.82403	.77303	.72542	.68095	.63940	.60057	.53032
14	.96565	.93256	.86996	.81185	.75788	.70773	.66112	.61778	.57748	.50507
15	.96324	.92792	.86135	.79985	.74301	.69047	.64186	.59689	.55526	.48102
16	.96084	.92330	.85282	.78803	.72845	.67362	.62317	.57671	.53391	.45811
17	.95844	.91871	.84438	.77639	.71416	.65720	.60502	.55720	.51337	.43630
18	.95605	.91414	.83602	.76491	.70016	.64117	.58739	.53836	.49363	.41552
19	.95367	.90959	.82774	.75361	.68643	.62553	.57029	.52016	.47464	.39573
20	.95129	.90506	.81954	.74247	.67297	.61027	.55368	.50257	.45639	.37689
21	.94892	.90056	.81143	.73150	.65978	.59539	.53755	.48557	.43883	.35894
22	.94655	.89608	.80340	.72069	.64684	.58086	.52189	.46915	.42196	.34185
23	.94419	.89162	.79544	.71004	.63416	.56670	.50669	.45329	.40573	.32557
24	.94184	.88719	.78757	.69954	.62172	.55288	.49193	.43796	.39012	.31007
25	.93949	.88277	.77977	.68921	.60953	.53939	.47761	.42315	.37512	.29530
26	.93714	.87838	.77205	.67902	.59758	.52623	.46369	.40884	.36069	.28124
27	.93481	.87401	.76440	.66899	.58586	.51340	.45019	.39501	.34682	.26785
28	.93248	.86966	.75684	.65910	.57437	.50088	.43708	.38165	.33348	.25509
29	.93015	.86533	.74934	.64936	.56311	.48866	.42435	.36875	.32065	.24295
30	.92783	.86103	.74192	.63976	.55207	.47674	.41199	.35628	.30832	.23138
31	.92552	.85675	.73458	.63031	.54125	.46511	.39999	.34423	.29646	.22036
32	.92321	.85248	.72730	.62099	.53063	.45377	.38834	.33259	.28506	.20987
33	.92091	.84824	.72010	.61182	.52023	.44270	.37703	.32134	.27409	.19987
34	.91861	.84402	.71297	.60277	.51003	.43191	.36604	.31048	.26355	.19035
35	.91632	.83982	.70591	.59387	.50003	.42137	.35538	.29998	.25342	.18129
36	.91403	.83564	.69892	.58509	.49022	.41109	.34503	.28983	.24367	.17266
37	.91175	.83149	.69200	.57644	.48061	.40107	.33498	.28003	.23430	.16444
38	.90948	.82735	.68515	.56792	.47119	.39128	.32523	.27056	.22529	.15661
39	.90721	.82323	.67837	.55953	.46195	.38174	.31575	.26141	.21662	.14915
40	.90495	.81914	.67165	.55126	.45289	.37243	.30656	.25257	.20829	.14205
41	.90269	.81506	.66500	.54312	.44401	.36335	.29763	.24403	.20028	.13528
42	.90044	.81101	.65842	.53509	.43530	.35448	.28896	.23578	.19257	.12884
43	.89820	.80697	.65190	.52718	.42677	.34584	.28054	.22781	.18517	.12270
44	.89596	.80296	.64545	.51939	.41840	.33740	.27237	.22010	.17805	.11686
45	.89372	.79896	.63905	.51171	.41020	.32917	.26444	.21266	.17120	.11130
46	.89149	.79499	.63273	.50415	.40215	.32115	.25674	.20547	.16461	.10600
47	.88927	.79103	.62616	.49670	.39427	.31331	.24920	.19852	.15828	.10095
48	.88705	.78710	.62026	.48936	.38654	.30567	.24200	.19181	.15219	.09614
49	.88484	.78318	.61412	.48213	.37896	.29822	.23495	.18532	.14634	.09156
50	.88263	.77929	.60804	.47500	.37153	.29094	.22811	.17905	.14071	.08720

* This table is reproduced by permission of the Society of Actuaries.

TABLE IV. AMOUNT OF I PER ANNUM

n	$\frac{1}{4}\%$	$\frac{1}{2}\%$	1%	$1\frac{1}{2}\%$	2%	$2\frac{1}{2}\%$	3%	$3\frac{1}{2}\%$	4%	5%
1	1.0000	1.0000	1.0000	1.0000	1.0000	1.0000	1.0000	1.0000	1.0000	1.0000
2	2.0025	2.0050	2.0100	2.0150	2.0200	2.0250	2.0300	2.0350	2.0400	2.0500
3	3.0075	3.0150	3.0301	3.0452	3.0604	3.0756	3.0909	3.1062	3.1216	3.1525
4	4.0150	4.0301	4.0604	4.0909	4.1216	4.1525	4.1836	4.2149	4.2465	4.3101
5	5.0251	5.0503	5.1010	5.1523	5.2040	5.2563	5.3091	5.3625	5.4163	5.5256
6	6.0376	6.0755	6.1520	6.2296	6.3081	6.3877	6.4684	6.5502	6.6330	6.8019
7	7.0527	7.1059	7.2135	7.3230	7.4343	7.5474	7.6625	7.7794	7.8983	8.1420
8	8.0704	8.1414	8.2857	8.4328	8.5830	8.7361	8.8923	9.0517	9.2142	9.5491
9	9.0905	9.1821	9.3685	9.5593	9.7546	9.9545	10.1591	10.3685	10.5828	11.0266
10	10.1133	10.2280	10.4622	10.7027	10.9497	11.2034	11.4639	11.7314	12.0061	12.5779
11	11.1385	11.2792	11.5668	11.8633	12.1687	12.4835	12.8078	13.1420	13.4864	14.2068
12	12.1664	12.3356	12.6825	13.0412	13.4121	13.7956	14.1920	14.6020	15.0258	15.9171
13	13.1968	13.3972	13.8093	14.2368	14.6803	15.1404	15.6178	16.1130	16.6268	17.7130
14	14.2298	14.4642	14.9474	15.4504	15.9739	16.5190	17.0863	17.6770	18.2919	19.5986
15	15.2654	15.5365	16.0969	16.6821	17.2934	17.9319	18.5989	19.2957	20.0236	21.5786
16	16.3035	16.6142	17.2579	17.9324	18.6393	19.3802	20.1569	20.9710	21.8245	23.6575
17	17.3443	17.6973	18.4304	19.2014	20.0121	20.8647	21.7616	22.7050	23.6975	25.8404
18	18.3876	18.7858	19.6147	20.4894	21.4123	22.3863	23.4144	24.4997	25.6454	28.1324
19	19.4336	19.8797	20.8109	21.7967	22.8406	23.9460	25.1169	26.3572	27.6712	30.5390
20	20.4822	20.9791	22.0190	23.1237	24.2974	25.5447	26.8704	28.2797	29.7781	33.0660
21	21.5334	22.0840	23.2392	24.4705	25.7833	27.1833	28.6765	30.2695	31.9692	35.7193
22	22.5872	23.1944	24.4716	25.8376	27.2990	28.8629	30.5368	32.3289	34.2480	38.5052
23	23.6437	24.3104	25.7163	27.2251	28.8450	30.5844	32.4529	34.4604	36.6179	41.4305
24	24.7028	25.4320	26.9735	28.6335	30.4219	32.3490	34.4265	36.6665	39.0826	44.5020
25	25.7646	26.5591	28.2432	30.0630	32.0303	34.1578	36.4593	38.9499	41.6459	47.7271
26	26.8290	27.6919	29.5256	31.5140	33.6709	36.0117	38.5530	41.3131	44.3117	51.1135
27	27.8961	28.8304	30.8209	32.9867	35.3443	37.9120	40.7096	43.7591	47.0842	54.6691
28	28.9658	29.9745	32.1291	34.4815	37.0512	39.8598	42.9309	46.2906	49.9676	58.4026
29	30.0382	31.1244	33.4504	35.9987	38.7922	41.8563	45.2189	48.9108	52.9663	62.3227
30	31.1133	32.2800	34.7849	37.5387	40.5681	43.9027	47.5754	51.6227	56.0849	66.4388
31	32.1911	33.4414	36.1327	39.1018	42.3794	46.0003	50.0027	54.4295	59.3283	70.7608
32	33.2716	34.6086	37.4941	40.6883	44.2270	48.1503	52.5028	57.3345	62.7015	75.2988
33	34.3547	35.7817	38.8690	42.2986	46.1116	50.3540	55.0778	60.3412	66.2095	80.0638
34	35.4406	36.9606	40.2577	43.9331	48.0338	52.6129	57.7302	63.4532	69.8579	85.0670
35	36.5292	38.1454	41.6603	45.5921	49.9945	54.9282	60.4621	66.6740	73.6522	90.3203
36	37.6206	39.3361	43.0769	47.2760	51.9944	57.3014	63.2759	70.0076	77.5983	95.8363
37	38.7146	40.5328	44.5076	48.9851	54.0343	59.7339	66.1742	73.4579	81.7022	101.6281
38	39.8114	41.7354	45.9527	50.7199	56.1149	62.2273	69.1594	77.0289	85.9703	107.7095
39	40.9109	42.9441	47.4123	52.4807	58.2372	64.7830	72.2342	80.7249	90.4091	114.0950
40	42.0132	44.1588	48.8864	54.2679	60.4020	67.4026	75.4013	84.5503	95.0255	120.7998
41	43.1182	45.3796	50.3752	56.0819	62.6100	70.0876	78.6633	88.5095	99.8265	127.8398
42	44.2260	46.6065	51.8790	57.9231	64.8622	72.8398	82.0232	92.6074	104.8196	135.2318
43	45.3366	47.8396	53.3978	59.7920	67.1595	75.6608	85.4839	96.8486	110.0124	142.9933
44	46.4499	49.0788	54.9318	61.6889	69.5027	78.5523	89.0484	101.2383	115.4129	151.1430
45	47.5661	50.3242	56.4811	63.6142	71.8927	81.5161	92.7199	105.7817	121.0294	159.7002
46	48.6850	51.5758	58.0459	65.5684	74.3306	84.5540	96.5015	110.4840	126.8706	168.6852
47	49.8067	52.8337	59.6263	67.5519	76.8172	87.6679	100.3965	115.3510	132.9454	178.1194
48	50.9312	54.0978	61.2226	69.5652	79.3535	90.8596	104.4084	120.3883	139.2632	188.0254
49	52.0585	55.3683	62.8348	71.6087	81.9406	94.1311	108.5406	125.6018	145.8337	198.4267
50	53.1887	56.6452	64.4632	73.6828	84.5794	97.4843	112.7969	130.9979	152.6671	209.3480

This table is reproduced by permission of the Society of Actuaries.

TABLE V. PRESENT VALUE OF I PER ANNUM

n	$\frac{1}{4}\%$	$\frac{1}{2}\%$	1%	$1\frac{1}{2}\%$	2%	$2\frac{1}{2}\%$	3%	$3\frac{1}{2}\%$	4%	5%
1	0.9975	0.9950	0.9901	0.9852	0.9804	0.9756	0.9709	0.9662	0.9615	0.9524
2	1.9925	1.9851	1.9704	1.9559	1.9416	1.9274	1.9135	1.8997	1.8861	1.8594
3	2.9851	2.9702	2.9410	2.9122	2.8839	2.8560	2.8286	2.8016	2.7751	2.7232
4	3.9751	3.9505	3.9020	3.8544	3.8077	3.7620	3.7171	3.6731	3.6299	3.5460
5	4.9627	4.9259	4.8534	4.7826	4.7135	4.6458	4.5797	4.5151	4.4518	4.3295
6	5.9478	5.8964	5.7955	5.6972	5.6014	5.5081	5.4172	5.3286	5.2421	5.0757
7	6.9305	6.8621	6.7282	6.5982	6.4720	6.3494	6.2303	6.1145	6.0021	5.7864
8	7.9107	7.8230	7.6517	7.4859	7.3255	7.1701	7.0197	6.8740	6.7327	6.4632
9	8.8885	8.7791	8.5660	8.3605	8.1622	7.9709	7.7861	7.6077	7.4353	7.1078
10	9.8639	9.7304	9.4713	9.2222	8.9826	8.7521	8.5302	8.3166	8.1109	7.7217
11	10.8368	10.6770	10.3676	10.0711	9.7868	9.5142	9.2526	9.0016	8.7605	8.3064
12	11.8073	11.6189	11.2551	10.9075	10.5753	10.2578	9.9540	9.6633	9.3851	8.8633
13	12.7753	12.5562	12.1337	11.7315	11.3484	10.9832	10.6350	10.3027	9.9856	9.3936
14	13.7410	13.4887	13.0037	12.5434	12.1062	11.6909	11.2961	10.9205	10.5631	9.8986
15	14.7042	14.4166	13.8651	13.3432	12.8493	12.3814	11.9379	11.5174	11.1184	10.3797
16	15.6650	15.3399	14.7179	14.1313	13.5777	13.0550	12.5611	12.0941	11.6523	10.8378
17	16.6235	16.2586	15.5623	14.9076	14.2919	13.7122	13.1661	12.6513	12.1657	11.2741
18	17.5795	17.1728	16.3983	15.6726	14.9920	14.3534	13.7535	13.1897	12.6593	11.6896
19	18.5332	18.0824	17.2260	16.4262	15.6785	14.9789	14.3238	13.7098	13.1339	12.0853
20	19.4845	18.9874	18.0456	17.1686	16.3514	15.5802	14.8775	14.2124	13.5903	12.4622
21	20.4334	19.8880	18.8570	17.9001	17.0112	16.1845	15.4150	14.6980	14.0292	12.8212
22	21.3800	20.7841	19.6604	18.6208	17.6580	16.7654	15.9369	15.1671	14.4511	13.1630
23	22.3241	21.6757	20.4558	19.3309	18.2922	17.3321	16.4436	15.6204	14.8568	13.4886
24	23.2660	22.5629	21.2434	20.0304	18.9139	17.8850	16.9355	16.0584	15.2470	13.7986
25	24.2055	23.4456	22.0232	20.7196	19.5235	18.4244	17.4131	16.4815	15.6221	14.0939
26	25.1426	24.3240	22.7952	21.3986	20.1210	18.9506	17.8768	16.8904	15.9828	14.3752
27	26.0774	25.1980	23.5596	22.0676	20.7069	19.4640	18.3270	17.2854	16.3296	14.6430
28	27.0000	26.0677	24.3164	22.7267	21.2813	19.9649	18.7641	17.6670	16.6631	14.8981
29	27.9400	26.9330	25.0658	23.3761	21.8444	20.4535	19.1885	18.0358	16.9837	15.1411
30	28.8679	27.7941	25.8077	24.0158	22.3965	20.9303	19.6004	18.3920	17.2920	15.3725
31	29.7034	28.6508	26.5423	24.6461	22.9377	21.3954	20.0004	18.7363	17.5885	15.5928
32	30.7166	29.5033	27.2696	25.2671	23.4683	21.8492	20.3888	19.0689	17.8736	15.8027
33	31.6375	30.3515	27.9897	25.8790	23.9886	22.2919	20.7658	19.3902	18.1476	16.0025
34	32.5561	31.1955	28.7027	26.4817	24.4986	22.7238	21.1318	19.7007	18.4112	16.1929
35	33.4724	32.0354	29.4086	27.0756	24.9986	23.1452	21.4872	20.0007	18.6646	16.3742
36	34.3865	32.8710	30.1075	27.6607	25.4888	23.5563	21.8323	20.2905	18.9083	16.5469
37	35.2982	33.7025	30.7995	28.2371	25.9695	23.9573	22.1672	20.5705	19.1426	16.7113
38	36.2077	34.5299	31.4847	28.8051	26.4406	24.3486	22.4925	20.8411	19.3679	16.8679
39	37.1149	35.3531	32.1630	29.3646	26.9026	24.7303	22.8082	21.1025	19.5845	17.0170
40	38.0199	36.1722	32.8347	29.9158	27.3555	25.1028	23.1148	21.3551	19.7928	17.1591
41	38.9226	36.9873	33.4997	30.4590	27.7995	25.4661	23.4124	21.5991	19.9931	17.2944
42	39.8230	37.7983	34.1581	30.9941	28.2348	25.8206	23.7014	21.8349	20.1856	17.4232
43	40.7212	38.6053	34.8100	31.5212	28.6616	26.1664	23.9819	22.0627	20.3708	17.5459
44	41.6172	39.4082	35.4555	32.0406	29.0800	26.5038	24.2543	22.2828	20.5488	17.6628
45	42.5109	40.2072	36.0945	32.5523	29.4902	26.8330	24.5187	22.4955	20.7200	17.7741
46	43.4024	41.0022	36.7272	33.0565	29.8923	27.1542	24.7754	22.7009	20.8847	17.8801
47	44.2916	41.7932	37.3537	33.5532	30.2866	27.4675	25.0247	22.8994	21.0429	17.9810
48	45.1787	42.5803	37.9740	34.0426	30.6731	27.7732	25.2667	23.0912	21.1951	18.0772
49	46.0635	43.3635	38.5881	34.5247	31.0521	28.0714	25.5017	23.2766	21.3415	18.1687
50	46.9462	44.1428	39.1961	34.9997	31.4236	28.3623	25.7298	23.4556	21.4822	18.2559

This table is reproduced by permission of the Society of Actuaries.

SELECTED ANSWERS

Exercise 1, page 5

2. Yes; 6.
3. 2 one-to-one correspondences exist between the given sets.

Exercise 2, page 10

2. (b) $\{x, y\}, \{x\}, \{y\}, \varnothing$; 4.
4. (a) A nn a is said to be *even* if there exists a nn b such that $a = 2b$.
5. (c) For example, $24 = 2 \cdot 2 \cdot 2 \cdot 3$.
8. (a) T.   (c) F.   (e) F.   (i) F.

Exercise 4, page 29

10. (i) Range: the set of all odd nn; the image of 3 is 5; the pre-image of 11 is 6; the function is one-one.
    (iii) Range: the set of all nn that are 1 more than a perfect square; the image of 3 is 2; the pre-images of 2 are 1 and 3; the function is many-one, since there does exist an element of the range (2, for example) which has more than one pre-image.
    (v) Range: $\{1, 2, 3, 4, 5\}$; the image of 3 is 3; the pre-image of 4 is 4; the function is one-one.
    (vii) Range: $\{16\}$; the image of 3 is 16; the pre-image of 16 is 3; the function is one-one.
11. (a) $f(x) = 5x$.

Exercise 5, page 35

6. (a) $8 \circ 2 = 14$; $\circ$ is closed, not commutative, not associative.
   (c) $8 \circ 2 = 17$; $\circ$ is closed, commutative, not associative.
   (f) $8 \circ 2 = 4$; $\circ$ is commutative, not closed, not associative.

Exercise 6, page 39

2. Subtraction.
5. (a) Yes, since $7 = 7/1$, and 7 and 1 are nn.

Exercise 7, page 43

1. (a) 5.   (c) Not defined.   (e) 42.   (g) 1451.
2. (a) (i) 10,111,010,100.   (iii) 21,432.
       (v) t44.   (b) (ii) 2,102,210.
3. (a) 14; 40.   (c) 24; 143.
   (e) 110; 1331.   (g) 214; 11,143.

4. (b) (i) 13; 30.   (iii) 30; 203.
     (v) 121; 2112.   (vii) 220; 10,033.
5. (b) (i) 14; 40.   (iii) 24; 143.
     (v) $e0t$; $t0e1$.   (vii) 20; 100.

Exercise 8, page 49

	(a)	(c)	(e)	(g)	(i)	(k)
1. Absolute values of numbers	2, 1	2, 1	2, 2	10, 5	10, 5	0, 1
Sum of numbers	3	1	0	-5	-15	1
Absolute value of sum	3	1	0	5	15	1
Sum of absolute values	3	3	4	15	15	1
3. Difference	1	3	4	-15	-5	-1
Product	2	-2	-4	-50	50	0
Quotient	2	-2	-1	-2	2	0

4. (a) ± 1.   (c) 0.   (e) There are none.
5. (c) $2 > -1$.   (c) $2 > -2$.   (g) $-10 < 5$.
     (i) $-10 < -5$.   (k) $0 < 1$.
6. (a) 10.   (c) 0.   (e) -10.

	(a)	(c)	(e)	(g)	(i)	(k)
7. Absolute value of product	2	2	4	50	50	0
Product of absolute values	2	2	4	50	50	0

9. (a) Always true, never true, never true, never true.

Exercise 9, page 57

2. (a) $A \cup B = \{2 \cdots 7\}$.   (c) $A \cap C = N$.   (e) $A \cup N = A$.
     (f) $A \cap N = N$.   (h) $B \cap D = \{3, 4, 5, 6, 7\}$.
5. $A(3, 2)$, $C(-5, 3)$, $E(0, 7)$.
12. (a) Range: $\{0 \cdots 9\}$; f is many-one.
     (c) Range: $\{-4 \cdots 3\}$; f is one-one.
     (e) Range: $\{-12 \cdots 9\}$; f is one-one.
     (h) Range: $\{7\}$; f is many-one.
     (l) Range: $\{-0.25 \cdots 6\}$; f is many-one.
     (n) Range: $\{0 \cdots 81\}$; f is many-one.
     (p) Range: $\{-7 \cdots 2\}$; f is many-one.
     (r) Range: $\{1 \cdots 6\}$; f is one-one.
14. (a) Range: $\{7, 11\}$; f is many-one.
     (c) Range: $\{10\} \cup \{0 \cdots 5\}$; f is many-one.

Exercise 10, page 63

2. $>$ is not reflexive, since it is not true for each real number a that $a > a$; $>$ is not symmetric, since it is not true that whenever $a > b$, then $b > a$; $>$ is transitive, since it is true that whenever $a > b$ and $b > c$, then $a > c$; $>$ is not an equivalence relation; $\geq$ is reflexive and transitive, but not symmetric, therefore not an equivalence relation.
3. (b) (i) In the set of all integers, $\vert$ is reflexive and transitive, but not symmetric.
     (iii) In the set of all positive rational numbers, $\vert$ is reflexive, symmetric and transitive, hence an equivalence relation.
     (v) In the set $\{1, 2, 4, 8\}$, $\vert$ is reflexive and transitive, but not symmetric.

4. (*a*) Not reflexive, since it is not true that each American is his own father; not symmetric since it is not true that whenever *a* is the father of *b*, then *b* is the father of *a*; not transitive, since it is not true that whenever *a* is the father of *b* and *b* is the father of *c*, then *a* is the father of *c*; not an equivalence relation.

    (*c*) Symmetric, not reflexive, not transitive.

Exercise 11, page 70

2. (*a*) Hint: Construct a rectangle with sides of lengths *a* and *b* + *c*; *a, b, c* may be any *positive* real numbers.

3. (*a*) Construct (how?) a right triangle with hypotenuse of length 2 and an arm of length 1; then the other arm will be of length $\sqrt{3}$ (why?). Or proceed somewhat similarly, making use of the already constructed length of $\sqrt{2}$.

Exercise 12, page 79

2. (*a*) $0.16666\cdots$.   (*c*) $0.040000\cdots$.

3. (*a*) 2/9.   (*c*) 41/33.   (*e*) 37/999.

10. For 0.77, rows 5, 6, 9 should be checked.

Exercise 13, page 89

4. (*a*) *If x is a real number and y is a real number, then* $x + y = y + x$; commutativity of addition (Axiom F2).

    (*c*) Transitivity of equality (Axiom F1).

    (*e*) *If a is a real number and b is a real number, then* $ab = ba$; commutativity of multiplication (Axiom F2).

    (*g*) *If a is a real number and b is a real number, then* $(1 + a) + b = 1 + (a + b)$; associativity of addition (Axiom F2).

    (*i*) Associativity of multiplication (Axiom F2), or closure and commutativity of multiplication (Axiom F2).

    (*k*) *If r is a real number, then* $1 \cdot r = r$. (Problem 1.)

Exercise 16, page 98

2. Either $x = 0$ or $y = 0$ (by Theorem R9).

4. Either $x = 0$ or $x = 0$, (by Theorem R9), hence $x = 0$ (by definition of "or").

5. (*b*) If $xy = 60$, then $x = 5$ and $y = 12$ (false).

    If $x = 5$ and $xy = 60$, then $y = 12$ (true).

    If $xy = 60$ and $y = 12$, then $x = 5$ (true).

6. (*b*) The equality of two angles in a triangle implies that the triangle is isosceles.

    In order for a triangle to be isosceles, it is sufficient that two angles of the triangle be equal.

    In order for a triangle to have two equal angles, it is necessary that the triangle be isosceles.

9. (*a*) 0 (MPZ).   (*d*) -77 [Theorem R10 (i)].

    (*g*) -8 [Definition (Exercise 14, Problem 3), Theorem R10 (iii), (i)].

    (*j*) -4 [Definition (Exercise 14, Problem 3)].

    (*m*) $-x^3$ [Same as (*g*)].   (*p*) $2x$ [Exercise 15, Problem 17].

    (*s*) $6xy$ [Associativity and commutativity of multiplication, Theorem R10 (iii)].

(v) $13x^2$ [Definition (Exercise 14, Problem 3), associativity and commutativity of multiplication, Theorem R10 (iii), RDL].

Exercise 17, page 102

6. $7 - 4 = 3, 7 - 3 = 4; 8 - 6 = 2, 8 - 2 = 6$; etc.
7. (a) $7x - 7y$.   (c) $xz - yz$.   (e) $(3 - 2)a$.
9. (a) ab.   (c) 0.   (e) $-5a$.   (g) $4a - 3b + 4c$.
   (i) $x^3 - 2x^2 + 4x$.   (k) $a + (1/a)$.
10. (c) Binomial; $a(b - c)$, $-(b - c)$.
    (e) Binomial; $-2a$, $-3a$.
    (g) Trinomial; $a - 3b + 7c$, $2a - b - 4c$, $a + b + c$.
    (i) Binomial.   (k) Binomial.
11. (a) -2.   (c) 0.   (e) -5.
    (g) 10.   (i) -57.   (k) 2.

Exercise 18, page 105

15. $\{x \mid x \neq 7\}$.
19. $10 \div 2 = 5$, $10 \div 5 = 2$; etc.
20. (a) $q = 1$ $r = 4$.   (c) $q = 32, r = 0$.   (e) $q = 3, r = 2$.
    (g) $q = 4, r = 3$.
21. (b) (i) $1 + (4/7)$.

Exercise 19, page 110

4. (a) $x^2 + 6x + 9$.   (c) $x^2 + 5x + 6$.
   (e) $x^2 - x - 6$.   (g) $4x^2 + 12xy + 9y^2$.
   (i) $4x^2 - 9y^2$.   (k) $6x^2 + 5xy - 6y^2$.
   (m) $6x^2 - 13xy + 6y^2$.   (o) $x^4 - 1$.
   (q) $x^2 + 2 + (1/x^2)$.   (s) $acx^2 + (ad + bc)x + bd$.
   (u) $(a + b)^2 - c^2$.   (w) $10y^2 - 8xy$.
   (y) $14x + 5$.
7. (a) $2(x + y)$.   (c) $3(x + y)(x - y)$.
   (e) $(x + 2)^2$.   (g) $(x - 1)(x - 2)$.
   (i) $(2x + 1)(x - 2)$.   (k) $(x - a)(x - b)$.
   (m) $(a + b + c)(a + b - c)$.   (o) $(6x + 1)(x - 6)$.

Exercise 23, page 143

5. (e) (i) $1/4$.
6. (a) 6.   (c) -3.   (e) $4i$.   (g) $2\sqrt{2}$.
   (i) $8i$.   (k) $4\sqrt{3}$. (m) $-4\sqrt{3}$. (o) $2i\sqrt{2}$.
   (q) $\sqrt{3}/3$. (s) $\sqrt{3}$.   (u) $i\sqrt{2}/8$. (w) $\sqrt{2}/2$.
7. (a) 2.4.   (c) 3.2.   (e) 3.9.   (g) 4.5.
   (i) 0.7.   (k) 0.8.   (m) 0.6.   (o) 0.2.
8. (a) $|x|$.   (c) $2i|x|$.   (e) -3.   (g) $|x - 3|$.
10. (a) $(7,7)$; $5,5$, $7\sqrt{2}$ lb.   (c) $(7, 1)$; $5,5$, $5\sqrt{2}$ lb.
    (e) $(0,0)$; $5,5$, 0 lb.   (g) $(5,12)$; $\sqrt{13},5,5$, 13 lb.
12. (a) 20.6 mi./hr.

Exercise 24, page 151

1. (a) 2 cis $0°$.   (c) 2 cis $180°$.   (e) $2\sqrt{2}$ cis $45°$.
   (g) $2\sqrt{2}$ cis $225°$.   (i) 2 cis $30°$.
   (k) 2 cis $210°$.   (m) 2 cis $60°$.
   (o) 2 cis $240°$.

3. (a) $5\sqrt{3} + 5i$.   (c) $5 + 5\sqrt{3}i$.
   (e) 1.   (g) -1.
   (i) $-2 + 2\sqrt{3}i$.   (k) $-2\sqrt{3} + 2i$.
   (m) $-5\sqrt{3} - 5i$.   (o) $-5 - 5\sqrt{3}i$.
   (q) $(1/2) - (\sqrt{3}/2)i$.   (s) $(\sqrt{3}/2) - (1/2)i$.

4. (a) 16.   (c) $512 - 512\sqrt{3}i$.
   (e) 16.   (g) 8.   (i) -1.

5. (a) $\pm [(\sqrt{2}/2) + (\sqrt{2}/2)i]$.   (c) $(\sqrt{6}/2) + (\sqrt{2}/2)i,\ -(\sqrt{6}/2) - (\sqrt{2}/2)i$.
   (e) $\pm 1,\ \pm i$.   (g) $\pm 1,\ \pm [(1/2) + (\sqrt{3}/2)i],\ \pm [(1/2) - (\sqrt{3}/2)i]$.
   (i) $\pm [(\sqrt{2}/2) + (\sqrt{2}/2)i],\ \pm [(-\sqrt{2}/2) + (\sqrt{2}/2)i]$.

8. (a) -1.   (c) $(1 \pm i\sqrt{3})/2$.

Exercise 25, page 164

1. (a) 512.   (c) -512.   (e) 256.
   (g) 256.   (i) 81.   (k) -81.
   (m) 162.   (o) 4096.   (q) 0.
   (s) Not defined.   (u) 1.   (w) 1.
   (y) 250.   (a') $2/125$.   (c') 58.
   (e') $1/2$.   (g') $1/3$.   (i') $1/10$.
   (k') $1/64$.   (m') 243.   (o') 64.
   (q') 2.   (s') 81.   (u') $16/81$.
   (w') $2/3$.   (y') $(3/2)i$.

2. (a) $1/a^2$; a nonzero complex.
   (c) $1/\sqrt{a}$; a nonzero real.
   (e) $1/a^3$; a nonzero complex.
   (g) $a + b$; $a + b$ nonzero complex.
   (i) a/b; b nonzero complex, a complex.
   (k) $11a$; a nonzero complex.
   (m) $2a$; a nonzero complex.
   (o) $(a + b)/ab$; a, b nonzero complex.
   (q) b/a; a, b nonzero complex.
   (s) $1/a^3$; a nonzero complex.
   (u) $a + b$; a, b nonzero complex.
   (w) a^{10}; a nonzero complex.
   (y) $1/a^2$; a nonzero real.
   (a') $\sqrt[6]{a}/a^2$; a positive real.
   (c') $a\sqrt[5]{a}$; a real.
   (e') $\sqrt{b}/\sqrt{a}$; a, b nonzero real.
   (g') $b\sqrt[3]{b}/a\sqrt[3]{a}$; a, b nonzero real.
   (i') $1/ab^3$; a, b nonzero real.
   (k') $(\sqrt{a} + \sqrt{b})/\sqrt{ab}$; a, b positive real.
   (m') $b\sqrt{b}/a\sqrt{a}$; a, b nonzero real.

3. (a) a^{-1}; a nonzero complex.
   (c) ab^{-1}; b nonzero complex, a complex.
   (e) $(a + b)^{1/2}$; $a + b$ real.
   (g) a^{-3}; a nonzero complex.
   (i) $a^{3/4}$; a non-negative real.
   (k) $a^{-1/3}$; a nonzero real.
   (m) $a^{1/3}$; a non-negative real.

    (o) a^6; a real.
    (q) $a^{-1/2}$; a nonzero real.
    (s) $3 \cdot 10^{-1}$.
    (u) ab^{-2}; a, b complex, $b \neq 0$.
    (w) $(a + b)^{-1}$; $a + b$ nonzero complex.
4. (a) a^7; a complex.
    (c) $1/a^3$; a nonzero complex.
    (e) a^7; a nonzero complex.
    (g) $(a^3 + 1)/a^5$; a nonzero complex.
    (i) c^2/a^2; a, b, c nonzero complex.
    (k) $4a^2b^4$; a, b complex.
    (m) $18a^4b^5$; a, b complex.
    (o) ab; a, b nonzero real.
    (q) a^3b^2; a, b nonzero complex.
    (s) $2a^{5/4}$; a non-negative real.
    (u) $4a$; a real.
    (w) $6ab\sqrt[6]{2ab/3}$; ab non-negative real.
    (y) $(x^2 + 1)^{-3/2}$; $x^2 + 1$ nonzero real.
5. (a) $-i$.   (c) i.   (e) $-i$.   (g) i.
   (i) $-i$.   (k) i.   (m) i.   (o) -1.
   (q) 1.
7. (a) 200.   (c) 0.03.   (e) 2.5×10^{-2}.
   (g) 1×10^1.   (i) 2.5×10^1.   (k) 9.3×10^7.
   (m) 6.78.   (o) 1.204×10^1.
8. (a) 1×10^3.
9. (a) 8.93×10^{-5} gram.   (c) (8.53×10^{10} years.
10. (a) 500 seconds.
11. (a) Range: All positive real numbers; one-one.
13. (a) Range: All positive real numbers; one-one.
    (c) Range: All negative real numbers; one-one.
    (e) Range: $\{0 \to 1\}$; many one.
15. (a) 2^{x+1}.   (c) $2^{2x} - 2^{-2x}$.   (e) $2^{2x} - 2 + 2^{-2x}$.

Exercise 26, page 170

1. (a) 11.   (c) $4x - 1$.   (e) 19.   (g) 4.
   (i) $2x^2 - 8x + 10$.   (k) 65.
2. (a) $fg(1) = 1/2$.   (b) $fg(x) = 2^{2x-3}$.
   (c) The domain of fg is the set of all real numbers.

Exercise 27, page 174

1. (a) -3.   (c) -1.   (e) 1.   (g) 3.
   (i) Nonexistent.   (k) -2.   (m) 0.   (o) 2.
2. (a) $x = \log_{10} 5$.   (c) $\log_{10} 2 \doteq 0.3010$.
3. (a) $10^{0.4771} \doteq 3$.   (c) $10^y = x$.

Exercise 28, page 182

4. (a) 18,15.   (c) 1.414.   (e) 1.096×10^{12}.
   (g) 23,940.   (i) 1.732.   (k) 961.8.
   (m) 10.66.   (p) 5.092.   (s) 5.810.
   (t) 0.3162.   (v) -0.06979.

Exercise 29, page 186

1. (a) No degree; constant.
   (e) Degree 2; quadratic.
   (i) Degree 1; linear.
   (m) Degree 2; quadratic.
   (q) Degree 3, cubic.
   (u) Degree 4, quartic.
   (y) Degree 1, linear.

   (c) Degree 0; constant.
   (g) No degree; constant.
   (k) Degree 2; quadratic.
   (o) Degree 2; quadratic.
   (s) Degree 3; cubic.
   (w) Degree 3, cubic.

3. (a) $n = 0, a_0 = 0$.
   (e) $n = 2, a_0 = 1, a_1 = 0, a_2 = 0$.
   (g) $n = 0, a_0 = 0$.
   (i) $n = 1, a_0 = -1, a_1 = 1$.
   (k) $n = 2, a_0 = -2, a_1 = 0, a_2 = 0$.
   (m) $n = 2, a_0 = 1, a_1 = -1, a_2 = 5$.
   (o) $n = 2, a_0 = -1, a_1 = 0, a_2 = 0$.
   (q) $n = 3, a_0 = 1, a_1 = -3, a_2 = 0, a_3 = 0$.
   (s) $n = 3, a_0 = -1, a_1 = 1, a_2 = 1, a_3 = 1$.
   (u) $n = 4, a_0 = 1, a_1 = 0, a_2 = -1, a_3 = 0, a_4 = 0$.
   (w) $n = 3, a_0 = 1, a_1 = 1, a_2 = -4, a_3 = -4$.
   (y) $n = 1, a_0 = 4, a_1 = 0$.

   (c) $n = 0, a_0 = -\sqrt{2}$.

5. (a) No degree; constant.
   (e) Degree 0; constant.
   (i) No degree; constant.
   (m) Degree 3, cubic.
   (q) Degree 2; quadratic.
   (u) Degree 2; quadratic.
   (y) Degree 3; cubic.

   (c) Degree 1; linear.
   (g) Degree 2; quadratic.
   (k) Degree 2; quadratic.
   (o) Degree 2; quadratic.
   (s) Degree 3; cubic.
   (w) No degree; constant.

6. (a) $x^3 + x^2 + x + 7 - \sqrt{2}$.
   (e) $2x + 2y - \sqrt{2}$.

   (c) $x^6 + 3x^3 - 3x^2 + 5x - 3$.
   (g) $x^3 + y^3 + 3x^2 - y^2 + x + 1$.

7. (a) $2x; 2y, -2y; x^2 - y^2$.
   (c) $2x^2 + x + 1; -3x + 3, 3x - 3; x^4 + x^3 - x^2 + 5x - 2$.
   (e) $x^2 + xy + y^2 + x - y; x^2 + xy + y^2 - x + y,$
       $x - y - x^2 - xy - y^2; x^3 - y^3$.
   (g) $x^3 + x^2 + 2x; x^3 + x^2 + 2, -x^3 - x^2 - 2; x^4 - 1$.

Exercise 30, page 193

1. (a) $q = x - 5, r = 12$.
   (e) $q = 2x^2 - 3x - 1, r = 4x + 2$.
   (g) $q = x^2 + 2x + 4, r = 0$.
   (i) $q = x^2 + ax + a^2, r = 0$.
   (k) $q = x^3 + ax^2 + a^2x + a^3, r = 0$.
   (m) $q = y^2 - 3xy + x^2, r = 0$.

   (c) $q = 2x^2 + x + 2, r = 11$.

3. (a) $x + 2 + [3/(x - 1)]$, for all complex x except $x = 1$.
   (c) $y^2 - 1 + [2/(y^2 + 1)]$, for all complex $y \neq \pm i$.

5. (a) $f(4) = 96, f(-4) = -184$.
       $f(1/2) = 5, f(-1/2) = 3/2$.
   (c) $f(4) = 800, f(-4) = 1056, f(1/2) = -3/2, f(-1/2) = -1$.

6. (a) $4x^4 - 2x^3 - 6x^2 = 2x^2(2x - 3)(x + 1)$; roots; $x = -1, 0, 3/2$.

Exercise 31, page 199

1. $-2/3$. 3. $-1/16$. 5. -1, $(a \neq b)$. 7. $-(a + b)$, $(a \neq b)$.

9. $-a/b$, $(b \neq 0, x \neq y)$. 11. $2a + b$, $(b \neq 2a)$.

13. $(x + y)/(x - 2y)$, $(x \neq 2y, 3y)$.

15. $x + 2$, $(x \neq 3)$. 17. $(b + a)/(b - a)$, $(a, b, a - b \neq 0)$.

19. $b/(1 + a)$, $(a \neq 0, -1)$. 21. $(x + 1)/(x - 1)$, $(x \neq \pm 1)$.

23. $2/(x^2 - 1)$, $(x \neq \pm 1)$. 25. $3/2a$, $(a, x - y \neq 0)$.

27. $y/(x + 2)$, $(x \neq \pm 2, y \neq 0)$.

29. $-4/3$, $(a, b \neq 0)$. 31. $2/(a + 3)^2$, $(a \neq \pm 3)$.

33. $ay/2x$, $(x, y, x + y \neq 0)$. 35. 2, $(a \neq 0$ or $b \neq 0, a - 2b \neq 0)$.

37. $59/72$. 39. $1/(1 + x)$, $(x \neq \pm 1)$.

41. $-12x/(x^2 - 9)$, $(x \neq \pm 3)$.

43. $(3x^2 - 3x + 2)/(x - 2)(x - 1)(x + 1)$, $(x \neq \pm 1, 2)$.

45. $-1/(x^2 - 1)$, $(x \neq \pm 1)$. 47. 0, $(a \neq b, b \neq c, a \neq c)$.

49. $x^2 + y^2$, $(x, y \neq 0)$.

51. $(r^2 + rs + s^2)/(r + s)$, $(r, s \neq 0, r \neq \pm s)$.

53. $(x - 1)/(x + 1)$, $(x \neq 0, \pm 1)$.

Exercise 32, page 204

2. (a) $a^3 - 3a^2b + 3ab^2 - b^3$.

   (c) $27a^3 + 54a^2b + 36ab^2 + 8b^3$.

   (e) $1 - 3x + 3x^2 - x^3$.

   (g) $16a^4 + 32a^3b + 24a^2b^2 + 8ab^3 + b^4$.

   (i) $1 + 4x + 6x^2 + 4x^3 + x^4$.

   (k) $a^5 - 5a^4b + 10a^3b^2 - 10a^2b^3 + 5ab^4 - b^5$.

   (m) $243a^5 + 810a^4b + 1080a^3b^2 + 720a^2b^3 + 240ab^4 + 32b^5$.

   (o) $1 - 5x + 10x^2 - 10x^3 + 5x^4 - x^5$.

3. 2.7.

Exercise 33, page 214

3. Length: 150 gar; width: 24 gar. 5. $x = 1.6$.

6. (a) 7. (c) $(1 \pm \sqrt{5})/2$. (e) $1/2, -2$.

   (g) ± 1 (i) $0, -1$. (k) $(-1 \pm \sqrt{-3})/2$.

8. (a) (i) $\{3, -3\}$; (ii) $\{3\}$. (c) (i) $\{-1 \leftrightarrow 3\}$; (ii) $\{1, 2, 3\}$.

   (e) (i) $\{2 \leftrightarrow 7\}$; (ii) $\{2, 3, 4, 5, 6, 7\}$.

Exercise 34, page 219

1. (a) $x = \pm 2$. (c) $x = -2, 3$. (e) $x = 0, 9/4$.

   (g) $x = 2, 3$. (i) $x = -1/3, -1/2$. (k) $x = 0$.

   (m) $x = 0$.

2. (a) $x = 4$. (c) $x = 16/9$. (e) $x = 1$. (g) $x = 4/9$.

   (i) No solution.

Exercise 35, page 224

2. (a) $x > 1$. (c) $x \geqslant -2/5$. (e) $-1 < x \leqslant 4$.

   (g) No solution. (i) $-2 < x \leqslant -1$.

3. (c) $x > 3$ or $x < -3$. (e) Interval $(-\sqrt{5}, \sqrt{5})$.

   (g) No solution. (i) Interval $(-3, 1)$.

   (k) Interval $(-4, 1)$. (m) $x > 2$ or $x < 0$.

   (o) Interval $(-2, 1/2)$. (q) No solution.

4. (b) $x = 2$ or $x = -5$. (d) $x = -2$ or $x = 5$.

   (f) $x > 4$ or $x < -6$.

Exercise 36, page 229

1. (a) $\{-2, \pm 1/3\}$.   (c) $\{-2/3, 3/2, -1 \pm \sqrt{2}\}$.

    (e) $\{0, 3, \pm 1/2\}$.   (g) $\{1/2, -1/3, \pm i\sqrt{2}\}$.

2. (a) $p(x) = (x + 2)(3x + 1)(3x - 1)$.

    (c) $p(x) = (3x + 2)(2x - 3)(x^2 + 2x - 1)$.

    (e) $p(x) = x(x - 3)(2x + 1)(2x - 1)$.

Exercise 37, page 234

6. (a) $x - 1 = 0$.   (c) $x^3 - 6x^2 + 11x - 6 = 0$.

    (e) $6x^2 - 5x + 1 = 0$.   (g) $x^2 - 4x + 13 = 0$.

    (i) $x^3 - x^2 + x - 1 = 0$.   (k) $3x^3 - 20x^2 + 87x - 50 = 0$.

Exercise 38, page 241

1. (a) A constant polynomial of no degree, whose graph is a straight line, the X-axis.

    (e) A second-degree, or quadratic, polynomial, whose graph only rises, both to the right and to the left of the origin. The graph is symmetric to the Y-axis, has one extremum (a minimum), and intercepts the axes only at the origin.

    (g) A fourth-degree, or quartic, polynomial; the rest of our discussion is as for (e) above. How, then, do the graphs differ?

    (j) The discussion in this case is exactly as in (e) above. How do the graphs differ?

    (l) A third-degree, or cubic, polynomial whose graph only rises to the left and only falls to the right of the origin. The graph has 0 or 2 extrema (it turns out to be 0) and intercepts the axes only at the origin.

    (n) A second-degree, or quadratic, polynomial whose graph eventually only rises on both right and left. It has one extremum (a minimum), no x-intercepts, and y-intercept 5.

    (p) A third-degree, or cubic, polynomial whose graph eventually only rises on the right and falls on the left. The graph has 0 or 2 extrema (it turns out to be 2), an x-intercept between 2 and 3, and a y-intercept of -5.

    (r) A cubic polynomial whose graph eventually only rises on the right and falls on the left. The graph has 0 or 2 extrema, and intercepts at the origin and $x = 3$.

    (t) A cubic polynomial, whose graph eventually only rises on the right and falls on the left. The graph has 0 or 2 extrema, x-intercepts 2, -1, -3, and y-intercept -6.

Exercise 39, page 246

2. (a) 1.7.   (c) 2.4.   (e) 2.8.   (g) 1.3.

    (i) 1.6.   (k) 1.8.   (m) 2.0.   (o) 7.5.

4. (a) No.   (b) One positive and either two negative or two imaginary roots.

    (d) 1.7.   (e) 1.67.

5. (a) No.   (b) Same as 4b.

    (d) 1.5.   (e) 1.52.

7. (b) -0.2, -2.1.

9. (a) One negative and either two positive or two imaginary roots; upper bound 1, lower bound −1.
   (c) One negative and either two positive or two imaginary roots; upper bound 2, lower bound −3.
   (e) Either two negative and two imaginary, or four imaginary roots; upper bound 0, lower bound −3.
10. (a) {3/2, −0.4, −2.6}.
    (c) {2/3, 2.1, −0.3, −1.9}.
11. $x = 4.088$.
12. (a) $x = 2.322$.   (c) $x = 5.288$.
13. (a) 3.322.   (c) 0.6309.

Exercise 40, page 256

1. (a) {(6, −3)}; neither.   (c) { }; inconsistent.
   (e) {(0, 2)}; neither.
2. (a) {(−2, 6, −15)}; neither.
   (c) { }; inconsistent.
   (e) {(2, 1/2 − 1)}; neither.
   (g) {(0, 0, 0)}; neither.
3. (a) {(0, 0), (3, 9)}.
   (c) {(2, 5), (−1 + 2i, −2 − 4i), (−1 − 2i, −2 + 4i)}.
   (e) {($\sqrt{10}$, 2$\sqrt{10}$), (−$\sqrt{10}$, −2$\sqrt{10}$), (2$\sqrt{10}$, $\sqrt{10}$), (−2$\sqrt{10}$, −$\sqrt{10}$)}.
4. (a) {(2, −3), (−4/3, 11/3)}.
   (c) {($\sqrt{2}$, 2), (−$\sqrt{2}$, 2), (−$\sqrt{2}$, −2), ($\sqrt{2}$, −2)}.

Exercise 41, page 261

1. (a) $(x, y) = (6, 1)$; minimum $C = 9$ cents.
   (c) $(x, y) = (0, 5)$ or (6, 1) or any point on the line segment joining these two points; minimum $C = 15$ cents.
2. (a) 5 cards, 1 box.
3. (a) 27 skate keys, 1 can opener.
   (c) 5 skate keys, 45 can openers.
   (e) 0 skate keys, 50 can openers.
4. (a) k skate keys, $50 - k$ can openers, where k is any member of the set {0, 1, 2, 3, 4, 5}. (But note that $k = 0$ involves minimum use of machine time.)
5. (a) 0 gram of Dis, 8 grams of Dat.
   (c) 2 grams of Dis, 6 grams of Dat.
   (e) 8 grams of Dis, 4 grams of Dat.

Exercise 42, page 267

1. $1,620.00.   3. 8%.   5. 1096.
7. (a) Not A. P.   (c) Not A. P.   (e) 49.   (g) 485.
10. (e) 1224.   (g) 11,985.
11. (a) $40 + (n - 1)8$.   (b) $232; $3400.

Exercise 43, page 270

1. $110.41; $121.90.
3. A: $130.00, $160.00, $190.00, $220.00, $250.00.
   B: $134.39, $180.61, $242.73, $326.20, $438.39.
5. $3\frac{1}{2}$%.   7. 18 yrs.; 17.5 yrs.; 28 yrs.

Exercise 44, page 273

1. (a) 512; 1023.   (c) Not G. P.
   (e) -1024; -682.   (g) 1/128; 1023/128.
3. $(1/2)^{12}$.
7. (a) 2.   (c) 100/9.   (e) 4.
9. 160 ft.

Exercise 45, page 276

1. \$135.48.   3. Better.   5. In the year 2000.

Exercise 46, page 279

2. \$2.67; \$2.69.

Exercise 47, page 280

2. (a) \$74.25.   (c) \$61.15.
3. \$712.97.   5. \$8195.40.   7. \$9173.80.

Exercise 48, page 282

1. \$715.84.   3. \$277.27.
5. (a) \$6921.72.   (b) \$(S/1.17304) = \$(0.85248S).
7. \$237.15.   9. \$242,974.   11. \$115.

Exercise 49, page 286

1. \$28,187.80.   3. \$426.21.   5. \$2575.29.
7. b, a, c.   9. 24%.   11. \$8110.90.

Exercise 50, page 294

1.

Grade	Frequency	Cumulative Frequency	Cumulative Relative Frequency
54	1	1	0.083
56	1	2	0.167
65	1	3	0.250
72	3	6	0.500
75	1	7	0.583
78	1	8	0.667
83	2	10	0.833
87	1	11	0.917
92	1	12	1.000

Class Intervals	Frequency	Cumulative Frequency	Cumulative Relative Frequency
50–60	2	2	0.167
60–70	1	3	0.250
70–80	5	8	0.667
80–90	3	11	0.917
90–100	1	12	1.000

3.

Letters	Frequency	Cumulative Frequency	Cumulative Relative Frequency
1	1	1	0.033
2	5	6	0.200
3	4	10	0.333
4	6	16	0.533
5	1	17	0.567
6	1	18	0.600
7	3	21	0.700
8	1	22	0.733
9	1	23	0.767
10	3	26	0.867
11	1	27	0.900
12	1	28	0.933
13	2	30	1.000

Class Intervals	Frequency	Cumulative Frequency	Cumulative Relative Frequency
0–3	10	10	0.333
3–6	8	18	0.600
6–9	5	23	0.767
9–12	5	28	0.933
12–15	2	30	1.000

6.

Hours	Frequency	Cumulative Frequency	Cumulative Relative Frequency
720	1	1	0.050
840	1	2	0.100
860	1	3	0.150
940	1	4	0.200
970	1	5	0.250
980	3	8	0.400
990	1	9	0.450
1010	1	10	0.500
1040	1	11	0.550
1100	1	12	0.600
1120	2	14	0.700
1130	1	15	0.750
1220	1	16	0.800
1280	1	17	0.850
1300	1	18	0.900
1340	1	19	0.950
1410	1	20	1.000

Class Intervals	Frequency	Cumulative Frequency	Cumulative Relative Frequency
700–800	1	1	0.050
800–900	2	3	0.150
900–1000	6	9	0.450
1000–1100	3	12	0.600
1100–1200	3	15	0.750
1200–1300	3	18	0.900
1300–1400	1	19	0.950
1400–1500	1	20	1.000

7. (a)

Score	Frequency	Cumulative Frequency	Cumulative Relative Frequency
51	1	1	0.067
55	1	2	0.133
58	1	3	0.200
62	1	4	0.267
64	1	5	0.333
67	1	6	0.400
71	1	7	0.467
73	1	8	0.533
74	1	9	0.600
75	1	10	0.667
77	1	11	0.733
78	1	12	0.800
90	1	13	0.867
91	1	14	0.933
94	1	15	1.000

Class Intervals	Frequency	Cumulative Frequency	Cumulative Relative Frequency
50–60	3	3	0.200
60–70	3	6	0.400
70–80	6	12	0.800
80–90	1	13	0.867
90–1000	2	15	1.000

Exercise 51, page 297

1. Ungrouped mean, 74.1; grouped mean, 75.0; ungrouped median, 72; grouped median, 76.0.
3. Ungrouped mean, 5.8; grouped mean, 5.6; ungrouped median, 4; grouped median, 4.9.
6. Ungrouped mean, 1066; grouped mean, 1065; ungrouped median, 1010; grouped median, 1033.
7. (a) Ungrouped mean, 72.0; grouped mean, 72.3; ungrouped median, 73; grouped median, 72.5.

Exercise 52, page 299

1. Ungrouped: 65; 83; 56; 87; 83.
   Grouped: 70.0; 83.3; 56.0; 89.3; 80.1.
3. Ungrouped: 3; 9; 2; 11; 7.
   Grouped: 2.2; 8.7; 0.9; 11.4; 7.3.
6. Ungrouped: 970; 1130; 840; 1300; 1120.
   Grouped: 933; 1200; 850; 1300; 1147.
7. (a) Ungrouped: 62; 78; 55; 91; 77.
       Grouped: 62.5; 78.8; 55.0; 92.5; 76.8.

Exercise 53, page 301

1. Ungrouped: 38; 18; 11.0.
   Grouped: 50; 13.3; 11.5.
3. Ungrouped: 12; 6; 3.7.
   Grouped: 15; 6.5; 3.8.

6. Ungrouped: 690; 160; 176.
   Grouped: 800; 267; 177.
7. (*a*) Ungrouped: 43; 16; 12.5.
   Grouped: 50; 16.3; 12.5.

Exercise 55, page 310
1. (*a*) 1/26.   (*c*) 5/26.   (*e*) 0.
2. (*a*) 1/6.   (*c*) 1/2.   (*e*) 1.   (*g*) 0.   (*i*) 5/6.
3. (*a*) 1/13.   (*c*) 1/52.   (*e*) 3/4.
6. (*b*) 1/4.   (*d*) 1/2.
7. (*b*) 1/8.   (*d*) 1/2.   (*e*) 1/2.

Exercise 56, page 314
1. 456,976.   2. (*a*) 67,600.   (*c*) 1,336,336.
3. (*u*) 12.   (*c*) 1/4.
4. (*a*) 216.   (*c*) 125/216.   (*e*) 5/72.
5. (*b*) 1/1024.
6. (*b*) 1/2704.   (*d*) 51/1352.   (*f*) 1/52.
7. (*a*) 1/32.   8. (*a*) 64.   (*c*) 32.

Exercise 57, page 317
2. (*a*) 1.   (*c*) 120.   (*e*) 479,001,600.
3. (*a*) 12.   (*c*) 95,040.   (*e*) 479,001,600.
5. (*a*) 7.   (*c*) 210.   (*e*) 2520.   (*g*) 5040.
7. (*a*) 6.   10. (*a*) 120.   (*c*) 24.   (*e*) 3125.
11. (*a*) 120.   (*c*) 1/5; 1/5; 2/5

Exercise 58, page 321
1 (*a*) 6   (*c*) 20   (*e*) 60
2 (*a*) 20   (*c*) 60.
4. (*a*) 362,880.   (*c*) 10,080.
6. 170.   8. 1/4.   10. 720.

Exercise 59, page 325
1. (*a*) 26.   (*b*) 358,800.   4. 4.
6. (*a*) 64.   (*c*) 24.   8. 450; 150; 200.
9. 72; 48.   11. 120.   13. 1/216; 1/1024.
15. (*a*) 1.   (*c*) 360.

Exercise 60, page 330
1. (*a*) 5.   (*c*) 35.   (*e*) 28.   (*g*) 1.
3. (*a*) 28.   5. 35.   7. 20; 15; 1; 1.
9. (*a*) 1/20.   (*c*) 9/20.   (*e*) 1/20.
12. 180.   14. 1326; 270,725.
16. 2197/20,825, or approximately 0.1.
18. (*a*) 358,800.   (*c*) 2600.   (*e*) 17,576.
20. 120; 64; 112.

Exercise 61, page 334
1. (*a*) $21x^2y^5$.   (*c*) $120x^7y^3$.   (*e*) $-120x^3y^7$.
   (*g*) $11,520x^2y^8$.   (*i*) $-10x$.

Exercise 62, page 338

1. (a) 1/2.   (b) 1/2.   (c) 1/6.   (d) 5/6.
   (e) 1/12.   (f) 5/12.
3. (a) 1/1024.   (c) 11/1024.   (e) 1013/1024.
5. (a) 1/221; 1/169.   (c) 188/221; 144/169.
7. (a) 1/35; 27/343.   (c) 4/35; 64/343.
   (e) 18/35; 144/343.

Exercise 63, page 341

1 (a) 0.6.   (b) 0.24; 0.24; 0.36; 0.16.
  (c) 0.096; 0.288; 0.432; 0.216; 0.064.
3. (a) 0.59049.   (c) 0.0729.   (e) 0.00045.   (g) 0.40951.
4. $65/81 \doteq 0.802$; $665/729 \doteq 0.912$.
6. $66\frac{2}{3}\%$; 75%.   8. 75%.   10. 2.9701%.

Exercise 64, page 345

1. The odds in favor of 1 are 0:1; of 2, 1:35; of 3, 1:17; of 4, 1:11; of 5, 1:8; of 6, 5:31; of 7, 1:5; of 8, 5:31; of 9, 1:8; of 10, 1:11; of 11, 1:17; of 12, 1:35.
3. 9/10.   5. (a) 0.001.   (b) − $3.99.   (c) $14.56 (loss).
6. Expense money: $10.

Exercise 65, page 352

2. (a) Using either the $2s$ or the $3s$ criterion, the coin is true.
   (b) Using either the $2s$ or the $3s$ criterion, the coin is untrue.
5. (a) Under either the $2s$ or the $3s$ criterion: Yes.
   (c) Under either the $2s$ or the $3s$ criterion: No.
   (e) Under the $2s$ criterion: Yes; under the $3s$ criterion: No.
   (g) The probability that this will happen is 1/1296, which means that either under the $2s$ criterion ($\doteq 0.05$), or under the $3s$ criterion ($\doteq 0.003$), the dice must be considered to be loaded.
7. (a) Under either the $2s$ or the $3s$ criterion: No.
   (c) Under the $2s$ criterion: No; under the $3s$ criterion: Yes.
   (e) Under either the $2s$ or the $3s$ criterion: Yes.
9. (a) A test is not feasible in this case.
   (c) A test is not feasible in this case.
   (e) A test is feasible in this case, under the $2s$ criterion. At least 85 right would demonstrate that Tom's claim is justified; fewer, and he would have to admit that it is not. Under the $3s$ criterion, a test is not feasible in this case.
12. Under the $2s$ criterion, at least 108; under the $3s$ criterion, at least 117.

Exercise 66, page 358

1. (a) $\begin{pmatrix} 2 & 3 \\ 4 & 5 \end{pmatrix}$.

   (b) $\begin{pmatrix} 2 & 3 \\ 4 & 5 \end{pmatrix}\begin{pmatrix} x \\ y \end{pmatrix} = \begin{pmatrix} 2x + 3y \\ 4x + 5y \end{pmatrix}$.

   (c) $\begin{pmatrix} 2 & 3 \\ 4 & 5 \end{pmatrix}\begin{pmatrix} 7 \\ 8 \end{pmatrix} = \begin{pmatrix} 38 \\ 68 \end{pmatrix}$.

   (d) $2 \times 2, 2 \times 1, 2 \times 1$.

3. (a) $\begin{pmatrix} 2 & 3 & 1 \\ 3 & -1 & -1 \end{pmatrix}$.

   (b) $\begin{pmatrix} 2 & 3 & 1 \\ 3 & -1 & -1 \end{pmatrix}\begin{pmatrix} x \\ y \\ z \end{pmatrix} = \begin{pmatrix} 2x + 3y + z \\ 3x - y - z \end{pmatrix}$.

(c) $\begin{pmatrix} 2 & 3 & 1 \\ 3 & -1 & -1 \end{pmatrix} \begin{pmatrix} 7 \\ 8 \\ 9 \end{pmatrix} = \begin{pmatrix} 47 \\ 4 \end{pmatrix}.$

(d) $2 \times 3, 3 \times 1, 2 \times 1.$

5. (a) $(3 \quad -2 \quad 1).$　　　　(b) $(3 \quad -2 \quad 1) \begin{pmatrix} x \\ y \\ z \end{pmatrix} = 3x - 2y + z.$

(c) $(3 \quad -2 \quad 1) \begin{pmatrix} 7 \\ 8 \\ 9 \end{pmatrix} = 14.$　　　　(d) $1 \times 3, 3 \times 1, 1 \times 1.$

7. (a) $(1 \quad 1).$　　　　(b) $(1 \quad 1) \begin{pmatrix} x \\ y \end{pmatrix} = x + y.$

(c) $(1 \quad 1) \begin{pmatrix} 7 \\ 8 \end{pmatrix} = 15.$　　　　(d) $1 \times 2, 2 \times 1, 1 \times 1.$

9. (a) $(1).$　　　　(b) $(1)(x) = x.$

(c) $(1)(7) = 7.$　　　　(d) $1 \times 1, 1 \times 1, 1 \times 1.$

11. (a) $\begin{pmatrix} 2 \\ 3 \end{pmatrix}.$　　　　(b) $\begin{pmatrix} 2 \\ 3 \end{pmatrix}(x) = \begin{pmatrix} 2x \\ 3x \end{pmatrix}.$

(c) $\begin{pmatrix} 2 \\ 3 \end{pmatrix}(7) = \begin{pmatrix} 14 \\ 21 \end{pmatrix}.$　　　　(d) $2 \times 1, 1 \times 1, 2 \times 1.$

13. (a) $\begin{pmatrix} 1 & 1 & 0 \\ 0 & 1 & 1 \\ 1 & 0 & 1 \end{pmatrix}.$　　　　(b) $\begin{pmatrix} 1 & 1 & 0 \\ 0 & 1 & 1 \\ 1 & 0 & 1 \end{pmatrix} \begin{pmatrix} x \\ y \\ z \end{pmatrix} = \begin{pmatrix} x + y \\ y + z \\ x + z \end{pmatrix}.$

(c) $\begin{pmatrix} 1 & 1 & 0 \\ 0 & 1 & 1 \\ 1 & 0 & 1 \end{pmatrix} \begin{pmatrix} 7 \\ 8 \\ 9 \end{pmatrix} = \begin{pmatrix} 15 \\ 17 \\ 16 \end{pmatrix}.$　　　　(d) $3 \times 3, 3 \times 1, 3 \times 1.$

Exercise 67, page 362

1. (a) $(5).$　　　　(c) $\begin{pmatrix} 1 & 2 \\ 2 & 4 \end{pmatrix}.$　　　　(e) $\begin{pmatrix} 1 & 2 & 3 \\ 2 & 4 & 6 \end{pmatrix}.$

(g) Scalar product: $(7 \quad -28 \quad 35).$

(i) Scalar product: $\begin{pmatrix} 4 & 8 \\ 8 & 4 \end{pmatrix}.$

(k) $(-5 \quad 4).$　　　　(m) $\begin{pmatrix} -8 & 9 \\ 22 & -1 \end{pmatrix}.$

(o) Nonexistent.　　　　(q) $\begin{pmatrix} 4 & 2 & 2 \\ 3 & 3 & 2 \\ 4 & 2 & 2 \end{pmatrix}.$

(s) $\begin{pmatrix} a & b \\ c & d \end{pmatrix}.$　　(u) $\begin{pmatrix} x \\ y \end{pmatrix}.$　　　　(w) $\begin{pmatrix} a & b & c \\ d & e & f \\ g & h & i \end{pmatrix}.$　　(y) $\begin{pmatrix} x \\ y \\ z \end{pmatrix}.$

4. (a)
$$AB = 10$$
$$BC = \begin{pmatrix} 10 & 12 & 14 \\ 20 & 24 & 28 \end{pmatrix}$$
$$(AB)C = (50 \quad 60 \quad 70)$$
$$A(BC) = (50 \quad 60 \quad 70).$$

(c)
$$AB = \begin{pmatrix} 5 & 10 \\ 20 & 15 \end{pmatrix}.$$
$$BC = \begin{pmatrix} 3 \\ 2 \end{pmatrix}$$
$$(AB)C = \begin{pmatrix} 15 \\ 10 \end{pmatrix}$$
$$A(BC) = \begin{pmatrix} 15 \\ 10 \end{pmatrix}$$

Exercise 68, page 368

1. (a) Multiplication is closed, commutative, associative; (1) is a unity in the given set; each element in the set except (0) has an inverse in the set.

(c) Multiplication is closed, associative, not commutative; there is no unity element in the given set; no element in the set has an inverse in the set.

(e) Multiplication is neither closed, commutative, nor associative; there is no unity element in the given set; no element in the set has an inverse in the set.

(g) Multiplication is closed, commutative, associative; $\begin{pmatrix} 1 & 0 \\ 0 & 1 \end{pmatrix}$ is a unity in the given set; each element in the set except $\begin{pmatrix} 0 & 0 \\ 0 & 0 \end{pmatrix}$ has an inverse in the set.

3. (a) $2, \begin{pmatrix} 3 & -1 \\ -1 & 1/2 \end{pmatrix}.$ (c) $-1, \begin{pmatrix} 3 & -1 \\ 2 & -1 \end{pmatrix}.$

(e) 0, no inverse.   (g) $1, \begin{pmatrix} 1 & 0 \\ 0 & 1 \end{pmatrix}.$

(i) 0, no inverse.

4. (a) $10, 2, \begin{pmatrix} 6 & 10 \\ 4 & 10 \end{pmatrix}, 20.$ (c) $7, 11, \begin{pmatrix} 4 & -5 \\ 1 & 18 \end{pmatrix}, 77.$

Exercise 70, page 375

1. (a) 37.   (c) 0.   (e) 8.   (g) 30.   (i) −77.   (k) 0.

3. (a) $p_1: 0, p_2: 1, p_3: 1, p_4: 2, p_5: 2, p_6: 3.$

(c) $p_{13}: 2, p_{14}: 3, p_{15}: 3, p_{16}: 4, p_{17}: 4, p_{18}: 5.$

4. (a) +.   (c) +.   (e) −.

Exercise 71, page 382

2. (a) p_4.   (c) p_2.   (e) p_3.   (g) p_3.

(i) p_1.   (k) p_1.

5. (a) $p_1^{-1} = p_1, p_3^{-1} = p_3, p_6^{-1} = p_6.$

7. (b) $\sum_P s = s(p_1) + s(p_2) + s(p_3) + s(p_4) + s(p_5) + s(p_6) = 0.$

(d) $\sum_Q f = f(p_1^{-1}) + f(p_2^{-1}) + f(p_3^{-1}) + f(p_4^{-1}) + f(p_5^{-1}) + f(p_6^{-1})$

12. (a) p_2.

Exercise 72, page 387

1. (c), (e), (g) Transposes identical with original matrices.

(i) $\begin{pmatrix} 1 & 2 & 3 \\ 2 & 4 & -1 \\ 2 & -7 & 5 \end{pmatrix}$.

(k) $\begin{pmatrix} 1 & 2 & 7 \\ 2 & 4 & 11 \\ 3 & 6 & 97 \end{pmatrix}$.

4. (a) $k = 2$.　　　(c) $k = 2 \cdot 3 = 6$.　　　(e) $k = (-1)(-1) = 1$.

Exercise 73, page 394

2. (a) -21.　　　(c) 63.　　　(e) -21.　　(g) 0.　　　(i) 0.

(k) 21.　　　(m) 84.　　　(o) 168.　　(q) $-abc$.

Exercise 74, page 402

2. (a) 0.　　　(c) 0.　　　(e) -394.　　(g) $(x - y)(y - z)(z - x)$.

Exercise 75, page 406

1. (a) $(1/37)\begin{pmatrix} 5 & 3 & -7 \\ -13 & 7 & 4 \\ -4 & 5 & 13 \end{pmatrix}$.　　　(c) No inverse exists.

(e) $\begin{pmatrix} 1/2 & 0 & 0 \\ 0 & 1/2 & 0 \\ 0 & 0 & 1/2 \end{pmatrix}$.　　　(g) $\begin{pmatrix} 1/2 & 0 & 0 \\ 0 & 1/3 & 0 \\ 0 & 0 & 1/5 \end{pmatrix}$.

(i) $\dfrac{1}{7}\begin{pmatrix} -13 & 12 & 22 \\ 31 & 1 & -11 \\ 14 & -7 & 0 \end{pmatrix}$.　　　(k) No inverse exists.

Exercise 76, page 408

1. (a) $\begin{pmatrix} x \\ y \\ z \end{pmatrix} = \begin{pmatrix} 1 \\ 1 \\ 1 \end{pmatrix}$.　　　(c) $\begin{pmatrix} x \\ y \\ z \end{pmatrix} = \begin{pmatrix} 0 \\ 0 \\ 0 \end{pmatrix}$.

2. (a) $\begin{pmatrix} x \\ y \\ z \end{pmatrix} = \begin{pmatrix} 1 \\ 0 \\ 1 \end{pmatrix}$.　　　(c) $\begin{pmatrix} x \\ y \\ z \end{pmatrix} = \begin{pmatrix} 52/77 \\ 30/77 \\ 21/77 \end{pmatrix}$.

(e) Equations are dependent. $\begin{pmatrix} x \\ y \\ z \end{pmatrix} = \begin{pmatrix} -161k \\ 76k \\ 3k \end{pmatrix}$, k any complex number.

Exercise 78, page 415

1. (a) Rain falls and I wear rubbers.

(c) If rain falls, I wear rubbers.

(e) Either I wear rubbers or rain does not fall.

(g) Rain does not fall if and only if I wear rubbers.

(i) If rain falls and I do not wear rubbers, I catch cold.

(k) If I do not wear rubbers, it rains and I catch cold.

(m) If the combination of falling rain and my catching cold does not occur, then I wear rubbers.

(*o*) The combination of no rain and my not wearing rubbers never occurs.

2. (*a*) *p*: They come. *q*: They go. *pq*.

(*c*) *p*: I win. *q*: I play. *p* + *q*′.

(*e*) *p*: Sticks will break my bones. *q*: Stones will break my bones. *pq*.

(*g*) *pq*′.   (i) *p* + *q*′.   (*k*) *p* + *q* + *p*′*q*′.

3. (*a*) *p*: I work. *q*: I eat.

  p′: I do not work, *q*′: I do not eat.

  pq: I work and I eat.

  p + *q*: I work or I eat.

  p * *q*: If I work, then I eat.

  q * *p*: If I eat, then I work.

  p ** *q*: I work if and only if I eat.

(*c*) *p*: All brides are beautiful.

  q: Everything is for the best.

  p′: Not all brides are beautiful.

  q′: Not everything is for the best.

  pq: All brides are beautiful and everything is for the best.

  p + *q*: All brides are beautiful or everything is for the best.

  p * *q*: If all brides are beautiful, then everything is for the best.

  q * *p*: If everything is for the best, then all brides are beautiful.

  p ** *q*: All bride are beautiful if and only if everything is for the best.

4. (*a*) For all *x*, *x* is a bride implies *x* is beautiful.

  All brides are beautiful.

  (Set of all women.)

(*c*) Not for all *x* is it the case that *x* is a bride implies *x* is beautiful.

  Not all brides are beautiful.

  (Set of all women.)

(*e*) For all *x*, *x* dreams.

  Everyone dreams.

  (Set of all people.)

(*g*) Not for all *x* is it the case that *x* dreams.

  Not everyone dreams.

  (Set of all people.)

(*i*) There does not exist an *x* such that *x* dreams.

  No one dreams.

  (Set of all people.)

(*k*) For all *x*, *x* knows her implies *x* loves her.

  To know her is to love her.

  (Set of all people.)

(*m*) There exists an *x* such that *x* is a man and *x* lives in our town.

  There lives a man in our town.

  (Set of all people.)

(*o*) There exists an *x* such that $x^2 = -1$.

  There exists a number whose square is -1.

  (Set of all numbers.)

(*q*) Not for all *x* is it the case that $x/x = 1$.

  It is not true that each complex number divided by itself is equal to 1.

  (Set of all complex numbers.)

5. Universal set: Set of all emus.

(x) $(x$ flies$)'$: All emus are incapable of flight.

$(x)'(x$ flies$)\cdot(\exists x)(x$ flies$)$: Not all emus but only some emus fly.

6. (a) $(x)(x$ is mortal$)$. (Universal set?)

(c) $(x)(x$ seems to whisper Louise$)$. (Universal set?)

(e) $[(\exists x)'(x$ volunteers$)] * ($I will do it myself$)$. (Universal set?)

(g) $[(\exists x)'(x$ moves$)] + [(x)(x$ dies$)]$. (Universal set?)

7. (a) (x). (c) $(\exists x)'$. (e) $(\exists x)$.

Exercise 79, page 420

5. (a) 0. (c) 1. (e) 1. (g) 0. (i) 0. (k) 1. (m) 0.

Exercise 80, page 424

5. (a) Statement: True.

 Inverse: If it is not a fish, then it does not swim. (False.)

 Converse: If it swims, then it is a fish. (False.)

 Contrapositive: If it does not swim, it is not a fish. (True.)

(c) Statement: True.

 Inverse: If it is not a whale, then it flies. (False.)

 Converse: If it does not fly, then it is a whale. (False.)

 Contrapositive: If it flies, then it is not a whale. (True.)

(e) Statement: True.

 Inverse: If an integer is not odd, then it is divisible by 2. (True.)

 Converse: If an integer is not divisible by 2, then it is odd. (True.)

 Contrapositive: If an integer is divisible by 2, it is not odd. (True.)

(g) Statement: True.

 Inverse: If a triangle is not scalene, it is isosceles. (True.)

 Converse: If a triangle is not isosceles, it is scalene. (True.)

 Contrapositive: If a triangle is isosceles, it is not scalene. (True.)

(i) Statement: False.

 Inverse: If the combination of rain and my not wearing rubbers does not occur, then I do not catch cold. (False.)

 Converse: If I catch cold, then it rains and I do not wear rubbers. (False.)

 Contrapositive: If I do not catch cold, then the combination of rain and my not wearing rubbers does not occur. (False.)

(k) Statement: True.

 Inverse: A sufficient condition for not residing in New York State is not residing in New York City. (False.)

 Converse: A necessary condition for residing in New York State is residing in New York City. (False.)

 Contrapositive: A sufficient condition for not residing in New York City is not residing in New York State. (True.)

(m) Statement: False.

 Inverse: Everyone who is bad lives long. (False.)

 Converse: Everyone who dies young is good. (False.)

 Contrapositive: Everyone who lives long is bad. (False.)

Exercise 81, page 428

1. (a) Some brides are unbeautiful.

(c) All brides are unbeautiful.

(e) Some roses are not red.

(g) Either he does not say "bananna" or she does not say "banahna."

(i) Some college men are not handsome and not rich.

(k) 5 ≯ 7 and 5 ≠ 7.

(m) No rectangle is a square.

(o) There exists a real number which is not negative and not positive.

(q) There exists a number which is real and not rational, or rational and not real.

(s) There exists a negative number whose cube is not negative.

(u) There exists a prime number which is not odd.

2. (a) Negation true. (c) Negation true.
   (e) Statement true. (g) Statement true.
   (i) Negation true.   (k) Negation true.

Exercise 82, page 431

6. Conclusion true.   8. Reasoning not valid.
10. Reasoning not valid.

Exercise 83, page 437

1. (c) Your sons are lunatics and unfit to serve on a jury.
   (e) Guinea pigs do not really appreciate Beethoven.

Exercise 84, page 443

2. (a) $(fh)g = e = f(hg)$.   (c) $(hh)g = g = h(hg)$.

3. (a) Let $\triangle ABC$ be such that $AB = BC$ and $AB \neq AC$. Define $e(ABC) = (ABC)$, $f(ABC) = (CBA)$. Then the group of $\triangle ABC$ is $\{e, f\}$, where e is an identity element and $ff = e$.

   (c) Let $\triangle ABC$ be equilateral. Define $e(ABC) = (ABC)$, $f(ABC) = (CBA)$, $g(ABC) = (ACB)$, $h(ABC) = (BCA)$, $i(ABC) = (BAC)$, $j(ABC) = (CAB)$. Then the group of $\triangle ABC$ is $\{e, f, g, h, i, j\}$, with multiplication table:

	e	f	g	h	i	j
e	e	f	g	h	i	j
f	f	e	j	i	h	g
g	g	h	e	f	j	i
h	h	g	i	j	f	e
i	i	j	h	g	e	f
j	j	i	f	e	g	h

4. (a) Not a group; the real number 0 has no multiplicative inverse in the set of real numbers.

   (c) Not a group; the rational number 0 has no multiplicative inverse in the set of rational numbers.

(e), (g), (i), (k), (s) Groups.

(m), (o), (q), (u) Not groups.

8. (a) The group is $\{p\}$, where $p(1) = 1$, and $p \cdot p = p$.

(b), (c) See Exercise 71, Problems 1 and 3.

9. (a) and (b) are abelian; (c) is not.

13. (a) A group.   (c) Not a group.   (e) Not a group.

INDEX